HIGHER MATHEMATICS

FOR

ENGINEERS AND PHYSICISTS

Higher Mathematics
for
Engineers and Physicists

BY

IVAN S. SOKOLNIKOFF, Ph.D.

Professor of Mathematics, University of Calfornia,
Los Angeles, California

AND

ELIZABETH S. SOKOLNIKOFF, Ph.D.

Assistant Professor of Mathematics, University of Wisconsin

SECOND EDITION

McGRAW-HILL BOOK COMPANY, INC.

NEW YORK AND LONDON

1941

PREFACE

The favorable reception of the First Edition of this volume appears to have sustained the authors' belief in the need of a book on mathematics beyond the calculus, written from the point of view of the student of applied science. The chief purpose of the book is to help to bridge the gap which separates many engineers from mathematics by giving them a bird's-eye view of those mathematical topics which are indispensable in the study of the physical sciences.

It has been a common complaint of engineers and physicists that the usual courses in advanced calculus and differential equations place insufficient emphasis on the art of formulating physical problems in mathematical terms. There may also be a measure of truth in the criticism that many students with pronounced utilitarian leanings are obliged to depend on books that are more distinguished for rigor than for robust uses of mathematics.

This book is an outgrowth of a course of lectures offered by one of the authors to students having a working knowledge of the elementary calculus. The keynote of the course is the practical utility of mathematics, and considerable effort has been made to select those topics which are of most frequent and immediate use in applied sciences and which can be given in a course of one hundred lectures. The illustrative material has been chosen for its value in emphasizing the underlying principles rather than for its direct application to specific problems that may confront a practicing engineer.

In preparing the revision the authors have been greatly aided by the reactions and suggestions of the users of this book in both academic and engineering circles. A considerable portion of the material contained in the First Edition has been rearranged and supplemented by further illustrative examples, proofs, and problems. The number of problems has been more than doubled. It was decided to omit the discussion of improper integrals and to absorb the chapter on Elliptic Integrals into

v

much enlarged chapters on Infinite Series and Differential
Equations. A new chapter on Complex Variable incorporates
some of the material that was formerly contained in the chapter
on Conformal Representation. The original plan of making
each chapter as nearly as possible an independent unit, in order
to provide some flexibility and to enhance the availability of the
book for reference purposes, has been retained.

I. S. S.
E. S. S.

MADISON, WISCONSIN,
  September, 1941.

CONTENTS

CHAPTER I

SECTION

INFINITE SERIES

CHAPTER II

FOURIER SERIES

CHAPTER III

SOLUTION OF EQUATIONS

CHAPTER VII
ORDINARY DIFFERENTIAL EQUATIONS

CHAPTER VIII
PARTIAL DIFFERENTIAL EQUATIONS

CHAPTER IX

VECTOR ANALYSIS

CHAPTER X

COMPLEX VARIABLE

CHAPTER XI
PROBABILITY

CHAPTER XII
EMPIRICAL FORMULAS AND CURVE FITTING

HIGHER MATHEMATICS FOR ENGINEERS AND PHYSICISTS

CHAPTER I

INFINITE SERIES

It is difficult to conceive of a single mathematical topic that occupies a more prominent place in applied mathematics than the subject of infinite series. Students of applied sciences meet infinite series in most of the formulas they use, and it is quite essential that they acquire an intelligent understanding of the concepts underlying the subject.

The first section of this chapter is intended to bring into sharper focus some of the basic (and hence more difficult) notions with which the reader became acquainted in the first course in calculus. It is followed by ten sections that are devoted to a treatment of the algebra and calculus of series and that represent the minimum theoretical background necessary for an intelligent use of series. Some of the practical uses of infinite series are indicated briefly in the remainder of the chapter and more fully in Chaps. II, VII, and VIII.

1. Fundamental Concepts. Familiarity with the concepts discussed in this section is essential to an understanding of the contents of this chapter.

FUNCTION. *The variable y is said to be a function of the variable x if to every value of x under consideration there corresponds at least one value of y.*

If x is the variable to which values are assigned at will, then it is called the *independent variable*. If the values of the variable y are determined by the assignment of values to the independent

1

variable x, then y is called the *dependent variable*. The functional dependence of y upon x is usually denoted by the equation*

$$y = f(x).$$

Unless a statement to the contrary is made, it will be supposed in this book that the variable x is permitted to assume real values only and that the corresponding values of y are also real. In this event the function $f(x)$ is called a *real function of the real variable x.* It will be observed that

(1-1) $$y = \sqrt{x}$$

does not represent a real function of x for all real values of x, for the values of y become imaginary if x is negative.   In order that the symbol $f(x)$ define a real function of x, it may be necessary to restrict the range of values that x may assume.   Thus, (1-1) defines a real function of x only if $x \geq 0$. On the other hand, $y = \sqrt{x^2 - 1}$ defines a real function of x only if $|x| \geq 1$.

SEQUENCES AND LIMITS.   Let some process of construction yield a succession of values

$$x_1, x_2, x_3, \cdots, x_n, \cdots,$$

where it is assumed that every x_i is followed by other terms. Such a succession of terms is called an *infinite sequence*.   Examples of sequences are

(a) $1, 2, 3, \cdots, n, \cdots,$

(b) $\dfrac{1}{2}, -\dfrac{1}{4}, \dfrac{1}{8}, -\dfrac{1}{16}, \cdots, (-1)^{n-1}\dfrac{1}{2^n}, \cdots,$

(c) $0, 2, 0, 2, \cdots, 1 + (-1)^n, \cdots.$

Sequences will be considered here only in connection with the theorems on infinite series,† and for this purpose it is necessary to have a definition of the limit of a sequence.

DEFINITION.   *The sequence $x_1, x_2, \cdots, x_n, \cdots$ is said to converge to the constant L as a limit if for any preassigned positive number ϵ, however small, one can find a positive integer p such that*

$$|x_n - L| < \epsilon \qquad \text{for all } n > p.$$

---

* Other letters are often used.   In particular, if more than one function enters into the discussion, the functions may be denoted by $f_1(x), f_2(x)$, etc.; by $f(x), g(x)$, etc.; by $F(x), G(x)$, etc.

† For a somewhat more extensive treatment, see I. S. Sokolnikoff, *Advanced Calculus*, pp. 3–21.

For convenience, this definition is frequently written in the compact form

$$\lim_{n \to \infty} x_n = L,$$

and L is called the *limit* of the sequence. If a variable x takes on these successive values $x_1, x_2, \cdots, x_n, \cdots$, then x is said to *approach* L *as a limit*. It follows from this definition that, of the sequences given above, (*b*) converges to the limit 0, whereas (*a*) and (*c*) are not convergent.

As an illustration, let the variable x assume the set of values

$$x_1 = 0.1, \qquad x_2 = 0.11, \qquad x_3 = 0.111, \cdots.$$

It is easily seen that

$$\lim_{n \to \infty} x_n = \frac{1}{9};$$

that is, corresponding to any $\epsilon > 0$, one can find a positive integer p such that

$$|L - x_n| \equiv \left| \frac{1}{9} - x_n \right| < \epsilon$$

for all values of n greater than p. Observe that

$$\frac{1}{9} - x_1 = \frac{1}{90}, \qquad \frac{1}{9} - x_2 = \frac{1}{900}, \cdots, \qquad \frac{1}{9} - x_n = \frac{1}{9 \cdot 10^n}.$$

Hence, for any ϵ that is chosen, it is necessary to demand that n be large enough so that

$$\frac{1}{9} - x_n \equiv \frac{1}{9 \cdot 10^n} < \epsilon.$$

The inequality is equivalent to

$$9 \cdot 10^n > \frac{1}{\epsilon},$$

and, taking logarithms to the base 10,*

$$\log 9 + n > \log \frac{1}{\epsilon}$$

or

$$n > -(\log 9 + \log \epsilon) = -\log 9\epsilon.$$

* From the definition of the logarithm, it follows that, if $A > B$, then $\log A > \log B$.

Thus, if p is chosen as any integer greater than $|-\log 9\epsilon|$, the inequality

$$\left| \frac{1}{9} - x_n \right| < \epsilon$$

will be satisfied for all values of n greater than p.

INFINITE SERIES.   Let u_1, u_2, u_3, $\cdots$ be an infinite sequence of real functions of a real variable x.   Then the symbol

$$(1\text{-}2) \qquad \sum_{n=1}^{\infty} u_n(x) \equiv u_1(x) + u_2(x) + \cdots + u_n(x) + \cdots$$

is called an *infinite series*.

If, in (1-2), x is assigned some fixed value, say $x = x_0$, there results the series of constants

$$(1\text{-}3) \qquad\qquad \sum_{n=1}^{\infty} u_n(x_0).$$

Denote by $s_n(x_0)$ the nth partial sum, that is, the sum of the first n terms, of the series (1-3) so that

$$s_n(x_0) = u_1(x_0) + u_2(x_0) + \cdots + u_n(x_0).$$

As n increases indefinitely, the sequence of constants

$$s_1(x_0), \ s_2(x_0), \ \cdots, \ s_n(x_0), \ \cdots$$

either will converge to a finite limit S or it will not converge to such a limit.   If

$$\lim_{n \to \infty} s_n(x_0) = S,$$

the series (1-2) is said to converge to the value S for $x = x_0$.*
If the series (1-2) converges for every value of x in some interval†
(a, b), then the series is said to be convergent in the interval (a, b).

As an example, consider the series

$$(1\text{-}4) \qquad\qquad 1 + x + x^2 + \cdots + x^{n-1} + \cdots.$$

If $x = \frac{1}{2}$, (1-4) becomes

$$1 + \frac{1}{2} + \frac{1}{4} + \cdots + \frac{1}{2^{n-1}} + \cdots,$$

---

* This limit S is usually called the *sum of the series* (1-3).

† This means that x can assume any real value between a and b and that a and b can be thought of as the end points of an interval of the x-axis.

which is convergent to the value 2. In order to establish this fact, note that

$$s_n = 1 + \frac{1}{2} + \frac{1}{4} + \cdots + \frac{1}{2^{n-1}}$$

is a geometric progression of ratio $\frac{1}{2}$, so that

$$s_n = \frac{1 - \dfrac{1}{2^n}}{1 - \dfrac{1}{2}} = 2 - \frac{1}{2^{n-1}}.$$

Hence, the absolute value of the difference between 2 and s_n is $1/2^{n-1}$, which can be made arbitrarily small by choosing n sufficiently large.

On the other hand, if $x = -1$, the series (1-4) becomes

$$1 - 1 + 1 - 1 + \cdots + (-1)^{n-1} + \cdots ,$$

which does not converge; for $s_{2n} = 0$ and $s_{2n-1} = 1$ for any choice of n and, therefore, $\lim_{n \to \infty} s_n$ does not exist. Moreover, if $x = 2$, the series (1-4) becomes

$$1 + 2 + 4 + \cdots + 2^{n-1} + \cdots ,$$

so that s_n increases indefinitely with n and $\lim_{n \to \infty} s_n$ does not exist. If an infinite series does not converge for a certain value of x, it is said to *diverge* or *be divergent* for that value of x. It will be shown later that the series (1-4) is convergent for $-1 < x < 1$ and divergent for all other values of x.

The definition of the limit, as given above, assumes that the value of the limit S is known. Frequently it is possible to infer the existence of S without actually knowing its value. The following example will serve to illustrate this point.

Example. Consider the series

$$s = 1 + \frac{1}{2!} + \frac{1}{3!} + \cdots + \frac{1}{n!} + \cdots ,$$

and compare the sum of its first n terms

$$s_n = 1 + \frac{1}{2!} + \frac{1}{3!} + \cdots + \frac{1}{n!}$$

with the sum of the geometrical progression

$$S_n = 1 + \frac{1}{2} + \frac{1}{2^2} + \cdots + \frac{1}{2^{n-1}}$$
$$= 2 - \frac{1}{2^{n-1}}.$$

The corresponding terms of S_n are never less than those of s_n; but, no matter how large n be taken, S_n is less than 2. Consequently, $s_n < 2$; and since the successive values of s_n form an increasing sequence of numbers, the sum of the first series must be greater than 1 and less than or equal to 2. A geometrical interpretation of this statement may help to fix the idea. If the successive values of s_n,

$$s_1 = 1,$$
$$s_2 = 1 + \frac{1}{2!} = 1.5,$$
$$s_3 = 1 + \frac{1}{2!} + \frac{1}{3!} = 1.667,$$
$$s_4 = 1 + \frac{1}{2!} + \frac{1}{3!} + \frac{1}{4!} = 1.708,$$
$$s_5 = 1 + \frac{1}{2!} + \frac{1}{3!} + \frac{1}{4!} + \frac{1}{5!} = 1.717,$$

are plotted as points on a straight line (Fig. 1), the points representing the sequence $s_1, s_2, \cdots, s_n, \cdots$ always move to the right but never

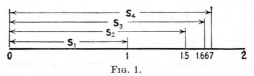

Fig. 1.

progress as far as the point 2. It is intuitively clear that there must be some point s, either lying to the left of 2 or else coinciding with it, which the numbers s_n approach as a limit. In this case the numerical value of the limit has not been ascertained, but its existence was established with the aid of what is known as the *fundamental principle*.

Stated in precise form the principle reads as follows: *If an infinite set of numbers $s_1, s_2, \cdots, s_n, \cdots$ forms an increasing sequence* (that is, $s_N > s_n$, when $N > n$) *and is such that every s_n is less than some fixed number M* (that is, $s_n < M$ for all values of n), *then s_n approaches a limit s that is not greater than M* (that is, $\lim_{n \to \infty} s_n = s \leq M$). The formulation of the principle for a decreasing sequence of numbers $s_1, s_2, \cdots, s_n, \cdots$, which are always greater than a certain fixed number m, will be left to the reader.

2. Series of Constants. The definition of the convergence of a series of functions evidently depends on a study of the behavior of series of constants. The reader has had some acquaintance with such series in his earlier study of mathematics, but it seems desirable to provide a summary of some essential theorems that will be needed later in this chapter. The following important theorem gives the necessary and sufficient condition for the convergence of an infinite series of constants:

THEOREM. *The infinite series of constants* $\sum\limits_{n=1}^{\infty} u_n$ *converges if and only if there exists a positive integer n such that for all positive integral values of* p

$$|s_{n+p} - s_n| \equiv |u_{n+1} + u_{n+2} + \cdots + u_{n+p}| < \epsilon,$$

where ϵ *is any preassigned positive constant.*

The necessity of the condition can be proved immediately by recalling the definition of convergence. Thus, assume that the series converges, and let its sum be S, so that

$$\lim_{n \to \infty} s_n = S$$

and also, for any fixed value of p,

$$\lim_{n \to \infty} s_{n+p} = S.$$

Hence,

$$\lim_{n \to \infty} (s_{n+p} - s_n) \equiv \lim_{n \to \infty} (u_{n+1} + u_{n+2} + \cdots + u_{n+p}) = 0,$$

which is another way of saying that

$$|u_{n+1} + u_{n+2} + \cdots + u_{n+p}| < \epsilon$$

for a sufficiently large value of n.

The proof of the sufficiency of the condition requires a fair degree of mathematical maturity and will not be given here.*

This theorem is of great theoretical importance in a variety of investigations, but it is seldom used in any practical problem requiring the testing of a given series. A number of tests for convergence, applicable to special types of series, will be given in the following sections.

It may be remarked that a sufficient condition that a series diverge is that the terms u_n do not approach zero as a limit when n increases indefinitely. Thus the necessary condition for convergence of a series is that $\lim\limits_{n \to \infty} u_n = 0$, but this condition is not

---

* See SOKOLNIKOFF, I. S., *Advanced Calculus*, pp. 11–13.

sufficient; that is, there are series for which $\lim\limits_{n \to \infty} u_n = 0$ but which are not convergent. A classical example illustrating this case is the harmonic series

$$1 + \frac{1}{2} + \frac{1}{3} + \cdots + \frac{1}{n} + \cdots,$$

in which S_n increases without limit as n increases.

Despite the fact that a proof of the divergence of the harmonic series is given in every good course in elementary calculus, it will be recalled here because of its importance in subsequent considerations. Since

$$\frac{1}{n+1} + \frac{1}{n+2} + \cdots + \frac{1}{n+n} > n \cdot \frac{1}{2n} = \frac{1}{2},$$

it is possible, beginning with any term of the series, to add a definite number of terms and obtain a sum greater than ½. If $n = 2$,

$$\frac{1}{3} + \frac{1}{4} > \frac{1}{2};$$

$n = 4$,

$$\frac{1}{5} + \frac{1}{6} + \frac{1}{7} + \frac{1}{8} > \frac{1}{2};$$

$n = 8$,

$$\frac{1}{9} + \frac{1}{10} + \cdots + \frac{1}{16} > \frac{1}{2};$$

$n = 16$,

$$\frac{1}{17} + \frac{1}{18} + \cdots + \frac{1}{32} > \frac{1}{2}.$$

Thus it is possible to group the terms of the harmonic series

$$1 + \frac{1}{2} + \left(\frac{1}{3} + \frac{1}{4}\right) + \left(\frac{1}{5} + \frac{1}{6} + \frac{1}{7} + \frac{1}{8}\right) + \cdots$$

in such a way that the sum of the terms in each parenthesis exceeds ½; and, since the series

$$1 + \frac{1}{2} + \frac{1}{2} + \frac{1}{2} + \cdots$$

is obviously divergent, the harmonic series is divergent also.

3. Series of Positive Terms. This section is concerned with series of the type

$$\sum_{n=1}^{\infty} a_n = a_1 + a_2 + \cdots + a_n + \cdots ,$$

where the a_n are positive constants. It is evident from the definition of convergence and from the fundamental principle (see Sec. 1) that the convergence of a series of positive constants will be established if it is possible to demonstrate that the partial sums s_n remain bounded. This means that there exists some positive number M such that $s_n < M$ for all values of n. The proof of the following important test is based on such a demonstration.

COMPARISON TEST. *Let $\sum_{n=1}^{\infty} a_n$ be a series of positive terms,*

and let $\sum_{n=1}^{\infty} b_n$ be a series of positive terms that is known to converge.

Then the series $\sum_{n=1}^{\infty} a_n$ is convergent if there exists an integer p such

that, for $n \geq p$, $a_n \leq b_n$. On the other hand, if $\sum_{n=1}^{\infty} c_n$ is a series of

positive terms that is known to be divergent and if $a_n \geq c_n$ for

$n \geq p$, then $\sum_{n=1}^{\infty} a_n$ is divergent also.

Since the convergence or divergence of a series evidently is not affected by the addition or subtraction of a finite number of terms, the proof will be given on the assumption that $p = 1$. Let $s_n = a_1 + a_2 + \cdots + a_n$, and let B denote the sum of the series $\sum_{n=1}^{\infty} b_n$ and B_n its nth partial sum. Then, since $a_n \leq b_n$ for all values of n, it follows that $s_n \leq B_n$ for all values of n. Hence, the s_n remain bounded, and the series $\sum_{n=1}^{\infty} a_n$ is convergent. On the other hand, if $a_n \geq c_n$ for all values of n and if the series $\sum_{n=1}^{\infty} c_n$ diverges, then the series $\sum_{n=1}^{\infty} a_n$ will diverge also.

There are two series that are frequently used as series for comparison.

a. The geometric series

(3-1) $$a + ar + ar^2 + \cdots + ar^n + \cdots ,$$

which the reader will recall* is convergent to $\dfrac{a}{1-r}$ if $|r| < 1$ and is divergent if $|r| \geq 1$.

b. The p series

$$(3\text{-}2) \qquad 1 + \frac{1}{2^p} + \frac{1}{3^p} + \cdots + \frac{1}{n^p} + \cdots ,$$

which converges if $p > 1$ and diverges if $p \leq 1$.

Consider first the case when $p > 1$, and write (3-2) in the form

$$(3\text{-}3) \quad 1 + \left(\frac{1}{2^p} + \frac{1}{3^p}\right) + \left(\frac{1}{4^p} + \frac{1}{5^p} + \frac{1}{6^p} + \frac{1}{7^p}\right) + \cdots$$
$$+ \left(\frac{1}{(2^{n-1})^p} + \cdots + \frac{1}{(2^n - 1)^p}\right) + \cdots ,$$

where the nth term of (3-3) contains 2^{n-1} terms of the series (3-2). Each term, after the first, of (3-3) is less than the corresponding term of the series

$$1 + 2 \cdot \frac{1}{2^p} + 4 \cdot \frac{1}{4^p} + \cdots + 2^{n-1} \frac{1}{(2^{n-1})^p} + \cdots ,$$

or

$$(3\text{-}4) \quad 1 + \frac{1}{2^{p-1}} + \frac{1}{(2^{p-1})^2} + \cdots + \frac{1}{(2^{p-1})^{n-1}} + \cdots .$$

Since the geometric series (3-4) has a ratio $1/2^{p-1}$ (which is less than unity for $p > 1$), it is convergent and, by the comparison test, (3-2) will converge also.

If $p = 1$, (3-2) becomes the harmonic series which has been shown to be divergent.

If $p < 1$, $1/n^p > 1/n$ for $n > 1$, so that each term of (3-2), after the first, is greater than the corresponding term of the harmonic series; hence, the series (3-2) is divergent also.

Example 1. Test the series

$$1 + \frac{1}{2^2} + \frac{1}{3^3} + \cdots + \frac{1}{n^n} + \cdots .$$

The geometric series

$$1 + \frac{1}{2^2} + \frac{1}{2^3} + \cdots + \frac{1}{2^n} + \cdots$$

* Since the sum of the geometric progression of n terms $a + ar + ar^2 + \cdots + ar^{n-1}$ is equal to $\dfrac{a - ar^n}{1 - r} = \dfrac{a}{1 - r}(1 - r^n)$.

is known to be convergent, and the terms of the geometric series are never less than the corresponding terms of the given series. Hence, the given series is convergent.

Example 2. Test the series

$$1 + \frac{1}{\log 2} + \frac{1}{\log 3} + \frac{1}{\log 4} + \cdots + \frac{1}{\log n} + \cdots .$$

Compare the terms of this series with the terms of the p series for $p = 1$,

$$1 + \frac{1}{2} + \frac{1}{3} + \frac{1}{4} + \cdots + \frac{1}{n} + \cdots .$$

The given series is divergent, for its terms (after the first) are greater than the corresponding terms of the p series, which diverges when $p = 1$.

RATIO TEST. *The series $\sum\limits_{n=1}^{\infty} a_n$ of positive terms is convergent if*

$$\lim_{n \to \infty} \frac{a_{n+1}}{a_n} = r < 1$$

and divergent if

$$\lim_{n \to \infty} \frac{a_{n+1}}{a_n} > 1.$$

If $\lim\limits_{n \to \infty} \dfrac{a_{n+1}}{a_n} = 1$, the series may converge or diverge.

Consider first the case when $r < 1$, and let q denote some constant between r and 1. Then there will be some positive integer N such that

$$\frac{a_{n+1}}{a_n} < q \qquad \text{for all } n \geq N.$$

Hence,

$$a_{N+1} < a_N q,$$
$$a_{N+2} < a_{N+1} q < a_N q^2,$$
$$a_{N+3} < a_{N+2} q < a_N q^3,$$
$$\cdots\cdots\cdots\cdots\cdots\cdots\cdots$$

and

$$a_{N+1} + a_{N+2} + a_{N+3} + \cdots < a_N(q + q^2 + q^3 + \cdots).$$

Since $q < 1$, the series in the right-hand member is convergent; therefore, the series in the left-hand member converges, also. It follows that the series $\sum\limits_{n=1}^{\infty} a_n$ is convergent.

If the limit of the ratio is greater than 1, then $a_{n+1} > a_n$ for every $n \geq N$ so that $\lim\limits_{n \to \infty} a_n \neq 0$, and hence the series $\sum\limits_{n=1}^{\infty} a_n$ is divergent.

It is important to observe that this theorem makes no reference to the magnitude of the ratio of a_{n+1}/a_n but deals solely with the *limit* of the ratio. Thus, in the case of the harmonic series the ratio is $a_{n+1}/a_n = n/(n+1)$, which remains less than 1 for all finite values of n, but the limit of the ratio is precisely equal to 1. Hence the test gives no information in this case.

Example 1. For the series

$$1 + \frac{2}{2} + \frac{3}{2^2} + \frac{4}{2^3} + \cdots + \frac{n}{2^{n-1}} + \cdots,$$

$$\lim_{n \to \infty} \frac{a_{n+1}}{a_n} = \lim_{n \to \infty} \frac{n+1}{2^n} \cdot \frac{2^{n-1}}{n} = \lim_{n \to \infty} \frac{1 + \dfrac{1}{n}}{2} = \frac{1}{2}$$

and, therefore, the series converges.

Example 2. The series

$$\frac{1}{10} + \frac{2!}{10^2} + \frac{3!}{10^3} + \cdots + \frac{n!}{10^n} + \cdots$$

is divergent, for

$$\lim_{n \to \infty} \frac{a_{n+1}}{a_n} = \lim_{n \to \infty} \frac{(n+1)!}{10^{n+1}} \frac{10^n}{n!} = \lim_{n \to \infty} \frac{n+1}{10} = \infty.$$

Example 3. Test the series

$$\frac{1}{1 \cdot 2} + \frac{1}{3 \cdot 4} + \frac{1}{5 \cdot 6} + \cdots + \frac{1}{(2n-1)2n} + \cdots.$$

Here

$$\lim_{n \to \infty} \frac{a_{n+1}}{a_n} = \lim_{n \to \infty} \frac{1}{(2n+1)(2n+2)} \cdot \frac{(2n-1)2n}{1}$$

$$= \lim_{n \to \infty} \frac{4n^2 - 2n}{4n^2 + 6n + 2} = \lim_{n \to \infty} \frac{1 - \dfrac{1}{2n}}{1 - \dfrac{3}{2n} + \dfrac{1}{2n^2}} = 1.$$

Hence, the test fails; but if the given series be compared with the p series for $p = 2$, it is seen to be convergent.

CAUCHY'S INTEGRAL TEST. *Let* $\displaystyle\sum_{n=1}^{\infty} a_n$ *be a series of positive terms such that* $a_{n+1} < a_n$. *If there exists a positive decreasing function* $f(x)$, *for* $x \geq 1$, *such that* $f(n) = a_n$, *then the given series converges if the integral*

$$\int_1^{\infty} f(x) \, dx$$

exists; the series diverges if the integral does not exist.

The proof of this test is deduced easily from the following graphical considerations. Each term a_n of the series may be thought of as representing the area of a rectangle of base unity and height $f(n)$ (see Fig. 2). The sum of the areas of the first n inscribed rectangles is less than $\int_1^{n+1} f(x)\, dx$, so that

$$s_{n+1} - a_1 \equiv a_2 + a_3 + \cdots + a_{n+1} < \int_1^{n+1} f(x)\, dx.$$

But $f(x)$ is positive, and hence

$$\int_1^{n+1} f(x)\, dx < \int_1^{\infty} f(x)\, dx.$$

If the integral on the right exists, it follows that the partial sums are bounded and, therefore, the series converges (see Sec. 1).

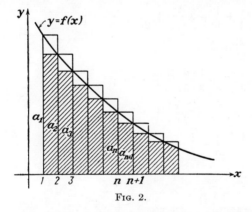

FIG. 2.

The sum of the areas of the circumscribed rectangles, $a_1 + a_2 + \cdots + a_n$, is greater than $\int_1^{n+1} f(x)\, dx$; hence, the series will diverge if the integral does not exist.

Example 1. Test the harmonic series

$$1 + \frac{1}{2} + \frac{1}{3} + \cdots + \frac{1}{n} + \cdots .$$

In this case, $f(x) = \frac{1}{x}$ and

$$\int_1^{\infty} \frac{1}{x}\, dx \equiv \lim_{n \to \infty} \int_1^n \frac{dx}{x} = \lim_{n \to \infty} \log n = \infty,$$

and the series is divergent.

Example 2. Apply Cauchy's test to the p series $\sum_{n=1}^{\infty} \dfrac{1}{n^p}$ where $p > 0$.

Taking $f(x) = \dfrac{1}{x^p}$, observe that

$$\int_1^n \frac{dx}{x^p} = \frac{1}{1-p} \, x^{1-p}\Big|_1^n, \qquad \text{if } p \neq 1,$$

$$= \log x\Big|_1^n, \qquad \text{if } p = 1.$$

Hence, $\displaystyle\int_1^{\infty} \dfrac{dx}{x^p}$ exists if $p > 1$ and does not exist if $p \leq 1$.

PROBLEMS

1. Test for convergence

(a) $\dfrac{1}{2} + \dfrac{1}{2 \cdot 2^2} + \dfrac{1}{3 \cdot 2^3} + \dfrac{1}{4 \cdot 2^4} + \cdots$;

(b) $\dfrac{1}{2} + \dfrac{1}{4} + \dfrac{1}{6} + \cdots + \dfrac{1}{2n} + \cdots$;

(c) $1 + \dfrac{2!}{2^2} + \dfrac{3!}{3^2} + \cdots$;

(d) $\dfrac{1}{3} + \dfrac{1 \cdot 2}{3 \cdot 5} + \dfrac{1 \cdot 2 \cdot 3}{3 \cdot 5 \cdot 7} + \cdots$;

(e) $\dfrac{1}{1 \cdot 2} + \dfrac{1}{2 \cdot 3} + \dfrac{1}{3 \cdot 4} + \cdots$;

(f) $1 + \dfrac{1}{3} + \dfrac{1}{5} + \dfrac{1}{7} + \cdots$;

(g) $\dfrac{1}{2} + \dfrac{2}{2^2} + \dfrac{3}{2^3} + \cdots$;

(h) $\dfrac{1}{2 \log 2} + \dfrac{1}{3 \log 3} + \dfrac{1}{4 \log 4} + \cdots$.

2. Use Cauchy's integral test to investigate the convergence of

(a) $\dfrac{1}{2} + \dfrac{1}{5} + \dfrac{1}{10} + \cdots + \dfrac{1}{1+n^2} + \cdots$;

(b) $1 + \dfrac{2}{1+2^2} + \dfrac{3}{2+3^2} + \cdots$.

3. Show that the series $\sum_{n=1}^{\infty} a_n$ of positive terms is divergent if na_n has a limit L which is different from 0. *Hint:* Let $\lim_{n \to \infty} na_n = L$ so that $na_n > L - \epsilon$ for n large enough. Hence, $a_n > \dfrac{L - \epsilon}{n}$.

4. Test for convergence

(a) $\displaystyle\sum_{n=1}^{\infty} \frac{1}{\sqrt{n}}$;

(b) $\displaystyle\sum_{n=1}^{\infty} \frac{n}{2^n}$;

(c) $\displaystyle\sum_{n=1}^{\infty} \frac{1}{\sqrt{n(n+1)}}$;

(d) $\displaystyle\sum_{n=1}^{\infty} \frac{n!}{n^2}$;

(e) $\displaystyle\sum_{n=1}^{\infty} \frac{1}{n \cdot 2^n}$;

(f) $\displaystyle\sum_{n=1}^{\infty} \frac{n^2}{n!}$;

(g) $\displaystyle\sum_{n=1}^{\infty} \frac{n!}{10^n}$;

(h) $\displaystyle\sum_{n=1}^{\infty} \frac{1}{n\sqrt{n}}$;

(i) $\displaystyle\sum_{n=0}^{\infty} \frac{1}{(2n+1)^2}$;

(j) $\displaystyle\sum_{n=0}^{\infty} \frac{n}{(2n+1)^2}$.

4. Alternating Series. A series whose terms are alternately positive and negative is called an *alternating series*. There is a simple test, due to Leibnitz, that establishes the convergence of many of these series.

TEST FOR AN ALTERNATING SERIES. *If the alternating series* $a_1 - a_2 + a_3 - a_4 + \cdots$, *where the* a_i *are positive, is such that* $a_{n+1} < a_n$ *and* $\lim_{n \to \infty} a_n = 0$, *then the series is convergent. Moreover, if S is the sum of the series, the numerical value of the difference between S and the nth partial sum is less than* a_{n+1}.

Since

$$s_{2n} = (a_1 - a_2) + (a_3 - a_4) + \cdots + (a_{2n-1} - a_{2n})$$
$$= a_1 - (a_2 - a_3) - \cdots - (a_{2n-2} - a_{2n-1}) - a_{2n},$$

it is evident that s_{2n} is positive and also that $s_{2n} < a_1$ for all values of n. Also, $s_2 < s_4 < s_6 < \cdots$, so that these partial sums tend to a limit S (by the fundamental principle). Since $s_{2n+1} = s_{2n} + a_{2n+1}$ and $\lim\limits_{n \to \infty} a_{2n+1} = 0$, it follows that the partial sums of odd order tend to this same limit.   Therefore, the series converges.   The proof of the second statement of the test will be left as an exercise for the reader.

Example 1.   The series

$$1 - \frac{1}{2} + \frac{1}{3} - \frac{1}{4} + \cdots$$

is convergent since $\lim\limits_{n \to \infty} \dfrac{1}{n} = 0$ and $\dfrac{1}{n+1} < \dfrac{1}{n}.$ Moreover, $s_4 = 1 - \frac{1}{2} + \frac{1}{3} - \frac{1}{4}$ differs from the sum S by less than $\frac{1}{5}$.

Example 2.   The series

$$1 - \frac{1}{2} + \frac{1}{3^1} - \frac{1}{4} + \frac{1}{3^2} - \frac{1}{6} + \frac{1}{3^3} - \cdots$$

is divergent.   Why?

5. Series of Positive and Negative Terms.   The alternating series and the series of positive constants are special types of the general series of constants in which the terms can be either positive or negative.

DEFINITION.   *If $u_1 + u_2 + \cdots + u_n + \cdots$ is an infinite series of terms such that the series of the absolute values of its terms, $|u_1| + |u_2| + \cdots + |u_n| + \cdots$, is convergent, then the series $u_1 + u_2 + \cdots + u_n + \cdots$ is said to be absolutely convergent. If the series of absolute values is not convergent, but the given series is convergent, then the given series is said to be conditionally convergent.*

Thus,

$$1 - \frac{1}{2} + \frac{1}{3} - \frac{1}{4} + \frac{1}{5} - \cdots$$

is convergent, but the series of absolute values,

$$1 + \frac{1}{2} + \frac{1}{3} + \frac{1}{4} + \frac{1}{5} + \cdots,$$

is not, so that the original series is conditionally convergent.

If a series is absolutely convergent, it can be shown that the series formed by changing the signs of any of the terms is also a convergent series.   This is an immediate result of the following theorem:

THEOREM. *If the series of absolute values $\sum\limits_{n=1}^{\infty} |u_n|$ is convergent,*

then the series $\sum\limits_{n=1}^{\infty} u_n$ is necessarily convergent.

Let

$$s_n = u_1 + u_2 + \cdots + u_n$$

and

$$t_n = |u_1| + |u_2| + \cdots + |u_n|.$$

If p_n denotes the sum of the positive terms occurring in s_n and $-q_n$ denotes the sum of the negative terms, then

(5-1) $$s_n = p_n - q_n$$

and

$$t_n = p_n + q_n.$$

The series $\sum\limits_{n=1}^{\infty} |u_n|$ is assumed to be convergent, so that

(5-2) $$\lim_{n \to \infty} t_n \equiv \lim_{n \to \infty} (p_n + q_n) \equiv L.$$

But p_n and q_n are positive and increasing with n and, since (5-2) shows that both remain less than L, it follows from the fundamental principle that both the p_n and q_n sequences converge. If

$$\lim_{n \to \infty} p_n = P \quad \text{and} \quad \lim_{n \to \infty} q_n = Q,$$

then (5-1) gives

$$\lim_{n \to \infty} s_n = \lim_{n \to \infty} (p_n - q_n) = P - Q,$$

which establishes the convergence of $\sum\limits_{n=1}^{\infty} u_n$.

Moreover, it can be shown that changing the order of the terms in an absolutely convergent series gives a series which is convergent to the same value as the original series.* However, conditionally convergent series do not possess this property. In fact, by suitably rearranging the order of the terms of a conditionally convergent series, the resulting series can be made to converge to any desired value. For example, it is known† that the sum of the series

$$1 - \frac{1}{2} + \frac{1}{3} - \frac{1}{4} + \cdots + \frac{(-1)^{n-1}}{n} + \cdots$$

---

* See SOKOLNIKOFF, I. S., Advanced Calculus, pp. 240–241.
† See Example 1, Sec. 13.

is $\log_e 2$. The fact that the sum of this series is less than 1 and greater than $\frac{1}{2}$ can be made evident by writing the series as

$$\left(1 - \frac{1}{2}\right) + \left(\frac{1}{3} - \frac{1}{4}\right) + \left(\frac{1}{5} - \frac{1}{6}\right) + \cdots,$$

which shows that the value of $s_n > \frac{1}{2}$ for $n > 2$; whereas, by writing it as

$$1 - \left(\frac{1}{2} - \frac{1}{3}\right) - \left(\frac{1}{4} - \frac{1}{5}\right) \cdots,$$

it is clear that $s_n < 1$ for $n \geq 2$. Some questions might be raised concerning the legitimacy of introducing parentheses in a convergent infinite series. The fact that the associative law holds unrestrictedly for convergent infinite series can be established easily directly from the definition of the sum of the infinite series. It will be shown* next that it is possible to rearrange the series

$$1 - \frac{1}{2} + \frac{1}{3} - \frac{1}{4} + \cdots$$

so as to obtain a new series whose sum is equal to 1. The positive terms of this series in their original order are

$$1, \quad \frac{1}{3}, \quad \frac{1}{5}, \quad \frac{1}{7}, \quad \frac{1}{9}, \cdots.$$

The negative terms are

$$-\frac{1}{2}, \quad -\frac{1}{4}, \quad -\frac{1}{6}, \quad -\frac{1}{8}, \cdots.$$

In order to form a series that converges to 1, first pick out, in order, as many positive terms as are needed to make their sum equal to or just greater than 1, then pick out just enough negative terms so that the sum of all terms so far chosen will be just less than 1, then more positive terms until the sum is just greater than 1, etc. Thus, the partial sums will be

$$s_1 = 1,$$

$$s_2 = 1 - \frac{1}{2} = \frac{1}{2},$$

$$s_4 = 1 - \frac{1}{2} + \frac{1}{3} + \frac{1}{5} = \frac{31}{30},$$

* General proof can be constructed along the lines of this example.

$$s_6 = 1 - \frac{1}{2} + \frac{1}{3} + \frac{1}{5} - \frac{1}{4} = \frac{47}{60},$$

$$s_7 = 1 - \frac{1}{2} + \frac{1}{3} + \frac{1}{5} - \frac{1}{4} + \frac{1}{7} + \frac{1}{9} = \frac{1307}{1260},$$

$$s_8 = 1 - \frac{1}{2} + \frac{1}{3} + \frac{1}{5} - \frac{1}{4} + \frac{1}{7} + \frac{1}{9} - \frac{1}{6} = \frac{1093}{1260},$$

. . . .

It is clear that the series formed by this method will have a sum equal to 1.

As another example, consider the conditionally convergent series

(5-3) $$1 - \frac{1}{\sqrt{2}} + \frac{1}{\sqrt{3}} - \frac{1}{\sqrt{4}} + \cdots .$$

Let the order of the terms in (5-3) be rearranged to give the series

(5-4) $$\left(1 + \frac{1}{\sqrt{3}} - \frac{1}{\sqrt{2}}\right) + \left(\frac{1}{\sqrt{5}} + \frac{1}{\sqrt{7}} - \frac{1}{\sqrt{4}}\right)$$
$$+ \left(\frac{1}{\sqrt{9}} + \frac{1}{\sqrt{11}} - \frac{1}{\sqrt{6}}\right) + \cdots .$$

The nth term of (5-4) is

$$a_n \equiv \frac{1}{\sqrt{4n-3}} + \frac{1}{\sqrt{4n-1}} - \frac{1}{\sqrt{2n}},$$

which is greater than

$$b_n \equiv \frac{1}{\sqrt{4n}} + \frac{1}{\sqrt{4n}} - \frac{1}{\sqrt{2n}} = \left(1 - \frac{1}{\sqrt{2}}\right)\frac{1}{\sqrt{n}}.$$

But the series $\sum_{n=1}^{\infty} b_n$ is divergent, and it follows that the series (5-4) must diverge.

Inasmuch as the series $\sum_{n=1}^{\infty} |u_n|$ is a series of positive terms, the tests that were developed in Sec. 3 can be applied in establishing the absolute convergence of the series $\sum_{n=1}^{\infty} u_n$. In particular, the ratio test can be restated in the following form:

RATIO TEST.   *The series* $\sum\limits_{n=1}^{\infty} u_n$ *is absolutely convergent if*

$$\lim_{n \to \infty} \left| \frac{u_{n+1}}{u_n} \right| < 1$$

and is divergent if

$$\lim_{n \to \infty} \left| \frac{u_{n+1}}{u_n} \right| > 1.$$

If the limit is unity, the test gives no information.

Example 1.   In the case of the series

$$1 + x + \frac{x^2}{2!} + \frac{x^3}{3!} + \frac{x^4}{4!} + \cdots,$$

$$\lim_{n \to \infty} \left| \frac{u_{n+1}}{u_n} \right| = \lim_{n \to \infty} \left| \frac{x^n}{n!} \frac{(n-1)!}{x^{n-1}} \right| = \lim_{n \to \infty} \left| \frac{x}{n} \right| = 0$$

for all values of x.   Hence, the series is convergent for all values of x and, in particular, the series

$$1 - 2 + \frac{2^2}{2!} - \frac{2^3}{3!} + \cdots$$

is absolutely convergent.

Example 2.   Consider the series

$$\frac{1}{1-x} + \frac{1}{2(1-x)^2} + \frac{1}{3(1-x)^3} + \cdots.$$

Here

$$\lim_{n \to \infty} \left| \frac{1}{(n+1)(1-x)^{n+1}} \cdot \frac{n(1-x)^n}{1} \right| = \lim_{n \to \infty} \left| \frac{n}{(n+1)(1-x)} \right|$$

$$= \lim_{n \to \infty} \left| \frac{1}{\left(1 + \dfrac{1}{n}\right)(1-x)} \right| = \frac{1}{|1-x|}.$$

Therefore, the series will converge if

$$\frac{1}{|1-x|} < 1 \quad \text{or} \quad 1 < |1-x|,$$

which is true for $x < 0$ and for $x > 2$.

For $x = 0$ and for $x = 2$ the limit is unity, but if $x = 0$ the series becomes the divergent harmonic series

$$1 + \frac{1}{2} + \frac{1}{3} + \cdots + \frac{1}{n} + \cdots,$$

and if $x = 2$ there results the convergent alternating series

$$-1 + \frac{1}{2} - \frac{1}{3} + \cdots + (-1)^n \frac{1}{n} + \cdots .$$

It follows that the original series converges for $x < 0$ and for $x \geq 2$ and diverges for $0 \leq x < 2$.

6. Algebra of Series. The following important theorems are stated without proof:*

THEOREM 1. *Any two convergent series*

$$U = u_1 + u_2 + \cdots + u_n + \cdots$$
$$V = v_1 + v_2 + \cdots + v_n + \cdots$$

can be added or subtracted term by term to give

$$U + V = (u_1 + v_1) + (u_2 + v_2) + \cdots + (u_n + v_n) + \cdots$$

or

$$U - V = (u_1 - v_1) + (u_2 - v_2) + \cdots + (u_n - v_n) + \cdots .$$

If the original series are both absolutely convergent, then the resulting series will be absolutely convergent also.

THEOREM 2. *If*

$$U = u_1 + u_2 + \cdots + u_n + \cdots$$

and

$$V = v_1 + v_2 + \cdots + v_n + \cdots$$

are two absolutely convergent series, then they can be multiplied like finite sums and the product series will converge to UV. *Moreover, the product series will be absolutely convergent. Thus,*

$$UV = u_1 v_1 + u_1 v_2 + u_2 v_1 + u_1 v_3 + u_2 v_2 + u_3 v_1 + \cdots .$$

THEOREM 3. *In an absolutely convergent series the positive terms by themselves form a convergent series and also the negative terms by themselves form a convergent series. If in a convergent series the positive terms form a divergent series, then the series of negative terms is also divergent and the original series is conditionally convergent.*

THEOREM 4. *If* $u_1 + u_2 + \cdots + u_n + \cdots$ *is an absolutely convergent series and if* $M_1, M_2, \cdots, M_n, \cdots$ *is any sequence of quantities whose numerical values are all less than some positive number* N, *then the series*

$$u_1 M_1 + u_2 M_2 + \cdots + u_n M_n + \cdots$$

is absolutely convergent.

* See SOKOLNIKOFF, I. S., Advanced Calculus, pp. 212–213, 241–245.

Example. Consider the series

$$\frac{\sin x}{1^3} - \frac{\sin 2x}{2^3} + \frac{\sin 3x}{3^3} - \cdots .$$

This series is absolutely convergent for all values of x, for the series

$$\frac{1}{1^3} - \frac{1}{2^3} + \frac{1}{3^3} - \cdots$$

is absolutely convergent and $|\sin nx| \leq 1$.

PROBLEMS

1. Show that the following series are divergent:

(a) $\dfrac{5}{2} - \dfrac{7}{4} + \dfrac{9}{6} - \dfrac{11}{8} + \cdots + (-1)^{n-1}\dfrac{2n+3}{2n} + \cdots$;

(b) $\dfrac{1}{2} - \dfrac{1}{2^2} + \dfrac{1}{3} - \dfrac{1}{3^2} + \dfrac{1}{4} - \dfrac{1}{4^2} + \cdots$;

(c) $\dfrac{2}{1} - \dfrac{3}{2} + \dfrac{4}{3} - \dfrac{5}{4} + \cdots$.

2. Test for convergence, and if the series is convergent determine whether it is absolutely convergent.

(a) $1 - \dfrac{1}{\sqrt{2}} + \dfrac{1}{\sqrt{3}} - \dfrac{1}{\sqrt{4}} + \cdots$;

(b) $\dfrac{1}{3} - \dfrac{1\cdot 3}{3\cdot 6} + \dfrac{1\cdot 3\cdot 5}{3\cdot 6\cdot 9} - \dfrac{1\cdot 3\cdot 5\cdot 7}{3\cdot 6\cdot 9\cdot 12} + \cdots$;

(c) $\dfrac{2}{1} - \dfrac{3}{2} + \dfrac{4}{3} - \dfrac{5}{4} + \cdots$.

3. For what values of x are the following series convergent?

(a) $x - \dfrac{x^2}{2} + \dfrac{x^3}{3} - \cdots + (-1)^{n-1}\dfrac{x^n}{n} + \cdots$;

(b) $1 - \dfrac{x^2}{2!} + \dfrac{x^4}{4!} - \dfrac{x^6}{6!} + \cdots$;

(c) $1 - x + x^2 - x^3 + \cdots$;

(d) $\dfrac{1}{x} + \dfrac{1}{2x^2} + \dfrac{1}{3x^3} + \cdots + \dfrac{1}{nx^n} + \cdots$.

4. Determine the intervals of convergence of the following series:

(a) $\dfrac{2x}{x+4} + \dfrac{1}{2}\left(\dfrac{2x}{x+4}\right)^2 + \dfrac{1}{3}\left(\dfrac{2x}{x+4}\right)^3 + \cdots$;

(b) $x + 2!x^2 + 3!x^3 + 4!x^4 + \cdots$;

(c) $1 + mx + \dfrac{m(m-1)}{2!}x^2 + \dfrac{m(m-1)(m-2)}{3!}x^3 + \cdots$.

where m is not a positive integer.

7. Continuity of Functions.   Uniform Convergence. Before proceeding with a discussion of infinite series of functions, it is necessary to have a clear understanding of the concept of continuity of functions.   The reader will recall that a function $f(x)$ is said to be continuous at a point $x = x_0$ if $\lim\limits_{x \to x_0} f(x) = f(x_0)$ regardless of how x approaches x_0.   From the discussion of the limit in Sec. 1, it appears that this concept can be defined in the following way:

DEFINITION.   *The function $f(x)$ is continuous at the point $x = x_0$ if, corresponding to any preassigned positive number ϵ, it is possible to find a positive number δ such that*

(7-1) $|f(x) - f(x_0)| < \epsilon$ *whenever* $|x - x_0| < \delta.$

The foregoing analytical definition of continuity is merely a formulation in exact mathematical language of the intuitive

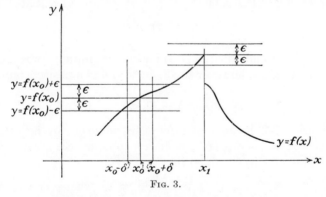

FIG. 3.

concept of continuity.   If the function $f(x)$ is represented by a graph and if it is continuous at the point $x = x_0$, then it is possible to find a strip bounded by the two parallel lines $x = x_0 + \delta$ and $x = x_0 - \delta$, such that the graph of the function will lie entirely within the strip bounded by the parallel lines $y = f(x_0) + \epsilon$ and $y = f(x_0) - \epsilon$ (Fig. 3).   But if the function is discontinuous at some point (such as $x = x_1$), then no interval about such a point can be found such that the graph of the function will lie entirely within the strip of width 2ϵ, where ϵ is arbitrarily small.

DEFINITION.   *A function is said to be continuous in an interval (a, b) if it is continuous at each point of the interval.*

If a finite number of functions that are all continuous in an interval (a, b) are added together, the sum also will be a continuous function in (a, b). The question arises as to whether this property will be retained in the case of an infinite series of continuous functions. Moreover, it is frequently desirable to obtain the derivative (or integral) of a function $f(x)$ by means of term-by-term differentiation (or integration) of an infinite series that defines $f(x)$. Unfortunately, such operations are not always valid, and many important investigations have led to erroneous results solely because of the improper handling of infinite series. A discussion of such questions requires an introduction of the property of uniform convergence of a series.

It was stated in Sec. 1 that the series

$$(7\text{-}2) \qquad u_1(x) + u_2(x) + \cdots + u_n(x) + \cdots$$

is convergent to the value S, when $x = x_0$, provided that

$$(7\text{-}3) \qquad \lim_{n \to \infty} s_n(x_0) = S.$$

The statement embodied in (7-3) means that for any preassigned positive number ϵ, however small, one can find a positive number N such that

$$|s_n(x_0) - S| < \epsilon \qquad \text{for all } n \geq N.$$

If the series (7-2) is convergent for every value of x in the interval (a, b), then the series (7-2) defines a function $S(x)$. Let x_0 be some value of x in (a, b), so that

$$|s_n(x_0) - S(x_0)| < \epsilon \quad \text{whenever } n \geq N.$$

It is important to note that, in general, the magnitude of N depends not only on the choice of ϵ, but also on the value of x_0.

This last remark may be clarified by considering the series

$$(7\text{-}4) \quad x + (x - 1)x + (x - 1)x^2 + \cdots$$
$$+ (x - 1)x^{n-1} + \cdots .$$

Since

$$s_n(x) = x + (x - 1)x + (x - 1)x^2 + \cdots + (x - 1)x^{n-1}$$
$$= x^n,$$

it is evident that

$$\lim_{n \to \infty} s_n(x) \equiv \lim_{n \to \infty} x^n = 0, \quad \text{if } 0 \leq x < 1.$$

Thus, $S(x) = 0$ for all values of x in the interval $0 \leq x < 1$, and therefore

$$|s_n(x) - S(x)| = |x^n - 0| = |x^n|.$$

Hence, the requirement that $|s_n(x) - S(x)| < \epsilon$, for an arbitrary ϵ, will be satisfied only if $x^n < \epsilon$. This inequality leads to the condition

$$n \log x < \log \epsilon.$$

Since $\log x$ is negative for x between 0 and 1, it follows that it is necessary to have

$$n > \frac{\log \epsilon}{\log x},$$

which clearly shows the dependence of N on both ϵ and x. In fact, if $\epsilon = 0.01$ and $x = 0.1$, n must be greater than $\log 0.01/\log 0.1$ $= -2/-1 = 2$, so that N can be chosen as any number greater than 2. If $\epsilon = 0.01$ and $x = 0.5$, N must be chosen larger than $\log 0.01/\log 0.5$, which is greater than 6. Since the values of $\log x$ approach zero as x approaches unity, it appears that the ratio $\log \epsilon/\log x$ will increase indefinitely and that it will be impossible to find a single value of N which will serve for $\epsilon = 0.01$ and for all values of x in $0 \leq x < 1$.

It should be noted that the discussion applies to the interval $(0, 1)$ and that it might be possible to find an N, depending on ϵ only, if some other interval were chosen. If the series and the interval are such that it is possible to find an N, for any preassigned ϵ, which will serve *for all values of x in the interval*, then the series is said to converge *uniformly* in the interval.

DEFINITION OF UNIFORM CONVERGENCE. *The series* $\sum\limits_{n=1}^{\infty} u_n(x)$ *is uniformly convergent in the interval* (a, b) *if, for any* $\epsilon > 0$, *there exists a positive number* N, *independent of the value of x in* (a, b), *such that*

$$|S(x) - s_n(x)| < \epsilon \qquad \textit{for all } n \geq N.$$

The distinction between uniform convergence and the type of convergence exemplified by the discussion of the series (7·4) will become apparent in the discussion of the series

$$(7 \cdot 5) \qquad 1 + x + x^2 + \cdots + x^n + \cdots,$$

where $-\frac{1}{2} \leq x \leq \frac{1}{2}$.

Since $s_n(x) = \dfrac{1 - x^n}{1 - x}$, it follows that

$$S(x) = \lim_{n \to \infty} s_n(x) = \lim_{n \to \infty} \left(\frac{1}{1 - x} - \frac{x^n}{1 - x} \right) = \frac{1}{1 - x}.$$

Then,

$$|S(x) - s_n(x)| = \left| \frac{x^n}{1 - x} \right|,$$

which will be less than an arbitrary $\epsilon > 0$ if

$$|x^n| < \epsilon(1 - x).$$

Hence,

$$n \log |x| < \log \epsilon(1 - x),$$

or

(7-6)
$$n > \frac{\log \epsilon(1 - x)}{\log |x|}.$$

Again, it appears that the choice of N will depend on both x and ϵ, but in this case it is possible to choose an N that will serve for all values of x in $(-\frac{1}{2}, \frac{1}{2})$. Observing that the ratio $\log \epsilon(1 - x)/\log |x|$ assumes its maximum value, for a fixed ϵ, when $x = +\frac{1}{2}$, it is evident that if N is chosen so that

$$N > \frac{\log \epsilon(\frac{1}{2})}{\log \frac{1}{2}} = 1 - \frac{\log \epsilon}{\log 2},$$

then the inequality (7-6) will be satisfied for all $n \geq N$.

Upon recalling the conditions for uniform convergence, it is seen that the series (7-5) converges uniformly for $-\frac{1}{2} \leq x \leq \frac{1}{2}$. However, it should be noted that (7-5) does not converge uniformly in the interval $(-1, 1)$. For, in this interval, the ratio appearing in (7-6) will increase indefinitely as x approaches the values ± 1. The discussion given above shows that the series (7-5) is uniformly convergent in any interval $(-a, a)$, where $a < 1$.

It may be remarked that the series (7-5) does not even converge for $x = \pm 1$. For $x = 1$, it is obviously divergent, and when $x = -1$ the series becomes

$$1 - 1 + 1 - 1 + \cdots .$$

If $-1 < x < 1$, (7-5) defines the function $\dfrac{1}{1 - x}$, which takes the value $\frac{1}{2}$ when $x = -1$.

As is often the case with definitions, the definition of uniform convergence is usually difficult to apply when the behavior of a particular series is to be investigated. There are available several tests for the uniform convergence of series, the simplest of which is associated with the name of the German mathematician Weierstrass.

THEOREM. (WEIERSTRASS M TEST). *Let*

$$(7\text{-}7) \qquad u_1(x) + u_2(x) + \cdots + u_n(x) + \cdots$$

be a series of functions of x defined in the interval (a, b). If there exists a convergent series of positive constants,

$$M_1 + M_2 + \cdots + M_n + \cdots,$$

such that $|u_i(x)| \leq M_i$ for all values of x in (a, b), then the series (7-7) is uniformly and absolutely convergent in (a, b).

Since, by hypothesis, the series of M's is convergent, it follows that for any prescribed $\epsilon > 0$ there exists an N such that

$$M_{n+1} + M_{n+2} + \cdots < \epsilon \quad \text{for all } n \geq N.$$

But $|u_i(x)| \leq M_i$ for all values of x in (a, b), so that

$$|u_{n+1}(x) + u_{n+2}(x) + \cdots| \leq M_{n+1} + M_{n+2} + \cdots < \epsilon$$

for all $n \geq N$ and for all values of x in (a, b). Therefore, the series (7-7) is uniformly and absolutely convergent in (a, b).

The fact that the Weierstrass test establishes the absolute convergence, as well as the uniform convergence, of a series means that it is applicable only to series which converge absolutely. There are other tests that are not so restricted, but these tests are more complex. It should be emphasized that a series may converge uniformly but not absolutely, and vice versa.

Example 1. Consider the series

$$\frac{\sin x}{1^2} + \frac{\sin 2x}{2^2} + \cdots + \frac{\sin nx}{n^2} + \cdots.$$

Since $|\sin nx| \leq 1$ for all values of x, the convergent series

$$\frac{1}{1^2} + \frac{1}{2^2} + \cdots + \frac{1}{n^2} + \cdots$$

will serve as an M series. It follows that the given series is uniformly and absolutely convergent in any interval, no matter how large.

Example 2. As noted earlier in this section, the series

$$1 + x + x^2 + \cdots + x^n + \cdots$$

converges uniformly in any interval $(-a, a)$, where $a < 1$. The series of positive constants

$$1 + a + a^2 + \cdots + a^n + \cdots$$

could be used as an M series in this case, since this series converges for $a < 1$ and $|x^i| \leq a^i$ for x in $(-a, a)$.

PROBLEMS

1. Show that the series (7-4) is uniformly convergent in the interval $(0, \frac{1}{2})$.

2. By using the definition of uniform convergence, show that

$$\frac{1}{x + 1} - \frac{1}{(x + 1)(x + 2)} - \cdots - \frac{1}{(x + n - 1)(x + n)} - \cdots$$

is uniformly convergent in the interval $0 \leq x \leq 1$.

Hint: Rewrite the series to show that $s_n(x) = \dfrac{1}{x + n}$ and therefore

$$|S(x) - s_n(x)| = \frac{1}{x + n}.$$

3. Test the following series for uniform convergence:

(a) $\dfrac{\cos x}{1^2} + \dfrac{\cos 3x}{3^2} + \dfrac{\cos 5x}{5^2} + \cdots$;

(b) $\dfrac{\sin 2x}{1 \cdot 3} + \dfrac{\sin 4x}{3 \cdot 5} + \dfrac{\sin 6x}{5 \cdot 7} + \cdots$;

(c) $1 + x \cos \theta + x^2 \cos 2\theta + x^3 \cos 3\theta + \cdots$, $|x| \leq x_1 < 1$;

(d) $\dfrac{\cos 2x}{2^\alpha} - \dfrac{\cos 3x}{3^\alpha} + \dfrac{\cos 4x}{4^\alpha} - \cdots$;

(e) $10x + 10^2 x^2 + 10^3 x^3 + \cdots$.

8. Properties of Uniformly Convergent Series.

As remarked in the preceding section, the concept of uniform convergence was introduced in order to allow the discussion of certain properties of infinite series. This section contains the statements* of three important theorems concerning uniformly convergent series.

THEOREM 1. *Let*

$$u_1(x) + u_2(x) + \cdots + u_n(x) + \cdots$$

be a series such that each $u_i(x)$ is a continuous function of x in the interval (a, b). If the series is uniformly convergent in (a, b), then the sum of the series is also a continuous function of x in (a, b).

* For proofs, see I. S. Sokolnikoff, Advanced Calculus, pp. 256–262.

COROLLARY. *A discontinuous function cannot be represented by a uniformly convergent series of continuous functions in the neighborhood of the point of discontinuity.*

THEOREM 2. *If a series of continuous functions,*

$$u_1(x) + u_2(x) + \cdots + u_n(x) + \cdots,$$

converges uniformly to $S(x)$ in (a, b), then

$$\int_\alpha^\beta S(x)\, dx = \int_\alpha^\beta u_1(x)\, dx + \int_\alpha^\beta u_2(x)\, dx + \cdots + \int_\alpha^\beta u_n(x)\, dx + \cdots,$$

where $a < \alpha < b$ and $a < \beta < b$.

THEOREM 3. *Let*

$$u_1(x) + u_2(x) + \cdots + u_n(x) + \cdots$$

be a series of differentiable functions that converges to $S(x)$ in (a, b). If the series

$$u_1'(x) + u_2'(x) + \cdots + u_n'(x) + \cdots$$

converges uniformly in (a, b), then it converges to $S'(x)$.

These theorems provide sufficient conditions only. It may be that the sum of the series is a continuous function when the series is not uniformly convergent. It is impossible to discuss necessary conditions in this brief introduction to uniform convergence. It may happen also that the series is differentiable or integrable term by term when it does not converge uniformly. In the chapter on Fourier series it will be shown that a discontinuous function can be represented by an infinite series of continuous functions. In that chapter, it is established that the series

$$2\left(\sin x - \frac{\sin 2x}{2} + \frac{\sin 3x}{3} - \cdots \right)$$

represents the function x for $-\pi < x < \pi$. But, if this series be differentiated term by term, the resulting series is

$$2(\cos x - \cos 2x + \cos 3x - \cdots),$$

which does not converge in $(-\pi, \pi)$; for the necessary condition for convergence, namely, that $\lim_{n \to \infty} |u_n| = 0$, does not hold for any value of x.

The series used in the first example of Sec. 7,

$$(8\text{-}1) \quad \frac{\sin x}{1^2} + \frac{\sin 2x}{2^2} + \frac{\sin 3x}{3^2} + \cdots + \frac{\sin nx}{n^2} + \cdots,$$

is uniformly convergent in any interval (a, b) and as such defines a continuous function $S(x)$. Moreover, the series can be integrated term by term to produce the integral of $S(x)$. The term-by-term derivative of (8-1) is

$$(8\text{-}2) \qquad \cos x + \tfrac{1}{2} \cos 2x + \tfrac{1}{3} \cos 3x + \cdots ,$$

which is convergent in $(0, \pi)$, but the M series for (8-2) cannot be found since $1 + \tfrac{1}{2} + \tfrac{1}{3} + \cdots$ is divergent. This merely suggests that (8-2) may not converge to the derivative of $S(x)$, but it does not say that it will not.

PROBLEMS

1. Test for uniform convergence the series obtained by term-by-term differentiation of the five series given in Prob. 3 of Sec. 7.

2. Test for uniform convergence the series obtained by term-by-term integration of the five series given in Prob. 3, Sec. 7.

9. Power Series. One of the most important types of infinite series of functions is the power series

$$(9\text{-}1) \qquad \sum_{n=0}^{\infty} a_n x^n \equiv a_0 + a_1 x + a_2 x^2 + \cdots + a_n x^n + \cdots ,$$

in which the a_i are independent of x. Some of the reasons for the usefulness of power series will become apparent in the discussion that follows.

Whenever a series of functions is used, the first question which arises is that of determining the values of the variable for which the series is convergent. The ratio test was applied for this purpose in the examples discussed in Sec. 5. In general, for a power series,

$$\lim_{n \to \infty} \left| \frac{u_{n+1}}{u_n} \right| = \lim_{n \to \infty} \left| \frac{a_n}{a_{n-1}} x \right| ,$$

so that the series converges if

$$\lim_{n \to \infty} \left| \frac{a_n}{a_{n-1}} x \right| < 1$$

and diverges if

$$\lim_{n \to \infty} \left| \frac{a_n}{a_{n-1}} x \right| > 1.$$

Therefore, the series will converge for those values of x for which

$$|x| < \lim_{n \to \infty} \left| \frac{a_{n-1}}{a_n} \right| .$$

If $\lim\limits_{n \to \infty} \left| \dfrac{a_{n-1}}{a_n} \right| = r$, it follows that the series will converge when x lies inside the interval $(-r, r)$, which is called the *interval of convergence*, the number r being called the *radius of convergence.* This discussion establishes the following theorem:

THEOREM. *If the series* $\sum\limits_{n=0}^{\infty} a_n x^n$ *is such that*

$$\lim_{n \to \infty} \left| \frac{a_{n-1}}{a_n} \right| = r,$$

then the series converges in the interval $-r < x < r$ *and diverges outside this interval. The series may or may not converge at the end points of the interval.*

Example 1. Consider the series

$$1 + x + \frac{x^2}{2} + \frac{x^3}{3} + \cdots + \frac{x^n}{n} + \cdots .$$

Since $\lim\limits_{n \to \infty} \left| \dfrac{a_{n-1}}{a_n} \right| = \lim\limits_{n \to \infty} \left| \dfrac{n}{n-1} \right| = 1$, the series converges for $-1 < x < 1$ and diverges for $|x| > 1$. At the end point $x = -1$ the series becomes

$$1 - 1 + \frac{1}{2} - \frac{1}{3} + \frac{1}{4} - \cdots$$

which is convergent. At the end point $x = 1$ the divergent series

$$1 + 1 + \frac{1}{2} + \frac{1}{3} + \frac{1}{4} + \cdots$$

is obtained. Hence, this power series is convergent for $-1 \leq x < 1$.

Example 2. The series

$$1 + x + 2!x^2 + \cdots + n!x^n + \cdots$$

will serve to demonstrate the fact that there are power series which converge only for the value $x = 0$. For

$$\lim_{n \to \infty} \left| \frac{a_{n-1}}{a_n} \right| = \lim_{n \to \infty} \left| \frac{(n-1)!}{n!} \right| = \lim_{n \to \infty} \frac{1}{n} = 0.$$

Obviously, the series converges for $x = 0$, as does every power series, but it diverges for every other value of x.

Power series in $x - h$ are frequently more useful than the special case in which the value of h is zero. A series of this type has the form

$$a_0 + a_1(x - h) + a_2(x - h)^2 + \cdots + a_n(x - h)^n + \cdots .$$

In this case the test ratio yields

$$\lim_{n \to \infty} \left| \frac{u_{n+1}}{u_n} \right| = \lim_{n \to \infty} \left| \frac{a_n}{a_{n-1}} \right| |x - h|.$$

If this limit is less than 1, the series is convergent; if greater than 1, the series is divergent; and if the limit is equal to 1, the test fails and the values of x, which make the limit equal to 1, must be investigated. Thus, if the series is

$$1 + (x - 1) + \frac{(x - 1)^2}{2^2} + \frac{(x - 1)^3}{3^2} + \cdots$$
$$+ \frac{(x - 1)^n}{n^2} + \cdots,$$

then

$$\lim_{n \to \infty} \left| \frac{u_{n+1}}{u_n} \right| = \lim_{n \to \infty} \left| \frac{(x - 1)^n}{n^2} \frac{(n - 1)^2}{(x - 1)^{n-1}} \right|$$
$$= \lim_{n \to \infty} \left(1 - \frac{2}{n} - \frac{1}{n^2} \right) |x - 1| = |x - 1|.$$

Therefore the series converges if $|x - 1| < 1$, or $0 < x < 2$, and diverges for $|x - 1| > 1$, or $x < 0$, $x > 2$. For $x - 1 = 1$, or $x = 2$, the series becomes

$$1 + 1 + \frac{1}{2^2} + \frac{1}{3^2} + \cdots + \frac{1}{n^2} + \cdots,$$

which is the p series for $p = 2$ and is therefore convergent. For $x - 1 = -1$, or $x = 0$, the series becomes

$$1 - 1 + \frac{1}{2^2} - \frac{1}{3^2} + \cdots + (-1)^n \frac{1}{n^2} + \cdots,$$

which is an alternating series of decreasing terms with $\lim_{n \to \infty} u_n = 0$ and is therefore convergent. Thus the series is convergent for $0 \le x \le 2$.

PROBLEM

Find the interval of convergence for each of the following series, and determine its behavior at the end points of the interval:

(a) $1 + x + x^2 + x^3 + \cdots$;

(b) $1 - x + \frac{x^2}{2!} - \frac{x^3}{3!} + \cdots$;

(c) $1 + (x + 1) + \frac{(x + 1)^2}{2} + \frac{(x + 1)^3}{3} + \cdots$;

(d) $1 - 2x + 3x^2 - 4x^3 + \cdots$;

(e) $1 + \dfrac{x}{2} + \dfrac{x^2}{2^2 \cdot 2} + \dfrac{x^3}{2^3 \cdot 3} + \cdots$;

(f) $(x - 2) - \dfrac{1}{2}(x - 2)^2 + \dfrac{1}{3}(x - 2)^3 - \cdots$;

(g) $x - \dfrac{x^3}{3} + \dfrac{x^5}{5} - \cdots$.

10. Properties of Power Series. The importance of power series in applied mathematics is due to the properties given in the theorems of this section, as will be evident from the applications discussed in succeeding sections.

THEOREM 1. *If $r > 0$ is the radius of convergence of a power series $\sum\limits_{n=0}^{\infty} a_n x^n$, then the series converges absolutely and uniformly for every value of x in any interval $a \le x \le b$ that is interior to $(-r, r)$.*

Since the interval (a, b) lies entirely within the interval $(-r, r)$, it is possible to choose a positive number c that is less than r but greater than $|a|$ and $|b|$. The interval (a, b) will then lie entirely within the interval $(-c, c)$; and it follows that, for $a \le x \le b$,

$$|a_n x^n| < |a_n c^n|.$$

The series of positive constants $\sum\limits_{n=0}^{\infty} |a_n c^n|$ is convergent, for $c < r$, and, accordingly, can be used as a Weierstrass M series establishing the absolute and uniform convergence of $\sum\limits_{n=0}^{\infty} a_n x^n$ in (a, b).

THEOREM 2. *A power series $\sum\limits_{n=0}^{\infty} a_n x^n$ defines a continuous function for all values of x in any closed interval (a, b) that is interior to the interval of convergence of the series.*

This statement is a direct consequence of the preceding theorem and of Theorem 1, Sec. 8.

THEOREM 3. *If the radius of convergence of the power series $\sum\limits_{n=0}^{\infty} a_n x^n$ is r, then the radii of convergence of the series $\sum\limits_{n=0}^{\infty} n a_n x^{n-1}$ and $\sum\limits_{n=0}^{\infty} \dfrac{a_n}{n + 1} x^{n+1}$, obtained by term-by-term differentiation and integration of the given series, are also r.*

If the radius of convergence can be determined from the ratio test, then the proof follows immediately from the fact that if

$$\lim_{n \to \infty} \left| \frac{a_{n-1}}{a_n} \right| = r, \qquad \text{then} \qquad \lim_{n \to \infty} \left| \frac{(n-1)a_{n-1}}{na_n} \right| = r \qquad \text{and}$$

$$\lim_{n \to \infty} \left| \frac{(n+1)a_{n-1}}{na_n} \right| = r.$$

Since the series obtained by term-by-term differentiation and integration are also power series, these processes can be repeated as many times as desired and the resulting series will be power series that converge in the interval $(-r, r)$. It follows from Theorem 1 that all these series are uniformly and absolutely convergent in any interval which is interior to $(-r, r)$. However, the behavior of these series at the end points $x = -r$ and $x = r$ must be investigated in each case.

For example, the series

$$1 + x + \frac{x^2}{2} + \frac{x^3}{3} + \cdots + \frac{x^n}{n} + \cdots$$

has unity for its radius of convergence. The series converges for $x = -1$ but is divergent for $x = 1$. The series obtained by term-by-term differentiation is

$$1 + x + x^2 + \cdots + x^n + \cdots,$$

which has the same radius of convergence but diverges at both $x = 1$ and $x = -1$. On the other hand, the series obtained by term-by-term integration is

$$x + \frac{x^2}{1 \cdot 2} + \frac{x^3}{2 \cdot 3} + \frac{x^4}{3 \cdot 4} + \cdots + \frac{x^{n+1}}{n(n+1)} + \cdots$$

which converges for both $x = 1$ and $x = -1$.

This discussion leads to the conclusion stated in the following theorem:

THEOREM 4. *A power series $\sum\limits_{n=0}^{\infty} a_n x^n$ may be differentiated and integrated term by term as many times as desired in any closed interval (a, b) that lies entirely within the interval of convergence of the given series.*

THEOREM 5. *If a power series $\sum\limits_{n=0}^{\infty} a_n x^n$ vanishes for all values of x lying in a certain interval about the point $x = 0$, then the* *coefficient of each power of x vanishes, that is,*

$$a_0 = 0, \qquad a_1 = 0, \qquad a_2 = 0, \cdots, \qquad a_n = 0, \cdots.$$

The reader may attempt to construct the proof of this theorem with the aid of Theorem 2 of this section.

11. Expansion of Functions in Power Series. It was stated in Theorem 2, Sec. 10, that a power series defines a continuous function of x in any interval which lies within the interval of convergence. This theorem suggests at once the possibility of using such a power series for the purpose of computation. For example, the values of sin x might be obtained by means of a power series. Accordingly, it becomes necessary to develop some method of obtaining such a power series, and this section is devoted to a derivation of Taylor's formula and a discussion of Taylor's series.

One of the simplest proofs of Taylor's formula will be given here.* It assumes that the given function $f(x)$ has a continuous nth derivative throughout the interval (a, b). Taylor's formula is obtained by integrating this nth derivative n times in succession between the limits a and x, where x is any point in (a, b). Thus,

$$\int_a^x f^{(n)}(x)\, dx = f^{(n-1)}(x)\Big|_a^x = f^{(n-1)}(x) - f^{(n-1)}(a),$$

$$\int_a^x \int_a^x f^{(n)}(x)\, (dx)^2 = \int_a^x f^{(n-1)}(x)\, dx - \int_a^x f^{(n-1)}(a)\, dx$$

$$= f^{(n-2)}(x) - f^{(n-2)}(a) - (x-a)f^{(n-1)}(a),$$

$$\int_a^x \int_a^x \int_a^x f^{(n)}(x)\, (dx)^3 = f^{(n-3)}(x) - f^{(n-3)}(a) - (x-a)f^{(n-2)}(a)$$

$$- \frac{(x-a)^2}{2!} f^{(n-1)}(a),$$

$$\cdots\cdots\cdots\cdots\cdots\cdots\cdots\cdots\cdots\cdots\cdots\cdots$$

$$\int_a^x \cdots \int_a^x f^{(n)}(x)\, (dx)^n = f(x) - f(a) - (x-a)f'(a)$$

$$- \frac{(x-a)^2}{2!} f''(a) - \cdots - \frac{(x-a)^{n-1}}{(n-1)!} f^{(n-1)}(a).$$

* For other proofs, see I. S. Sokolnikoff, Advanced Calculus, pp. 291–295.

Solving for $f(x)$ gives

$$(11\text{-}1) \quad f(x) = f(a) + (x - a)f'(a) + \frac{(x - a)^2}{2!} f''(a)$$

$$+ \cdots + \frac{(x - a)^{n-1}}{(n - 1)!} f^{(n-1)}(a) + R_n,$$

where

$$(11\text{-}2) \qquad R_n = \int_a^x \cdots \int_a^x f^{(n)}(x) \, (dx)^n.$$

The formula given by (11-1) is known as Taylor's formula and the particular form of R_n given in (11-2) is called the integral form of the remainder after n terms. The foregoing can be stated in the form of a theorem.

TAYLOR'S THEOREM.   *Any function $f(x)$ that possesses a continuous derivative $f^{(n)}(x)$ in the interval (a, b) can be expanded in the form (11-1) for all values of x in (a, b).*

The term R_n, which represents the difference between $f(x)$ and the polynomial of degree $n - 1$ in $x - a$, is frequently more useful when expressed in a different form.   Since*

$$\int_a^x f^{(n)}(x) \, dx = (x - a)f^{(n)}(\xi), \qquad \text{where } a < \xi < x,$$

repeated integration gives

$$(11\text{-}3) \quad R_n = \int_a^x \cdots \int_a^x f^{(n)}(x) \, (dx)^n = \frac{(x - a)^n}{n!} f^{(n)}(\xi).$$

The right-hand member of (11-3) is the Lagrangian form of the remainder after n terms.

The special form of Taylor's formula that is obtained by setting $a = 0$ is known as the Maclaurin formula.   In this case

$$(11\text{-}4) \quad f(x) = f(0) + f'(0)x + f''(0) \frac{x^2}{2!} + \cdots$$

$$+ f^{(n-1)}(0) \frac{x^{n-1}}{(n - 1)!} + R_n,$$

where

$$R_n = f^{(n)}(\xi) \frac{x^n}{n!}, \qquad 0 < \xi < x.$$

---

* The student will recall from elementary calculus that

$$\int_a^b \varphi(x) \, dx = (b - a)\varphi(\xi), \qquad \text{where } a < \xi < b.$$

Taylor's formula with the Lagrangian form of the remainder is often encountered in a somewhat different form, which results from setting $x - a = h$. Since $a < \xi < x$, ξ can be written in the form $a + \theta h$, where $0 < \theta < 1$. Hence, (11-1) becomes

$$(11\text{-}5) \quad f(a + h) = f(a) + f'(a)h + f''(a)\frac{h^2}{2!} + \cdots$$

$$+ f^{(n-1)}(a)\frac{h^{n-1}}{(n-1)!} + f^{(n)}(a + \theta h)\frac{h^n}{n!}, \quad \text{where } 0 < \theta < 1.$$

In this derivation of Taylor's formula, it was assumed that $f(x)$ possesses a continuous nth derivative, and as a result it appeared that then $f(x)$ could be expressed as a polynomial of degree n in $x - a$. It should be noted, however, that only the first n coefficients of this polynomial are constants, for the coefficient of $(x - a)^n$ is a function of ξ and the value of ξ is dependent upon the choice of x. It may happen that $f(x)$ possesses derivatives of all orders and that the remainder R_n approaches zero as a limit when $n \to \infty$ regardless of the choice of x in (a, b). If such is the case, the infinite series

$$(11\text{-}6) \quad f(a) + f'(a)(x - a) + f''(a)\frac{(x - a)^2}{2!} + \cdots$$

$$+ f^{(n)}(a)\frac{(x - a)^n}{n!} + \cdots$$

is convergent and, in general,* it converges to $f(x)$.

The series given in (11-6) is called the Taylor's series expansion, or representation, of the function $f(x)$ about the point $x = a$. The special form of (11-6) that is obtained when $a = 0$, namely,

$$(11\text{-}7) \quad f(0) + f'(0)x + f''(0)\frac{x^2}{2!} + \cdots + f^{(n)}(0)\frac{x^n}{n!} + \cdots$$

is called Maclaurin's series.

Example. Find the Taylor's series expansion of $\cos x$ in powers of $x - \frac{\pi}{2}$.

Since

$$f(x) = \cos x, \qquad f\left(\frac{\pi}{2}\right) = 0;$$

$$f'(x) = -\sin x, \qquad f'\left(\frac{\pi}{2}\right) = -1;$$

---

* For a further discussion of this point, see I. S. Sokolnikoff, Advanced Calculus, pp. 296–298.

$$f''(x) = -\cos x, \qquad f''\left(\frac{\pi}{2}\right) = 0;$$

$$f'''(x) = \sin x, \qquad f'''\left(\frac{\pi}{2}\right) = 1;$$

$$f^{IV}(x) = \cos x, \qquad f^{IV}\left(\frac{\pi}{2}\right) = 0;$$

$$\dots\dots\dots\dots\dots\dots\dots\dots\dots\dots\dots;$$

it follows that the result is

$$\cos x = -\left(x - \frac{\pi}{2}\right) + \frac{1}{3!}\left(x - \frac{\pi}{2}\right)^3 - \frac{1}{5!}\left(x - \frac{\pi}{2}\right)^5 + \cdots.$$

Since it is often possible to obtain a power series expansion of a function $f(x)$ by some other method, the question arises as to the relation of such an expansion to the Taylor's series expansion for $f(x)$. For example, a power series expansion for the function $\frac{1}{1-x}$ is obtained easily by division, giving

$$\frac{1}{1-x} = 1 + x + x^2 + \cdots + x^n + \cdots.$$

The reader can check the fact that the Maclaurin expansion for this function is identical with the power series obtained by division. That this is not an exceptional case is established in the following theorem:

UNIQUENESS THEOREM. *There is only one possible expansion of a function in a power series in $x - a$; and, therefore, if such an expansion be found in any manner whatsoever, it must coincide with Taylor's expansion about the point a.*

Suppose that $f(x)$ could be represented by two power series in $x - a$, so that

$$f(x) = a_0 + a_1(x - a) + a_2(x - a)^2 + \cdots$$
$$+ a_n(x - a)^n + \cdots$$

and

$$f(x) = b_0 + b_1(x - a) + b_2(x - a)^2 + \cdots$$
$$+ b_n(x - a)^n + \cdots.$$

Since both these expansions represent $f(x)$ in the vicinity of a, there must be some interval about the point $x = a$ in which both the expansions are valid. Then, in this interval,

$$\sum_{n=0}^{\infty} a_n(x - a)^n = \sum_{n=0}^{\infty} b_n(x - a)^n,$$

or

$$\sum_{n=0}^{\infty} (a_n - b_n)(x - a)^n = 0.$$

It follows from Theorem 5, Sec. 10, that

$$a_n - b_n = 0, \quad (n = 0, 1, 2, \cdots),$$

or

$$a_n = b_n, \quad (n = 0, 1, 2, \cdots).$$

Hence, the two power series expansions are identical.

Taylor's formula is frequently more useful in a slightly modified form. Let

$$x - a \equiv h,$$

so that

$$x = a + h.$$

Then

$$f(x) = f(a) + f'(a)(x - a) + \frac{f''(a)}{2!} (x - a)^2 + \cdots$$
$$+ \frac{f^{(n-1)}(a)}{(n - 1)!} (x - a)^{n-1} + \frac{f^{(n)}(\xi)}{n!} (x - a)^n$$

becomes

$$(11\text{-}8) \quad f(a + h) = f(a) + f'(a)h + \frac{f''(a)}{2!} h^2 + \cdots$$
$$+ \frac{f^{(n-1)}(a)}{(n - 1)!} h^{n-1} + \frac{f^{(n)}(a + \theta h)}{n!} h^n,$$

in which $0 < \theta < 1$, so that $a < a + \theta h < a + h$.

PROBLEMS

1. Find the expansion of each of the following functions in power series in x:

    (a) e^x,   (b) $\sin x$,   (c) $\cos x$,   (d) $\tan^{-1} x$,
    (e) $\sin^{-1} x$,   (f) $\sec x$,   (g) $\tan x$,   (h) $e^{\sin x}$.

2. Expand

    (a) $\log x$ in powers of $x - 1$;

    (b) $\tan x$ in powers of $x - \dfrac{\pi}{4}$;

    (c) e^x in powers of $x - 2$;

    (d) $\sin x$ in powers of $x - \dfrac{\pi}{6}$;

    (e) $2 + x^2 - 3x^5 + 7x^6$ in powers of $x - 1$.

3. Show that sin x can be developed about any point a in a series (11-8) which converges for all values of h.

4. Differentiate term by term the power series in x for sin x and thus obtain the power series in x for cos x. What is the interval of convergence of the resulting series?

5. Divide the series $\sin x \equiv x - \dfrac{x^3}{3!} + \dfrac{x^5}{5!} - \cdots$ by the series $\cos x \equiv 1 - \dfrac{x^2}{2!} + \dfrac{x^4}{4!} - \cdots$, and thus obtain the series for tan x.

6. Differentiate the series for $\sin^{-1} x$ to obtain the expansion in powers of x for $(1 - x^2)^{-\frac{1}{2}}$. Find the interval of convergence. Is convergence absolute? Investigate the behavior of the series at the end points of the interval of convergence.

7. Establish with the aid of Maclaurin's series that

$$(a + b)^m \equiv k(1 + x)^m = k \left[1 + mx + \frac{m(m - 1)}{2!} x^2 + \cdots \right],$$

where m is not a positive integer.

This series is convergent for $|x| < 1$ and divergent when $|x| > 1$. A complete discussion of this series will be found in Sokolnikoff's Advanced Calculus. Some facts are:

If $x = 1$, convergence is absolute if $m > 0$;
If $x = 1$, convergence is conditional if $0 > m > -1$;
If $x = -1$, convergence is absolute if $m > 0$;
If $x = -1$, series diverges when $m < 0$;
If $x = 1$, series diverges when $m \leq -1$.

8. Let $f(y) = \sum\limits_{n=0}^{\infty} b_n y^n$ and $y = \sum\limits_{n=0}^{\infty} a_n x^n$ be convergent power series. If $f(y)$ is a polynomial, then the powers of y in terms of x can be determined by repeated multiplications and thus the expansion for $f(y)$ in powers of x can be obtained. But if $f(y)$ is an infinite series, this procedure may not be valid. Inasmuch as the power series in x is always convergent for $x = 0$ and since the value of y for $x = 0$ is a_0, it is clear that the interval of convergence of $\sum\limits_{n=0}^{\infty} b_n y^n$ must include a_0 if the series for $f(y)$, in powers of x, is to converge. But if $a_0 = 0$, then $f(y)$ surely can be expanded in power series in x by this method, for the point 0 is contained in the interval of convergence of $\sum\limits_{n=0}^{\infty} b_n y^n$.

Apply this method to deriving the series in powers of x for $e^{\sin x}$ by setting

$$y = \sin x = x - \frac{x^3}{3!} + \frac{x^5}{5!} - \cdots$$

and

$$e^y = 1 + y + \frac{y^2}{2!} + \frac{y^3}{3!} + \cdots .$$

Explain why this method fails to produce the series in powers of x for $\log (1 + e^x)$, where $e^x = y$.

12. Application of Taylor's Formula. In this section two illustrations of the application of Taylor's formula will be given, and in each case the remainder will be investigated to determine the error made in using the sum of the first n terms of the expansion instead of the function itself.

1. *Calculate the Value of* sin 10°. Since 10° is closer to 0° than to any other value of x for which the values of sin x and its derivatives are known, the Maclaurin expansion for sin x will be determined and evaluated for $x = 10° = \pi/18$ radian. Then

$$f(x) = f(0) + f'(0)x + \frac{f''(0)}{2!} x^2 + \cdots + \frac{f^{(n-1)}(0)}{(n-1)!} x^{n-1}$$
$$+ \frac{f^{(n)}(\xi)}{n!} x^n,$$

where $0 < \xi < \dfrac{\pi}{18}$.

Since

$$\begin{array}{ll} f(x) = \sin x, & f(0) = 0; \\ f'(x) = \cos x, & f'(0) = 1; \\ f''(x) = -\sin x, & f''(0) = 0; \\ f'''(x) = -\cos x, & f'''(0) = -1; \\ \cdots\cdots\cdots\cdots\cdots\cdots\cdots\cdots & \cdots; \\ f^{(n)}(x) = \sin\left(x + \dfrac{n\pi}{2}\right), & f^{(n)}(0) = \sin \dfrac{n\pi}{2}; \end{array}$$

therefore,

$$\sin x = x - \frac{x^3}{3!} + \frac{x^5}{5!} - \frac{x^7}{7!} + \cdots + \frac{x^n}{n!} f^{(n)}(\xi).$$

Here,

$$R_n(x) \equiv \frac{x^n}{n!} f^{(n)}(\xi) = \frac{x^n}{n!} f^{(n)}(\theta x), \qquad 0 < \theta < 1,$$
$$= \frac{x^n}{n!} \sin\left(\theta x + \frac{n\pi}{2}\right).$$

If only the terms through x^7 (or x^8) are used in computing $\sin \pi/18$, the error will be

$$R_9\left(\frac{\pi}{18}\right) = \left(\frac{\pi}{18}\right)^9 \frac{1}{9!} \sin\left(\theta\,\frac{\pi}{18} + \frac{9}{2}\,\pi\right) = \left(\frac{\pi}{18}\right)^9 \frac{1}{9!} \cos\frac{\theta\pi}{18}$$

$$< \left(\frac{\pi}{18}\right)^9 \frac{1}{9!},$$

so that

$$\sin\frac{\pi}{18} = \frac{\pi}{18} - \left(\frac{\pi}{18}\right)^3 \frac{1}{3!} + \left(\frac{\pi}{18}\right)^5 \frac{1}{5!} - \left(\frac{\pi}{18}\right)^7 \frac{1}{7!},$$

with an error less than $\left(\dfrac{\pi}{18}\right)^9 \dfrac{1}{9!}$.

2. *Compute the Value of* $e^{1.1}$. It can be established readily, by expanding e^x in Maclaurin's series and evaluating for $x = 1$, that $e = 2.71828 \cdots$. In order to compute the value of $e^{1.1}$, the expansion of e^x about $x = 1$ will be used. The expansion is

$$f(x) = f(1) + f'(1)(x - 1) + \frac{f''(1)}{2!}\,(x - 1)^2 + \cdots$$

$$+ \frac{f^{(n)}(\xi)}{n!}\,(x - 1)^n.$$

Since

$$f(x) = e^x, \qquad f(1) = e;$$
$$f'(x) = e^x, \qquad f'(1) = e;$$
$$\cdots\cdots\cdots\cdots\cdots\cdots\cdots$$
$$f^{(n)}(x) = e^x, \qquad f^{(n)}(1) = e;$$

and

$$f^{(n)}(\xi) = e^\xi, \qquad 1 < \xi < x;$$

therefore

$$e^x = e + e(x - 1) + \frac{e}{2!}\,(x - 1)^2 + \cdots + \frac{e}{(n - 1)!}\,(x - 1)^{n-1}$$

$$+ \frac{e^\xi}{n!}\,(x - 1)^n.$$

Here

$$R_n = \frac{e^\xi}{n!}\,(x - 1)^n,$$

so that the error made in using only four terms is

$$R_4 = \frac{e^\xi}{4!}\,(x - 1)^4.$$

If $x = 1.1$,

$$e^{1.1} = e\left[1 + 0.1 + \frac{(0.1)^2}{2!} + \frac{(0.1)^3}{3!}\right] + \frac{e^\xi}{4!}\,(0.1)^4$$

$$= 1.105166e + \frac{0.0001}{24}\,e^\xi.$$

Thus, $e^{1.1} = 1.105166e$ with an error of $(0.0001/24)e^{\xi}$. Since ξ lies between 1 and 1.1 and since e^{ξ} is an increasing function, e^{ξ} is certainly less than e^2. An approximate value of e^2 is 7, and the error is certainly less than $0.0007/24 = 0.00003$. Therefore,

$$e^{1.1} = 1.1052e,$$

correct to four decimal places.

13. Evaluation of Definite Integrals by Means of Power Series. One of the most important applications of infinite series is their use in computing numerical values of definite integrals, such as $\int_0^1 e^{-x^2}\, dx$, in which the indefinite integral cannot be found in closed form. Moreover, the values of many transcendental functions are computed most easily by this method. Several examples of this use of infinite series are given in this section.

Example 1.   Consider

$$\log (1 + x) = \int_0^x \frac{dz}{1 + z} = \int_0^x (1 + z)^{-1}\, dz.$$

Since

$$(1 + z)^{-1} = 1 - z + z^2 - z^3 + \cdots$$

for $|z| < 1$, it follows that

$$\log (1 + x) = \int_0^x \frac{dz}{1 + z} = \int_0^x dz - \int_0^x z\, dz + \int_0^x z^2\, dz - \cdots$$
$$= x - \frac{x^2}{2} + \frac{x^3}{3} - \cdots.$$

Example 2.   Since

$$\sin^{-1} x = \int_0^x \frac{dz}{\sqrt{1 - z^2}}$$
$$= \int_0^x \left(1 + \frac{1}{2} z^2 + \frac{1 \cdot 3}{2 \cdot 4} z^4 + \frac{1 \cdot 3 \cdot 5}{2 \cdot 4 \cdot 6} z^6 + \cdots \right) dz,$$

if $|z| < 1$, therefore

$$\sin^{-1} x = x + \frac{1}{2} \frac{x^3}{3} + \frac{1 \cdot 3}{2 \cdot 4} \frac{x^5}{5} + \cdots.$$

It is evident that this method of obtaining the expansion of $\sin^{-1} x$ is much less complicated than the direct application of Taylor's formula.

Example 3.   In order to evaluate the integral

$$I = \int_0^h \frac{2a\, dx}{\sqrt{2g(h - x)(2ax - x^2)}},$$

express it as

$$\sqrt{\frac{a}{g}} \int_0^h \frac{dx}{\sqrt{hx - x^2}} \left(1 - \frac{x}{2a}\right)^{-\frac{1}{2}},$$

and then replace $\left(1 - \dfrac{x}{2a}\right)^{-\frac{1}{2}}$ by its expansion in powers of $\dfrac{x}{2a}$, giving

$$\sqrt{\frac{a}{g}} \int_0^h \left[1 + \frac{1}{2}\left(\frac{x}{2a}\right) + \frac{1 \cdot 3}{2 \cdot 4}\left(\frac{x}{2a}\right)^2 \right.$$
$$\left. + \frac{1 \cdot 3 \cdot 5}{2 \cdot 4 \cdot 6}\left(\frac{x}{2a}\right)^3 + \cdots \right] \frac{dx}{\sqrt{hx - x^2}}.$$

If this integral is expressed as

$$\sqrt{\frac{a}{g}} \left[\int_0^h \frac{dx}{\sqrt{hx - x^2}} + \int_0^h \frac{1}{2}\left(\frac{x}{2a}\right) \frac{dx}{\sqrt{hx - x^2}} \right.$$
$$\left. + \int_0^h \frac{1 \cdot 3}{2 \cdot 4}\left(\frac{x}{2a}\right)^2 \frac{dx}{\sqrt{hx - x^2}} + \cdots \right]$$

and each integral evaluated, there results

$$I = \pi \sqrt{\frac{a}{g}} \left[1 + \left(\frac{1}{2}\right)^2 \frac{h}{2a} + \left(\frac{1 \cdot 3}{2 \cdot 4}\right)^2 \left(\frac{h}{2a}\right)^2 \right.$$
$$\left. + \left(\frac{1 \cdot 3 \cdot 5}{2 \cdot 4 \cdot 6}\right)^2 \left(\frac{h}{2a}\right)^3 + \cdots \right].$$

This expression gives the period of the simple pendulum. By making the change of variable $x = h \sin^2 \varphi$, the integral reduces to

$$I = 2 \sqrt{\frac{a}{g}} \int_0^{\frac{\pi}{2}} (1 - k^2 \sin^2 \varphi)^{-\frac{1}{2}} \, d\varphi,$$

where $k^2 = h/2a$.

This is the form used in the discussion of the simple pendulum given in Sec. 71. In this illustration, h denotes the height of the pendulum bob and a the length of the pendulum.

Example 4. The integral $\displaystyle\int_0^1 \frac{e^x - e^{-x}}{x} \, dx$ cannot be evaluated by the usual method for evaluating a definite integral, for the indefinite integral cannot be obtained. Moreover, the expansion for $\dfrac{e^x - e^{-x}}{x}$, if obtained directly with the aid of Maclaurin's formula, would lead to an extremely complicated expression for each derivative. The expansion is most easily obtained by using the separate expansions for e^x and e^{-x}. Thus,

$$e^x = 1 + x + \frac{x^2}{2!} + \frac{x^3}{3!} + \cdots,$$
$$e^{-x} = 1 - x + \frac{x^2}{2!} - \frac{x^3}{3!} + \cdots,$$

and

$$e^x - e^{-x} = 2\left(x + \frac{x^3}{3!} + \frac{x^5}{5!} + \cdots \right).$$

Hence,

$$\int_0^1 \frac{e^x - e^{-x}}{x}\, dx = 2\left(1 + \frac{1}{3\cdot 3!} + \frac{1}{5\cdot 5!} + \cdots \right) = 2.1145.$$

Example 5. In order to evaluate the integral $\int_0^\pi e^{\sin x}\, dx$, recall that

$$e^u = 1 + u + \frac{u^2}{2!} + \frac{u^3}{3!} + \cdots ,$$

so that

$$e^{\sin x} = 1 + \sin x + \frac{\sin^2 x}{2!} + \frac{\sin^3 x}{3!} + \cdots .$$

Then

$$\int_0^\pi e^{\sin x}\, dx = \int_0^\pi \left(1 + \sin x + \frac{\sin^2 x}{2!} + \frac{\sin^3 x}{3!} + \cdots \right) dx$$

$$= 2\int_0^{\frac{\pi}{2}} \left(1 + \sin x + \frac{\sin^2 x}{2!} + \frac{\sin^3 x}{3!} + \cdots \right) dx,$$

which can be evaluated with the aid of the Wallis formula

$$\int_0^{\frac{\pi}{2}} \sin^n x\, dx = \int_0^{\frac{\pi}{2}} \cos^n x\, dx = \frac{(n-1)(n-3)\cdots 2 \text{ or } 1}{n(n-2)\cdots 2 \text{ or } 1}\, \alpha,$$

where $\alpha = 1$, if n is odd, and $\alpha = \frac{\pi}{2}$, if n is even.

In order to justify the term-by-term integration, it is sufficient to show that the series in the integrand is uniformly convergent. That such is the case is obvious if one considers

$$1 + 1 + \frac{1}{2!} + \frac{1}{3!} + \cdots$$

as the Weierstrass M series.

PROBLEMS

1. Calculate cos 10°, and estimate the maximum error committed by neglecting terms after x^6.

2. Find the interval of convergence of the expansion of e^x in power series in x. Determine the number of terms necessary to compute $e^{1.1}$ accurate to four decimal places from this expansion, and compare the result with illustration 2, Sec. 12.

3. Compute sin 33°, correct to four decimal places.

4. Expand the integrand of $\int_0^x \dfrac{dx}{1 + x^2}$ in power series in x, and integrate term by term.   Compare the result with that of Prob. 1(d), Sec. 11.

5. Compute $\sqrt[5]{35} = 2(1 + \tfrac{3}{32})^{\frac{1}{5}}$, correct to five decimal places.

6. Develop the power series in x for $\sin^{-1} x$ and hence establish that

$$\frac{\pi}{6} = \frac{1}{2} + \frac{1}{2} \cdot \frac{1}{3} \left(\frac{1}{2}\right)^3 + \frac{1 \cdot 3}{2 \cdot 4} \cdot \frac{1}{5} \left(\frac{1}{2}\right)^5 + \cdots .$$

7. Show, by squaring and adding the power series for $\sin x$ and $\cos x$, that

$$\sin^2 x + \cos^2 x = 1.$$

8. Evaluate by using series expansions of the integrands

(a) $\displaystyle\int_0^1 \sin (x^2)\, dx;$ (b) $\displaystyle\int_0^{\frac{1}{3}} \frac{\sin x\, dx}{\sqrt{1 - x^2}};$

(c) $\displaystyle\int_0^1 \frac{\sin x}{x}\, dx;$ (d) $\displaystyle\int_0^x e^{-x^2}\, dx;$

(e) $\displaystyle\int_0^x \cos (x^2)\, dx;$ (f) $\displaystyle\int_0^1 (2 - \cos x)^{-\frac{1}{2}}\, dx$

$$= \int_0^1 \left[2 - \left(1 - 2 \sin^2 \frac{x}{2}\right)\right]^{-\frac{1}{2}} dx$$

$$= \int_0^1 \left(1 + 2 \sin^2 \frac{x}{2}\right)^{-\frac{1}{2}} dx;$$

(g) $\displaystyle\int_{0.9}^1 \frac{\log x}{1 - x}\, dx = \int_0^{0.1} \frac{\log(1 - z)}{z}\, dz;$ (h) $\displaystyle\int_0^x \frac{\cos x\, dx}{\sqrt{x}};$

(i) $\displaystyle\int_0^x e^{\tan x}\, dx.*$

9. Show, by multiplication of series, that

$$(1 + x + x^2 + \cdots)^2 = 1 + 2x + 3x^2 + \cdots$$
$$= (1 - x)^{-2}.$$

10. Expand to terms in x^6

(a) $\sqrt{\cos x};$

(b) $\dfrac{\sin x}{e^x - 1};$

(c) $\dfrac{e^x}{1 + e^x}.$

11. Determine the magnitude of α, if the error in the approximation $\sin \alpha \doteq \alpha$ is not to exceed 1 per cent.

Hint: $\dfrac{\alpha - \sin \alpha}{\alpha} = 0.01$ and $\sin \alpha = \alpha - \dfrac{\alpha^3}{3!} + \dfrac{\alpha^5}{5!} - \cdots .$

* See form 787, B. O. Peirce, A Short Table of Integrals.

14. Rectification of Ellipse. Elliptic Integrals. In spite of its importance and apparent simplicity, the problem of finding the length of an elliptical arc is not usually considered in elementary calculus. This is because the integral that arises is incapable of evaluation in terms of elementary functions. However, the evaluation can be effected by means of series expansion of the integrand function, as will be shown in this section.

Let the equation of the ellipse be

$$\frac{x^2}{a^2} + \frac{y^2}{b^2} = 1, \qquad a > b.$$

The length of arc from $(0, b)$ to (x_1, y_1) is given by the integral

$$(14\text{-}1) \qquad s = \int_0^{x_1} \sqrt{1 + \left(\frac{dy}{dx}\right)^2}\, dx.$$

Computing dy/dx and substituting its value in (14-1) gives

$$s = \int_0^{x_1} \sqrt{1 + \frac{b^2}{a^2}\frac{x^2}{a^2 - x^2}}\, dx = \int_0^{x_1} \sqrt{\frac{a^2 - \dfrac{a^2 - b^2}{a^2} x^2}{a^2 - x^2}}\, dx.$$

Recalling the fact that the numerical eccentricity of the ellipse is $k = \sqrt{a^2 - b^2}/a$, the integral given above can be written as

$$(14\text{-}2) \qquad s = \int_0^{x_1} \sqrt{\frac{a^2 - k^2 x^2}{a^2 - x^2}}\, dx,$$

where $k^2 < 1$.

Let $x = a \sin \theta$; then $dx = a \cos \theta\, d\theta$, and (14-2) becomes

$$(14\text{-}3) \qquad s = a \int_0^{\varphi} \sqrt{1 - k^2 \sin^2 \theta}\, d\theta.$$

The series expansion of the integrand function is most easily obtained by writing it as $(1 - k^2 \sin^2 \theta)^{\frac{1}{2}}$ and expanding by use of the binomial theorem. Then (14-3) is replaced by

$$s = a \int_0^{\varphi} \left(1 - \frac{1}{2} k^2 \sin^2 \theta - \frac{1}{8} k^4 \sin^4 \theta - \cdots \right) d\theta,$$

and term-by-term integration* gives

---

* Term-by-term integration is valid here, for the series

$$1 + \frac{1}{2} k^2 + \cdots + \frac{1 \cdot 3 \cdots (2n - 3)}{2 \cdot 4 \cdots 2n} k^{2n} + \cdots$$

serves as a Weierstrass M series.

$$(14\text{-}4) \quad s = a\left[\varphi - \frac{1}{2}k^2 \int_0^\varphi \sin^2\theta\,d\theta - \frac{1}{8}k^4 \int_0^\varphi \sin^4\theta\,d\theta - \cdots \right.$$

$$\left. - \frac{1\cdot 3\cdot 5\,\cdots\,(2n-3)}{2\cdot 4\cdot 6\,\cdots\,2n}\,k^{2n}\int_0^\varphi \sin^{2n}\theta\,d\theta - \cdots \right].$$

If (14-4) is used, it is possible to evaluate s for particular values of k and φ. However, the integral in (14-3) is so important that there are extensive tables* giving its value for many choices of k and φ. This integral for the value of $a = 1$ is called the elliptic integral of the second kind and is denoted by the symbol $E(k, \varphi)$. If $\varphi = \pi/2$, the integral is called the complete elliptic integral of the second kind, which is denoted by the symbol E.

The elliptic integral of the second kind having been defined, it seems desirable to mention the elliptic integral of the first kind, although the latter arises in considering the motion of a simple pendulum and will be discussed in more detail in Sec. 71. The elliptic integral of the first kind, $F(k, \varphi)$, has the form

$$(14\text{-}5) \qquad F(k, \varphi) = \int_0^\varphi \frac{d\theta}{\sqrt{1 - k^2\sin^2\theta}}.$$

The complete elliptic integral of the first kind, which arises when $\varphi = \pi/2$, is denoted by the symbol K. Values of $F(k, \varphi)$ and of K are also tabulated, but the evaluation can be obtained from (14-5) by means of series expansion of the integrand. Thus, one has the expansion

$$(14\text{-}6) \quad F(k, \varphi) = \varphi + \frac{1}{2}k^2 \int_0^\varphi \sin^2\theta\,d\theta + \frac{3}{8}k^4 \int_0^\varphi \sin^4\theta\,d\theta$$

$$+ \cdots + \frac{1\cdot 3\,\cdots\,(2n-1)}{2\cdot 4\,\cdots\,2n}\,k^{2n}\int_0^\varphi \sin^{2n}\theta\,d\theta + \cdots .$$

15. Discussion of Elliptic Integrals. The elliptic integral of the first kind is a function defined by the integral

$$(15\text{-}1) \qquad F(k, \varphi) \equiv \int_0^\varphi \frac{d\theta}{\sqrt{1 - k^2\sin^2\theta}}, \qquad k^2 < 1.$$

* See the brief table in B. O. Peirce, A Short Table of Integrals, pp. 121–123.

If $\sin \theta$ is replaced by z, (15-1) becomes

$$(15\text{-}2) \qquad \bar{F}(k, x) = \int_0^x \frac{dz}{\sqrt{(1 - z^2)(1 - k^2 z^2)}}, \qquad k^2 < 1.$$

This is an alternative form of the elliptic integral of the first kind.

Similarly, the same change of variable transforms the integral of the second kind

$$(15\text{-}3) \qquad E(k, \varphi) = \int_0^\varphi \sqrt{1 - k^2 \sin^2 \theta} \, d\theta, \qquad k^2 < 1,$$

into

$$(15\text{-}4) \qquad \bar{E}(k, x) = \int_0^x \sqrt{\frac{1 - k^2 z^2}{1 - z^2}} \, dz, \qquad k^2 < 1.$$

It will be recalled that any integral of the type

$$\int R(x, \sqrt{ax^2 + bx + c}) \, dx,$$

where R is a rational function of the variables x and

$$\sqrt{ax^2 + bx + c},$$

is integrable in terms of the elementary functions, *i.e.*, power, trigonometric, and logarithmic functions. It can be shown that the integration of integrals of the type

$$(15\text{-}5) \qquad \int R(x, \sqrt{ax^3 + bx^2 + cx + d}) \, dx$$

and

$$(15\text{-}6) \qquad \int R(x, \sqrt{ax^4 + bx^3 + cx^2 + dx + e}) \, dx$$

requires, in general, the introduction of new functions obtained from the elliptic integrals.

The evaluation of (15-5) and (15-6) can be reduced to the evaluation of integrals of the elementary types and the following new types:

a. Elliptic integral of the first kind:

$$\bar{F}(k, x) \equiv \int_0^x \frac{dz}{\sqrt{(1 - z^2)(1 - k^2 z^2)}}, \qquad \text{or}$$

$$F(k, \varphi) \equiv \int_0^\varphi \frac{d\theta}{\sqrt{1 - k^2 \sin^2 \theta}}.$$

b. Elliptic integral of the second kind:

$$\bar{E}(k, x) \equiv \int_0^x \sqrt{\frac{1 - k^2 z^2}{1 - z^2}} \, dz, \qquad \text{or}$$

$$E(k, \varphi) \equiv \int_0^\varphi \sqrt{1 - k^2 \sin^2 \theta} \, d\theta.$$

c. Elliptic integral of the third kind:

$$\overline{\Pi}(n, k, x) \equiv \int_0^x \frac{dz}{(1 + nz^2)\sqrt{(1 - z^2)(1 - k^2z^2)}},$$

or

$$\Pi(n, k, \varphi) \equiv \int_0^\varphi \frac{d\theta}{(1 + n\sin^2\theta)\sqrt{1 - k^2\sin^2\theta}}.$$

The problem of reducing the integrals of expressions involving square roots of cubics and quartics to normal forms is not difficult, but it is tedious and will be omitted here.* Integrals involving

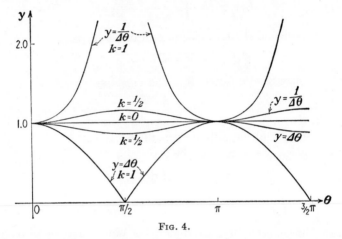

Fig. 4.

square roots of polynomials of degree higher than the fourth lead, in general, to more complicated functions, the so-called hyper-elliptic functions.

The graphs of the integrands of the integrals of the first and second kinds are of some interest (see Fig. 4). For $k = 0$,

$$\Delta\theta \equiv \sqrt{1 - k^2\sin^2\theta} \quad \text{and} \quad \frac{1}{\Delta\theta} \equiv \frac{1}{\sqrt{1' - k^2\sin^2\theta}}$$

both become equal to 1, and the corresponding integrals are both equal to φ. For $0 < k < 1$, the curve $y = 1/\Delta\theta$ lies entirely above the line $y = 1$ and the curve $y = \Delta\theta$ lies entirely below it. As φ increases,

* For a detailed account see Goursat-Hedrick, Mathematical Analysis, vol. 1, p. 226. A monograph, Elliptic Functions by H. Hancock, may also be consulted.

$F(k, \varphi)$ and $E(k, \varphi)$ increase continuously, F being always the larger. As k increases, φ being fixed, the value of $F(k, \varphi)$ increases and that of $E(k, \varphi)$ decreases. Also $F(k, \pi) = 2K$ and $E(k, \pi) = 2E$, for the curves are symmetrical about $\theta = \pi/2$. If $\pi/2 < \varphi < \pi$, it is obvious from the figure that

$$(15\text{-}7) \qquad \begin{aligned} F(k, \varphi) &= 2K - F(k, \pi - \varphi), \\ E(k, \varphi) &= 2E - E(k, \pi - \varphi). \end{aligned}$$

Moreover,

$$(15\text{-}8) \qquad \begin{aligned} F(k, m\pi + \varphi) &= 2mK + F(k, \varphi), \\ E(k, m\pi + \varphi) &= 2mE + E(k, \varphi), \end{aligned}$$

where m is an integer.

Since the values of K and E, and of $F(k, \varphi)$ and $E(k, \varphi)$ for $\varphi \leq \pi/2$, are tabulated, the relations (15-7) and (15-8) permit the evaluation of $F(k, \varphi)$ and $E(k, \varphi)$ for all values of φ.

The discussion* above was restricted to values of $k^2 < 1$. If $k^2 = 1$, $y = \Delta\theta$ becomes $y = |\cos \theta|$ and $y = 1/\Delta\theta$ becomes $y = |\sec \theta|$.

Consider

$$(15\text{-}9) \qquad u = \int_0^x \frac{dz}{\sqrt{(1 - z^2)(1 - k^2 z^2)}} = \int_0^\varphi \frac{d\theta}{\sqrt{1 - k^2 \sin^2 \theta}},$$

where $x = \sin \varphi$.

For a fixed value of k, (15-9) defines $u = \bar{F}(x)$ or $u = F(\varphi)$. The function resulting from the solution of (15-9) for φ in terms of u is called the amplitude of u and is denoted by am $(u, \bmod k)$, or more simply by $\varphi = $ am u. It will be assumed that the equation $u = F(\varphi)$ can be solved for φ. Since $\varphi = $ am u,

$$x = \sin \varphi \equiv \sin \text{ am } u \equiv \text{sn } u.$$

Moreover,

$$\cos \varphi \equiv \sqrt{1 - x^2} \equiv \sqrt{1 - \text{sn}^2 u} \equiv \text{cn } u.$$

Finally,

$$\Delta\varphi \equiv \sqrt{1 - k^2 x^2} \equiv \text{dn } u.$$

The functions sn u, cn u, and dn u are called the *elliptic functions*.

From the definitions, it is obvious that

$$\text{am } (0) = 0, \quad \text{sn } (0) = 0, \quad \text{cn } (0) = 1, \quad \text{dn } (0) = 1;$$
$$\text{am } (-u) = -\text{am } u, \text{sn } (-u) = -\text{sn } u, \text{cn } (-u) = \text{cn } u, \text{dn } (-u)$$
$$= \text{dn } u.$$

The elliptic functions are periodic functions and in some respects resemble the trigonometric functions. There exists a complete set of

* See Prob. 1, at the end of this section.

formulas connecting the elliptic functions analogous to the set for the trigonometric functions.*

An interesting application of elliptic integrals to electrical problems is found in the calculation of the magnetic flux density in the plane of a circular loop of radius a carrying a steady current I.

Upon applying the law of Biot and Savart† to a circular loop of radius a, the flux density B at any point P in the plane of the wire is given by

$$(15\text{-}10) \qquad B = \frac{I}{4\pi} \int_C \frac{\sin{(r,\,s)}\,ds}{r^2},$$

where C is the circumference of the loop, r is the radius vector

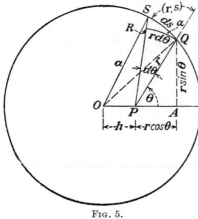

FIG. 5.

from P to an element of arc ds, and $(r,\,s)$ is the angle between r and this element (Fig. 5).

If the point P is at the center of the loop, then $(r,\,s) = 90°, r = a$, and the integral is easily evaluated to give

$$B = \frac{I}{4\pi}\frac{2\pi a}{a^2} = \frac{I}{2a},$$

a familiar result.

If, however, the point P is not at the center, the evaluation of the integral is not so easy. Consider the triangle RQS, where the side $RQ = r\,d\theta$ makes an angle α with ds. It is clear that $ds \cos \alpha = r\,d\theta$; and, since $\alpha = 90° - (r,\,s)$, it follows that

$$\cos \alpha = \sin{(r,\,s)}.$$

Hence,

$$ds = \frac{r\,d\theta}{\sin{(r,\,s)}}.$$

* See APPEL, P., and E. LACOUR, Fonctions elliptiques; PEIRCE, B. O., A Short Table of Integrals; GREENHILL, A. G., The Application of Elliptic Functions.

† This formula is known to engineers as Ampere's formula. See, for example, E. Bennett, Introductory Electrodynamics for Engineers. The system of units used here is the "rational" system of units used in M. Mason and W. Weaver, Electromagnetic Field.

The substitution of this value in (15-10) yields

$$(15\text{-}11) \qquad\qquad B = \frac{I}{4\pi} \int_0^{2\pi} \frac{d\theta}{r}$$

for the magnetic flux density at P.

Now, from triangle OQA, it is evident that

$$\sqrt{a^2 - (r \sin \theta)^2} = r \cos \theta + h,$$

which, after squaring both sides and simplifying, becomes

$$r^2 + 2rh \cos \theta + (h^2 - a^2) = 0.$$

Solving for r gives

$$r = -h \cos \theta \pm \sqrt{h^2 \cos^2 \theta + a^2 - h^2};$$

and, since r is always positive, the radical must be taken with the positive sign. Substituting this value of r in (15-11) gives

$$B = \frac{I}{4\pi} \int_0^{2\pi} \frac{d\theta}{-h \cos \theta + \sqrt{h^2 \cos^2 \theta + a^2 - h^2}},$$

or, upon rationalization of the denominator,

$$B = \frac{I}{4\pi} \int_0^{2\pi} \frac{-h \cos \theta - \sqrt{h^2 \cos^2 \theta + a^2 - h^2}}{h^2 - a^2} \, d\theta$$

$$= \frac{I}{4\pi(a^2 - h^2)} \left(\int_0^{2\pi} h \cos \theta \, d\theta + \int_0^{2\pi} \sqrt{a^2 - h^2 \sin^2 \theta} \, d\theta \right).$$

The first of these integrals is zero, and the second is an elliptic integral of the second kind, so that

$$B = \frac{Ia}{4\pi(a^2 - h^2)} \int_0^{2\pi} \sqrt{1 - \frac{h^2}{a^2} \sin^2 \theta} \, d\theta$$

$$= \frac{Ia}{\pi(a^2 - h^2)} \int_0^{\frac{\pi}{2}} \sqrt{1 - k^2 \sin^2 \theta} \, d\theta,$$

where $k = h/a$. This integral can be evaluated for any k with the aid of the tables of elliptic integrals.

PROBLEMS

1. Prove that

$$\int_0^{\varphi} \frac{d\varphi}{\sqrt{1 - l^2 \sin^2 \varphi}} = \frac{1}{l} \int_0^{\psi} \frac{d\alpha}{\sqrt{1 - l^{-2} \sin^2 \alpha}}, \qquad l > 1.$$

Hint: Change the variable by setting $l^2 \sin^2 \varphi = \sin^2 \alpha$.

2. Plot, with the aid of Peirce's tables, $F(k, \varphi)$, where $k = \sin \alpha$, using α as abscissa and $F(k, \varphi)$ as ordinate. Draw 10 curves on the same sheet of rectangular coordinate paper for $\varphi = 0$, $\varphi = 10$, $\varphi = 20$, $\varphi = 30$, $\varphi = 40$, $\varphi = 50$, $\cdots$, $\varphi = 90$.

3. Plot four curves representing $F(k, \varphi)$ on the same sheet of rectangular coordinate paper. Use φ as abscissa and the values of k as 0, $\frac{1}{2}$, $\sqrt{3}/2$, and 1.

4. Plot the integrand of $\int_0^\varphi \dfrac{d\varphi}{\sqrt{1 - k^2 \sin^2 \varphi}}$ for the values of $k = 0$, $\frac{1}{2}$, and 1. Use φ as abscissa. The areas under the curves give the values of the elliptic integrals.

5. Compute the value of $F(0, \pi/2)$.

6. The major and minor axes of an elliptical arch are 200 ft. and 50 ft., respectively. Find the length of the arch. Compute the length of the arch between the points where $x = 0$ and $x = 25$. Use Peirce's tables.

7. Plot with the aid of Peirce's tables $E(k, \varphi)$, where $k = \sin \alpha$. Use α's as abscissas and $E(k, \varphi)$ as ordinates. Draw 10 curves on the same sheet of rectangular coordinate paper for $\varphi = 0$, 10, 20, $\cdots$, 90.

8. Plot on a sheet of rectangular coordinate paper the four curves representing $E(k, \varphi)$. Use φ as abscissa. The four curves are for $k = 0$, $\frac{1}{2}$, $\sqrt{3}/2$, and 1.

9. Plot the integrand of $\int_0^\varphi \sqrt{1 - k^2 \sin^2 \varphi} \, d\varphi$ for the values of $k = 0$, $\frac{1}{2}$, and 1. Use φ as abscissa. Compare the result with that of Prob. 4. What can be said about the relative magnitudes of $F(k, \varphi)$ and $E(k, \varphi)$?

10. Show that $\int_0^\varphi \dfrac{d\varphi}{\sqrt{1 + k^2 \sin^2 \varphi}}$ is an elliptic integral of the first kind.

Hint: Change the variable by setting $\sin \varphi = \dfrac{1}{k} \tan x$.

11. Show that

$$\int_0^{\frac{\pi}{2}} \frac{dx}{\sqrt{\sin x}} = \int_0^{\frac{\pi}{2}} \frac{dx}{\sqrt{\cos x}} = \sqrt{2} \int_0^{\frac{\pi}{2}} \frac{d\varphi}{\sqrt{1 - \frac{1}{2} \sin^2 \varphi}}.$$

Hint: Set $\sqrt{\cos x} = \cos \varphi$.

Note that the integral is improper but that it is easy to show its convergence.

12. Show that

$$\int_0^{\frac{\pi}{2}} \frac{\sin^2 \theta \, d\theta}{\sqrt{1 - k^2 \sin^2 \theta}} = \frac{1}{k^2} (K - E).$$

Hint: $\sin^2 \theta = \dfrac{1}{k^2} - \dfrac{1}{k^2}(1 - k^2 \sin^2 \theta)$.

13. Show that

$$K \equiv \int_0^{\frac{\pi}{2}} \frac{d\theta}{\sqrt{1 - k^2 \sin^2 \theta}}$$

$$= \frac{\pi}{2} \left[1 + \left(\frac{1}{2}\right)^2 k^2 + \left(\frac{1 \cdot 3}{2 \cdot 4}\right)^2 k^4 + \left(\frac{1 \cdot 3 \cdot 5}{2 \cdot 4 \cdot 6}\right)^2 k^6 + \cdots \right] \text{ if } k^2 < 1.$$

14. Find the length of one arch of the sine curve.

15. Find the length of the portion of $y = \sin x$ lying between $x = 1$ and $x = 2$.

16. Given:

$$F\left(\frac{1}{2}, \varphi\right) \equiv \int_0^{\varphi} \frac{d\theta}{\sqrt{1 - \frac{1}{4}\sin^2 \theta}}.$$

Find K and sn $\frac{2}{3}K$.

17. Show that $\displaystyle\int \frac{d\theta}{\sqrt{a - \cos \theta}}$, where $a > 1$, is an elliptic integral.

18. Show that the length of arc of an ellipse of semiaxes a and b is given by

$$s = 4a \int_0^{\frac{\pi}{2}} \sqrt{1 - e^2 \sin^2 \theta} \, d\theta$$

$$= 2\pi a \left(1 - \frac{e^2}{4} - \frac{3}{64} e^4 - \cdots \right), \text{ where } e \text{ is the eccentricity.}$$

16. Approximate Formulas in Applied Mathematics. It is frequently necessary to introduce approximations in order to make readily usable the results of mathematical investigations. For example, an engineer seldom finds it necessary to use the exact formula for the curvature of a curve whose equation is $y = f(x)$, namely,

$$(16\text{-}1) \qquad\qquad K = \frac{\dfrac{d^2 y}{dx^2}}{\left[1 + \left(\dfrac{dy}{dx}\right)^2\right]^{\frac{3}{2}}},$$

since in most applications the slope dy/dx is small enough to permit the use of the approximate formula

$$(16\text{-}2) \qquad\qquad K \doteq \frac{d^2 y}{dx^2}.$$

Many such approximations are obtained by using the first few terms of the Taylor's series expansion in place of the function itself. Thus, the formula (16-2) is obtained from (16-1) by neglecting all except the first term in the expansion of $[1 + (dy/dx)^2]^{-3/2}$ in powers of dy/dx.

1. *Small Errors.* The values of physical quantities determined by experiment are subject to errors due to inaccuracies arising in the measurements of the quantities involved. It is often necessary to know the size of such errors.

Let a capillary tube contain a column of mercury. The radius R of the tube can be determined by measuring the length L and the weight W of the column of mercury. Let L be measured in centimeters and W in grams. Since the density of mercury is $\rho = 13.6$,

$$R = \sqrt{\frac{W}{\pi \rho L}} = 0.153 \sqrt{\frac{W}{L}}.$$

The principal error arises in the measurement of L. Let L be the true value, and let $L' = L + \epsilon$ be the observed value. Then, if R is the true value of the radius, let $R' = R + \eta$ be the computed value. The error in measuring W is negligible because of the high accuracy of the balance. It follows that

$$R = 0.153 \sqrt{\frac{W}{L}} \quad \text{and} \quad R' = 0.153 \sqrt{\frac{W}{L'}}$$

or

$$R + \eta = 0.153 \sqrt{\frac{W}{L + \epsilon}}.$$

Therefore,

$$\begin{aligned} \eta &= 0.153 \left(\sqrt{\frac{W}{L + \epsilon}} - \sqrt{\frac{W}{L}} \right) \\ &= 0.153 \sqrt{\frac{W}{L}} \left[\left(1 + \frac{\epsilon}{L} \right)^{-1/2} - 1 \right] \\ &= R \left(-\frac{\epsilon}{2L} + \frac{3}{8} \frac{\epsilon^2}{L^2} - \cdots \right). \end{aligned}$$

Since ϵ is small compared with L, it follows that η is approximately given by $-\frac{1}{2} R \frac{\epsilon}{L}$. Clearly, ϵ can be either positive or negative.

2. *Crank and Connecting Rod.* If one end of a straight line PQ (see Fig. 6) is required to move on a circle, while the other

end moves on a straight line which passes through the center of the circle, the resulting motion is called connecting-rod motion. This kind of motion arises in a steam engine in which one end of the connecting rod is attached to the crank PB and therefore moves in a circle whose radius is the length of the crank, while the other end is attached to the crosshead and moves along a straight line.

Let r be the length of the crank, l the length of the connecting rod, and s the displacement of the crosshead from the position A,

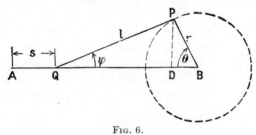

Fig. 6.

in which the connecting rod and crank lie in a straight line. Then,

$$AB = l + r,$$

and

$$AB = AQ + QD + DB = s + l \cos \varphi + r \cos \theta.$$

Moreover,

$$PD = l \sin \varphi = r \sin \theta,$$

so that

$$\sin \varphi = \frac{r}{l} \sin \theta$$

and

$$\cos \varphi = \sqrt{1 - \frac{r^2}{l^2} \sin^2 \theta}.$$

Therefore,

$$s + l \left(1 - \frac{r^2}{l^2} \sin^2 \theta \right)^{\frac{1}{2}} + r \cos \theta = l + r$$

or

$$s = l \left[1 - \left(1 - \frac{r^2}{l^2} \sin^2 \theta \right)^{\frac{1}{2}} \right] + r(1 - \cos \theta).$$

If

$$\left(1 - \frac{r^2}{l^2} \sin^2 \theta \right)^{\frac{1}{2}}$$

be replaced by its expansion, it follows that

$$s = l \left[\frac{1}{2} \frac{r^2}{l^2} \sin^2 \theta + \frac{1}{8} \left(\frac{r^2}{l^2} \right)^2 \sin^4 \theta + \cdots \right] + r(1 - \cos \theta)$$

$$= \left(\frac{r^2}{2l} \sin^2 \theta + \frac{r^4}{8l^3} \sin^4 \theta + \cdots \right) + r(1 - \cos \theta).$$

If r is small compared with l, the displacement of the crosshead is given approximately by $r(1 - \cos \theta)$.

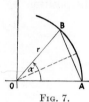

FIG. 7.

3. *Surveying.*   In railroad surveying, it is frequently useful to know the amount of difference between the length of a circular arc and the length of its corresponding chord.

Let r be the radius of curvature of the arc AB (Fig. 7), and let α be the angle intercepted by the arc.   Then, if s is the length of the arc AB and c is the length of chord AB, $s = r\alpha$ and $c = 2r \sin \frac{\alpha}{2}$.

Since

$$\sin x = x - \frac{x^3}{3!} + \frac{x^5}{5!} \cos \xi,$$

where $0 < \xi < x$, the error in using only the first two terms of the expansion is certainly less than $\left| \frac{x^5}{5!} \right|$.   Then,

$$c = 2r \sin \frac{\alpha}{2} = 2r \left(\frac{\alpha}{2} - \frac{\alpha^3}{8 \cdot 6} \right)$$

with an error less than

$$2r \left(\frac{\alpha^5}{32 \cdot 120} \right) = \frac{r\alpha^5}{1920}.$$

Therefore,

$$s - c = r\alpha - r\alpha + \frac{\alpha^3 r}{24} = \frac{\alpha^3 r}{24}$$

with an error that is less than $r\alpha^5/1920$.

4. *Vertical Motion under Earth's Attraction.*   Let it be required to determine the velocity of a body of mass m that is falling from a height s_0 above the center of the earth and is subject to the earth's attraction alone.

Let F be the attraction on the earth's surface and F' be the attraction at a distance h from the surface (Fig. 8).   Then

$$F = \frac{kmm'}{r^2} \quad \text{and} \quad F' = \frac{kmm'}{(r+h)^2},$$

where m' is the mass of the earth, k is the gravitational constant, and r is the radius of the earth.   Hence,

$$\frac{F}{F'} = \frac{(r+h)^2}{r^2}.$$

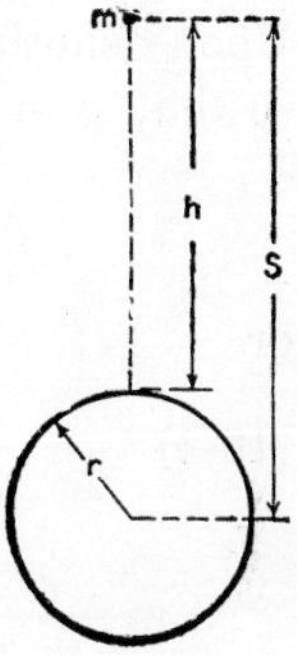

Also, let g be the acceleration at the surface of the earth and g' be the acceleration at a distance h above the surface, so that $F = mg$ and $F' = mg'$.   It follows that

$$\frac{F}{F'} = \frac{g}{g'} = \frac{(r+h)^2}{r^2} = \frac{s^2}{r^2},$$

and, therefore,

$$g' = \frac{gr^2}{s^2}.$$

FIG. 8.

But

$$g' = -\frac{d^2s}{dt^2},$$

so that

$$\frac{d^2s}{dt^2} = -\frac{gr^2}{s^2}.$$

This equation can be solved for $v = ds/dt$ by the following device: Multiplying both members by $2\,ds/dt$ and integrating give

$$\left(\frac{ds}{dt}\right)^2 = \frac{2gr^2}{s} + C,$$

where C is the constant of integration.   If the initial velocity $(ds/dt)_{s=s_0}$ is zero, then $C = -2gr^2/s_0$ and hence

$$\left(\frac{ds}{dt}\right)^2 = 2gr^2\left(\frac{1}{s} - \frac{1}{s_0}\right).$$

But $s = r + h$ and $ds/dt = v$, so that the equation becomes

$$v^2 = 2gr^2\left(\frac{1}{r+h} - \frac{1}{s_0}\right).$$

This formula can be used to calculate the terminal velocity (*i.e.*, the velocity at the earth's surface) when the body is released from any height.   Thus, setting $h = 0$ gives

(16-3) $$v^2 = 2gr^2 \left(\frac{1}{r} - \frac{1}{s_0} \right).$$

Upon denoting by h_0 the initial height above the earth's surface, so that $s_0 = r + h_0$, (16-3) can be written as

$$v^2 = 2gr^2 \left(\frac{1}{r} - \frac{1}{r + h_0} \right),$$

or

(16-4) $$v^2 = 2gr \left(1 - \frac{r}{r + h_0} \right).$$

Now $\dfrac{r}{r + h_0} = \left(1 + \dfrac{h_0}{r} \right)^{-1}$; and if $\dfrac{h_0}{r} < 1$, then series expansion is permissible, so that

$$\frac{r}{r + h_0} = 1 - \frac{h_0}{r} + \left(\frac{h_0}{r} \right)^2 - \cdots .$$

Hence, if $h_0/r < 1$, (16-4) can be replaced by

$$v^2 = 2gr \left[\frac{h_0}{r} - \left(\frac{h_0}{r} \right)^2 + \left(\frac{h_0}{r} \right)^3 - \cdots \right].$$

Moreover, if h_0 is very small compared with r, then the powers of h_0/r higher than the first can be neglected* and

$$v^2 = 2gh_0,$$

which is the familiar formula for the terminal velocity of a body falling freely from a height h_0 that is not too great.

It follows from (16-3) that the square of the terminal velocity will be less than $2gr^2(1/r) = 2gr$.   Moreover, for large values of s_0 the terminal velocity will be very close to $\sqrt{2gr}$.   Accordingly, if a body falls from a very great distance it would attain a terminal velocity (air resistance being neglected) of approximately

$$\sqrt{2gr} = 6.95 \text{ miles per second.}$$

The results stated in the last paragraph may receive a different interpretation.   Suppose a body were projected outward from the earth's surface with a velocity of more than $\sqrt{2gr} = 6.95$ miles per second.   The previous discussion shows that, if air

* Since the series is alternating, the error will be less than $2gr(h_0/r)^2$.

resistance is neglected, the body would travel an infinite distance. This velocity is called the critical velocity or the velocity of escape.

It may be recalled that the earth's rotation exerts a centrifugal force on a particle which is falling toward the earth and that this force diminishes the effect of the force due to the earth's attraction. For a particle of mass m on the surface of the earth at the equator, this centrifugal force is

$$\frac{mv^2}{r} = \frac{m\omega^2 r^2}{r} = m\omega^2 r = \frac{mg}{289} \text{ dynes,}$$

where $\omega = 0.00007292$ radian per second is the angular velocity of the earth, $r = 6,370,284$ m., and $g = 980$ cm. per second per second. At a distance s from the center of the earth, this force is

$$m\omega^2 s = \frac{mgs}{289r}.$$

But the earth's attraction at this distance is $F = mg'$. Since $g' = gr^2/s^2$,

$$F = \frac{mgr^2}{s^2}.$$

If the particle is to be in equilibrium,

$$\frac{mgs}{289r} = \frac{mgr^2}{s^2},$$

so that

$$s^3 = 289r^3 \qquad \text{or} \qquad s = 6.6r = 26,000 \text{ miles approx.}$$

Thus, if all other forces are neglected, a particle would be in equilibrium at approximately 22,000 miles above the earth's surface. This gives a very rough approximation to the extent of the earth's atmosphere. The actual thickness of the atmospheric layer is supposed to be considerably smaller.

PROBLEMS

1. The mass of the moon is nearly one-eighty-first that of the earth, and its radius is approximately three-elevenths that of the earth. Determine the velocity of escape for a body projected from the moon. Acceleration of gravity on the surface of the moon is one-sixth that on the surface of the earth.

2. Show that the time required for a body to reach the surface of the earth in Illustration 4, Sec. 16, is

$$t = \frac{\sqrt{s_0}}{8r} \left(\sqrt{s_0 s - s^2} + \frac{s_0}{2} \cos^{-1} \frac{2s - s_0}{s_0} \right).$$

Hint:

$$\frac{ds}{dt} = -\sqrt{2gr^2} \left(\frac{1}{s} - \frac{1}{s_0} \right)^{\frac{1}{2}}.$$

3. If the earth is considered as a homogeneous sphere at rest, then the force of attraction on a particle within the sphere can be shown to be proportional to the distance of the particle from the center. Let a hole be bored through the center of the earth, the air exhausted, and a stone released from rest at the surface of the earth. Show that the velocity of the stone at the center of the earth is about 5 miles per second.

Hint:

$$m \frac{d^2s}{dt^2} = -\frac{mg}{r} s,$$

where s is the distance of the stone from the center of the earth and r is the radius of the earth.

CHAPTER II

FOURIER SERIES

17. Preliminary Remarks. It is frequently necessary to find the equation of a curve that passes through a certain number of given points lying in the xy-plane. This can be accomplished in an infinite number of ways. Thus, if there are three given points, the coefficients of

$$(17\text{-}1) \qquad\qquad y = a_0 + a_1x + a_2x^2$$

can be chosen so that the resulting parabola will pass through the three given points. This is accomplished by solving the three linear equations, in a_0, a_1, and a_2, that arise when the coordinates of the given points are substituted in (17-1). If there are four given points, it is impossible, in general, to determine a_0, a_1, and a_2 so that the parabola (17-1) will pass through all four points, since the four linear equations in a_0, a_1, and a_2 will be, in general, incompatible. However, it will be possible to determine the coefficients of

$$(17\text{-}2) \qquad\qquad y = a_0 + a_1x + a_2x^2 + a_3x^3$$

so that the curve defined by (17-2) passes through all four points.

The determination of the equation of a curve passing through a set of given points is not unique. Thus, if four points are given, it is possible to determine a curve whose equation is (17-2) which passes through them. But it is also possible to determine the coefficients of

$$y = b_0 + b_1x + b_2 \sin x + b_3x^5$$

so that the curve defined by this equation will pass through the given points. Obviously this curve will not coincide with that defined by (17-2). The type of curve can be varied at will, but the number of coefficients to be determined must equal the number of given points.

If a curve is defined by the equation $y = f(x)$, it is possible, as indicated above, to make the curve whose equation is

(17-3) $\quad y = a_0 + a_1 \cos x + a_2 \cos 2x + \cdots + a_n \cos nx$
$$+ b_1 \sin x + b_2 \sin 2x + \cdots + b_n \sin nx$$

pass through any $2n + 1$ points of $y = f(x)$ in the interval from $x = 0$ to $x = 2\pi$. The question arises as to whether it is possible to make the curve $y = f(x)$ coincide with that defined by (17-3) at all points of the interval $(0, 2\pi)$ by increasing indefinitely the number of terms in (17-3). It is already known that it is possible, under rather severe restrictions, to represent $f(x)$ by an infinite series in powers of x. This was accomplished with the aid of Taylor's series. The analogous problem of representing $f(x)$ by an infinite trigonometric series was developed by Fourier and will be discussed in the succeeding sections.

Whereas the representation of a function $f(x)$ in Taylor's series demands that $f(x)$ possess derivatives of all orders, the development in a trigonometric series

$$(17\text{-}4) \qquad \sum_{n=0}^{\infty} (a_n \cos nx + b_n \sin nx)$$

is possible for a much larger group of functions. In fact, many periodic* functions having a finite number of ordinary discontinuities can be represented by infinite series of trigonometric functions. The term ordinary (or finite) discontinuity is used to describe the situation that arises when the function $f(x)$ suffers a finite jump at some point $x = x_0$ (see Fig. 9).

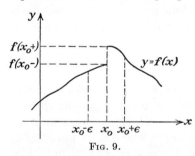

FIG. 9.

Analytically, this means that the two limiting values of $f(x)$, as x approaches x_0 from the right-hand and the left-hand sides, exist but are unequal; *i.e.*,

$$\lim_{\epsilon \to 0} f(x_0 + \epsilon) \neq \lim_{\epsilon \to 0} f(x_0 - \epsilon).$$

In order to economize on space, these right-hand and left-hand limits are written as $f(x_0+)$ and $f(x_0-)$, respectively, so that the foregoing inequality can be written as

$$f(x_0+) \neq f(x_0-).$$

* A function is said to be periodic of period a if $f(x) = f(x + a)$.

Inasmuch as each term of (17-4) is a periodic function of period 2π, it is necessary to restrict the discussion of the representation of functions by series of the type (17-4) to those functions which have period 2π. Or, what amounts to the same thing, the problem of representing a non-periodic function can be restricted to some interval of width 2π, and the function defined outside this interval so that it is periodic. For the present, it will be assumed that the interval in which $f(x)$ is considered is the interval $(-\pi, \pi)$ and that outside this interval the function is defined by the equation $f(x + 2\pi) = f(x)$. Of course, any interval $(a, a + 2\pi)$ would do equally well.

The theory of Fourier series is one of the most beautiful developments of analysis, and it serves as an indispensable instrument in the treatment of nearly every physical problem. Solutions of such important problems as sound vibration, propagation of electric currents and wireless waves, heat conduction, and mechanical vibrations give but a mere indication of its value.

The following section contains the celebrated theorem giving conditions on $f(x)$ that are sufficient to permit its representation by a Fourier series, and also a derivation* of the formulas for the Fourier coefficients (that is, the coefficients in the trigonometric series).

18. Dirichlet Conditions. Derivation of Fourier Coefficients.
THEOREM. *Let $f(x)$ be a function defined arbitrarily in the interval $-\pi \le x \le \pi$, and outside this interval defined by the equation $f(x + 2\pi) = f(x)$. If $f(x)$ has a finite number of points of ordinary discontinuity and a finite number of maxima and minima in the interval $-\pi \le x \le \pi$, then it can be represented by the series*

$$\frac{a_0}{2} + \sum_{k=1}^{\infty} (a_k \cos kx + b_k \sin kx),$$

with

$$a_k = \frac{1}{\pi} \int_{-\pi}^{\pi} f(t) \cos kt\, dt,$$

$$b_k = \frac{1}{\pi} \int_{-\pi}^{\pi} f(t) \sin kt\, dt, \qquad (k = 0, 1, 2, \cdots),$$

* For a more extended treatment, see I. S. Sokolnikoff, Advanced Calculus, Chap. XI.

which converges at every point $x = x_0$ *of the interval to the value**

$$\frac{f(x_0+) + f(x_0-)}{2}.$$

The restrictions imposed upon the function $f(x)$ in this theorem are known as the *Dirichlet conditions.*

The following demonstration that the Fourier coefficients a_k and b_k have the form given in the theorem assumes that the Fourier series development of the function $f(x)$, namely,

$$(18\text{-}1) \qquad f(x) = \frac{a_0}{2} + \sum_{k=1}^{\infty} (a_k \cos kx + b_k \sin kx)$$

can be integrated term by term in the interval $(-\pi, \pi)$. The proof that if a function $f(x)$ satisfies the Dirichlet conditions then its Fourier series expansion actually converges to $f(x)$ is too involved to be given here.†

In order to determine a_0, multiply (18-1) by dx and integrate term by term from $-\pi$ to π. Since

$$\int_{-\pi}^{\pi} \cos nx \, dx = \int_{-\pi}^{\pi} \sin nx \, dx = 0 \text{ for } n = 1, 2, \cdots$$

and, hence,

$$\int_{-\pi}^{\pi} f(x) \, dx = a_0 \pi,$$

there results

$$(18\text{-}2) \qquad a_0 = \frac{1}{\pi} \int_{-\pi}^{\pi} f(x) \, dx.$$

The coefficient a_n of the general cosine term can be obtained by multiplying both members of (18-1) by $\cos nx \, dx$ and performing term-by-term integration from $-\pi$ to π. Since, for all integral values of m and n,

$$\int_{-\pi}^{\pi} \sin mx \cos nx \, dx = 0$$

and

$$\int_{-\pi}^{\pi} \cos mx \cos nx \, dx = 0, \qquad \text{for } m \neq n,$$

---

* If $f(x)$ is continuous at the point $x = x_0$, then $f(x_0+) = f(x_0-) = f(x_0)$, so that at all points of continuity the series converges to $f(x)$. At the points of ordinary discontinuity, it converges to the arithmetic mean of the values of the right- and left-hand limits.

† KNOPP, K., Theory and Application of Infinite Series, p. 356; CARSLAW, H. S., Fourier's Series and Integrals, p. 207.

there results

$$\int_{-\pi}^{\pi} f(x) \cos nx \, dx = a_n \int_{-\pi}^{\pi} \cos^2 nx \, dx = a_n \pi.$$

Therefore,

(18-3) $$a_n = \frac{1}{\pi} \int_{-\pi}^{\pi} f(x) \cos nx \, dx.$$

It should be observed that (18-3) becomes (18-2) for $n = 0$.

Similarly, by multiplying (18-1) by $\sin nx \, dx$ and performing term-by-term integration from $-\pi$ to π, one obtains

(18-4) $$b_n = \frac{1}{\pi} \int_{-\pi}^{\pi} f(x) \sin nx \, dx.$$

It can be shown that if the values of the function are not equal at the end points of the interval $(-\pi, \pi)$, that is, if $f(-\pi) \neq f(\pi)$, then at these end points the Fourier series expansion for $f(x)$ converges to $\frac{1}{2}[f(-\pi) + f(\pi)]$.

The student will convince himself that, if the function $f(x)$ is defined in the interval from 0 to 2π, then the coefficients a_n and b_n in (18-1) are given by the formulas

$$a_n = \frac{1}{\pi} \int_0^{2\pi} f(x) \cos nx \, dx \quad \text{and} \quad b_n = \frac{1}{\pi} \int_0^{2\pi} f(x) \sin nx \, dx.$$

19. Expansion of Functions in Fourier Series. This section contains some illustrative examples of expansion of functions, satisfying the Dirichlet conditions in the interval $(-\pi, \pi)$, in the series

(19-1) $$\frac{a_0}{2} + \sum_{n=1}^{\infty} (a_n \cos nx + b_n \sin nx),$$

where the coefficients a_n and b_n are given by the formulas

(19-2) $$a_n = \frac{1}{\pi} \int_{-\pi}^{\pi} f(x) \cos nx \, dx$$

and

(19-3) $$b_n = \frac{1}{\pi} \int_{-\pi}^{\pi} f(x) \sin nx \, dx.$$

Illustrative Example 1. Expand $f(x) = x$ in Fourier series in the interval $-\pi \leq x \leq \pi$. Calculating the coefficients a_n and b_n gives

$$a_n = \frac{1}{\pi} \int_{-\pi}^{\pi} x \cos nx \, dx = 0,$$

and

$$b_n = \frac{1}{\pi} \int_{-\pi}^{\pi} x \sin nx \, dx = -\frac{2}{n} \cos n\pi.$$

Hence,

$$x = 2[(-\tfrac{1}{1} \cos \pi) \sin x + (-\tfrac{1}{2} \cos 2\pi) \sin 2x$$
$$+ (-\tfrac{1}{3} \cos 3\pi) \sin 3x + \cdots]$$

or

$$x = 2\left(\sin x - \frac{\sin 2x}{2} + \frac{\sin 3x}{3} - \cdots \right).$$

In this particular case, only the sine terms remain. It may be noted that whenever the function $f(x)$ is an odd function, that is, when $f(-x) = -f(x)$, then $a_n = 0$, for $n = 0, 1, 2 \cdots$, since, for such a function,

$$\int_{-\pi}^{0} f(x) \cos nx \, dx = -\int_{0}^{\pi} f(x) \cos nx \, dx.$$

Similarly, if $f(x)$ is an even function, that is, when $f(-x) = f(x)$ then $b_n = 0$, for $n = 1, 2, 3, \cdots$, since

$$\int_{-\pi}^{0} f(x) \sin nx \, dx = -\int_{0}^{\pi} f(x) \sin nx \, dx,$$

so that the function would be represented by a series of cosine terms.

If in the foregoing illustration the first four terms be plotted by composition of

$$y = 2 \sin x, \quad y = -\sin 2x, \quad y = \tfrac{2}{3} \sin 3x, \quad y = -\tfrac{1}{2} \sin 4x,$$

the curve

$$y = 2 \sin x - \sin 2x + \tfrac{2}{3} \sin 3x - \tfrac{1}{2} \sin 4x$$

is obtained. It is represented on Fig. 10. As the number of terms is increased, the approximating curves approach $y = x$ as a limit for all values of x, $-\pi < x < \pi$, but not for $x = \pm\pi$. Since the series has period 2π, it represents the discontinuous function shown in Fig. 11 by a series of parallel lines. It should be noted that each term of the series is continuous and the function from which the series was derived is continuous, but the function represented by the series has finite discontinuities at

$x = \pm(2k + 1)\pi$. At such points the series converges to zero, which is one-half the value of the sum of the right- and left-hand limits.

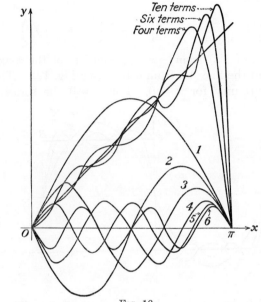

Fig. 10.

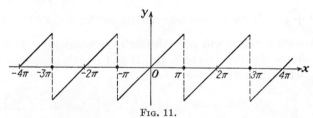

Fig. 11.

Illustrative Example 2. Develop $f(x)$ in Fourier series in the interval $(-\pi, \pi)$, if

$$f(x) = 0, \qquad \text{for } -\pi < x < 0,$$
$$= \pi, \qquad \text{for } \quad 0 < x < \pi.$$

Now

$$a_0 = \frac{1}{\pi} \left(\int_{-\pi}^{0} 0 \cdot dx + \int_{0}^{\pi} \pi \, dx \right) = \pi,$$

$$a_n = \frac{1}{\pi} \int_{0}^{\pi} \pi \cos nx \, dx = 0,$$

$$b_n = \frac{1}{\pi} \int_0^\pi \pi \sin nx \, dx = \frac{1}{n}(1 - \cos n\pi).$$

The series is then

$$\frac{\pi}{2} + 2\left(\frac{\sin x}{1} + \frac{\sin 3x}{3} + \frac{\sin 5x}{5} + \cdots\right).$$

The graph of $f(x)$ from $-\pi$ to π consists of the x-axis from $-\pi$ to 0, and the line AB from 0 to π (see Fig. 12). There is a finite discontinuity for $x = 0$. For $x = 0$ the series reduces

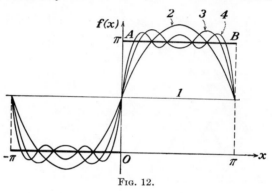

Fig. 12.

to $\pi/2$, which is equal to half the sum of $\lim_{\epsilon \to 0} f(0 - \epsilon)$ and $\lim_{\epsilon \to 0} f(0 + \epsilon)$. It may be observed from the series that every approximation curve will pass through the point $(0, \pi/2)$. The figure shows the first, second, third, and fourth approximation curves, whose equations are

$$y = \frac{\pi}{2}, \quad y = \frac{\pi}{2} + 2\sin x, \quad y = \frac{\pi}{2} + 2\left(\sin x + \frac{\sin 3x}{3}\right),$$

$$y = \frac{\pi}{2} + 2\left(\sin x + \frac{\sin 3x}{3} + \frac{\sin 5x}{5}\right),$$

as well as the graph of $f(x)$.

At $x = \pm\pi$ the series reduces to $\pi/2$, and again every approximation curve gives this same value for the ordinate at $\pm\pi$. This value is one-half the sum of $f(-\pi+)$ and $f(\pi-)$.

Illustrative Example 3. Let $f(x)$ be defined by the relations

$$f(x) = -\pi, \quad \text{if } -\pi < x < 0,$$
$$= x, \quad \text{if } 0 < x < \pi;$$

then the Fourier coefficients for $f(x)$ are given by

$$a_0 = \frac{1}{\pi} \int_{-\pi}^{\pi} f(x)\, dx = \frac{1}{\pi} \left(\int_{-\pi}^{0} -\pi\, dx + \int_{0}^{\pi} x\, dx \right)$$

$$= \frac{1}{\pi} \left(-\pi^2 + \frac{\pi^2}{2} \right) = -\frac{\pi}{2},$$

$$a_n = \frac{1}{\pi} \int_{-\pi}^{\pi} f(x) \cos nx\, dx = \frac{1}{\pi} \left(\int_{-\pi}^{0} -\pi \cos nx\, dx \right.$$

$$\left. + \int_{0}^{\pi} x \cos nx\, dx \right)$$

$$= \frac{1}{\pi} \left(0 + \frac{\cos n\pi}{n^2} - \frac{1}{n^2} \right)$$

$$= \frac{1}{\pi} \left(\frac{\cos n\pi - 1}{n^2} \right),$$

$$b_n = \frac{1}{\pi} \int_{-\pi}^{\pi} f(x) \sin nx\, dx = \frac{1}{\pi} \left(\int_{-\pi}^{0} -\pi \sin nx\, dx \right.$$

$$\left. + \int_{0}^{\pi} x \sin nx\, dx \right)$$

$$= \frac{1}{\pi} \left(\frac{\pi}{n} - \frac{\pi}{n} \cos n\pi - \frac{\pi}{n} \cos n\pi \right)$$

$$= \frac{1}{n} (1 - 2 \cos n\pi).$$

Therefore,

$$f(x) = -\frac{\pi}{4} - \frac{2}{\pi} \cos x - \frac{2}{\pi} \frac{\cos 3x}{3^2} - \frac{2}{\pi} \frac{\cos 5x}{5^2} - \cdots$$

$$+ 3 \sin x - \frac{\sin 2x}{2} + \frac{3 \sin 3x}{3} - \frac{\sin 4x}{4} + \frac{3 \sin 5x}{5} - \cdots$$

When $x = 0$, the series reduces to

$$-\frac{\pi}{4} - \frac{2}{\pi} \left(\frac{1}{1^2} + \frac{1}{3^2} + \frac{1}{5^2} + \cdots \right),$$

which must coincide with (see Fig. 13)

$$\frac{f(0+) + f(0-)}{2} = -\frac{\pi}{2}.$$

Thus,

$$-\frac{\pi}{4} - \frac{2}{\pi} \left(\frac{1}{1^2} + \frac{1}{3^2} + \frac{1}{5^2} + \cdots \right) = -\frac{\pi}{2}.$$

Hence,

$$\frac{1}{1^2} + \frac{1}{3^2} + \frac{1}{5^2} + \cdots = \frac{\pi^2}{8}.$$

Also, for $x = \pm\pi$, the series gives

$$-\frac{\pi}{4} + \frac{2}{\pi}\left(\frac{1}{1^2} + \frac{1}{3^2} + \frac{1}{5^2} + \cdots\right) = 0,$$

since

$$\frac{f(-\pi+) + f(\pi-)}{2} = 0.$$

This example suggests the use of Fourier series in evaluating sums of series of constants.

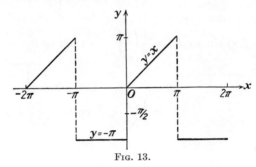

Fig. 13.

PROBLEMS

1. Show that

$$x^2 = \frac{\pi^2}{3} + 4 \sum_{n=1}^{\infty} (-1)^n \frac{\cos nx}{n^2}, \quad (-\pi \le x \le \pi).$$

2. If

$$f(x) = -x \qquad \text{for } -\pi < x < 0,$$
$$= 0 \qquad \text{for } \quad 0 < x < \pi,$$

then

$$f(x) = \frac{\pi}{4} - \frac{2}{\pi} \sum_{n=1}^{\infty} \frac{\cos (2n-1)x}{(2n-1)^2} + \sum_{n=1}^{\infty} \frac{(-1)^n \sin nx}{n}.$$

3. If

$$f(x) = 0 \qquad \text{for } -\pi \le x \le 0,$$
$$= \sin x \qquad \text{for } \quad 0 \le x \le \pi,$$

then

$$f(x) = \frac{1}{\pi} - \frac{2}{\pi} \sum_{n=1}^{\infty} \frac{\cos 2nx}{4n^2 - 1} + \frac{1}{2} \sin x.$$

4. If $f(x) = e^x$ in the interval $(0, 2\pi)$, then

$$e^x = \frac{e^{2\pi} - 1}{\pi} \left(\frac{1}{2} + \sum_{n=1}^{\infty} \frac{\cos nx}{1 + n^2} - \sum_{n=1}^{\infty} \frac{n \sin nx}{1 + n^2} \right).$$

5. Deduce from Prob. 1 that

$$\sum_{n=1}^{\infty} (-1)^{n-1} \frac{1}{n^2} = \frac{\pi^2}{12}.$$

6. Show that

$$\cos \alpha x = \frac{\sin \pi \alpha}{\pi \alpha} + \sum_{n=1}^{\infty} (-1)^n \frac{2\alpha \sin \pi \alpha}{\pi (\alpha^2 - n^2)} \cos nx,$$

if $-\pi \le x \le \pi$.

7. Deduce from Prob. 6 that

$$\cot \pi \alpha = \frac{1}{\pi} \left(\frac{1}{\alpha} - \sum_{n=1}^{\infty} \frac{2\alpha}{n^2 - \alpha^2} \right).$$

8. Deduce from the expansion of $f(x) = x + x^2$ in Fourier series in the interval $(-\pi, \pi)$ that

$$\sum_{n=1}^{\infty} \frac{1}{n^2} = \frac{\pi^2}{6}.$$

9. Expand $x \sin x$ and $x \cos x$ in Fourier series in the interval $(0, 2\pi)$.

10. Find the Fourier series expansion for $f(x)$, if

$$f(x) = \frac{\pi}{2} \qquad \text{for } -\pi < x < \frac{\pi}{2},$$

$$= 0 \qquad \text{for } \frac{\pi}{2} < x < \pi.$$

20. Sine and Cosine Series. The Fourier expansion for $f(x)$ in $(-\pi, \pi)$ has the form (19-1), in which the coefficients a_n and b_n are given by (19-2) and (19-3). As previously observed (Sec. 19), if $f(x)$ is an even function, (19-1) reduces to a series containing only cosine terms; and if $f(x)$ is an odd function, (19-1) reduces to a series containing only sine terms. Now suppose that it is desired that $f(x)$ be expanded in a Fourier series which will be used for the interval 0 to π only. In that case, it is frequently convenient to obtain the expansion in terms of sines alone or in terms of cosines alone. For this purpose, define

$$F(x) \equiv f(x) \qquad \text{for } 0 < x < \pi$$

and

$$F(x) \equiv f(-x) \qquad \text{for } -\pi < x < 0,$$

so that $F(x)$ is an even function identical with $f(x)$ in $0 < x < \pi$.
For an even function:

$$
\begin{aligned}
b_n &= \frac{1}{\pi} \int_{-\pi}^{\pi} F(x) \sin nx \, dx \\
&= \frac{1}{\pi} \left[\int_{-\pi}^{0} F(x) \sin nx \, dx + \int_{0}^{\pi} F(x) \sin nx \, dx \right] \\
&= \frac{1}{\pi} \left[-\int_{0}^{\pi} F(-x) \sin (-nx)(-dx) + \int_{0}^{\pi} F(x) \sin nx \, dx \right] \\
&= \frac{1}{\pi} \left[-\int_{0}^{\pi} F(x) \sin nx \, dx + \int_{0}^{\pi} F(x) \sin nx \, dx \right] = 0,
\end{aligned}
$$

and

$$
\begin{aligned}
a_n &= \frac{1}{\pi} \int_{-\pi}^{\pi} F(x) \cos nx \, dx \\
&= \frac{1}{\pi} \left[\int_{-\pi}^{0} F(x) \cos nx \, dx + \int_{0}^{\pi} F(x) \cos nx \, dx \right] \\
&= \frac{1}{\pi} \left[\int_{0}^{\pi} F(x) \cos nx \, dx + \int_{0}^{\pi} F(x) \cos nx \, dx \right] \\
&= \frac{2}{\pi} \int_{0}^{\pi} F(x) \cos nx \, dx.
\end{aligned}
$$

Hence, in the expansion of $F(x)$ in the interval $-\pi < x < \pi$, only
the cosine terms appear. Moreover, $F(x)$ is identical with $f(x)$
for $0 < x < \pi$. Therefore,*

$$(20\text{-}1) \quad f(x) = \frac{a_0}{2} + a_1 \cos x + a_2 \cos 2x + \cdots + a_n \cos nx + \cdots$$

in the interval $(0, \pi)$, where

$$(20\text{-}2) \qquad a_n = \frac{2}{\pi} \int_{0}^{\pi} f(x) \cos nx \, dx.$$

Similarly, if $F(x)$ be defined so that

$$F(x) \equiv f(x) \qquad \text{for } 0 < x < \pi$$

and

$$F(x) \equiv -f(-x) \qquad \text{for } -\pi < x < 0,$$

---

* If $f(x)$ has a finite discontinuity at the point $x = x_0$, then the left-hand
member of (20-1) is defined to be $\frac{1}{2}[f(x_0+) + f(x_0-)]$.

then the a_n all vanish and

(20-3) $f(x) = b_1 \sin x + b_2 \sin 2x + \cdots + b_n \sin nx + \cdots ,$
where

(20-4) $b_n = \dfrac{2}{\pi} \displaystyle\int_0^{\pi} f(x) \sin nx \, dx.$

Thus, $f(x)$ can be represented in the interval $0 < x < \pi$ by either
(20-1) or (20-3). Frequently, one series is more desirable than
the other.

Example. As has been determined already (see Illustrative Example
1, Sec. 19), the expansion for $f(x) = x$ in a sine series is

$$x = 2 \left(\sin x - \frac{\sin 2x}{2} + \frac{\sin 3x}{3} - \cdots \right).$$

This series represents $f(x) = x$ in the interval $(-\pi, \pi)$. If one is inter-

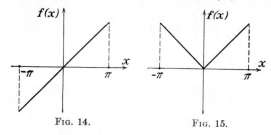

Fig. 14.   Fig. 15.

ested in the values of the function in the interval $(0, \pi)$, the same function can be expanded in a series of cosines.

In fact, in the interval $(0, \pi)$,

$$x = \frac{\pi}{2} - \frac{4}{\pi} \left(\frac{\cos x}{1} + \frac{\cos 3x}{3^2} + \frac{\cos 5x}{5^2} + \cdots \right),$$

since

$$a_0 = \frac{2}{\pi} \int_0^{\pi} x \, dx = \pi$$

and

$$a_n = \frac{2}{\pi} \int_0^{\pi} x \cos nx \, dx = \frac{2}{n^2 \pi} [(-1)^n - 1].$$

The sine series represents the odd function shown in Fig. 14 and the
cosine series the even function in Fig. 15. The two graphs are identical
in the interval $(0, \pi)$.

PROBLEMS

1. Show that if c is a constant, then, in $0 < x < \pi$,

$$c = c \frac{4}{\pi} \left(\sin x + \frac{\sin 3x}{3} + \frac{\sin 5x}{5} + \cdots \right).$$

2. Give sine and cosine developments of $y = x \sin x$ in the interval $(0, \pi)$.

3. Show that, in $(0, \pi)$,

$$x^2 = \frac{2}{\pi} \left[\left(\frac{\pi^2}{1} - \frac{4}{1^3} \right) \sin x - \frac{\pi^2}{2} \sin 2x + \left(\frac{\pi^2}{3} - \frac{4}{3^3} \right) \sin 3x \right.$$
$$\left. - \frac{\pi^2}{4} \sin 4x + \cdots \right].$$

4. Prove that, if $f(x)$ is any function of x, it can be expressed as the sum of an even function of x and an odd function of x.

5. Show that, if $f(x) = x$ for $0 < x < \pi/2$ and $f(x) = \pi - x$ for $\pi/2 < x < \pi$, then

$$f(x) = \frac{\pi}{4} - \frac{2}{\pi} \left(\frac{\cos 2x}{1^2} + \frac{\cos 6x}{3^2} + \frac{\cos 10x}{5^2} + \cdots \right).$$

6. Show that

$$\log \left(2 \sin \frac{x}{2} \right) = - \sum_{n=1}^{\infty} \frac{\cos nx}{n}, \quad \text{if } 0 < x < \pi.$$

7. Find the expansion in the series of sines, if

$$f(x) = \frac{\pi}{4} x, \qquad \text{for } 0 \leq x \leq \frac{\pi}{2},$$
$$= \frac{\pi}{4} (\pi - x), \qquad \text{for } \frac{\pi}{2} \leq x \leq \pi.$$

8. Expand $f(x) = e^x$ in the series of cosines in the interval $(0, \pi)$.

21. Extension of Interval of Expansion. The methods developed up to this point restrict the interval in which $f(x)$ can be expanded in a Fourier series to $(-\pi, \pi)$. In many problems, it is desirable to develop $f(x)$ in a Fourier series that will be valid over a wider interval. In order to obtain an expansion that will hold for the interval $(-l, l)$, change the variable by replacing x by $\frac{l}{\pi} z$. Then $f(x) = f\left(\frac{l}{\pi} z \right)$ can be developed in a Fourier series in z,

$$(21\text{-}1) \quad f\left(\frac{l}{\pi} z \right) = \frac{a_0}{2} + \sum_{n=1}^{\infty} a_n \cos nz + \sum_{n=1}^{\infty} b_n \sin nz,$$

in which

$$a_n = \frac{1}{\pi} \int_{-\pi}^{\pi} f\left(\frac{lz}{\pi} \right) \cos nz \, dz$$

and

$$b_n = \frac{1}{\pi} \int_{-\pi}^{\pi} f\left(\frac{lz}{\pi}\right) \sin nz \, dz.$$

The expression (21-1) will be valid for $-\pi < z < \pi$; but $z = \pi x/l$ so that (21-1) becomes

$$(21\text{-}2) \quad f(x) = \frac{a_0}{2} + \sum_{n=1}^{\infty} a_n \cos \frac{n\pi x}{l} + \sum_{n=1}^{\infty} b_n \sin \frac{n\pi x}{l}.$$

Also,

$$a_n = \frac{1}{\pi} \int_{-\pi}^{\pi} f\left(\frac{lz}{\pi}\right) \cos nz \, dz = \frac{1}{l} \int_{-l}^{l} f(x) \cos \frac{n\pi x}{l} \, dx$$

and

$$b_n = \frac{1}{\pi} \int_{-\pi}^{\pi} f\left(\frac{lz}{\pi}\right) \sin nz \, dz = \frac{1}{l} \int_{-l}^{l} f(x) \sin \frac{n\pi x}{l} \, dx.$$

Example. Develop $f(x)$ in Fourier series in the interval $(-2, 2)$, if $f(x) = 0$ for $-2 < x < 0$ and $f(x) = 1$ for $0 < x < 2$. Here

$$a_0 = \frac{1}{2}\left(\int_{-2}^{0} 0 \cdot dx + \int_{0}^{2} 1 \cdot dx\right) = 1,$$

$$a_n = \frac{1}{2}\left(\int_{-2}^{0} 0 \cdot \cos \frac{n\pi x}{2} \, dx + \int_{0}^{2} 1 \cdot \cos \frac{n\pi x}{2} \, dx\right) = \frac{1}{n\pi} \sin \frac{n\pi x}{2}\Big|_{0}^{2} = 0,$$

$$b_n = \frac{1}{2}\left(\int_{-2}^{0} 0 \cdot \sin \frac{n\pi x}{2} \, dx + \int_{0}^{2} 1 \cdot \sin \frac{n\pi x}{2} \, dx\right) = \frac{1}{n\pi}(1 - \cos n\pi).$$

Therefore,

$$f(x) = \frac{1}{2} + \frac{2}{\pi}\left(\sin \frac{\pi x}{2} + \frac{1}{3} \sin \frac{3\pi x}{2} + \frac{1}{5} \sin \frac{5\pi x}{2} + \cdots\right).$$

PROBLEMS

1. The expansion of $f(x)$ is desired for $0 < x < l$. If $F(x) \equiv f(x)$ for $0 < x < l$ and $F(x) \equiv -f(-x)$ for $-l < x < 0$ [that is, $F(x)$ is defined as an odd function], show that the expansion of $F(x)$ and $f(x)$ for $0 < x < l$ is

$$\sum_{n=1}^{\infty} b_n \sin \frac{n\pi x}{l},$$

where

$$b_n = \frac{2}{l} \int_{0}^{l} f(x) \sin \frac{n\pi x}{l} \, dx.$$

If $\varphi(x) \equiv f(x)$ for $0 < x < l$ and $\varphi(x) \equiv f(-x)$ for $-l < x < 0$ [that is, $\varphi(x)$ is defined as an even function], show that the expansion of $\varphi(x)$

and $f(x)$ for $0 < x < l$ is

$$\frac{a_0}{2} + \sum_{n=1}^{\infty} a_n \cos \frac{n\pi x}{l},$$

where

$$a_n = \frac{2}{l} \int_0^l f(x) \cos \frac{n\pi x}{l} \, dx.$$

2. Using the results of the preceding problem, obtain the sine and cosine expansions of the following functions:

    (*a*) $f(x) = 1$ in the interval $(0, 2)$;
    (*b*) $f(x) = x$ in the interval $(0, 1)$;
    (*c*) $f(x) = x^2$ in the interval $(0, 3)$.

3. Expand $f(x) = \cos \pi x$ in the interval $(-1, 1)$.

4. Expand

$$f(x) = \tfrac{1}{4} - x, \qquad \text{if } 0 < x < \tfrac{1}{2},$$
$$= x - \tfrac{3}{4}, \qquad \text{if } \tfrac{1}{2} < x < 1,$$

in the series of sines.

5. Find the expansion in the series of cosines, if

$$f(x) = 0, \qquad \text{if } 0 < x < 1,$$
$$= 1, \qquad \text{if } 1 < x < 2.$$

6. Expand $f(x) = |x|$ in the series of cosines in the interval $(-1, 1)$.

7. Show that the series

$$\frac{l}{\pi} \sum_{n=1}^{\infty} \frac{1}{n} \sin \frac{2n\pi x}{l}$$

represents $\tfrac{1}{2}l - x$ when $0 < x < l$.

8. Find the expansion in the series of cosines, if

$$f(x) = 1 \qquad \text{when } 0 < x < \pi,$$
$$= 0 \qquad \text{when } \pi < x < 2\pi.$$

22. Complex Form of Fourier Series.   The Fourier series

$$(22\text{-}1) \qquad f(x) = \frac{a_0}{2} + \sum_{n=1}^{\infty} (a_n \cos nx + b_n \sin nx),$$

with

$$a_n = \frac{1}{\pi} \int_{-\pi}^{\pi} f(t) \cos nt \, dt, \qquad b_n = \frac{1}{\pi} \int_{-\pi}^{\pi} f(t) \sin nt \, dt,$$

can be written, with the aid of the Euler formula*

$$(22\text{-}2) \qquad e^{iu} = \cos u + i \sin u,$$

* See Sec. 73.

in an equivalent form, namely,

$$(22\text{-}3) \qquad f(x) = \sum_{n=-\infty}^{n=+\infty} c_n e^{inx},$$

where the coefficients c_n are defined by the equation

$$(22\text{-}4) \qquad c_n = \frac{1}{2\pi} \int_{-\pi}^{\pi} f(t) e^{-int}\, dt.$$

The index of summation n in (22-3) runs through the set of all positive and negative integral values including zero.

The equivalence of (22-3) and (22-1) can be established in the following manner: Substituting from (22-2) in (22-4) gives, for $n > 0$,

$$\begin{aligned} c_n &= \frac{1}{2\pi} \int_{-\pi}^{\pi} f(t)\,(\cos nt - i \sin nt)\, dt \\ &= \frac{1}{2\pi} \int_{-\pi}^{\pi} f(t) \cos nt\, dt - \frac{i}{2\pi} \int_{-\pi}^{\pi} f(t) \sin nt\, dt \\ &= \frac{a_n}{2} - i\frac{b_n}{2}. \end{aligned}$$

A similar calculation for $n < 0$ gives

$$c_{-n} = \frac{a_n}{2} + i\frac{b_n}{2},$$

while

$$c_0 = \frac{a_0}{2}.$$

Now (22-3) can be written in the form

$$f(x) = c_0 + \sum_{n=1}^{\infty} c_n e^{inx} + \sum_{n=1}^{\infty} c_{-n} e^{-inx}.$$

Making use of the expressions for the c_n just found gives

$$\begin{aligned} f(x) &= \frac{a_0}{2} + \sum_{n=1}^{\infty} \frac{a_n - ib_n}{2} e^{inx} + \sum_{n=1}^{\infty} \frac{a_n + ib_n}{2} e^{-inx} \\ &= \frac{a_0}{2} + \sum_{n=1}^{\infty} a_n \frac{e^{inx} + e^{-inx}}{2} - i\sum_{n=1}^{\infty} b_n \frac{e^{inx} - e^{-inx}}{2}. \end{aligned}$$

Recalling that

$$e^{iu} + e^{-iu} = 2 \cos u \quad \text{and} \quad e^{iu} - e^{-iu} = 2i \sin u$$

gives

$$f(x) = \frac{a_0}{2} + \sum_{n=1}^{\infty} (a_n \cos nx + b_n \sin nx),$$

which establishes the identity of (22-3) with (22-1).

PROBLEM

Show that the Fourier series in the interval $(-l, l)$ can be written in the form

$$f(x) = \sum_{n=-\infty}^{n=+\infty} c_n e^{\frac{in\pi x}{l}}$$

where

$$c_n = \frac{1}{2l} \int_{-l}^{l} f(t) e^{-\frac{in\pi t}{l}} \, dt.$$

23. Differentiation and Integration of Fourier Series. Some general rules concerning differentiation and integration of infinite series were given in Sec. 8. It may be added here that, if the Fourier series represents a function $f(x)$, then the term-by-term integral of the series will converge to the integral of $f(x)$. Thus, in Sec. 20 it was found that the function x can be expanded in a cosine series in $(0, \pi)$ to give

$$(23\text{-}1) \quad x = \frac{\pi}{2} - \frac{4}{\pi} \left(\frac{\cos x}{1^2} + \frac{\cos 3x}{3^2} + \frac{\cos 5x}{5^2} + \cdots \right).$$

The term-by-term integral of this series gives

$$(23\text{-}2) \quad \frac{x^2}{2} = \int_0^x \frac{\pi}{2} \, dx - \frac{4}{\pi} \left(\int_0^x \frac{\cos x}{1^2} \, dx + \int_0^x \frac{\cos 3x}{3^2} \, dx \right.$$
$$\left. + \int_0^x \frac{\cos 5x}{5^2} \, dx + \cdots \right) = \frac{\pi}{2} x - \frac{4}{\pi} \left(\frac{\sin x}{1^3} + \frac{\sin 3x}{3^3} \right.$$
$$\left. + \frac{\sin 5x}{5^3} + \cdots \right).$$

On account of the presence of the term $\pi x/2$ in the right member of this equation, the resulting series is not a Fourier series. However, if the sine series development for x (Illustrative Example 1, Sec. 19) be substituted in this term and the like terms collected, the resulting series will be the development of $x^2/2$ in $(0, \pi)$ in a sine series.

The series resulting from term-by-term differentiation of a Fourier series converges more slowly than the original series, and, in fact, it may diverge.   Thus, term-by-term differentiation of

$$x = 2\left(\sin x - \frac{\sin 2x}{2} + \frac{\sin 3x}{3} - \cdots\right)$$

gives the series

$$2(\cos x - \cos 2x + \cos 3x - \cdots),$$

which is divergent, as was observed in Sec. 8.   Accordingly, great caution must be exercised in differentiating Fourier series termwise.*

24. Orthogonal Functions.   A set of continuous functions

(24-1) $u_1(x), u_2(x), \cdots, u_n(x), \cdots,$

which do not vanish identically in the interval $a \le x \le b$, is said to be *orthogonal* with respect to the interval (a, b) if the functions $u_i(x)$ satisfy the relations

(24-2) $\int_a^b u_i(x)u_j(x)\, dx = 0,$ if $i \ne j.$

For $i = j$, (24-2) becomes

$$\int_a^b [u_i(x)]^2\, dx \equiv c_i^2,$$

where c_i^2 certainly is not zero.

If each of the orthogonal functions $u_i(x)$ be divided by c_i, there will be obtained a system of *normal* orthogonal functions,

$$v_1(x) = \frac{u_1(x)}{c_1}, \qquad v_2(x) = \frac{u_2(x)}{c_2}, \cdots, \qquad v_n(x) = \frac{u_n(x)}{c_n}, \cdots,$$

that are characterized by the property that

(24-3) $\int_a^b v_i(x)v_j(x)\, dx = 0,$ if $i \ne j,$
                                      $= 1,$ if $i = j.$

Consider a set of normal orthogonal functions $v_i(x)$, and assume that an arbitrary function $f(x)$ can be expanded in a series

---

* Some important theorems in regard to this will be found in I. S. Sokolnikoff, Advanced Calculus, Sec. 108.

(24-4) $\quad f(x) = a_1v_1(x) + a_2v_2(x) + \cdots + a_nv_n(x) + \cdots$

$$\equiv \sum_{i=1}^{\infty} a_iv_i(x),$$

which can be integrated term by term. Multiplying both sides of (24-4) by $v_j(x)$ and integrating term by term between the limits a and b yield

$$\int_a^b f(x)v_j(x) \, dx = \sum_{i=1}^{\infty} a_i \int_a^b v_i(x)v_j(x) \, dx,$$

which, by virtue of (24-3), gives the formula

(24-5) $\qquad a_i = \int_a^b f(x)v_i(x) \, dx, \qquad (i = 1, 2, 3, \cdots).$

The numbers a_i are known as the Fourier coefficients of the function $f(x)$ associated with the system of normal and orthogonal functions

$$v_1(x), \, v_2(x), \, \cdots, \, v_n(x), \, \cdots.$$

The set of functions

$$\frac{1}{\sqrt{2\pi}}, \frac{\cos x}{\sqrt{\pi}}, \frac{\sin x}{\sqrt{\pi}}, \frac{\cos 2x}{\sqrt{\pi}}, \frac{\sin 2x}{\sqrt{\pi}}, \cdots, \frac{\cos nx}{\sqrt{\pi}}, \frac{\sin nx}{\sqrt{\pi}}, \cdots$$

is obviously a normal orthogonal set in the interval $(-\pi, \pi)$, and the development of a function $f(x)$ with the aid of this particular set of orthogonal functions is precisely the Fourier development of $f(x)$. Among many other useful sets of orthogonal functions are the functions of Bessel and Legendre, which are of frequent occurrence in applied mathematics and will be used in the discussion of some important problems in Secs. 101, 113, and 114.

CHAPTER III

SOLUTION OF EQUATIONS

Students of engineering, physics, chemistry, and other sciences meet the problem of the solution of equations at every stage of their work. This chapter gives a brief outline of some of the algebraic, graphical, and numerical methods of obtaining the real roots of equations with real coefficients, of types that occur frequently in the applied sciences. It also contains a short summary of those parts of the theory of determinants and the theory of matrices that are immediately applicable to the solution of systems of linear equations.

25. Graphical Solutions. The subject of the solution of equations will be introduced by considering a simple problem that any engineer may be called upon to solve.

It is required to design a hollow cast-iron sphere, 1 in. in thickness, that will just float in water. It is assumed that the air in the cavity is completely exhausted. The specific gravity of cast iron will be denoted by ρ, for convenience.

By the law of Archimedes, the weight of the sphere must equal the weight of the displaced water. This gives the condition on the radius of the sphere, namely,

$$\tfrac{4}{3}\pi x^3 = \tfrac{4}{3}\pi\rho[x^3 - (x - 1)^3].$$

Simplifying gives

(25-1) $$x^3 - 3\rho x^2 + 3\rho x - \rho = 0.$$

It will be convenient to remove the second-degree term in (25-1). To accomplish this, let $x = y + k$, giving

$$y^3 + 3y^2k + 3yk^2 + k^3 - 3\rho(y^2 + 2yk + k^2) + 3\rho(y + k) - \rho = 0,$$

or

$$y^3 + (3k - 3\rho)y^2 + (3k^2 - 6\rho k + 3\rho)y + k^3 - 3\rho k^2 + 3\rho k - \rho = 0.$$

Choosing $k = \rho$ makes the equation reduce to

(25-2) $$y^3 + (3\rho - 3\rho^2)y - 2\rho^3 + 3\rho^2 - \rho = 0.$$

83

For cast iron, $\rho = 7.5$, and (25-2) becomes

(25-3) $y^3 - 146.25y - 682.5 = 0.$

If (25-3) is solved, the solution of (25-1) is also determined, since $x = y + 7.5$.

A graphical method of solution will be used.   The solution of (25-3) is equivalent to the simultaneous solution of the system

(25-4) $\begin{cases} z = y^3, \\ z = 146.25y + 682.5. \end{cases}$

The accompanying figure (Fig. 16) represents the graphs of the

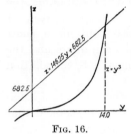

FIG. 16.

two functions of (25-4); since they inter-sect at $y = 14.0$, this value gives an approximate solution of (25-3).   The cor-responding solution of (25-1) is $x = 21.5$. From the graph, it is clear that there is only one real solution of (25-4) and hence of (25-3).

This graphical method can be applied to any cubic equation.   The general fourth-degree equation (quartic) can also be reduced to a form that is convenient for graphical methods of solution.

Consider the quartic

$$x^4 + ax^3 + bx^2 + cx + d = 0.$$

Let $x = y + k$, as in the cubic equation.   This substitution gives

$$y^4 + y^3(4k + a) + y^2(6k^2 + 3ak + b)$$
$$+ y(4k^3 + 3ak^2 + 2bk + c) + k^4 + ak^3 + bk^2 + ck + d = 0.$$

In order to remove the term in y^3, choose $k = -\dfrac{a}{4}$.   This reduces the equation to the form

$$y^4 + Ay^2 + By + C = 0.$$

If $A > 0$, the further transformation $y = \sqrt{A}\, z$ is made, and the equation is reduced to

$$A^2 z^4 + A^2 z^2 + B \sqrt{A}\, z + C = 0,$$

or

$$z^4 + z^2 + pz + q = 0.$$

The solutions of this equation are the same as the solutions of the simultaneous system

$$u = z^4 + z^2,$$
$$u = -pz - q.$$

The graphs of these two functions are easily plotted, and the solutions can be read from the graph. In case $A < 0$, the transformation would be $y = \sqrt{-A}\, z$, which leads to the equation

$$z^4 - z^2 + pz + q = 0$$

and the graphical solution of the system

$$u = z^4 - z^2,$$
$$u = -pz - q.$$

This method of solution for the real roots of an equation is also applicable to many transcendental equations. In order to solve

$$Ax - B \sin x = 0,$$

write it as

$$ax - \sin x = 0,$$

and plot the curves of the simultaneous system

$$y = \sin x,$$
$$y = ax.$$

Similarly, the equation

$$a^x - x^2 = 0$$

can be solved graphically by plotting the curves of the equivalent simultaneous system

$$y = a^x,$$
$$y = x^2.$$

PROBLEMS

1. Solve graphically

   (a) $2^x - x^2 = 0$,

   (b) $x^4 - x - 1 = 0$,

   (c) $x^5 - x - 0.5 = 0$,

   (d) $e^x + x = 0$.

2. Find, graphically, the root of

$$\tan x - x = 0$$

nearest $\tfrac{3}{2}\pi$.

26. Algebraic Solution of Cubic.   The graphical method of solution is perfectly general, but its accuracy depends upon the accurate construction of the graphs of the equations in the simultaneous systems. This is often extremely laborious and, at most, yields only an approximate value of the roots.

In the case of the linear equation $ax + b = 0$, where $a \neq 0$, the solution is $x = -b/a$.   For the quadratic equation $ax^2 + bx + c = 0$, where $a \neq 0$, there are two solutions given by $x = \dfrac{-b \pm \sqrt{b^2 - 4ac}}{2a}$.

The question naturally arises as to the possibility of obtaining expressions for the roots of algebraic equations of degree higher than 2. This section will be devoted to a derivation of the solutions of the general cubic equation

$$a_0 x^3 + a_1 x^2 + a_2 x + a_3 = 0, \qquad a_0 \neq 0.$$

Dividing through by a_0 gives

(26-1) $$x^3 + bx^2 + cx + d = 0,$$

and the x^2 term can be removed by making the change of variable

$$x = y - \frac{b}{3}.$$

The resulting equation is

(26-2) $$y^3 + py + q = 0,$$

where

$$p = c - \frac{b^2}{3}$$

and

$$q = d - \frac{bc}{3} + \frac{2b^3}{27}.$$

In order to solve (26-2), assume that

(26-3) $$y = A + B,$$

so that

$$y^3 = A^3 + B^3 + 3AB(A + B).$$

Substitute in this last equation for $A + B$, from (26-3), and there is obtained the equation

(26-4) $$y^3 - 3ABy - (A^3 + B^3) = 0.$$

A comparison of (26-4) with (26-2) shows that

$$3AB = -p \quad \text{and} \quad A^3 + B^3 = -q,$$

or

(26-5) $\qquad A^3B^3 = -\dfrac{p^3}{27} \quad$ and $\quad A^3 + B^3 = -q.$

If B^3 is eliminated by substituting from the second of Eqs. (26-5) into the first, there appears the quadratic equation in A^3,

$$(A^3)^2 + qA^3 - \frac{p^3}{27} = 0,$$

whose roots are

$$A^3 = \frac{-q \pm \sqrt{q^2 + \dfrac{4p^3}{27}}}{2}.$$

The solution for B^3 yields precisely the same values. However, in order to satisfy Eq. (26-5), choose*

(26-6) $\qquad \begin{cases} A^3 = \dfrac{-q + \sqrt{q^2 + \dfrac{4p^3}{27}}}{2}, \\[4ex] B^3 = \dfrac{-q - \sqrt{q^2 + \dfrac{4p^3}{27}}}{2}. \end{cases}$

If the values of y are to be determined from (26-3), it is necessary to find the cube roots of A^3 and B^3. Recall that if $x^3 = a^3$, then the solutions for x are given by a, ωa, and $\omega^2 a$, where $\omega = -\dfrac{1}{2} + \dfrac{\sqrt{3}}{2}i$ and $\omega^2 = -\dfrac{1}{2} - \dfrac{\sqrt{3}}{2}i$ are the complex roots of unity. Hence, if one cube root of A^3 be denoted by α and one cube root of B^3 by β, the cube roots of A^3 are

$$\alpha, \qquad \omega\alpha, \qquad \text{and} \qquad \omega^2\alpha,$$

whereas those of B^3 are

$$\beta, \qquad \omega\beta, \qquad \text{and} \qquad \omega^2\beta.$$

It would appear that there are nine choices for y, but it should be remembered that the values must be paired so that $3AB = -p$. The only pairs that satisfy this condition are α and β, $\omega\alpha$ and $\omega^2\beta$, and $\omega^2\alpha$ and $\omega\beta$. Hence, the values of y are

(26-7) $\qquad y_1 = \alpha + \beta, \qquad y_2 = \omega\alpha + \omega^2\beta, \qquad y_3 = \omega^2\alpha + \omega\beta,$

where

$$\alpha = \sqrt[3]{\frac{-q + \sqrt{q^2 + \dfrac{4p^3}{27}}}{2}} \qquad \text{and} \qquad \beta = \sqrt[3]{\frac{-q - \sqrt{q^2 + \dfrac{4p^3}{27}}}{2}}.$$

* The opposite choice for the values of A^3 and B^3 simply interchanges their role in what follows.

The solutions of (26-1) can be obtained from the values given in (26-7) by recalling that $x = y - b/3$.

The expressions for α and β are quite complicated, and when the quantity under the square-root sign has a negative value the values of α and β cannot, in general, be determined. This is the so-called irreducible case of the cubic, which can, however, be solved by using a trigonometric method. This method will be described later in the section, but first it is important to find a criterion that will determine in advance which method should be used.

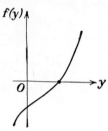

FIG. 17.

In order to determine the character of the roots of (26-2), whose coefficients are assumed to be real, consider the function

$$f(y) \equiv y^3 + py + q$$

and its maximum and minimum values. Since

$$f'(y) = 3y^2 + p,$$

it appears that, if $p > 0$, then $f'(y)$ is always positive and $f(y)$ is an increasing function. In this case the graph of $f(y)$ has the form shown in Fig. 17, and there is evidently only one real value for which $f(y) = 0$.

If $p < 0$, however, $f'(y)$ is zero when $y = \pm \sqrt{-p/3}$. Since $f''(y) = 6y$, it follows that $y = + \sqrt{-p/3}$ gives a minimum value to $f(y)$, whereas $y = - \sqrt{-p/3}$ furnishes a maximum value. The corresponding values of $f(y)$ are

$$q + \frac{2}{3} p \sqrt{-\frac{p}{3}}$$

and

$$q - \frac{2}{3} p \sqrt{-\frac{p}{3}}.$$

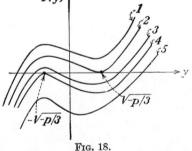

FIG. 18.

The graph of $f(y)$ will have the appearance of one of the curves in Fig. 18.

It is evident that $f(y) = 0$ will have only one real root if the graph of $f(y)$ has the appearance shown by (1) or (5), that is, if the maximum and minimum values of $f(y)$ are of the same sign. Hence,

$$\left(q + \frac{2}{3} p \sqrt{-\frac{p}{3}}\right) \left(q - \frac{2}{3} p \sqrt{-\frac{p}{3}}\right) > 0,$$

or

$$q^2 + \tfrac{4}{27} p^3 > 0,$$

is the condition that (26-2) have only one real root. It may be observed that this condition is automatically satisfied if $p \geqq 0$. It should be noted that, if $p = 0$, Eq. (26-2) reduces to $y^3 + q = 0$, which obviously has only one real root.

If (26-2) has three real and distinct roots, then the graph of $f(y)$ must have the appearance shown in (3), and it follows that the maximum and minimum values must be of opposite sign. Hence,

$$q^2 + \tfrac{4}{27}\, p^3 < 0$$

is the condition for three real and unequal roots.

If $q^2 + \tfrac{4}{27}p^3 = 0$, either the maximum or the minimum value of $f(y)$ must be zero [see (2) and (4)], and (26-2) will have three real roots, of which two will be equal (a so-called double root).

The expression

$$(26\text{-}8) \qquad\qquad \Delta \equiv -27q^2 - 4p^3$$

is called the discriminant of the cubic equation (26-2), for its value determines the character of the roots of the equation. The discriminant for (26-1), obtained by replacing p and q in (26-8) by their values in terms of b, c, and d, is

$$(26\text{-}9) \qquad\qquad \Delta \equiv 18bcd - 4b^3d + b^2c^2 - 4c^3 - 27d^2.$$

It may be worth noting that the discriminant of any algebraic equation, with leading coefficient unity, is the product of the squares of the differences of the roots taken two at a time. Inasmuch as

$$(x_1 - x_2)^2(x_2 - x_3)^2(x_3 - x_1)^2 = (y_1 - y_2)^2(y_2 - y_3)^2(y_3 - y_1)^2,$$

the discriminant has the same value for (26-1) and (26-2).

In view of the definition of Δ, it follows that

if $\Delta < 0$, one root is real and two are complex;
if $\Delta = 0$, all the roots are real and two are equal;
if $\Delta > 0$, the three roots are real and unequal.

Example. Consider the cubic equation

$$x^3 + 3x^2 + 9x - 1 = 0.$$

From (26-9), it follows that $\Delta = -2592$, and hence there will be one real root and two complex roots. Setting $x = y - 1$ yields the reduced cubic

$$y^3 + 6y - 8 = 0,$$

and substituting $p = 6$ and $q = -8$ in (26-6) gives $A^3 = 4 + 2\sqrt{6}$ and $B^3 = 4 - 2\sqrt{6}$. Therefore, the solutions for y are

$$\sqrt[3]{4 + 2\sqrt{6}} + \sqrt[3]{4 - 2\sqrt{6}}, \qquad \omega \sqrt[3]{4 + 2\sqrt{6}} + \omega^2 \sqrt[3]{4 - 2\sqrt{6}},$$

$$\text{and} \qquad \omega^2 \sqrt[3]{4 + 2\sqrt{6}} + \omega \sqrt[3]{4 - 2\sqrt{6}}.$$

The solutions of the original equation can now be obtained by recalling that $x = y - 1$.

The discussion of the solution of the cubic equation will be concluded by giving the derivation of the expressions for the roots in the case where the roots are real and unequal (that is, when $\Delta \equiv -27q^2 - 4p^3 > 0$).

Let

$$-\frac{q}{2} = r \cos \theta$$

and

$$\sqrt{-\left(\frac{p^3}{27} + \frac{q^2}{4}\right)} = r \sin \theta.$$

Then*

$$\alpha = (r \cos \theta + ir \sin \theta)^{1/3} = r^{1/3}\left(\cos \frac{\theta}{3} + i \sin \frac{\theta}{3}\right)$$

and

$$\beta = (r \cos \theta - ir \sin \theta)^{1/3} = r^{1/3}\left(\cos \frac{\theta}{3} - i \sin \frac{\theta}{3}\right).$$

If it is noted that

$$\omega = \cos \frac{2\pi}{3} + i \sin \frac{2\pi}{3}$$

and

$$\omega^2 = \cos \frac{2\pi}{3} - i \sin \frac{2\pi}{3},$$

it is easily checked that the expressions for

$$y_1 \equiv \alpha + \beta, \qquad y_2 \equiv \omega\alpha + \omega^2\beta, \qquad y_3 \equiv \omega^2\alpha + \omega\beta,$$

become

(26-10) $$y_1 = 2r^{1/3} \cos \frac{\theta}{3}, \qquad y_2 = 2r^{1/3} \cos \frac{\theta + 2\pi}{3},$$

$$y_3 = 2r^{1/3} \cos \frac{\theta + 4\pi}{3}.$$

Since

$$r = \sqrt{-\frac{p^3}{27}}$$

and

$$\cos \theta = -\frac{q}{2}\sqrt{-\frac{27}{p^3}},$$

the values of y_1, y_2, and y_3 can be obtained directly from the coefficients of (26-2) or (26-1).

---

* By De Moivre's theorem $(\cos \theta + i \sin \theta)^n = \cos n\theta + i \sin n\theta$.

Example. Determine the real roots of

$$x^3 - 3x^2 + 3 = 0.$$

Here

$$\Delta = -4(-27)(3) - 27(9) > 0,$$

and the roots are all real and unequal. Since $p = -3$ and $q = 1$, it follows that $r = 1$ and $\cos \theta = -\frac{1}{2}$. Hence,

$$\theta = \frac{2\pi}{3},$$

and

$$y_1 = 2 \cos \frac{2\pi}{9}, \qquad y_2 = 2 \cos \frac{8\pi}{9}, \qquad y_3 = 2 \cos \frac{14\pi}{9}.$$

The solutions of the general quartic equation

$$x^4 + bx^3 + cx^2 + dx + e = 0$$

can be found, but the methods of obtaining the expressions for the roots depend upon the solution of an auxiliary cubic equation. Moreover, these expressions are, in general, so involved that they are practically useless for computation.* It has been shown that the ordinary operations of algebra are, in general, insufficient for the purpose of obtaining exact solutions of algebraic equations of degree higher than 4. However, it is possible to obtain the expressions for the solutions of the general equation of the fifth degree with the aid of elliptic integrals.

The reader should not confuse the problem of obtaining expressions for the exact solutions of the general algebraic equation with that of calculating numerical approximations to the roots of specific equations which have numerical coefficients. The latter problem will be discussed in Secs. 28 and 29, and it will be shown that the real roots of such equations can be computed to any desired degree of accuracy. Moreover, if the roots are rational they can always be determined exactly.

PROBLEMS

Determine the roots of the following equations:

(a) $y^3 - 2y - 1 = 0$;

(b) $y^3 - 146.25y - 682.5 = 0$;

(c) $x^3 - x^2 - 5x - 3 = 0$;

(d) $x^3 - 2x^2 - x + 2 = 0$;

(e) $x^3 - 6x^2 + 6x - 2 = 0$;

(f) $x^3 + 6x^2 + 3x + 18 = 0$;

(g) $2x^3 + 3x^2 + 3x + 1 = 0$.

---

* See DICKSON, L. E., First Course in Theory of Equations, pp. 50–54; BURNSIDE, W. S., and A. W. PANTON, Theory of Equations, vol. 1, pp. 121–142.

27. Some Algebraic Theorems. The student of any applied science is usually interested in obtaining numerical values, correct to a certain number of decimal places, for the roots of equations. Unless the roots are rational, the expressions for the exact roots, provided that they can be found at all, are usually complicated and the process of determining numerical values from them is tedious. Accordingly, it is distinctly useful to consider other methods of finding these numerical values. Horner's method, Newton's method, and the method of interpolation are the ones most frequently used; they will be discussed in Secs. 28 and 29. However, all these methods are based on the assumption that a root has first been isolated, that is, that there have been determined two values of the variable such that between them lies one and only one root. In many practical problems the physical setup is a guide in this isolation process. This section contains a review of some theorems* from the theory of equations that provide preliminary information as to the character and location of the roots.

THEOREM 1. (Fundamental Theorem of Algebra.) *Every algebraic equation*

$$f(x) \equiv a_0 x^n + a_1 x^{n-1} + \cdots + a_{n-1} x + a_n = 0$$

has a root.

It should be noted that this theorem does not hold for non-algebraic equations. For example, the equation $e^x = 0$ has no root.

THEOREM 2. (Remainder Theorem.) *If the polynomial*

$$f(x) \equiv a_0 x^n + a_1 x^{n-1} + \cdots + a_{n-1} x + a_n$$

is divided by $x - b$ until the remainder is independent of x, then this remainder has the value $f(b)$.

THEOREM 3. (Factor Theorem.) *If $f(b) = 0$, then $x - b$ is a factor of the polynomial $f(x)$ and b is a root of $f(x) = 0$.*

This theorem follows directly from Theorem 2. In many cases the easiest way to compute the value of $f(b)$ is to perform the division of $f(x)$ by $x - b$. This is a particularly useful

---

* Those students who are not already familiar with these theorems and their proofs will benefit by referring to H. B. Fine, College Algebra, pp. 425–453, and L. E. Dickson, First Course in the Theory of Equations, Chap. II.

method when the factor theorem is being used for the purpose of determining the roots of $f(x) = 0$. For if $x - b$ is a factor of $f(x)$, it follows that $f(x) = (x - b) g(x)$, where $g(x)$ is a polynomial of degree one less than that of $f(x)$. Obviously the roots of $g(x) = 0$ will be the remaining roots of $f(x) = 0$, so that only $g(x) = 0$ need be considered in attempting to find these roots. Moreover, when $f(x)$ is divided by $x - b$ the quotient is $g(x)$. If synthetic division is used, the computation is usually quite simple.

Example. If $f(x) = x^3 + 2x^2 + 2x + 1$ is divided by $x + 1$, the quotient is $x^2 + x + 1$ and the remainder is zero. Hence, $x = -1$ is a root of $f(x) = 0$ and the remaining roots are determined by solving $x^2 + x + 1 = 0$.

THEOREM 4. *Every algebraic equation of degree n has exactly n roots if a root of multiplicity m is counted as m roots.*

A root b of $f(x) = 0$ is said to be a root of multiplicity m if $(x - b)^m$ is a factor of $f(x)$ but $(x - b)^{m+1}$ is not a factor of $f(x)$.

It follows from Theorems 3 and 4 that the polynomial of degree n can be factored into n linear factors, so that

$$f(x) \equiv a_0x^n + a_1x^{n-1} + \cdots + a_{n-1}x + a_n$$
$$= a_0(x - x_1)(x - x_2) \cdots (x - x_n).$$

THEOREM 5. *If*

$$f(x) = a_0x^n + a_1x^{n-1} + \cdots + a_{n-1}x + a_n$$

has integral coefficients and if $f(x) = 0$ has the rational root b/c, where b and c are integers without a common divisor, then b is an exact divisor of a_n and c is an exact divisor of a_0.

Example. Consider the equation

$$f(x) \equiv 2x^3 + x^2 + x - 1 = 0.$$

The only possible rational roots are ± 1 and $\pm \frac{1}{2}$. Since $f(1) = 3$, $f(-1) = -3, f(-\frac{1}{2}) = -\frac{3}{2}$, and $f(\frac{1}{2}) = 0$, it follows that $\frac{1}{2}$ is the only rational root. As a matter of fact, if $f(x)$ is divided by $x - \frac{1}{2}$ the quotient is $2x^2 + 2x + 2$ whose factors are 2, $x - \omega$, and $x - \omega^2$, where ω and ω^2 are the complex roots of unity.*

THEOREM 6. *Given $f(x) \equiv x^n + a_1x^{n-1} + \cdots + a_{n-1}x + a_n$ $= 0$. If $f(a)$ and $f(b)$ are of opposite sign, then there exists at least*

* See Sec. 26 and the example following Theorem 9 of this section.

one root of $f(x) = 0$ between a and b.   Moreover, the number of such roots is odd.

Graphically this means that $y = f(x)$ must cross the x-axis an odd number of times between a and b.

Example.   If $f(x) \equiv 8x^3 - 12x^2 - 2x + 3 = 0$,

$$f(-1) = -15, \qquad f(0) = 3; \qquad f(1) = -3, \qquad f(2) = 15.$$

Since $f(-1)$ is negative and $f(0)$ is positive, there is at least one root between -1 and 0.   Similarly, there is a root between 0 and 1, and another between 1 and 2.

THEOREM 7.   (Descartes' Rule of Signs.)   *The number of positive real roots of an algebraic equation $f(x) = 0$ with real coefficients is either equal to the number of variations in sign of $f(x)$ or less than that number by a positive even integer.   The number of negative real roots of $f(x) = 0$ is either equal to the number of variations in sign of $f(-x)$ or less than that number by a positive even integer.*

Example. $f(x) \equiv 8x^3 - 12x^2 - 2x + 3$ has two changes in sign, and therefore there are either two or no positive roots of $f(x) = 0$.   Also, $f(-x) \equiv -8x^3 - 12x^2 + 2x + 3$ has only one change in sign, and $f(x)$ must have one negative root.

THEOREM 8.   *Every algebraic equation of odd degree, with real coefficients, and leading coefficient positive has at least one real root whose sign is opposite to that of the constant term.*

Example.   Since $f(x) \equiv 8x^3 - 12x^2 - 2x + 3 = 0$ is of odd degree and the constant term is positive, it follows that there must be at least one negative root.

THEOREM 9.   *If an algebraic equation $f(x) = 0$ with real coefficients has a root $a + bi$, where $b \neq 0$, and a and b are real, it also has the root $a - bi$.*

Example.   Thus, $x^3 - 1 = 0$ has the root $-\frac{1}{2} + \frac{1}{2}\sqrt{3}\,i$, and therefore it has the root $-\frac{1}{2} - \frac{1}{2}\sqrt{3}\,i$.   This theorem states that imaginary roots always occur in pairs.

PROBLEMS

1. Find all the roots of the following equations:

(a) $x^3 + 2x^2 - 4x - 8 = 0$;
(b) $2x^3 - x^2 - 5x - 2 = 0$;
(c) $4x^4 + 4x^3 + 3x^2 - x - 1 = 0$;
(d) $2x^4 - 3x^3 - 3x - 2 = 0$.

2. Isolate the roots of the following equations between consecutive integers:

(a) $x^3 - 2x^2 - x + 1 = 0$;
(b) $2x^3 + 4x^2 - 2x - 3 = 0$;
(c) $x^3 + 5x^2 + 6x + 1 = 0$;
(d) $x^4 - 5x^2 + 3 = 0$.

28. Horner's Method. Many readers are already familiar with Horner's method of determining the value, to any desired number of decimal places, of the real roots of algebraic equations. However, the development given here is somewhat different from that used in the texts on algebra, in that it depends on Taylor's series expansion.

Suppose that the equation is

(28-1) $\qquad f(x) \equiv a_0 x^n + a_1 x^{n-1} + \cdots + a_{n-1} x + a_n = 0$

and that it is known that the equation has a root between c and $c + 1$, where c is an integer. If $f(x)$ is expanded in Taylor's series in powers of $x - c$, there will result* a polynomial in $x - c$, namely,

$$f(x) = f(c) + f'(c)(x - c) + \frac{f''(c)}{2!}(x - c)^2 + \cdots$$
$$+ \frac{f^{(n-1)}(c)}{(n-1)!}(x - c)^{n-1} + \frac{f^{(n)}(c)}{n!}(x - c)^n.$$

Now, let $x - c = x_1$ and $\dfrac{f^{(r)}(c)}{r!} = A_{n-r}$. Then (28-1) is replaced by

(28-2) $\quad f_1(x_1) \equiv A_n + A_{n-1} x_1 + \cdots + A_1 x_1^{n-1} + A_0 x_1^n = 0$.

Since (28-1) had a root between c and $c + 1$ and since $x_1 = x - c$, it is evident that (28-2) has a root between 0 and 1. By the use of Theorem 6, Sec. 27, this root can be isolated between d and $d + 0.1$, where d has the form $a/10$ and $0 \leq a < 9$. Moreover, $f_1(x_1) = f(x_1 + c)$; and it follows that, if f_1 has a root between d and $d + 0.1$, then f has a root between $c + d$ and $c + d + 0.1$. It should be noted that c may be negative but that d will always be positive or zero.

The function $f_1(x_1)$ can be expanded in Taylor's series in powers of $x_1 - d$; and, if $x_2 = x_1 - d$, there will be obtained an equation

$$f_2(x_2) = B_n + B_{n-1} x_2 + \cdots + B_1 x_2^{n-1} + B_0 x_2^n = 0.$$

But $f_1(x_1) = 0$ has a root between d and $d + 0.1$; and since $x_2 = x_1 - d$, it follows that $f_2(x_2) = 0$ will have a root between 0 and 0.1.

This process can be continued as long as desired, each step determining another decimal place of the root of the original equation (28-1).

---

* Since $f(x)$ is a polynomial of the nth degree, the derivatives of order higher than n are all zero.

The solution of a specific equation may help to clarify the procedure. Let it be required to find the values of the real roots of the equation

$$F(x) \equiv x^4 + x^3 - 3x^2 - 6x - 3 = 0.$$

Since there is only one variation in sign, $F(x)$ has at most one positive root. $F(-x)$ has three variations, and so there will be at most three negative roots. The only possibilities for rational roots are ± 1 and ± 3. Since $F(-1) = 0$, it follows that $x = -1$ is a root. Moreover, if $F(x)$ is divided by $x + 1$, the quotient is $f(x) = x^3 - 3x - 3$. Hence, the remaining roots of $F(x) = 0$ are the three roots of

$$f(x) \equiv x^3 - 3x - 3 = 0.$$

It is easily checked that $f(x) = 0$ has no rational roots. Also, $\Delta = 108 - 243$, so that there is only one real root which, since $f(2) = -1$ and $f(3) = 15$, must lie between 2 and 3. Therefore, $f(x)$ will be expanded in powers of $x - 2$. Since

$$
\begin{array}{ll}
f(x) = x^3 - 3x - 3, & f(2) = -1, \\
f'(x) = 3x^2 - 3, & f'(2) = 9, \\
f''(x) = 6x, & f''(2) = 12, \\
f'''(x) = 6, & f'''(2) = 6,
\end{array}
$$

the expansion becomes

$$f(x) = -1 + 9(x - 2) + \frac{12}{2!}(x - 2)^2 + \frac{6}{3!}(x - 2)^3.$$

Replacing $x - 2$ by x_1 gives

$$f_1(x_1) \equiv -1 + 9x_1 + 6x_1^2 + x_1^3 = 0.$$

Since the real root of this equation lies between 0 and 1, the x_1^2 and x_1^3 terms do not contribute very much to the value of $f_1(x_1)$. Hence, a first approximation to the root can be obtained by setting $9x_1 - 1 = 0$. This gives $x_1 = \frac{1}{9} = 0.111 \cdots$, and suggests that the root probably lies between 0.1 and 0.2. It is easy to show that $f_1(0.1) = -0.039$ and $f_1(0.2) = 1.048$; there is thus a root between 0.1 and 0.2, and it is evidently closer to 0.1. Therefore, $f(x) = 0$ has a root between 2.1 and 2.2.

Expanding $f_1(x_1)$ in powers of $x_1 - 0.1$ gives

$$f_1(x_1) = -0.039 + 10.23(x_1 - 0.1) + \frac{12.6}{2!}(x_1 - 0.1)^2 + \frac{6}{3!}(x_1 - 0.1)^3,$$

and replacing $x_1 - 0.1$ by x_2 yields

$$f_2(x_2) = -0.039 + 10.23x_2 + 6.3x_2^2 + x_2^3 = 0.$$

Now $10.23x_2 - 0.039 = 0$ gives the approximation $x_2 = 0.0038$, and testing 0.003 and 0.004 reveals that $f_2(0.003) = -0.008253273$ and

$f_2(0.004) = +0.002020864$. Thus, the root lies between 0.003 and 0.004 and is closer to 0.004. If it is desired to determine the root of $f(x) = 0$ to three decimal places only, this value will be 2.104. If more decimal places are desired, the process can be continued. It should be noted that in each succeeding step the terms of the second and third degree contribute less, so that the linear approximation becomes better.

PROBLEMS

1. Apply Horner's method to find the cube root of 25, correct to three decimal places.

2. Determine the real roots of $x^3 - 2x - 1 = 0$ by Horner's method.

3. Determine the root of $x^4 + x^3 - 7x^2 - x + 5 = 0$, which lies between 2 and 3.

4. Determine the real root of $2x^3 - 3x^2 + x - 1 = 0$.

5. Determine the roots of $x^3 - 3x^2 + 3 = 0$.

6. Find, correct to three decimal places, the value of the root of $x^5 + 3x^3 - 2x^2 + x + 1 = 0$, which lies between -1 and 0.

7. A sphere 2 ft. in diameter is formed of wood whose specific gravity is $\frac{2}{3}$. Find to three significant figures the depth h to which the sphere will sink in water. $\left[\text{The volume of a spherical segment is}\, \pi h^2 \left(r - \dfrac{h}{3}\right).\right]$ The volume of the submerged segment is equal to the volume of the displaced water, which must weigh as much as the sphere. Since water weighs 62.5 lb. per cubic foot,

$$\pi h^2 \left(r - \frac{h}{3}\right) 62.5 = \frac{4}{3}\pi r^3 \frac{2}{3}\, 62.5$$

and, since $r = 1$,

$$h^3 - 3h^2 + \tfrac{8}{3} = 0.$$

29. Newton's Method. Horner's method of obtaining a numerical solution of an equation is probably the most useful scheme for solving algebraic equations, but it is not applicable to trigonometric, exponential, or logarithmic equations. A method applicable to these types as well as to algebraic equations was developed by Sir Isaac Newton sometime before 1676.

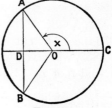

FIG. 19.

Newton applied his method to an algebraic equation, but it will be introduced here in the solution of a problem involving a trigonometric function.

Let it be required to find the angle subtended at the center of a circle by an arc whose length is double the length of its chord

(Fig. 19). Let the arc BCA be an arc of length $2BA$. Let $2x$ be the angle (measured in radians) subtended at the center of the circle. Then, arc $BCA = 2xr$ and $BA = 2\,DA = 2r\sin x$. If arc $BCA = 2BA$, then $2xr = 4r\sin x$, or $x - 2\sin x = 0$.

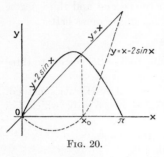

The graphical solution of equations of this type was discussed in Sec. 25. A first approximation can be obtained by graphical means. If $y = x$ and $y = 2\sin x$ are plotted, it appears from the graph (Fig. 20) that they intersect for x lying between 108° and 109°, or, expressing this in radians,

Fig. 20.

$$1.8850 < x < 1.9024.$$

If $x_1 = 1.8850$ be chosen as the first approximation, the question of improving this value will be discussed first from the following graphical considerations.

If the part of the curve $y = x - 2\sin x$ in the vicinity of the root be drawn on a large scale, it will have the appearance shown in Fig. 21. It is clear from the graph that adding to x_1 the

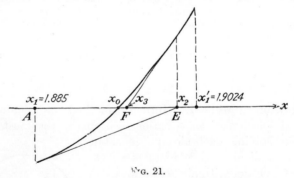

Fig. 21.

distance AE, cut off by the tangent line to the curve at $x_1 = 1.8850$, will give a value x_2 which is a better approximation to the actual root x_0. But AE is the subtangent at x_1 and is equal to $-\dfrac{f(x_1)}{f'(x_1)}$, where $f(x) = x - 2\sin x$. Thus,*

$$x_2 = x_1 - \frac{f(x_1)}{f'(x_1)}.$$

* See, in this connection, Prob. 8, at the end of this section.

Similarly, upon using x_2 as the second approximation and observing that $-\dfrac{f(x_2)}{f'(x_2)}$ is the subtangent EF, the third approximation is found to be

$$x_3 = x_2 - \frac{f(x_2)}{f'(x_2)},$$

and in general the nth approximation x_n is given by

(29-1) $$x_n = x_{n-1} - \frac{f(x_{n-1})}{f'(x_{n-1})}, \quad (n = 2, 3, \cdots).$$

Since $x_1 = 1.885$, the formula gives

$$x_2 = x_1 - \frac{f(x_1)}{f'(x_1)} = x_1 - \frac{x_1 - 2 \sin x_1}{1 - 2 \cos x_1}$$

$$= 1.8850 - \frac{1.8850 - 1.9022}{1 + 0.6180} = 1.8956.$$

In a similar way,

$$x_3 = x_2 - \frac{f(x_2)}{f'(x_2)} = 1.8956 - \frac{1.8956 - 2 \sin 1.8956}{1 - 2 \cos 1.8956} = 1.8955.$$

It follows that the angle subtended by the arc is 3.7910 radians.

The use of Newton's method requires some preliminary examination of the equation. It may happen that the equation is of such a character that the second approximation to x_0 will be worse than the first. A careful examination of the following sketches of four types of functions, sketched in the vicinity of their roots, reveals the fact that some care must be exercised in applying Newton's method. For all four figures, it is assumed that x_0 has been isolated between x_1 and x_1'. The graphical interpretation of the correction $-\dfrac{f(x_1)}{f'(x_1)}$ as the subtan-

Fig. 22.

gent must be kept in mind throughout this discussion. If x_1 is used as the first approximation, then x_2 will be obtained as the second approximation by using Newton's method; if x_1' is used, then x_2' will be obtained.

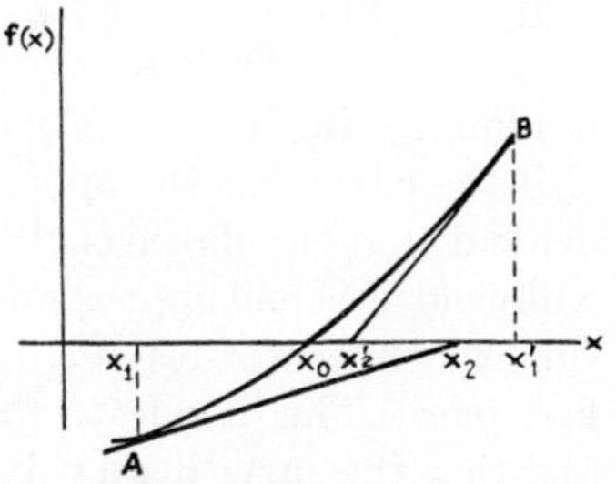

In Fig. 22, both x_2 and x_2' are closer to x_0 than x_1 or x_1'. In this case the method would work regardless of which value is chosen as the first approximation. In Fig. 23, x_2 is better than the first approximation x_1, but x_2' is worse than x_1'. It appears from

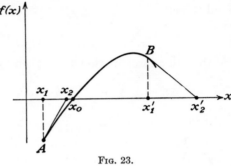

FIG. 23.

the figure that this occurs because the curve is concave down between x_1 and x_1', and hence $f''(x) < 0$, whereas $f(x_1) < 0$ and

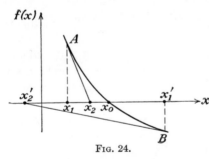

FIG. 24.

$f(x_1') > 0$. A similar situation would obtain if the curve is concave up, so that $f''(x) > 0$ (Fig. 24). The reader will readily convince himself from an inspection of Fig. 23 that caution must be exercised in the choice of the first approximation if the curve has a maximum (or a minimum) in the vicinity of x_0.

If the curve has the appearance indicated in Fig. 25, then it is evident that the choice of either x_1 or x_1' as the first approximation will yield a second approximation which is worse than the first one. This is due to the fact that the curve has a point of inflection between x_1 and x_1'.

From the foregoing discussion, it is apparent that Newton's method should not be

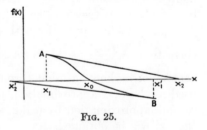

FIG. 25.

applied before making an investigation of the behavior of the first and second derivatives of $f(x)$ in the vicinity of the root. The conclusions drawn from this discussion can be summarized in the following practical rule for determining the choice of the first approximation: *If $f'(x)$ and $f''(x)$ do not vanish in the given interval (x_1, x_1') and if the signs of $f(x_1)$ and $f(x_1')$ are opposite, then the first approximation should be chosen as that one of the two end points for which $f(x)$ and $f''(x)$ have the same sign.*

It can be proved* that if the single-valued continuous function $f(x)$ is of such a nature that $f(x)$ = 0 has only one real root in (x_1, x_1') and both $f'(x)$ and $f''(x)$ are continuous and do not vanish in (x_1, x_1'), then repeated applications of Newton's method will determine the value of the root of $f(x) = 0$ to any desired number of decimal places.

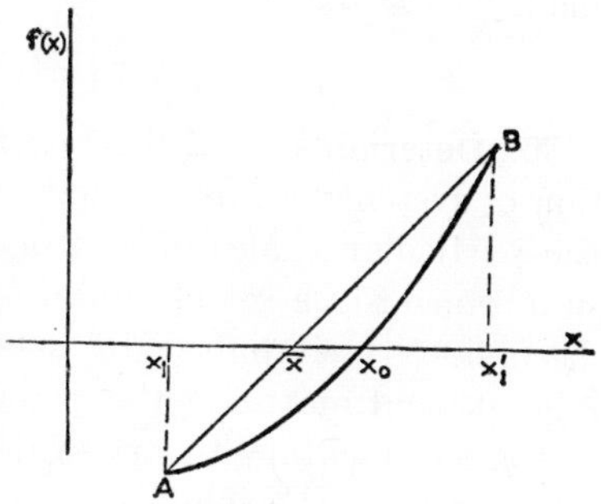

Fig. 26.

The cases to which Newton's method does not apply can be treated by a method of interpolation (*regula falsi*) that is applicable to any equation.

Let $\bar{x}$ be the value of x for which the chord AB intersects the x-axis. From similar triangles (Fig. 26),

$$\frac{\bar{x} - x_1}{-f(x_1)} = \frac{x_1' - \bar{x}}{f(x_1')}.$$

Solving for $\bar{x}$ gives

$$\bar{x} = \frac{x_1 f(x_1') - x_1' f(x_1)}{f(x_1') - f(x_1)}.$$

The value $\bar{x}$ is clearly a better approximation than either x_1 or x_1'.

PROBLEMS

1. Solve Prob. 7, Sec. 28, by Newton's method. Also, apply the method of interpolation.

2. Determine the angle subtended at the center of a circle by a chord which cuts off a segment whose area is one-quarter of that of the circle.

3. Find the roots of $e^x - 4x = 0$, correct to four decimal places.

4. Solve $x - \cos x = 0$.

* See WEBER, H., Algebra, 2d ed. vol. 1, pp. 380–382; COATE, G. T., On the Convergence of Newton's Method of Approximation, *Amer. Math. Monthly.* vol. 44, pp. 464–466, 1937.

5. Solve $x = \tan x$ in the vicinity of $x = \frac{3}{2}\pi$.

6. Solve $x + e^x = 0$.

7. Solve $x^4 - x - 1 = 0$.

8. Show with the aid of Taylor's series that, if $x = x_1$ is an approximate root of $f(x) = 0$, then the nth approximation is, in general, determined from the formula (29-1).

Hint: $f(x) = f(x_1) + f'(x_1)(x - x_1) + \cdots + \dfrac{f^{(n)}(x_1)}{n!}(x - x_1)^n + \cdots$;

and if $f(x_2) \doteq 0$, then

$$0 \doteq f(x_1) + f'(x_1)(x_2 - x_1).$$

30. Determinants of the Second and Third Order.   The solution of systems of linear equations involves the determination of the particular values of two or more variables that will satisfy simultaneously a set of equations in those variables.   Since the discussion is simplified by using certain properties of determinants and matrices, the remainder of this chapter is devoted to some elementary theory of determinants and matrices and its application to the solution of systems of linear equations.

Consider first a system composed of two linear equations in two unknowns, namely,

(30-1)
$$\begin{cases} a_1x + b_1y = k_1, \\ a_2x + b_2y = k_2. \end{cases}$$

If y is eliminated between these two equations, there is obtained the equation

(30-2) $$(a_1b_2 - a_2b_1)x = k_1b_2 - k_2b_1;$$

and if x is eliminated, there results

(30-3) $$(a_1b_2 - a_2b_1)y = a_1k_2 - a_2k_1.$$

If the expression $a_1b_2 - a_2b_1$ is not zero, the two equations (30-2) and (30-3) can be solved to give values for x and y.   That the values so obtained are actually the solutions of the system (30-1) can be verified by substitution in Eqs. (30-1).

The expression $a_1b_2 - a_2b_1$ occurs as the coefficient for both x and y.   Denote it by the symbol

(30-4) $$a_1b_2 - a_2b_1 \equiv \begin{vmatrix} a_1 & b_1 \\ a_2 & b_2 \end{vmatrix}.$$

This symbol is called a determinant of the second order.   It is also called the determinant of the coefficients of the system

(30-1), for the elements of its first column are the coefficients of x and the elements of its second column are the coefficients of y. Using this notation, (30-2) and (30-3) become

$$(30\text{-}5) \qquad \begin{vmatrix} a_1 \ b_1 \\ a_2 \ b_2 \end{vmatrix} x = \begin{vmatrix} k_1 \ b_1 \\ k_2 \ b_2 \end{vmatrix}, \qquad \begin{vmatrix} a_1 \ b_1 \\ a_2 \ b_2 \end{vmatrix} y = \begin{vmatrix} a_1 \ k_1 \\ a_2 \ k_2 \end{vmatrix}.$$

The definition (30-4) provides the method of evaluating the symbol. If

$$D \equiv \begin{vmatrix} a_1 \ b_1 \\ a_2 \ b_2 \end{vmatrix} \neq 0,$$

the unique solution of (30-1) can be written as

$$x = \frac{\begin{vmatrix} k_1 \ b_1 \\ k_2 \ b_2 \end{vmatrix}}{D}, \qquad y = \frac{\begin{vmatrix} a_1 \ k_1 \\ a_2 \ k_2 \end{vmatrix}}{D}.$$

If $D = 0$, $a_1 b_2 = a_2 b_1$ or $a_1/a_2 = b_1/b_2$. But if the corresponding coefficients of the two equations are proportional, the two lines, whose equations are given by (30-1), are parallel (if $a_1/a_2 \neq k_1/k_2$) or coincident (if $a_1/a_2 = b_1/b_2 = k_1/k_2$). In the first case, the determinants appearing as the right-hand members of the equations in (30-5) will be different from zero and there will be no solution for x and y. In the second case, these determinants, as well as D, are zero and any pair of values x, y that satisfies one equation of the system will satisfy the other equation, also.

Example 1. For the system

$$\begin{array}{l} 2x - 3y = -4 \\ 3x - y = 1, \end{array} \qquad D = \begin{vmatrix} 2 & -3 \\ 3 & -1 \end{vmatrix} = -2 + 9 = 7,$$

$$x = \frac{\begin{vmatrix} -4 & -3 \\ 1 & -1 \end{vmatrix}}{7} = 1. \qquad y = \frac{\begin{vmatrix} 2 & -4 \\ 3 & 1 \end{vmatrix}}{7} = 2.$$

Example 2. For the system

$$\begin{array}{l} 2x - 3y = 4 \\ 6x - 9y = 5, \end{array} \qquad D = \begin{vmatrix} 2 & -3 \\ 6 & -9 \end{vmatrix} = 0,$$

but

$$\frac{2}{6} = \frac{-3}{-9} \neq \frac{4}{5}.$$

The two lines whose equations are given are parallel.

Example 3. For the system

$$2x - 3y = 4 \qquad D = \begin{vmatrix} 2 & -3 \\ 6 & -9 \end{vmatrix} = 0,$$
$$6x - 9y = 12,$$
$$\frac{2}{6} = \frac{-3}{-9} = \frac{4}{12}.$$

The two lines are coincident.

Consider next the system of three linear equations in three unknowns,

$$(30\text{-}6) \qquad \begin{cases} a_1x + b_1y + c_1z = k_1, \\ a_2x + b_2y + c_2z = k_2, \\ a_3x + b_3y + c_3z = k_3. \end{cases}$$

If these equations are multiplied, respectively, by

$$b_2c_3 - b_3c_2, \qquad b_3c_1 - b_1c_3, \qquad b_1c_2 - b_2c_1,$$

and the resulting equations are added, the sum is

$$(30\text{-}7) \quad (a_1b_2c_3 - a_1b_3c_2 + a_2b_3c_1 - a_2b_1c_3 + a_3b_1c_2 - a_3b_2c_1)x$$
$$= k_1b_2c_3 - k_1b_3c_2 + k_2b_3c_1 - k_2b_1c_3 + k_3b_1c_2 - k_3b_2c_1.$$

The coefficient of x in (30-7) can be denoted by the symbol

$$(30\text{-}8) \quad D \equiv \begin{vmatrix} a_1 & b_1 & c_1 \\ a_2 & b_2 & c_2 \\ a_3 & b_3 & c_3 \end{vmatrix} \equiv a_1b_2c_3 - a_1b_3c_2 + a_2b_3c_1 - a_2b_1c_3 \\ + a_3b_1c_2 - a_3b_2c_1.$$

This symbol is called a determinant of the third order. It is also the determinant of the coefficients of the system (30-6).

Using the notation of (30-8), Eq. (30-7) can be written as

$$Dx \equiv \begin{vmatrix} a_1 & b_1 & c_1 \\ a_2 & b_2 & c_2 \\ a_3 & b_3 & c_3 \end{vmatrix} x = \begin{vmatrix} k_1 & b_1 & c_1 \\ k_2 & b_2 & c_2 \\ k_3 & b_3 & c_3 \end{vmatrix}.$$

Similarly it can be shown that

$$\begin{vmatrix} a_1 & b_1 & c_1 \\ a_2 & b_2 & c_2 \\ a_3 & b_3 & c_3 \end{vmatrix} y = \begin{vmatrix} a_1 & k_1 & c_1 \\ a_2 & k_2 & c_2 \\ a_3 & k_3 & c_3 \end{vmatrix},$$

and

$$\begin{vmatrix} a_1 & b_1 & c_1 \\ a_2 & b_2 & c_2 \\ a_3 & b_3 & c_3 \end{vmatrix} z = \begin{vmatrix} a_1 & b_1 & k_1 \\ a_2 & b_2 & k_2 \\ a_3 & b_3 & k_3 \end{vmatrix}.$$

If $D \neq 0$, the unique solutions for x, y, and z can be obtained as

$$(30\text{-}9) \quad x = \frac{\begin{vmatrix} k_1 & b_1 & c_1 \\ k_2 & b_2 & c_2 \\ k_3 & b_3 & c_3 \end{vmatrix}}{D}, \qquad y = \frac{\begin{vmatrix} a_1 & k_1 & c_1 \\ a_2 & k_2 & c_2 \\ a_3 & k_3 & c_3 \end{vmatrix}}{D}, \qquad z = \frac{\begin{vmatrix} a_1 & b_1 & k_1 \\ a_2 & b_2 & k_2 \\ a_3 & b_3 & k_3 \end{vmatrix}}{D}.$$

In order to show that the values of x, y, and z, given in (30-9), actually satisfy Eqs. (30-6), these values can be substituted in the given equations.

If $D = 0$, the three equations (30-6) are either inconsistent or dependent. A detailed analytic discussion of these cases will be given in Sec. 35. Since the three equations of (30-6) are the equations of three planes, a geometrical interpretation will now be given.

If the three equations are inconsistent, the three planes are all parallel, or two are parallel and are cut by the third plane in two parallel lines. In either case, there is obviously no solution for x, y, and z. If the equations are dependent, all three planes intersect in the same line or all three planes coincide. In either case there will be an infinite number of solutions for x, y, and z.

Example. For the system

$$\begin{array}{r} 3x - y - z = 2, \\ x - 2y - 3z = 0, \\ 4x + y + 2z = 4. \end{array} \qquad D = \begin{vmatrix} 3 & -1 & -1 \\ 1 & -2 & -3 \\ 4 & 1 & 2 \end{vmatrix} = 2.$$

Therefore,

$$x = \frac{\begin{vmatrix} 2 & -1 & -1 \\ 0 & -2 & -3 \\ 4 & 1 & 2 \end{vmatrix}}{2} = \frac{2}{2} = 1, \qquad y = \frac{\begin{vmatrix} 3 & 2 & -1 \\ 1 & 0 & -3 \\ 4 & 4 & 2 \end{vmatrix}}{2} = \frac{4}{2} = 2,$$

$$z = \frac{\begin{vmatrix} 3 & -1 & 2 \\ 1 & -2 & 0 \\ 4 & 1 & 4 \end{vmatrix}}{2} = -\frac{2}{2} = -1.$$

PROBLEMS

1. Evaluate

$$\begin{vmatrix} 1 & 2 & 3 \\ 2 & -1 & 4 \\ 3 & -1 & -2 \end{vmatrix}, \quad \begin{vmatrix} 2 & 0 & -3 \\ 1 & 4 & 2 \\ -1 & 1 & -2 \end{vmatrix}, \text{ and } \begin{vmatrix} 4 & -2 & 1 \\ 5 & 0 & -1 \\ 2 & 3 & -3 \end{vmatrix}.$$

2. Find the solutions of the following systems of equations by using determinants:

(a) $5x - 4y = 3,$
　　$2x + 3y = 7;$
(b) $2x + 3y - 2z = 4,$
　　$x + y - z = 2,$
　　$3x - 5y + 3z = 0;$
(c) $3x - 2y = 7,$
　　$3y + 2z = 6,$
　　$2x + 3z = 1;$
(d) $3x + 2y + 2z = 3,$
　　$x - 4y + 2z = 4,$
　　$2x + y + z = 2.$

31. Determinants of the nth Order. Determinants of the second and third orders were defined in the preceding section. These are merely special cases of the definition of the determinants of any order n. Instead of a symbol with 2^2 or 3^2 elements, the determinant of the nth order is defined as the symbol, with n rows and n columns,

$$D \equiv \begin{vmatrix} a_{11} & a_{12} & \cdots & a_{1n} \\ a_{21} & a_{22} & \cdots & a_{2n} \\ \hdotsfor{4} \\ \hdotsfor{4} \\ a_{n1} & a_{n2} & \cdots & a_{nn} \end{vmatrix},$$

which stands for the sum* of the $n!$ terms $(-1)^k a_{k_1 1} a_{k_2 2} \cdots a_{k_n n}$, where $k_1, k_2, \cdots, k_n$ are the numbers $1, 2, \cdots, n$ in some order. The integer k is defined as the number of *inversions of order* of the subscripts $k_1, k_2, \cdots, k_n$ from the normal order $1, 2, \cdots, n$, where a particular arrangement is said to have k inversions of order if it is necessary to make k successive interchanges of adjacent elements† in order to make the arrangement assume the normal order. There are $n!$ terms since there are $n!$ permutations of the n first subscripts. Moreover, it is evident that each term contains as a factor one and only one element from each row and one and only one element from each column.

---

* This sum is sometimes called the expansion of the determinant.

† It should be noted that it is not necessary to specify that the interchanges should be of adjacent elements, for it can be proved that, if any particular arrangement can be obtained by k interchanges of adjacent elements and also by k' interchanges of some other type, then k and k' are always either both even or both odd. Hence, the sign of the term is independent of the particular succession of interchanges.

Example. Consider the third-order determinant

$$D = \begin{vmatrix} a_{11} & a_{12} & a_{13} \\ a_{21} & a_{22} & a_{23} \\ a_{31} & a_{32} & a_{33} \end{vmatrix}.$$

The six terms of the expansion are, apart from sign,

$$a_{11}a_{22}a_{33}, \qquad a_{11}a_{32}a_{23}, \qquad a_{21}a_{12}a_{33},$$
$$a_{21}a_{32}a_{13}, \qquad a_{31}a_{12}a_{23}, \qquad a_{31}a_{22}a_{13}.$$

The first term, in which the first subscripts have the normal order, is called the diagonal term, and its sign is positive. In the second term the arrangement 132 requires the interchange of 2 and 3 to make it assume the normal order; therefore, $k = 1$, and the term has a negative sign. Similarly, the third term has a negative sign. The fourth term will have a positive sign, for the arrangement 231 requires the interchange of 3 and 1 followed by the interchange of 2 and 1 in order to assume the normal order. Similarly, it appears that the fifth term will have a positive sign. In the sixth term, it is necessary to make three interchanges (3 and 2, 3 and 1, and 2 and 1) in order to arrive at the normal order; hence, this term will have a negative sign. As a result of this investigation, it follows that

$$D = a_{11}a_{22}a_{33} - a_{11}a_{32}a_{23} - a_{21}a_{12}a_{33} + a_{21}a_{32}a_{13} + a_{31}a_{12}a_{23} - a_{31}a_{22}a_{13}$$

It is evident that if k is equal to zero or an even number the term will have a positive sign, whereas if k is odd the term will be negative.

PROBLEM

Find the signs of the six terms involving a_{11} in the expansion of the determinant

$$\begin{vmatrix} a_{11} & a_{12} & a_{13} & a_{14} \\ a_{21} & a_{22} & a_{23} & a_{24} \\ a_{31} & a_{32} & a_{33} & a_{34} \\ a_{41} & a_{42} & a_{43} & a_{44} \end{vmatrix}.$$

32. Properties of Determinants. 1. *The value of a determinant is not changed if in the symbol the elements of corresponding rows and columns are interchanged.*

If

$$D \equiv \begin{vmatrix} a_{11} & a_{12} & \cdots & a_{1n} \\ a_{21} & a_{22} & \cdots & a_{2n} \\ \cdots & \cdots & \cdots & \cdots \\ a_{n1} & a_{n2} & \cdots & a_{nn} \end{vmatrix},$$

then the determinant formed by interchanging the corresponding rows and columns is

$$D' \equiv \begin{vmatrix} a_{11} & a_{21} & \cdots & a_{n1} \\ a_{12} & a_{22} & \cdots & a_{n2} \\ \cdots\cdots\cdots\cdots\cdots \\ a_{1n} & a_{2n} & \cdots & a_{nn} \end{vmatrix}.$$

Any term $(-1)^k a_{k_1 1} a_{k_2 2} \cdots a_{k_n n}$ of D, where $k_1, k_2, \cdots, k_n$ are the numbers $1, 2, \cdots, n$ in some order, will correspond to a term $(-1)^l a_{k_1 1} a_{k_2 2} \cdots a_{k_n n}$ of D', for each determinant must contain every possible term that is a product of one and only one element from each row and each column. But the number of inversions is the same for the term of D as it is for the term of D', owing to the fact that the corresponding first subscripts are the same. It follows that each term of D occurs also in D', and conversely each term of D' occurs also in D.

Example. If

$$D \equiv \begin{vmatrix} 2 & .5 & 3 \\ 1 & -1 & 4 \\ -3 & -2 & 1 \end{vmatrix} = -66,$$

then

$$D' \equiv \begin{vmatrix} 2 & 1 & -3 \\ 5 & -1 & -2 \\ 3 & 4 & 1 \end{vmatrix} = -66.$$

2. *An interchange of any two rows or of any two columns of a determinant will merely change the sign of the determinant.*

If D is the original determinant and D'' is the determinant having the ith and jth rows of D interchanged, then the expansion of D'' will have the first subscripts of each term the same as those of the corresponding term of D, except that i and j will be interchanged. Since it requires one interchange to restore i and j to their original order in each term, the sign of every term will be changed. Thus, $D'' = -D$.

Example. If

$$D \equiv \begin{vmatrix} 2 & 5 & 3 \\ 1 & -1 & 4 \\ -3 & -2 & 1 \end{vmatrix} = -66,$$

then

$$D'' = \begin{vmatrix} 2 & 5 & 3 \\ -3 & -2 & 1 \\ 1 & -1 & 4 \end{vmatrix} = 66.$$

3. *If any two rows or any two columns of a determinant are identical, the value of the determinant is zero.*

For, by property 2, if these two rows (or columns) were interchanged, the sign of D should be changed. But since these two rows (or columns) are identical, D remains unchanged. Therefore, $D = -D$, and hence $D = 0$.

Example. If

$$D \equiv \begin{vmatrix} 2 & -1 & 2 \\ 3 & 4 & 3 \\ -2 & 5 & -2 \end{vmatrix},$$

then

$$D = 0.$$

4. *If each element of any row or any column be multiplied by m, the value of the determinant is multiplied by m.*

This follows from the definition of the determinant. Since one and only one element of any row or column occurs in each term, each term will be multiplied by m and therefore the value of the determinant is multiplied by m.

Example 1. If

$$D \equiv \begin{vmatrix} 2 & 5 & 3 \\ 1 & -1 & 4 \\ -3 & -2 & 1 \end{vmatrix} = -66$$

and

$$\bar{D} \equiv \begin{vmatrix} 2 & 5 & 3 \\ 1 & -1 & 4 \\ -6 & -4 & 2 \end{vmatrix},$$

which has each element of the last row twice the corresponding element of the last row of D, then

$$\bar{D} = -132 \quad \text{and} \quad \bar{D} = 2D.$$

Example 2. If

$$D \equiv \begin{vmatrix} 6 & 4 & 8 \\ 9 & 2 & 1 \\ -6 & 3 & -1 \end{vmatrix},$$

then

$$D \equiv 2 \begin{vmatrix} 3 & 2 & 4 \\ 9 & 2 & 1 \\ -6 & 3 & -1 \end{vmatrix} = 2 \cdot 3 \begin{vmatrix} 1 & 2 & 4 \\ 3 & 2 & 1 \\ -2 & 3 & -1 \end{vmatrix}.$$

5. *From properties 3 and 4, it follows that the value of a determinant is zero if any two rows or any two columns have corresponding elements proportional.*

6. *The product of two determinants D and D', both of order n, is the nth-order determinant D'' which has as the element in its ith row and jth column the sum*

$$\sum_{k=1}^{n} a_{ik}b_{kj} \equiv a_{i1}b_{1j} + a_{i2}b_{2j} + \cdots + a_{in}b_{nj},$$

which is formed by multiplying each element a_{ik} of the ith row of D by the corresponding element b_{kj} of the jth column of D'.

Thus, if

$$D = \begin{vmatrix} a_{11} & a_{12} \\ a_{21} & a_{22} \end{vmatrix} \quad \text{and} \quad D' = \begin{vmatrix} b_{11} & b_{12} \\ b_{21} & b_{22} \end{vmatrix},$$

then

$$D \cdot D' \equiv D'' = \begin{vmatrix} a_{11}b_{11} + a_{12}b_{21} & a_{11}b_{12} + a_{12}b_{22} \\ a_{21}b_{11} + a_{22}b_{21} & a_{21}b_{12} + a_{22}b_{22} \end{vmatrix}.$$

Example.   The product of the following determinants is easily found by expanding the product determinant:

$$\begin{vmatrix} \sin x & \cos x & 1 \\ \sec x & \tan x & 1 \\ \csc x & \cot x & 1 \end{vmatrix} \cdot \begin{vmatrix} \sin x & \sec x & \csc x \\ \cos x & -\tan x & -\cot x \\ -1 & -1 & -1 \end{vmatrix}$$

$$= \begin{vmatrix} 0 & \tan x - \sin x - 1 & -\cos x \cot x \\ \tan x + \sin x - 1 & 0 & \sec x \csc x - 2 \\ \cos x \cot x & \sec x \csc x - 2 & 0 \end{vmatrix}$$

$$= 2 \cos^2 x (2 - \sec x \csc x).$$

33. Minors.   The method of evaluating a determinant by the use of the definition of Sec. 31 is exceedingly tedious, especially if $n \geq 4$.   There are other schemes for this evaluation, and these require the definition of the minors of a determinant.   The simplest of these schemes will be described and used here.

If, in the determinant D, the ith row and the jth column be suppressed, the resulting determinant A_{ij} (which is of order one less than the order of D) is called the minor of the element a_{ij}, which is in the ith row and jth column.

Example.   If

$$D \equiv \begin{vmatrix} a_{11} & a_{12} & a_{13} & a_{14} \\ a_{21} & a_{22} & a_{23} & a_{24} \\ a_{31} & a_{32} & a_{33} & a_{34} \\ a_{41} & a_{42} & a_{43} & a_{44} \end{vmatrix},$$

then

$$A_{23} \equiv \begin{vmatrix} a_{11} & a_{12} & a_{14} \\ a_{31} & a_{32} & a_{34} \\ a_{41} & a_{42} & a_{44} \end{vmatrix}.$$

From the definition of a determinant, it is evident that $a_{ij}A_{ij}$ is composed of all the terms of D which contain the element a_{ij} as a factor, except for the possibility that all the signs may be reversed. Then the expression $(-1)^{k_1}a_{11}A_{11}$ is composed of all the terms of D containing a_{11} as a factor; $(-1)^{k_2}a_{21}A_{21}$ is composed of all the terms containing a_{21} as a factor; $(-1)^{k_3}a_{31}A_{31}$ is composed of all the terms containing a_{31} as a factor; etc.　But D is composed of all the terms containing a_{11}, a_{21}, a_{31}, $\cdots$, a_{n1} as a factor, and so

$$D = (-1)^{k_1}a_{11}A_{11} + (-1)^{k_2}a_{21}A_{21} + \cdots + (-1)^{k_n}a_{n1}A_{n1}.$$

It can be proved* that $k_1 = 1 + 1$. $k_2 = 2 + 1$, $k_3 = 3 + 1$, $\cdots$, $k_n = n + 1$, so that

$$D = a_{11}A_{11} - a_{21}A_{21} + \cdots + (-1)^{n+1}a_{n1}A_{n1}.$$

In the above development for D the elements a_{11}, a_{21}, $\cdots$, a_{n1} are the elements of the first column of D. Similarly, the value of D can be formed by taking the elements of any other column or of any row.

Using the ith column gives

$$D = (-1)^{k_1}a_{1i}A_{1i} + (-1)^{k_2}a_{2i}A_{2i} + \cdots + (-1)^{k_n}a_{ni}A_{ni},$$

where $k_1 = i + 1$, $k_2 = i + 2$, $\cdots$, $k_n = i + n$.　Similarly, using the ith row gives

$$D = (-1)^{k_1}a_{i1}A_{i1} + (-1)^{k_2}a_{i2}A_{i2} + \cdots + (-1)^{k_n}a_{in}A_{in},$$

where $k_1 = i + 1$, $k_2 = i + 2$, $\cdots$, $k_n = i + n$.　It may be observed that each k_r is equal to the sum of the subscripts of its a_{ij} and is thus equal to the sum of the number of the row and the number of the column in which this element occurs.　This development is known as the *expansion by minors*, or the *simple Laplace development*.

Since the term *cofactor* is frequently used in applications of this type of development, it will be defined here.　*The cofactor C_{ij} of an element a_{ij} is defined as the signed minor, that is,*

$$C_{ij} = (-1)^{i+j}A_{ij}.$$

---

* Dickson, L. E., First Course in Theory of Equations, pp. 101–127; Fine, H. B., College Algebra, pp. 492–519.

Thus, the expression for D can be written as

$$D = \sum_{i=1}^{n} (-1)^{i+j} a_{ij} A_{ij} = \sum_{j=1}^{n} (-1)^{i+j} a_{ij} A_{ij},$$

or as

$$D = \sum_{i=1}^{n} a_{ij} C_{ij} = \sum_{j=1}^{n} a_{ij} C_{ij}.$$

Example.

$$
\begin{vmatrix} 3 & 4 & 0 & 6 \\ 0 & 5 & 2 & 1 \\ 0 & 3 & 4 & 0 \\ 1 & 2 & 7 & 1 \end{vmatrix}
= 3\begin{vmatrix} 5 & 2 & 1 \\ 3 & 4 & 0 \\ 2 & 7 & 1 \end{vmatrix}
- 0\begin{vmatrix} 4 & 0 & 6 \\ 3 & 4 & 0 \\ 2 & 7 & 1 \end{vmatrix}
+ 0\begin{vmatrix} 4 & 0 & 6 \\ 5 & 2 & 1 \\ 2 & 7 & 1 \end{vmatrix}
- 1\begin{vmatrix} 4 & 0 & 6 \\ 5 & 2 & 1 \\ 3 & 4 & 0 \end{vmatrix}
$$

$$
= 3\left[-3\begin{vmatrix} 2 & 1 \\ 7 & 1 \end{vmatrix} + 4\begin{vmatrix} 5 & 1 \\ 2 & 1 \end{vmatrix} - 0\begin{vmatrix} 5 & 2 \\ 2 & 7 \end{vmatrix} \right]
$$

$$
- 1\left[4\begin{vmatrix} 2 & 1 \\ 4 & 0 \end{vmatrix} - 0\begin{vmatrix} 5 & 1 \\ 3 & 0 \end{vmatrix} + 6\begin{vmatrix} 5 & 2 \\ 3 & 4 \end{vmatrix} \right]
$$

$$
= -9(2 - 7) + 12(5 - 2) - 4(0 - 4) - 6(20 - 6)
$$

$$
= 13.
$$

Here, the first expansion is made by using the elements of the first column, for it contains two zeros (the third row is an equally good choice). The expansion of the first third-order determinant is made by using the elements of the second row, but the third column could be used to equal advantage. In the expansion of the last third-order determinant the first row was chosen, but the third row and the second and third columns provide equally good choices.

The following theorem is given here because of its frequent use in many fields of pure and applied mathematics:

THEOREM. *The sum* $\sum_{j=1}^{n} a_{ij} C_{kj}$ *is zero, if* $k \neq i$.

Each term of this sum is formed by taking the product of the cofactor of an element of the kth row by the corresponding element of the ith row. This is the expansion of a determinant whose ith and kth rows are identical and whose value is accordingly zero. Similarly, it follows that $\sum_{i=1}^{n} a_{ij} C_{ik} = 0$, if $k \neq j$.

Example. Let

$$D \equiv \begin{vmatrix} 3 & -1 & 2 \\ 1 & 2 & -1 \\ 4 & -3 & -2 \end{vmatrix}.$$

Then,

$$C_{11} = -7, \qquad C_{12} = -2, \qquad C_{13} = -11$$

and the sum

$$\sum_{j=1}^{3} a_{3j}C_{1j} = -28 + 6 + 22 = 0.$$

Similarly,

$$\sum_{j=1}^{3} a_{2j}C_{1j} = -7 - 4 + 11 = 0.$$

By using the theory of determinants, the solution of a system of n non-homogeneous linear equations in n unknowns can be obtained. The rule for effecting the solution will be stated but not proved.* The proof for the cases when $n = 2$ and $n = 3$ has already been given in Sec. 30.

Cramer's Rule. Let

$$(33\text{-}1) \quad \begin{aligned} a_{11}x_1 + a_{12}x_2 + \cdots + a_{1n}x_n &= k_1, \\ a_{21}x_1 + a_{22}x_2 + \cdots + a_{2n}x_n &= k_2, \\ &\cdots\cdots\cdots\cdots\cdots\cdots\cdots \\ a_{n1}x_1 + a_{n2}x_2 + \cdots + a_{nn}x_n &= k_n \end{aligned}$$

be a system of n equations in the unknowns $x_1, x_2, \cdots, x_n$, such that the determinant

$$D = \begin{vmatrix} a_{11} & a_{12} & \cdots & a_{1n} \\ a_{21} & a_{22} & \cdots & a_{2n} \\ \cdots & \cdots & \cdots & \cdots \\ a_{n1} & a_{n2} & \cdots & a_{nn} \end{vmatrix}$$

of the coefficients is not zero. The system (33-1) has a unique solution given by

$$x_1 = \frac{D_1}{D}, \qquad x_2 = \frac{D_2}{D}, \cdots, \qquad x_n = \frac{D_n}{D},$$

where D_i is the determinant formed by replacing the elements $a_{1i}, a_{2i}, a_{3i}, \cdots, a_{ni}$ of the ith column of D by $k_1, k_2, k_3, \cdots, k_n$, respectively.

Example. Solve, by Cramer's rule, the system

$$\begin{aligned} 3x + y + 2z &= 3, \\ 2x - 3y - z &= -3, \\ x + 2y + z &= 4. \end{aligned}$$

* DICKSON, L. E., First Course in Theory of Equations, pp. 114–115.

Here

$$D = \begin{vmatrix} 3 & 1 & 2 \\ 2 & -3 & -1 \\ 1 & 2 & 1 \end{vmatrix} = 8$$

and

$$x = \frac{\begin{vmatrix} 3 & 1 & 2 \\ -3 & -3 & -1 \\ 4 & 2 & 1 \end{vmatrix}}{8} = \frac{8}{8} = 1, \qquad y = \frac{\begin{vmatrix} 3 & 3 & 2 \\ 2 & -3 & -1 \\ 1 & 4 & 1 \end{vmatrix}}{8} = \frac{16}{8} = 2,$$

$$z = \frac{\begin{vmatrix} 3 & 1 & 3 \\ 2 & -3 & -3 \\ 1 & 2 & 4 \end{vmatrix}}{8} = \frac{-8}{8} = -1.$$

PROBLEMS

1. Evaluate

$$\begin{vmatrix} 1 & -2 & 0 & 3 \\ -1 & 4 & 1 & 2 \\ 2 & 0 & -1 & -3 \\ 3 & 1 & 0 & 1 \end{vmatrix}, \begin{vmatrix} 2 & -1 & 3 & 0 \\ 1 & 4 & 0 & 2 \\ 1 & 1 & 3 & 5 \\ -1 & 0 & 2 & 0 \end{vmatrix}, \text{ and } \begin{vmatrix} 1 & 3 & 2 & -1 \\ 0 & 4 & -3 & 2 \\ -3 & 1 & 0 & 1 \\ 1 & 2 & 0 & -4 \end{vmatrix}.$$

2. Solve, by Cramer's rule, the systems

(a) $x + 2y + 3z = 3,$
$2x - y + z = 6,$
$3x + y - z = 4.$

(b) $2x + y + 3z = 2,$
$3x - 2y - 2z = 1,$
$x - y + z = -1.$

(c) $x + 2y = 1,$
$2x - y - 2z = 3,$
$-x + y + 3z = 2.$

(d) $2x + y + 3z + w = -2,$
$5x + 3y - z - w = 1,$
$x - 2y + 4z + 3w = 4,$
$3x - y + z = 2.$

34. Matrices and Linear Dependence.

In order to discuss the systems arising in the succeeding sections, it is convenient to give a short introduction to the theory of matrices.*

An $m \times n$ matrix is defined as a system of mn quantities a_{ij} arranged in a rectangular array of m rows and n columns. If $m = n$, the array is called a square matrix of order n. The quantities a_{ij} are called the elements of the matrix. Thus,

$$(34\text{-}1) \quad A \equiv \begin{vmatrix} a_{11} & a_{12} & \cdots & a_{1n} \\ a_{21} & a_{22} & \cdots & a_{2n} \\ \cdots\cdots\cdots\cdots\cdots \\ \cdots\cdots\cdots\cdots\cdots \\ a_{m1} & a_{m2} & \cdots & a_{mn} \end{vmatrix} \quad \text{or} \quad \begin{pmatrix} a_{11} & a_{12} & \cdots & a_{1n} \\ a_{21} & a_{22} & \cdots & a_{2n} \\ \cdots\cdots\cdots\cdots\cdots \\ \cdots\cdots\cdots\cdots\cdots \\ a_{m1} & a_{m2} & \cdots & a_{mn} \end{pmatrix},$$

* For detailed treatment see M. Bocher, Introduction to Higher Algebra, pp. 20–53; L. E. Dickson, Modern Algebraic Theories, pp. 39–63.

where double bars or parentheses are used to enclose the array of elements. If the order of the elements in (34-1) is changed or if any element is changed, a different matrix results. Any two matrices A and B are said to be equal if and only if every element of A is equal to the corresponding element of B, that is, if $a_{ij} = b_{ij}$ for every i and j.

If the matrix is square, it is possible to form from the elements of the matrix a determinant whose elements have the same arrangement as those of the matrix. The determinant is called the *determinant of the matrix*. From any matrix, other matrices can be obtained by striking out any number of rows and columns. Certain of these matrices will be square matrices, and the determinants of these matrices are called the determinants of the matrix. For an $m \times n$ matrix, there are square matrices of orders 1, 2, $\cdots$, p, where p is equal to the smaller of the numbers m and n.

Example. The 2×3 matrix

$$A \equiv \begin{pmatrix} a_{11} & a_{12} & a_{13} \\ a_{21} & a_{22} & a_{23} \end{pmatrix}$$

contains the first-order square matrices (a_{11}), (a_{12}), (a_{23}), etc., obtained by striking out any two columns and any one row. It also contains the second-order square matrices

$$\begin{pmatrix} a_{11} & a_{12} \\ a_{21} & a_{22} \end{pmatrix}, \qquad \begin{pmatrix} a_{11} & a_{13} \\ a_{21} & a_{23} \end{pmatrix}, \qquad \begin{pmatrix} a_{12} & a_{13} \\ a_{22} & a_{23} \end{pmatrix},$$

obtained by striking out any column of A.

In many applications, it is useful to employ the notion of the rank of a matrix A. This is defined in terms of the determinants of A. *A matrix A is said to be of rank r if there exists at least one r-rowed determinant of A that is not zero, whereas all determinants of A of order higher than r are zero.**

Example. If

$$A \equiv \begin{pmatrix} 1 & 0 & 1 & 3 \\ 2 & 1 & 0 & -2 \\ -1 & -1 & 1 & 5 \end{pmatrix},$$

---

* In case an $m \times n$ matrix contains no determinants of order higher than r, obviously r is the smaller of the numbers m and n, and the matrix is said to be of rank r.

the third-order determinants are

$$\begin{vmatrix} 1 & 0 & 1 \\ 2 & 1 & 0 \\ -1 & -1 & 1 \end{vmatrix} = 0, \qquad \begin{vmatrix} 1 & 0 & 3 \\ 2 & 1 & -2 \\ -1 & -1 & 5 \end{vmatrix} = 0, \qquad \begin{vmatrix} 1 & 1 & 3 \\ 2 & 0 & -2 \\ -1 & 1 & 5 \end{vmatrix} = 0,$$

$$\begin{vmatrix} 0 & 1 & 3 \\ 1 & 0 & -2 \\ -1 & 1 & 5 \end{vmatrix} = 0.$$

Since

$$\begin{vmatrix} 1 & 0 \\ 2 & 1 \end{vmatrix} \neq 0,$$

there is at least one second-order determinant different from zero, whereas all third-order determinants of A are zero. Therefore, the rank of A is 2.

It should be observed that a matrix is said to have *rank zero if all of its elements are zero.*

The notion of linear dependence is of importance in connection with the study of systems of linear equations, and it will be considered next.

A set of m, $m \geq 2$, quantities $f_1, f_2, f_3, \cdots, f_m$ (which may be constants or functions of any number of variables) is said to be linearly dependent if there exist m constants $c_1, c_2, \cdots, c_m$, which are not all zero, such that

(34-2) $$c_1 f_1 + c_2 f_2 + \cdots + c_m f_m \equiv 0.$$

If no such constants exist, the quantities f_i are said to be *linearly independent.*

Example. If the f_i are the polynomials

$$f_1(x, y, z) \equiv 2x^2 - 3xy + 4z,$$
$$f_2(x, y, z) \equiv x^2 + 2xy - 3z,$$
$$f_3(x, y, z) \equiv 4x^2 + xy - 2z,$$

and if the constants are chosen as $c_1 = 1$, $c_2 = 2$, $c_3 = -1$, then

$$c_1 f_1 + c_2 f_2 + c_3 f_3 \equiv 0.$$

Therefore, these three polynomials are linearly dependent.

It is evident that, whenever the set of quantities is linearly dependent, at least one of the f_i can be expressed as a linear combination of the others. Thus, from (34-2), if $c_1 \neq 0$, then

$$f_1 = a_2 f_2 + a_3 f_3 + \cdots + a_m f_m,$$

where

$$a_2 = -\frac{c_2}{c_1}, \qquad a_3 = -\frac{c_3}{c_1}, \text{ etc.}$$

The definition of linear dependence requires the existence of at least one constant $c_i \neq 0$, and therefore the solution for f_i is assured.

Obviously, in most cases it would be extremely difficult to apply the definition in order to establish the linear dependence (or independence) of a given set of quantities. In case the quantities f_i are linear functions of n variables, there is a simple test which will be stated without proof.*

THEOREM. *The m linear functions*

$$f_i \equiv a_{i1}x_1 + a_{i2}x_2 + \cdots + a_{in}x_n, \quad (i = 1, 2, \cdots, m),$$

are linearly dependent if and only if the matrix of the coefficients is of rank $r < m$. Moreover, there are exactly r of the f_i that form a linearly independent set.

If $m > n$, obviously $r < m$, and it follows that any set of m linear functions in less than m unknowns must be linearly dependent.

The fact that the polynomials

$$f_1 \equiv 2x - 3y + 4z,$$
$$f_2 \equiv x + 2y - 3z,$$
$$f_3 \equiv 4x + y - 2z,$$

are linearly dependent can be determined by observing that the matrix of the coefficients,

$$A \equiv \begin{pmatrix} 2 & -3 & 4 \\ 1 & 2 & -3 \\ 4 & 1 & -2 \end{pmatrix},$$

is of rank 2.

35. Consistent and Inconsistent Systems of Equations. A set of equations that have at least one common solution is said to be a *consistent set* of equations. A set for which there exists no common solution is called an *inconsistent set*.

The question of consistency is frequently of practical importance. For example, in setting up problems in electrical networks, there are often more conditions than there are variables.

---

* DICKSON, L. E., Modern Algebraic Theories, pp. 55–60; BOCHER, M., Introduction to Higher Algebra, pp. 34–38.

This leads to a system in which there are more equations than there are unknowns. It is important to have a method for testing whether all the conditions can be satisfied simultaneously.

THEOREM 1. *Consider a system of m linear equations in n unknowns,*

(35-1)
$$\begin{cases} a_{11}x_1 + a_{12}x_2 + \cdots + a_{1n}x_n = k_1, \\ a_{21}x_1 + a_{22}x_2 + \cdots + a_{2n}x_n = k_2, \\ \dots\dots\dots\dots\dots\dots\dots\dots\dots\dots\dots\dots, \\ a_{m1}x_1 + a_{m2}x_2 + \cdots + a_{mn}x_n = k_m, \end{cases}$$

where at least one $k_i \neq 0$. *If the matrix of the coefficients is of rank r, Eqs.* (35-1) *are consistent provided that the rank of*

$$K \equiv \begin{pmatrix} a_{11} & a_{12} & \cdots & a_{1n} & k_1 \\ a_{21} & a_{22} & \cdots & a_{2n} & k_2 \\ \dots\dots\dots\dots\dots\dots \\ a_{m1} & a_{m2} & \cdots & a_{mn} & k_m \end{pmatrix}$$

is also r.

The matrix K is called the *augmented matrix*. The proof of this theorem will be found in any standard work on higher algebra.

Example 1. Consider the system

$$2x + 3y = 1,$$
$$x - 2y = 4,$$
$$4x - y = 9.$$

Since

$$A \equiv \begin{pmatrix} 2 & 3 \\ 1 & -2 \\ 4 & -1 \end{pmatrix}$$

is of rank 2, the equations are consistent if

$$K \equiv \begin{pmatrix} 2 & 3 & 1 \\ 1 & -2 & 4 \\ 4 & -1 & 9 \end{pmatrix}$$

is also of rank 2. This condition is satisfied; for the determinant of K is zero, and there exists a second-order determinant of K that is different from zero.

Example 2. The system

$$2x + 3y = 1,$$
$$x - 2y = 4,$$
$$4x - y = 6$$

is inconsistent, because

$$K = \begin{pmatrix} 2 & 3 & 1 \\ 1 & -2 & 4 \\ 4 & -1 & 6 \end{pmatrix}$$

is of rank 3, whereas the matrix A is of rank 2.

In the case in which there are n equations in n unknowns, the theorem on consistent equations shows that if the determinant of A is zero, so that the rank of A is $r < n$, then the rank of K must be r also, if the set of equations is to be consistent. If the rank of K is greater than r, the set of equations is inconsistent. This provides the analytic discussion that should accompany the geometric discussion given for $n = 3$ in Sec. 30.

If the set of equations is consistent and the rank of A is r, then it can be shown that $n - r$ of the unknowns can be given arbitrary values, and the values of the remaining r unknowns are determined uniquely in terms of those $n - r$ arbitrary values. These $n - r$ unknowns cannot be chosen at random, for the $m \times r$ matrix of the coefficients of the remaining r unknowns must have rank r if these unknowns are to be uniquely determined.

Example 3. Solve the system

$$\begin{aligned} x - y + 2z &= 3, \\ x + y - 2z &= 1, \\ x + 3y - 6z &= -1. \end{aligned}$$

Since A and K are both of rank 2, the equations are consistent. If either y or z is chosen arbitrarily the matrix of the coefficients of the remaining variables will have rank 2. If $z = k$, the equations to be solved are

$$\begin{aligned} x - y &= 3 - 2k, \\ x + y &= 1 + 2k, \\ x + 3y &= -1 + 6k. \end{aligned}$$

Solving the first two for x and y gives $x = 2$ and $y = 2k - 1$. These values are seen to satisfy the third equation. Therefore, the solutions $x = 2$, $y = 2k - 1$, $z = k$ satisfy the original system for all values of k.

The preceding discussion has dealt with non-homogeneous linear equations. In case the k_i are all zero, the system becomes the set of homogeneous equations

$$(35\text{-}2) \quad \left\{ \begin{aligned} a_{11}x_1 + a_{12}x_2 + \cdots + a_{1n}x_n &= 0, \\ a_{21}x_1 + a_{22}x_2 + \cdots + a_{2n}x_n &= 0, \\ \cdots\cdots\cdots\cdots\cdots\cdots\cdots\cdots\cdots\cdots\cdots\cdots\cdots&, \\ a_{m1}x_1 + a_{m2}x_2 + \cdots + a_{mn}x_n &= 0. \end{aligned} \right.$$

Obviously, $x_1 = x_2 = \cdots = x_n = 0$ is a solution of (35-2). It may happen that there are other solutions. If $a_1, a_2, \cdots, a_n$ is a solution of (35-2), it is evident that $ka_1, ka_2, \cdots, ka_n$, where k is an arbitrary constant, will be a solution, also. The condition for solutions different from the $x_1 = x_2 = \cdots = x_n = 0$ solution will be stated without proof.

THEOREM 2. *The system* (35-2) *will have a solution different from the solution* $x_1 = x_2 = \cdots = x_n = 0$, *if the rank of the matrix of the coefficients is less than* n.

It follows that if the number of equations is less than the number of unknowns, that is, if $m < n$, there are always solutions other than the obvious zero solution. If $m = n$, there exist other solutions if the determinant of the square matrix of the coefficients is zero. As in the case of the non-homogeneous system, if the $m \times n$ matrix of the coefficients is of rank r, then $n - r$ of the unknowns can be specified arbitrarily and the remaining r unknowns will be uniquely determined, provided that the rank of the matrix of the remaining unknowns is r.

Example 4.   Consider the system

$$2x - y + 3z = 0,$$
$$x + 2y - z = 0,$$
$$3x + 4y + z = 0.$$

Here

$$|A| \equiv \begin{vmatrix} 2 & -1 & 3 \\ 1 & 2 & -1 \\ 3 & 4 & 1 \end{vmatrix} = 10.$$

Therefore, $x = 0$, $y = 0$, $z = 0$ is the only solution.

Example 5.   Consider

$$3x - 2y = 0,$$
$$x + 4y = 0,$$
$$2x - y = 0,$$

for which the matrix of the coefficients is of rank 2. Since the number of unknowns is 2, $x = 0$, $y = 0$ is the only solution.

Example 6.   Consider

$$2x - y + 3z = 0,$$
$$3x + 2y + z = 0,$$
$$x + 3y - 2z = 0,$$
$$5x + y + 4z = 0.$$

Here,

$$A \equiv \begin{pmatrix} 2 & -1 & 3 \\ 3 & 2 & 1 \\ 1 & 3 & -2 \\ 5 & 1 & 4 \end{pmatrix},$$

which is of rank 2. Since the number of unknowns is 3, the system has solutions other than $x = 0$, $y = 0$, $z = 0$. Let $z = k$, and solve any two of the equations for x and y. If the first two are chosen, $x = -k$ and $y = k$. By substitution, it is easily verified that $x = -k$, $y = k$, $z = k$ satisfies all four equations for any choice of k.

Example 7. Consider

$$\begin{aligned} 2x - 4y + z &= 0, \\ 3x + y - 2z &= 0. \end{aligned}$$

For this system,

$$A = \begin{pmatrix} 2 & -4 & 1 \\ 3 & 1 & -2 \end{pmatrix},$$

which is of rank 2. Since the number of unknowns is greater than the number of equations, there exist other solutions. Let $z = k$, and solve the two equations for x and y. There results $x = \frac{1}{2}k$ and $y = \frac{1}{2}k$. Thus, $x = \frac{1}{2}k$, $y = \frac{1}{2}k$, $z = k$ is a solution for any choice of k.

Example 8. Consider

$$\begin{aligned} x - y + z &= 0, \\ 2x + 3y + z &= 0, \\ 3x + 2y + 2z &= 0. \end{aligned}$$

Here,

$$|A| = \begin{vmatrix} 1 & -1 & 1 \\ 2 & 3 & 1 \\ 3 & 2 & 2 \end{vmatrix} = 0.$$

Since the determinant of A is zero, there are solutions different from $x = 0$, $y = 0$, $z = 0$. Let $z = k$, and solve any two of the equations. If the first two are chosen, $x = -\frac{4}{5}k$, $y = \frac{1}{5}k$, $z = k$. It is verifiable by substitution that these values satisfy all three equations, whatever be the choice of k.

PROBLEMS

1. Investigate the following systems and find solutions whenever the systems are consistent:

(a) $\begin{aligned} x - 2y &= 3, \\ 2x + y &= 1, \\ 3x - y &= 4. \end{aligned}$

(b) $\begin{aligned} 2x + y - z &= 1, \\ x - 2y + z &= 3, \\ 4x - 3y + z &= 5. \end{aligned}$

(c) $\begin{aligned} 3x + 2y &= 4, \\ x - 3y &= 1, \\ 2x + 5y &= -1. \end{aligned}$

(d) $\begin{aligned} 2x - y + 3z &= 4, \\ x + y - 3z &= -1, \\ 5x - y + 3z &= 7. \end{aligned}$

2. Investigate for consistency, and obtain non-zero solutions when they exist.

(a) $x + 3y - 2z = 0,$
     $2x - y + z = 0.$

(b) $x - 2y = 0,$
     $3x + y = 0,$
     $2x - y = 0.$

(c) $3x - 2y + z = 0,$
     $x + 2y - 2z = 0,$
     $2x - y + 2z = 0.$

(d) $2x - 4y + 3z = 0,$
     $x + 2y - 2z = 0,$
     $3x - 2y + z = 0.$

(e) $4x - 2y + z = 0,$
     $2x - y + 3z = 0,$
     $2x - y - 2z = 0,$
     $6x - 3y + 4z = 0.$

(f) $x + 2y + 2z = 0,$
     $3x - y + z = 0,$
     $2x + 3y + 2z = 0,$
     $x + 4y - 2z = 0.$

CHAPTER IV

PARTIAL DIFFERENTIATION

36. Functions of Several Variables. Most of the functions considered in the preceding chapters depended on a single independent variable. This chapter is devoted to a study of functions depending on more than one independent variable.

A simple example of a function of two independent variables x and y is

$$z = xy,$$

which can be thought to represent the area of a rectangle whose sides are x and y. Again, the volume v of a rectangular parallelepiped whose edges are x, y, and z, namely,

$$v = xyz,$$

is an example of a function of three independent variables x, y, and z. A function u of n independent variables x_1, x_2, $\cdots$, x_n can be denoted by

$$u = f(x_1, x_2, \cdots, x_n).$$

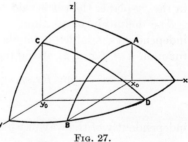

A real function of a single independent variable x, say $y = f(x)$, can be represented graphically by a curve in the xy-plane. Analogously, a real function $z = f(x, y)$, of two independent variables x and

Fig. 27.

y, can be thought to represent a surface in the three-dimensional space referred to a set of coordinate axes x, y, z (Fig. 27). However, one must not become too much dependent on geometric interpretations, for such interpretations may prove to be of more hindrance than help. For instance, the function $v = xyz$, representing the volume of a rectangular parallelepiped, depends on three independent variables x, y, and z and hence cannot be conveniently represented geometrically in a space of three dimensions.

Corresponding to the definition of continuity of a function of a single independent variable x (see Sec. 7), it will be said that a function $z = f(x, y)$ is continuous at the point (x_0, y_0) provided that a small change in the values of x and y produces a small change in the value of z. More precisely, if the value of the function $z = f(x, y)$ at the point (x_0, y_0) is z_0, then the continuity of the function at the point (x_0, y_0) means that*

$$(36\text{-}1) \qquad \lim_{\substack{x \to x_0 \\ y \to y_0}} f(x, y) = f(x_0, y_0) = z_0.$$

In writing the left-hand member of (36-1), it is assumed that the limit is independent of the mode of approach of (x, y) to (x_0, y_0).

The statement embodied in (36-1) is another way of saying that

$$f(x, y) = f(x_0, y_0) + \epsilon,$$

where $\lim\limits_{\substack{x \to x_0 \\ y \to y_0}} \epsilon = 0$; that is, *if the function $f(x, y)$ is continuous at (x_0, y_0), then its value in the neighborhood of the point (x_0, y_0) can be made to differ from the value at the point (x_0, y_0) by as little as desired.*

If a function is continuous at all points of some region R in the xy-plane, then it is said to be *continuous in the region R.*

The definition of continuity of a function of more than two independent variables is similar. Thus, the continuity of the function $u = f(x, y, z)$ at the point (x_0, y_0, z_0) means that

$$\lim_{\substack{x \to x_0 \\ y \to y_0 \\ z \to z_0}} f(x, y, z) = f(x_0, y_0, z_0),$$

independently of the way in which (x, y, z) approaches (x_0, y_0, z_0).

PROBLEM

Describe the surfaces represented by the following equations:

(a) $x + 2y = 3$, (b) $x - y + z = 1$, (c) $x = 2$, (d) $z = y$,
(e) $2x - 3y + 7z = 1$, (f) $x^2 - y^2 = 0$, (g) $y^2 + z^2 = 25$,
(h) $y^2 = 2x$, (i) $x^2 + y^2 - 10x = 0$, (j) $x^2 + y^2 + z^2 = 1$,
(k) $x^2 + z^2 = y$, (l) $x^2 + 2y^2 + z = 0$, (m) $x^2 + y^2 = z^2$,

* For details, see I. S. Sokolnikoff, Advanced Calculus, Chap. III.

$(n)\ \dfrac{x^2}{9} + \dfrac{y^2}{4} - \dfrac{z^2}{2} = 1,\ (o)\ \dfrac{x^2}{9} - \dfrac{y^2}{4} - \dfrac{z^2}{2} = 1,$

$(p)\ \dfrac{x^2}{a^2} - \dfrac{y^2}{b^2} - \dfrac{z^2}{c^2} = 1,\ (q)\ \dfrac{x^2}{a^2} - \dfrac{y^2}{b^2} = 2cz,$

$(r)\ \dfrac{x^2}{a^2} + \dfrac{y^2}{b^2} = 2cz,\ \ \ \ (s)\ \dfrac{x^2}{a^2} + \dfrac{y^2}{b^2} = c^2z^2.$

37. Partial Derivatives. The analytical definition of the derivative of a function $y = f(x)$, of a single variable x, is

$$\frac{df}{dx} \equiv \lim_{\Delta x \to 0} \frac{\Delta y}{\Delta x} = \lim_{\Delta x \to 0} \frac{f(x + \Delta x) - f(x)}{\Delta x}.$$

This derivative can be interpreted geometrically as the slope of the curve represented by the equation $y = f(x)$ (Fig. 28).

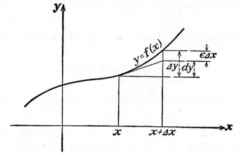

Fig. 28.

It is natural to extend the definition of the derivative to functions of several variables in the following way: Consider the function $z = f(x, y)$ of two independent variables x and y. If y is held fast, z becomes a function of the single variable x and its derivative with respect to x can be computed in the usual way. Let Δz_x denote the increment in the function $z = f(x, y)$ when y is kept fixed and x is changed by an amount Δx; that is,

$$\Delta z_x = f(x + \Delta x, y) - f(x, y).$$

Then,

$$\lim_{\Delta x \to 0} \frac{\Delta z_x}{\Delta x} = \lim_{\Delta x \to 0} \frac{f(x + \Delta x, y) - f(x, y)}{\Delta x}$$

is called the *partial derivative of z with respect to x* and is denoted by the symbol $\partial z/\partial x$, or z_x, or f_x.

Similarly, the partial derivative of z with respect to y is defined by

$$\frac{\partial z}{\partial y} \equiv \lim_{\Delta y \to 0} \frac{f(x, y + \Delta y) - f(x, y)}{\Delta y}.$$

In general, if $u = f(x_1, x_2, \cdots, x_n)$ is a function of n independent variables $x_1, x_2, \cdots, x_n$, then $\partial u/\partial x_i$ denotes the derivative of u with respect to x_i when the remaining variables are treated as constants.   Thus, if

$$z = x^3 + x^2 y + y^3,$$

then

$$\frac{\partial z}{\partial x} = 3x^2 + 2xy \quad \text{and} \quad \frac{\partial z}{\partial y} = x^2 + 3y^2.$$

Also, if $u = \sin (ax + by + cz)$, then

$$\frac{\partial u}{\partial x} = a \cos (ax + by + cz) \text{ (both } y \text{ and } z \text{ held constant)};$$

$$\frac{\partial u}{\partial y} = b \cos (ax + by + cz) \text{ (both } x \text{ and } z \text{ held constant)};$$

$$\frac{\partial u}{\partial z} = c \cos (ax + by + cz) \text{ (both } x \text{ and } y \text{ held constant)}.$$

In the case of $z = f(x, y)$, it is easy to provide a simple geometric interpretation of partial derivatives (Fig. 27).   The equation $z = f(x, y)$ is the equation of a surface; and if x is given the fixed value x_0, $z = f(x_0, y)$ is the equation of the curve AB on the surface, formed by the intersection of the surface and the plane $x = x_0$.   Then $\partial z/\partial y$ gives the value of the slope at any point of AB.   Similarly, if y is given the constant value y_0, then $z = f(x, y_0)$ is the equation of the curve CD on the surface, and $\partial z/\partial x$ gives the slope at any point of CD.

PROBLEMS

1. Find $\partial z/\partial x$ and $\partial z/\partial y$ for each of the following functions:

(a) $z = y/x$; (b) $z = x^3 y + \tan^{-1} (y/x)$; (c) $z = \sin xy + x$;
(d) $z = e^x \log y$; (e) $z = x^2 y + \sin^{-1} x$.

2. Find $\partial u/\partial x$, $\partial u/\partial y$, and $\partial u/\partial z$ for each of the following functions:

(a) $u = x^2 y + yz - xz^2$; (b) $u = xyz + \log xy$;
(c) $u = z \sin^{-1} (x/y)$; (d) $u = (x^2 + y^2 + z^2)^{1/2}$;
(e) $u = (x^2 + y^2 + z^2)^{-1/2}$.

38. Total Differential. In the case of a function of one variable, $y = f(x)$, the derivative of y with respect to x is defined as

$$\lim_{\Delta x \to 0} \frac{\Delta y}{\Delta x} \equiv f'(x),$$

so that $\Delta y / \Delta x = f'(x) + \epsilon$, where $\lim_{\Delta x \to 0} \epsilon = 0$. Therefore,

$$f(x + \Delta x) - f(x) \equiv \Delta y = f'(x)\,\Delta x + \epsilon\,\Delta x,$$

where ϵ is an infinitesimal which vanishes with Δx. Then,

$$f'(x)\,\Delta x \equiv f'(x)\,dx$$

is defined as the differential dy.

For the independent variable x, the terms "increment" and "differential" are synonymous (that is, $\Delta x \equiv dx$). However, it should be noted that the differential dy (of the dependent variable y) and the increment Δy differ by an amount $\epsilon\,\Delta x$ (see Fig. 28).

The differential of a function of several independent variables is defined similarly. Let $z = f(x, y)$, and let x and y acquire the respective increments Δx and Δy. Then,

$$\Delta z = f(x + \Delta x, y + \Delta y) - f(x, y).$$

If $z = f(x, y)$ is a continuous function, then, as Δx and Δy approach zero in any manner, Δz also approaches zero as a limit. It will be assumed here that $f(x, y)$ is continuous and that $\partial f / \partial x$ and $\partial f / \partial y$ are also continuous.

The expression for Δz can be put in a more useful form by adding and subtracting the term $f(x, y + \Delta y)$. Then,

$$\Delta z = f(x + \Delta x, y + \Delta y) - f(x, y + \Delta y) + f(x, y + \Delta y) - f(x, y).$$

But

$$\lim_{\Delta x \to 0} \frac{f(x + \Delta x, y + \Delta y) - f(x, y + \Delta y)}{\Delta x} = \frac{\partial f(x, y + \Delta y)}{\partial x},$$

so that

$$f(x + \Delta x, y + \Delta y) - f(x, y + \Delta y) = \left[\frac{\partial f(x, y + \Delta y)}{\partial x} + \epsilon_1 \right] \Delta x,$$

where $\lim_{\Delta x \to 0} \epsilon_1 = 0$. Moreover,

$$\lim_{\Delta y \to 0} \frac{\partial f(x, y + \Delta y)}{\partial x} = \frac{\partial f(x, y)}{\partial x},$$

since the derivative is continuous.   Therefore,

$$\frac{\partial f(x, y + \Delta y)}{\partial x} = \frac{\partial f(x, y)}{\partial x} + \epsilon_2,$$

where $\lim_{\Delta y \to 0} \epsilon_2 = 0.$

In like manner,

$$f(x, y + \Delta y) - f(x, y) = \left[\frac{\partial f(x, y)}{\partial y} + \epsilon' \right] \Delta y,$$

where $\lim_{\Delta y \to 0} \epsilon' = 0.$ It follows that

$$\Delta z = \frac{\partial f(x, y)}{\partial x} \Delta x + \frac{\partial f(x, y)}{\partial y} \Delta y + \epsilon \, \Delta x + \epsilon' \, \Delta y,$$

in which $\epsilon = \epsilon_1 + \epsilon_2.$

The expression

$$\frac{\partial f}{\partial x} \Delta x + \frac{\partial f}{\partial y} \Delta y \equiv \frac{\partial f}{\partial x} dx + \frac{\partial f}{\partial y} dy$$

is defined as the *total differential* of z and denoted by dz.   In general, if $u = f(x_1, x_2, \cdots, x_n)$, the total differential is given by

$$(38\text{-}1) \qquad du = \frac{\partial f}{\partial x_1} dx_1 + \frac{\partial f}{\partial x_2} dx_2 + \cdots + \frac{\partial f}{\partial x_n} dx_n.$$

The expression for the total differential is called the *principal part* of the increment Δu, and is a close approximation to Δu for sufficiently small values of $dx_1, dx_2, \cdots,$ and dx_n.   As in the case of a function of a single independent variable, the differential of each independent variable is identical with the increment of that variable, but the differential of the dependent variable differs from the increment.

If all of the variables except one, say x_i, are considered as constants, the resulting differential is called the partial differential and is denoted by

$$d_{x_i} u = \frac{\partial f}{\partial x_i} dx_i.$$

The partial differential expresses, approximately, the change in u due to a change $\Delta x_i \equiv dx_i$ in the independent variable x_i. On the other hand, the total differential du expresses, approximately, the change in u due to changes $dx_1, dx_2, \cdots, dx_n$ in all the independent variables x_1, x_2, $\cdots$, x_n. It may be noted that the total differential is equal to the sum of the partial differentials. Physically, this corresponds to the principle of superposition of effects. When a number of changes are taking place simultaneously in any system, each one proceeds as if it were independent of the others and the total change is the sum of the effects due to the independent changes.

Example 1. A metal box without a top has inside dimensions $6 \times 4 \times 2$ ft. If the metal is 0.1 ft. thick, find the actual volume of the metal used and compare it with the approximate volume found by using the differential.

The actual volume is ΔV, where

$$\Delta V = 6.2 \times 4.2 \times 2.1 - 6 \times 4 \times 2 = 54.684 - 48 = 6.684 \text{ cu. ft.}$$

Since $V = xyz$, where $x = 6$, $y = 4$, $z = 2$,

$$dV = yz\,dx + xz\,dy + xy\,dz$$
$$= 8(0.2) + 12(0.2) + 24(0.1) = 6.4 \text{ cu. ft.}$$

Example 2. Two sides of a triangular piece of land (Fig. 29) are measured as 100 ft. and 125 ft., and the included angle is measured as 60°. If the possible errors are 0.2 ft. in measuring the sides and 1° in measuring the angle, what is the approximate error in the area?

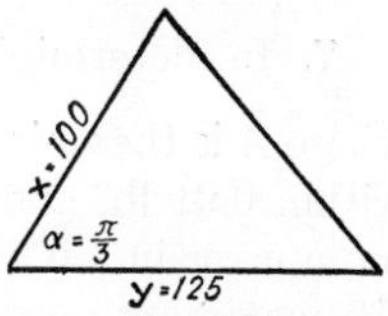

x=100
$\alpha = \frac{\pi}{3}$
y=125
FIG. 29.

Since $A = \frac{1}{2}xy \sin \alpha$,

$$dA = \frac{1}{2}(y \sin \alpha\,dx + x \sin \alpha\,dy + xy \cos \alpha\,d\alpha),$$

and the approximate error is therefore

$$dA = \frac{1}{2}\left[125\left(\frac{\sqrt{3}}{2}\right)(0.2) + 100\left(\frac{\sqrt{3}}{2}\right)(0.2) \right.$$
$$\left. + 100(125)\left(\frac{1}{2}\right)\frac{\pi}{180} \right] = 74.0 \text{ sq. ft.}$$

PROBLEMS

1. A closed cylindrical tank is 4 ft. high and 2 ft. in diameter (inside dimensions). What is the approximate amount of metal in the wall and the ends of the tank if they are 0.2 in. thick?

2. The angle of elevation of the top of a tower is found to be 30°, with a possible error of 0.5°. The distance to the base of the tower is found to be 1000 ft., with a possible error of 0.1 ft. What is the possible error in the height of the tower as computed from these measurements?

3. What is the possible error in the length of the hypotenuse of a right triangle if the legs are found to be 11.5 ft. and 7.8 ft., with a possible error of 0.1 ft. in each measurement?

4. The constant C in Boyle's law $pv = C$ is calculated from the measurements of p and v. If p is found to be 5000 lb. per square foot with a possible error of 1 per cent and v is found to be 15 cu. ft. with a possible error of 2 per cent, find the approximate possible error in C computed from these measurements.

5. The volume v, pressure p, and absolute temperature T of a perfect gas are connected by the formula $pv = RT$, where R is a constant. If $T = 500°$, $p = 4000$ lb. per square foot, and $v = 15.2$ cu. ft., find the approximate change in p when T changes to 503° and v to 15.25 cu. ft.

6. In estimating the cost of a pile of bricks measured as $6 \times 50 \times 4$ ft., the tape is stretched 1 per cent beyond the estimated length. If the count is 12 bricks to 1 cu. ft. and bricks cost \$8 per thousand, find the error in cost.

7. In determining specific gravity by the formula $s = \dfrac{A}{A - W}$, where A is the weight in air and W is the weight in water, A can be read within 0.01 lb. and W within 0.02 lb. Find approximately the maximum error in s if the readings are $A = 1.1$ lb. and $W = 0.6$ lb. Find the maximum relative error $\Delta s/s$.

8. The equation of a perfect gas is $pv = RT$. At a certain instant a given amount of gas has a volume of 16 cu. ft. and is under a pressure of 36 lb. per square inch. Assuming $R = 10.71$, find the temperature T. If the volume is increasing at the rate of $\frac{1}{3}$ cu. ft. per second and the pressure is decreasing at the rate $\frac{1}{8}$ lb. per square inch per second, find the rate at which the temperature is changing.

9. The period of a simple pendulum with small oscillations is

$$T = 2\pi \sqrt{\frac{l}{g}}.$$

If T is computed using $l = 8$ ft. and $g = 32$ ft. per second per second, find the approximate error in T if the true values are $l = 8.05$ ft. and $g = 32.01$ ft. per second per second. Find also the percentage error.

10. The diameter and altitude of a can in the shape of a right circular cylinder are measured as 4 in. and 6 in., respectively. The possible error in each measurement is 0.1 in. Find approximately the maximum possible error in the values computed for the volume and the lateral surface.

39. Total Derivatives. Thus far, it has been assumed that x and y were independent variables. It may be that x and y

are both functions of one independent variable t, so that z becomes a function of this single independent variable. In such a case, z may have a derivative with respect to t.

Let $z = f(x, y)$, where $x = \varphi(t)$ and $y = \psi(t)$; these functions are assumed to be differentiable. If t is given an increment Δt, then x, y, and z will have corresponding increments Δx, Δy, and Δz, which approach zero with Δt. As in the case when x and y were independent variables,

$$\Delta z = \frac{\partial f}{\partial x} \Delta x + \frac{\partial f}{\partial y} \Delta y + \epsilon_1 \Delta x + \epsilon_2 \Delta y.$$

Then,

$$\frac{\Delta z}{\Delta t} = \frac{\partial f}{\partial x} \frac{\Delta x}{\Delta t} + \frac{\partial f}{\partial y} \frac{\Delta y}{\Delta t} + \epsilon_1 \frac{\Delta x}{\Delta t} + \epsilon_2 \frac{\Delta y}{\Delta t}$$

and

(39-1) $$\frac{dz}{dt} = \frac{\partial f}{\partial x} \frac{dx}{dt} + \frac{\partial f}{\partial y} \frac{dy}{dt}.$$

Moreover, from (39-1) it appears that

$$dz = \frac{\partial f}{\partial x} dx + \frac{\partial f}{\partial y} dy$$

gives the expression for the differential in this case as well as when x and y are independent variables.

The general case, in which

$$z = f(x_1, x_2, \cdots, x_n)$$

with

$$x_1 = \varphi_1(t), \qquad x_2 = \varphi_2(t), \cdots, \qquad x_n = \varphi_n(t),$$

can be treated similarly to show that

$$\frac{dz}{dt} = \frac{\partial f}{\partial x_1} \frac{dx_1}{dt} + \frac{\partial f}{\partial x_2} \frac{dx_2}{dt} + \cdots + \frac{\partial f}{\partial x_n} \frac{dx_n}{dt}$$

and

$$dz = \frac{\partial f}{\partial x_1} dx_1 + \frac{\partial f}{\partial x_2} dx_2 + \cdots + \frac{\partial f}{\partial x_n} dx_n.$$

In case $t = x$ (39-1) becomes

$$\frac{dz}{dx} = \frac{\partial f}{\partial x} + \frac{\partial f}{\partial y} \frac{dy}{dx} \equiv \frac{\partial z}{\partial x} + \frac{\partial z}{\partial y} \frac{dy}{dx}.$$

This formula can be used to calculate the derivative of a function of x defined implicitly by the equation $f(x, y) = 0$. Let $z = f(x, y)$, so that

$$\frac{dz}{dx} = \frac{\partial f}{\partial x} + \frac{\partial f}{\partial y} \frac{dy}{dx}.$$

Since $z = f(x, y) = 0$, it follows that $dz/dx = 0$ and

$$\frac{dy}{dx} = - \frac{\partial f/\partial x}{\partial f/\partial y},$$

provided that $\partial f/\partial y \neq 0$.

As an example, let

$$x^2 y + y^2 x - 1 = 0$$

define y as an implicit function of x. Then,

$$\frac{dy}{dx} = - \frac{2xy + y^2}{x^2 + 2xy}$$

for all values of x and y for which the denominator does not vanish.

It was noted that the total differential of a function

$$z = f(x_1, x_2, \cdots, x_n), \quad \text{where } x_i = \varphi_i(t),$$

is given by

$$dz = \frac{\partial f}{\partial x_1} dx_1 + \frac{\partial f}{\partial x_2} dx_2 + \cdots + \frac{\partial f}{\partial x_n} dx_n.$$

It will be proved next that the same formula can be applied to calculate the differential even when the variables x_i are functions of several independent variables $t_1, t_2, \cdots, t_m$. Thus, consider

$$z = f(x_1, x_2, \cdots, x_n), \quad \text{where } x_i = \varphi_i(t_1, t_2, \cdots, t_m).$$

In order to find the partial derivative of $f(x_1, x_2, \cdots, x_n)$ with respect to one of the variables, say t_k, the remaining variables are held fixed so that $f(x_1, x_2, \cdots, x_n)$ becomes a function of the single variable t_k. Then,

$$(39\text{-}2) \quad \begin{cases} \dfrac{\partial f}{\partial t_1} = \dfrac{\partial f}{\partial x_1} \dfrac{\partial x_1}{\partial t_1} + \dfrac{\partial f}{\partial x_2} \dfrac{\partial x_2}{\partial t_1} + \cdots + \dfrac{\partial f}{\partial x_n} \dfrac{\partial x_n}{\partial t_1}, \\[2ex] \dfrac{\partial f}{\partial t_2} = \dfrac{\partial f}{\partial x_1} \dfrac{\partial x_1}{\partial t_2} + \dfrac{\partial f}{\partial x_2} \dfrac{\partial x_2}{\partial t_2} + \cdots + \dfrac{\partial f}{\partial x_n} \dfrac{\partial x_n}{\partial t_2}, \\[2ex] \cdots\cdots\cdots\cdots\cdots\cdots\cdots\cdots\cdots\cdots\cdots\cdots\cdots \\[1ex] \dfrac{\partial f}{\partial t_m} = \dfrac{\partial f}{\partial x_1} \dfrac{\partial x_1}{\partial t_m} + \dfrac{\partial f}{\partial x_2} \dfrac{\partial x_2}{\partial t_m} + \cdots + \dfrac{\partial f}{\partial x_n} \dfrac{\partial x_n}{\partial t_m}. \end{cases}$$

If the first equation of (39-2) is multiplied by dt_1, the second by dt_2, etc., and the resulting equations are added, there results

$$\frac{\partial f}{\partial t_1} dt_1 + \frac{\partial f}{\partial t_2} dt_2 + \cdots + \frac{\partial f}{\partial t_m} dt_m$$

$$= \frac{\partial f}{\partial x_1} \left(\frac{\partial x_1}{\partial t_1} dt_1 + \frac{\partial x_1}{\partial t_2} dt_2 + \cdots + \frac{\partial x_1}{\partial t_m} dt_m \right)$$

$$+ \frac{\partial f}{\partial x_2} \left(\frac{\partial x_2}{\partial t_1} dt_1 + \frac{\partial x_2}{\partial t_2} dt_2 + \cdots + \frac{\partial x_2}{\partial t_m} dt_m \right)$$

$$+ \ldots\ldots\ldots\ldots\ldots\ldots\ldots\ldots\ldots\ldots$$

$$+ \frac{\partial f}{\partial x_n} \left(\frac{\partial x_n}{\partial t_1} dt_1 + \frac{\partial x_n}{\partial t_2} dt_2 + \cdots + \frac{\partial x_n}{\partial t_m} dt_m \right)$$

or

(39-3) $$df = \frac{\partial f}{\partial x_1} dx_1 + \frac{\partial f}{\partial x_2} dx_2 + \cdots + \frac{\partial f}{\partial x_n} dx_n.$$

This establishes the validity of the formula (38-1) in all cases where the first partial derivatives are continuous functions, irrespective of whether the independent variables are x_1, x_2, $\cdots$, x_n or t_1, t_2, $\cdots$, t_m.

An important special case of the formula (39-3) arises in aerodynamics and other branches of applied mathematics. Consider a function $u = f(x, y, z, t)$ of four variables x, y, z, and t. The total differential of u is

(39-4) $$du = \frac{\partial f}{\partial x} dx + \frac{\partial f}{\partial y} dy + \frac{\partial f}{\partial z} dz + \frac{\partial f}{\partial t} dt$$

$$\equiv \frac{\partial u}{\partial x} dx + \frac{\partial u}{\partial y} dy + \frac{\partial u}{\partial z} dz + \frac{\partial u}{\partial t} dt.$$

Let it be supposed that x, y, and z are not independent variables, but functions of the variable t. In such a case, u will depend on t explicitly, and also implicitly through x, y, and z. Dividing both members of (39-4) by dt gives

(39-5) $$\frac{du}{dt} = \frac{\partial u}{\partial x} \frac{dx}{dt} + \frac{\partial u}{\partial y} \frac{dy}{dt} + \frac{\partial u}{\partial z} \frac{dz}{dt} + \frac{\partial u}{\partial t}.$$

On the other hand, if the variables x, y, and z are functions of t and of some other set of independent variables r, s, $\cdots$, one must replace dx/dt, dy/dt, and dz/dt in the right-hand member of (39-5) by $\partial x/\partial t$, $\partial y/\partial t$, and $\partial z/\partial t$, respectively, and du/dt in the left-hand member by $\partial u/\partial t$. The partial derivative with respect to t which appears in the left-hand member differs from that appearing in the right-hand member, since the latter is computed from $u = f(x, y, z, t)$ by fixing the variables x, y, and z and differentiating the resulting function with respect to t. In order to indicate the distinction between the meanings of the two partial derivatives with respect to t, one can write

$$\frac{Du}{\partial t} = \frac{\partial u}{\partial x}\frac{\partial x}{\partial t} + \frac{\partial u}{\partial y}\frac{\partial y}{\partial t} + \frac{\partial u}{\partial z}\frac{\partial z}{\partial t} + \frac{\partial u}{\partial t}.$$

The fact that the total differential of a composite function has the same form irrespective of whether the variables involved are independent or not permits one to use the same formulas for calculating differentials as those established for the functions of a single variable. Thus,

$$d(u + v) = du + dv,$$
$$d(uv) = \frac{\partial(uv)}{\partial u}\,du + \frac{\partial(uv)}{\partial v}\,dv$$
$$= v\,du + u\,dv,$$

etc.

Example 1. If $u = xy + yz + zx$, and $x = t$, $y = e^{-t}$, and $z = \cos t$,

$$\frac{du}{dt} = (y + z)\frac{dx}{dt} + (x + z)\frac{dy}{dt} + (x + y)\frac{dz}{dt}$$
$$= (e^{-t} + \cos t)(1) + (t + \cos t)(-e^{-t}) + (t + e^{-t})(-\sin t)$$
$$= e^{-t} + \cos t - te^{-t} - e^{-t}\cos t - t\sin t - e^{-t}\sin t.$$

This example illustrates the fact that this method of computing du/dt is often shorter than the old method in which the values of x, y, and z in terms of t are substituted in the expression for u before the derivative is computed.

Example 2. If $f(x, y) = x^2 + y^2$, where $x = r\cos\varphi$ and $y = r\sin\varphi$, then

$$\frac{\partial f}{\partial r} = \frac{\partial f}{\partial x}\frac{\partial x}{\partial r} + \frac{\partial f}{\partial y}\frac{\partial y}{\partial r} = 2x\cos\varphi + 2y\sin\varphi = 2r\cos^2\varphi + 2r\sin^2\varphi = 2r.$$

$$\frac{\partial f}{\partial\varphi} = \frac{\partial f}{\partial x}\frac{\partial x}{\partial\varphi} + \frac{\partial f}{\partial y}\frac{\partial y}{\partial\varphi} = 2x(-r\sin\varphi) + 2y(r\cos\varphi)$$
$$= -2r^2\cos\varphi\sin\varphi + 2r^2\cos\varphi\sin\varphi = 0.$$

Also,

$$df = 2r\,dr \quad \text{or} \quad df = 2x\,dx + 2y\,dy.$$

Example 3.   Let $z = e^{xy}$, where $x = \log (u + v)$ and $y = \tan^{-1} (u/v)$. Then,

$$\frac{\partial z}{\partial x} = ye^{xy}, \qquad \frac{\partial z}{\partial y} = xe^{xy}, \qquad \frac{\partial x}{\partial u} = \frac{1}{u + v}, \qquad \text{and} \qquad \frac{\partial y}{\partial u} = \frac{v}{v^2 + u^2}.$$

Hence,

$$\frac{\partial z}{\partial u} = \frac{\partial z}{\partial x} \frac{\partial x}{\partial u} + \frac{\partial z}{\partial y} \frac{\partial y}{\partial u} = \frac{ye^{xy}}{u + v} + \frac{xe^{xy}v}{v^2 + u^2}.$$

Similarly,

$$\frac{\partial z}{\partial v} = \frac{ye^{xy}}{u + v} - \frac{xe^{xy}u}{v^2 + u^2}.$$

The same results can be obtained by noting that

$$dz = ye^{xy}\, dx + xe^{xy}\, dy.$$

But

$$dx = \frac{\partial x}{\partial u}\, du + \frac{\partial x}{\partial v}\, dv = \frac{1}{u + v}\, du + \frac{1}{u + v}\cdot dv$$

and

$$dy = \frac{\partial y}{\partial u}\, du + \frac{\partial y}{\partial v}\, dv = \frac{v}{v^2 + u^2}\, du - \frac{u}{v^2 + u^2}\, dv.$$

Hence,

$$dz = ye^{xy}\, \frac{du + dv}{u + v} + xe^{xy}\, \frac{v\, du - u\, dv}{v^2 + u^2}$$

$$= \left(\frac{ye^{xy}}{u + v} + \frac{xe^{xy}v}{v^2 + u^2} \right) du + \left(\frac{ye^{xy}}{u + v} - \frac{xe^{xy}u}{v^2 + u^2} \right) dv.$$

But

$$dz = \frac{\partial z}{\partial u}\, du + \frac{\partial z}{\partial v}\, dv;$$

and since du and dv are independent differentials, equating the coefficients of du and dv in the two expressions for dz gives

$$\frac{\partial z}{\partial u} = \frac{ye^{xy}}{u + v} + \frac{xe^{xy}v}{v^2 + u^2}$$

and

$$\frac{\partial z}{\partial v} = \frac{ye^{xy}}{u + v} - \frac{xe^{xy}u}{v^2 + u^2}.$$

PROBLEMS

1. If $u = xyz$ and $x = a \cos \theta$, $y = a \sin \theta$, $z = k\theta$, find $du/d\theta$.

2. If $u = x^2 - y^2$ and $y = r \sin \theta$ and $x = r \cos \theta$, find $\partial u/\partial r$ and $\partial u/\partial \theta$.

3. If $u = xy - yz$ and $x = r + s$, $y = r - s$, $z = t$, find $\partial u/\partial r$, $\partial u/\partial s$, and $\partial u/\partial t$.

4. If $z = e^{xy}$, $x = \log \sqrt{u^2 + v^2}$, and $y = \tan^{-1}\dfrac{u}{v}$, find $\partial z/\partial u$ and $\partial z/\partial v$.

5. If $z = f(x + u, y + v)$, show that $\partial z/\partial x = \partial z/\partial u$ and $\partial z/\partial y = \partial z/\partial v$.

6. If $u = x^2 y + y^2 z + z^2 x$, verify that

$$\frac{\partial u}{\partial x} + \frac{\partial u}{\partial y} + \frac{\partial u}{\partial z} = (x + y + z)^2.$$

7. (a) Find du/dt, if $u = e^x \sin yz$ and $x = t^2$, $y = t - 1$, $z = 1/t$.
(b) Find $\partial u/\partial r$ and $\partial u/\partial \theta$, if $u = x^2 - 4y^2$ and $x = r \sec \theta$, $y = r \tan \theta$.

8. (a) Find $\partial u/\partial x$ and du/dx, if $u = x^2 + y^2$ and $y = \tan x$.
(b) Given $V = f(x, y, z)$, where $x = r \cos \theta$, $y = r \sin \theta$, $z = t$. Compute $\partial V/\partial r$, $\partial V/\partial \theta$, $\partial V/\partial t$ in terms of $\partial V/\partial x$, $\partial V/\partial y$, and $\partial V/\partial z$.

9. If f is a function of u and v, where $u = \sqrt{x^2 + y^2}$ and $v = \tan^{-1}\dfrac{y}{x}$, find $\partial f/\partial x$, $\partial f/\partial y$, and $\sqrt{(\partial f/\partial x)^2 + (\partial f/\partial y)^2}$.

40. Euler's Formula. A function $f(x_1, x_2, \cdots, x_n)$ of n variables $x_1, x_2, \cdots, x_n$ is said to be *homogeneous of degree m* if the function is multiplied by λ^m when the arguments $x_1, x_2, \cdots, x_n$ are replaced by $\lambda x_1, \lambda x_2, \cdots, \lambda x_n$, respectively. For example, $f(x, y) = x^2/\sqrt{x^2 + y^2}$ is homogeneous of degree 1, because the substitution of λx for x and λy for y yields $\lambda x^2/\sqrt{x^2 + y^2}$. Again, $f(x, y) = \dfrac{1}{y} + \dfrac{\log x - \log y}{x}$ is homogeneous of degree -1, whereas $f(x, y, z) = z^2/\sqrt[3]{x^2 + y^2}$ is homogeneous of degree $\frac{4}{3}$.

There is an important theorem, due to Euler, concerning homogeneous functions.

EULER'S THEOREM. *If $u = f(x_1, x_2, \cdots, x_n)$ is homogeneous of degree m and has continuous first partial derivatives, then*

$$x_1 \frac{\partial f}{\partial x_1} + x_2 \frac{\partial f}{\partial x_2} + \cdots + x_n \frac{\partial f}{\partial x_n} = mf(x_1, x_2, \cdots, x_n).$$

The proof of the theorem follows at once upon substituting

$$x_1' = \lambda x_1, \qquad x_2' = \lambda x_2, \cdots, \qquad x_n' = \lambda x_n.$$

Then, since $f(x_1, x_2, \cdots, x_n)$ is homogeneous of degree m,

$$f(x_1', x_2', \cdots, x_n') = \lambda^m f(x_1, x_2, \cdots, x_n).$$

Differentiating with respect to λ gives

$$\frac{\partial f}{\partial x_1'} x_1 + \frac{\partial f}{\partial x_2'} x_2 + \cdots + \frac{\partial f}{\partial x_n'} x_n = m\lambda^{m-1}f(x_1, x_2, \cdots, x_n).$$

If λ is set equal to 1, then $x_1 = x_1'$, $x_2 = x_2'$, $\cdots$, $x_n = x_n'$ and the theorem follows.

PROBLEM

Verify Euler's theorem for each of the following functions:

(a) $f(x, y, z) = x^2y + xy^2 + 2xyz$;

(b) $f(x, y) = \sqrt{y^2 - x^2}\, \sin^{-1} \dfrac{x}{y}$;

(c) $f(x, y) = \dfrac{1}{y^2} + \dfrac{\log x - \log y}{x^2}$;

(d) $f(x, y, z) = \dfrac{z^2}{\sqrt{x^2 - y^2}}$;

(e) $f(x, y, z) = (x^2 + y^2 + z^2)^{-\frac{1}{2}}$;

(f) $f(x, y) = e^{x/y}$;

(g) $f(x, y) = \dfrac{\sqrt{x + y}}{y}$;

(h) $f(x, y) = \dfrac{x^2 + y^2}{x^2 - y^2}$.

41. Differentiation of Implicit Functions. It was noted in Sec. 39 that the derivative of a function of x which is defined implicitly by the equation $f(x, y) = 0$ could be calculated by applying the expression for the total derivative. This section contains a more detailed discussion of this method.

The equation $f(x, y) = 0$ may define either x or y as an implicit function of the other. If the equation can be solved for y to give $y = \varphi(x)$, then the substitution of $y = \varphi(x)$ in $f(x, y) = 0$ gives an identity. Hence, $f(x, y) = 0$ may be regarded as a composite function of x, where x enters implicitly in y. If $u = f(x, y)$, then

$$du = \frac{\partial f}{\partial x} dx + \frac{\partial f}{\partial y} dy = 0,$$

so that

(41-1) $$\frac{dy}{dx} = -\frac{\partial f/\partial x}{\partial f/\partial y}, \qquad \text{if } \frac{\partial f}{\partial y} \neq 0.$$

It will be observed that this discussion tacitly assumes that $f(x, y) = 0$ has a real solution for y for every value of x. If (41-1) is applied formally to $x^2 + y^2 = 0$, it is readily checked that $\dfrac{dy}{dx} = -\dfrac{x}{y}$. This result is absurd for real values of x and y, inasmuch as the only real values of x and y that satisfy $x^2 + y^2 = 0$ are $x = 0$ and $y = 0$.

Example 1. Find dy/dx, if $3x^3y^2 + x \cos y = 0$. Here,

$$\frac{\partial f}{\partial x} = 9x^2y^2 + \cos y, \qquad \frac{\partial f}{\partial y} = 6x^3y - x \sin y,$$

so that

$$\frac{dy}{dx} = -\frac{9x^2y^2 + \cos y}{6x^3y - x \sin y}.$$

The relation $f(x, y, z) = 0$ may define any one of the variables as an implicit function of the other two. Let x and y be independent variables. Then $f(x, y, z) = 0$ defines z as an implicit function of x and y, and

$$dz = \frac{\partial z}{\partial x} dx + \frac{\partial z}{\partial y} dy.$$

But

$$df = \frac{\partial f}{\partial x} dx + \frac{\partial f}{\partial y} dy + \frac{\partial f}{\partial z} dz = 0.$$

Therefore, by substitution,

$$\frac{\partial f}{\partial x} dx + \frac{\partial f}{\partial y} dy + \frac{\partial f}{\partial z} \left(\frac{\partial z}{\partial x} dx + \frac{\partial z}{\partial y} dy \right) = 0.$$

This can be written as

$$\left(\frac{\partial f}{\partial x} + \frac{\partial f}{\partial z} \frac{\partial z}{\partial x} \right) dx + \left(\frac{\partial f}{\partial y} + \frac{\partial f}{\partial z} \frac{\partial z}{\partial y} \right) dy = 0.$$

Since dx and dy are independent differentials and the above relation holds for all values of dx and dy, it follows that

$$\frac{\partial f}{\partial x} + \frac{\partial f}{\partial z} \frac{\partial z}{\partial x} = 0$$

and

$$\frac{\partial f}{\partial y} + \frac{\partial f}{\partial z} \frac{\partial z}{\partial y} = 0.$$

If $\partial f/\partial z \neq 0$, these equations can be solved to give

(41-2) $$\frac{\partial z}{\partial x} = -\frac{\partial f/\partial x}{\partial f/\partial z}, \qquad \frac{\partial z}{\partial y} = -\frac{\partial f/\partial y}{\partial f/\partial z}.$$

Example 2. If $x^2 + 2y^2 - 3xz = 0$, then, by (41-2),

$$\frac{\partial z}{\partial x} = -\frac{2x - 3z}{-3x}, \qquad \frac{\partial z}{\partial y} = -\frac{4y}{-3x}.$$

Frequently, it is necessary to calculate the derivatives of a function that is defined implicitly by a pair of simultaneous equations

(41-3)
$$\begin{cases} f(x, y, z) = 0, \\ \varphi(x, y, z) = 0. \end{cases}$$

If each of these equations is solved for one of the variables, say z, to yield

$$z = F(x, y) \qquad \text{and} \qquad z = \Phi(x, y),$$

then one is led to consider the equation resulting from the elimination of z, namely,

$$F(x, y) - \Phi(x, y) = 0.$$

This equation may be thought to define y as an implicit function of x, and one can apply the method discussed earlier in this section to calculate dy/dx.

However, the elimination of one of the variables from the simultaneous equations (41-3) may prove to be difficult, and it is simpler to use the following procedure: The differentiation of (41-3) gives

$$df = \frac{\partial f}{\partial x}\,dx + \frac{\partial f}{\partial y}\,dy + \frac{\partial f}{\partial z}\,dz = 0$$

and

$$d\varphi = \frac{\partial \varphi}{\partial x}\,dx + \frac{\partial \varphi}{\partial y}\,dy + \frac{\partial \varphi}{\partial z}\,dz = 0.$$

These equations can be solved for the ratios to give

$$dx : dy : dz = \begin{vmatrix} \dfrac{\partial f}{\partial y} & \dfrac{\partial f}{\partial z} \\ \dfrac{\partial \varphi}{\partial y} & \dfrac{\partial \varphi}{\partial z} \end{vmatrix} : \begin{vmatrix} \dfrac{\partial f}{\partial z} & \dfrac{\partial f}{\partial x} \\ \dfrac{\partial \varphi}{\partial z} & \dfrac{\partial \varphi}{\partial x} \end{vmatrix} : \begin{vmatrix} \dfrac{\partial f}{\partial x} & \dfrac{\partial f}{\partial y} \\ \dfrac{\partial \varphi}{\partial x} & \dfrac{\partial \varphi}{\partial y} \end{vmatrix},$$

from which the derivatives can be written down at once.

Example 3. Let

$$f(x, y, z) \equiv x^2 + y^2 + z^2 - a^2 = 0$$

and

$$\varphi(x, y, z) \equiv x^2 - y^2 - 2z^2 - b^2 = 0.$$

Then,

$$dx : dy : dz = \begin{vmatrix} 2y & 2z \\ -2y & -4z \end{vmatrix} : \begin{vmatrix} 2z & 2x \\ -4z & 2x \end{vmatrix} : \begin{vmatrix} 2x & 2y \\ 2x & -2y \end{vmatrix}$$

$$= -4yz : 12xz : -8xy.$$

$$\frac{dy}{dx} = \frac{12xz}{-4yz}, \qquad \frac{dz}{dx} = \frac{-8xy}{-4yz}, \text{ etc.}$$

Another important case arises from a consideration of a pair of simultaneous equations

(41-4)
$$\begin{cases} f(x, y, u, v) = 0, \\ \varphi(x, y, u, v) = 0, \end{cases}$$

which may be thought to define u and v as implicit functions of the variables x and y.

Differentiating (41-4) gives

(41-5)
$$\begin{cases} df = \dfrac{\partial f}{\partial x} dx + \dfrac{\partial f}{\partial y} dy + \dfrac{\partial f}{\partial u} du + \dfrac{\partial f}{\partial v} dv = 0, \\ d\varphi = \dfrac{\partial \varphi}{\partial x} dx + \dfrac{\partial \varphi}{\partial y} dy + \dfrac{\partial \varphi}{\partial u} du + \dfrac{\partial \varphi}{\partial v} dv = 0. \end{cases}$$

But, since u and v are regarded as functions of x and y,

$$du = \frac{\partial u}{\partial x} dx + \frac{\partial u}{\partial y} dy$$

and

$$dv = \frac{\partial v}{\partial x} dx + \frac{\partial v}{\partial y} dy.$$

Substituting for du and dv in (41-5) gives

$$\left(\frac{\partial f}{\partial x} + \frac{\partial f}{\partial u} \frac{\partial u}{\partial x} + \frac{\partial f}{\partial v} \frac{\partial v}{\partial x} \right) dx + \left(\frac{\partial f}{\partial y} + \frac{\partial f}{\partial u} \frac{\partial u}{\partial y} + \frac{\partial f}{\partial v} \frac{\partial v}{\partial y} \right) dy = 0,$$

$$\left(\frac{\partial \varphi}{\partial x} + \frac{\partial \varphi}{\partial u} \frac{\partial u}{\partial x} + \frac{\partial \varphi}{\partial v} \frac{\partial v}{\partial x} \right) dx + \left(\frac{\partial \varphi}{\partial y} + \frac{\partial \varphi}{\partial u} \frac{\partial u}{\partial y} + \frac{\partial \varphi}{\partial v} \frac{\partial v}{\partial y} \right) dy = 0.$$

Since the variables x and y are independent, the coefficients of dx and dy must vanish, and this leads to a set of four equations for the determination of $\partial u/\partial x$, $\partial u/\partial y$, $\partial v/\partial x$, and $\partial v/\partial y$. Thus, one obtains

$$\frac{\partial u}{\partial x} = - \frac{\begin{vmatrix} \dfrac{\partial f}{\partial x} & \dfrac{\partial f}{\partial v} \\ \dfrac{\partial \varphi}{\partial x} & \dfrac{\partial \varphi}{\partial v} \end{vmatrix}}{\begin{vmatrix} \dfrac{\partial f}{\partial u} & \dfrac{\partial f}{\partial v} \\ \dfrac{\partial \varphi}{\partial u} & \dfrac{\partial \varphi}{\partial v} \end{vmatrix}},$$

and similar expressions for $\partial u/\partial y$, $\partial v/\partial x$, and $\partial v/\partial y$. It is assumed in the foregoing discussion that all the derivatives involved are continuous and that

$$J \equiv \begin{vmatrix} \dfrac{\partial f}{\partial u} & \dfrac{\partial f}{\partial v} \\[2mm] \dfrac{\partial \varphi}{\partial u} & \dfrac{\partial \varphi}{\partial v} \end{vmatrix} \neq 0.$$

Example 4. If

$$x + y^3 + u^3 + v^3 = 0,$$
$$x^3 + y - u^4 + v^4 = 0,$$

then

$$\frac{\partial u}{\partial x} = - \frac{\begin{vmatrix} 1 & 3v^2 \\ 3x^2 & 4v^3 \end{vmatrix}}{\begin{vmatrix} 3u^2 & 3v^2 \\ -4u^3 & 4v^3 \end{vmatrix}} = \frac{9x^2v^2 - 4v^3}{12(u^2v^3 + v^2u^3)}.$$

PROBLEMS

1. Obtain $\partial v/\partial x$, $\partial u/\partial y$, and $\partial v/\partial y$ in Example 4, Sec. 41.

2. Compute dy/dx, if $x^3 + y^3 - 3xy = 1$.

3. Find dy/dx if

$$x^2 - y^2 - z^2 - a^2 = 0,$$
$$x^2y - y^2z + xz^2 - a^3 = 0.$$

4. Obtain $\partial u/\partial x$ and $\partial v/\partial y$, if

$$ue^v - xy + v = 0,$$
$$ve^y - xv + u = 0.$$

5. If $x = f(u, v)$ and $y = g(u, v)$, then differentiation with respect to x gives

$$1 = \frac{\partial x}{\partial u}\frac{\partial u}{\partial x} + \frac{\partial x}{\partial v}\frac{\partial v}{\partial x},$$
$$0 = \frac{\partial y}{\partial u}\frac{\partial u}{\partial x} + \frac{\partial y}{\partial v}\frac{\partial v}{\partial x},$$

from which $\partial u/\partial x$ and $\partial v/\partial x$ can be computed. Consider the pair of equations

$$x = u^2 - v^2,$$
$$y = uv,$$

and obtain $\partial u/\partial x$, $\partial u/\partial y$, $\partial v/\partial x$, and $\partial v/\partial y$.

6. Apply the method outlined in Prob. 5 to find $\partial u/\partial x$, $\partial v/\partial x$, $\partial u/\partial y$, and $\partial v/\partial y$, if

(a) $\begin{cases} x = u + v, \\ y = 3u + 2v; \end{cases}$

(b) $\begin{cases} 2x = v^2 - u^2, \\ y = uv. \end{cases}$

7. If $x = r \cos \theta$ and $y = r \sin \theta$, find $\partial r/\partial x$ and $\partial \theta/\partial x$.

8. If $w = uv$ and

$$(a) \quad \begin{cases} u^2 + v + x = 0, \\ v^2 - u - y = 0, \end{cases}$$

one can obtain $\partial w/\partial x$ as follows: Differentiation of w with respect to x gives $\dfrac{\partial w}{\partial x} = u \dfrac{\partial v}{\partial x} + v \dfrac{\partial u}{\partial x}$. The values of $\partial u/\partial x$ and $\partial v/\partial x$ can be calculated from (a) by the method of Prob. 5. Find the expressions for $\partial w/\partial x$ and $\partial w/\partial y$.

9. If $z = uv$ and

$$u^2 + v^2 - x - y = 0,$$
$$u^2 - v^2 + 3x + y = 0,$$

find $\partial z/\partial x$.

10. If $z = u^2 + v^2$ and

$$x = u^2 - v^2,$$
$$y = uv,$$

find $\partial z/\partial x$.

11. If $z = u^2 + v^2$ and

$$u = r \cos \theta,$$
$$v = r \sin \theta,$$

find $\partial z/\partial r$ and $\partial z/\partial \theta$.

12. If $r = (x^2 + y^2)^{1/2}$ and $\theta = \tan^{-1} \dfrac{y}{x}$, find $\partial r/\partial x$ and $\partial \theta/\partial x$.

13. (a) Find dy/dx, if $x \sec y + x^3 y^2 = 0$.
(b) Find $\partial z/\partial x$ and $\partial z/\partial y$, if $x^3 y - \sin z + z^3 = 0$.

14. Let $u \equiv x + y + z = 0$ and $v \equiv x^2 + y^2 + z^2 - a^2 = 0$. Find $dx : dy : dz$.

15. Find $\partial u/\partial x$, $\partial v/\partial x$, $\partial u/\partial y$, and $\partial v/\partial y$, if

$$u^2 + v^2 + y^2 - 2x = 0,$$
$$u^3 + v^3 - x^3 + 3y = 0.$$

16. Find $\partial w/\partial x$ and $\partial w/\partial y$, if $w = u/v$ and

$$x = u + v,$$
$$y = 3u + 2v.$$

17. Show that $\dfrac{\partial z}{\partial x} \dfrac{\partial x}{\partial z} = 1$ and $\dfrac{\partial x}{\partial y} \dfrac{\partial y}{\partial z} \dfrac{\partial z}{\partial x} = -1$, if $f(x, y, z) = 0$. Note that, in general, $\partial z/\partial x$ and $\partial x/\partial z$ are not reciprocals.

18. Find $\partial u/\partial x$, if

$$u^2 - v^2 - x^3 + 3y = 0,$$
$$u + v - y^2 - 2x = 0.$$

19. Prove that

$$\frac{\partial u}{\partial x} \frac{\partial y}{\partial u} + \frac{\partial v}{\partial x} \frac{\partial y}{\partial v} = 0,$$

if $F(x, y, u, v) = 0$ and $G(x, y, u, v) = 0$.

20. Show that $\left(\dfrac{\partial z}{\partial r}\right)^2 + 1/r^2 \left(\dfrac{\partial z}{\partial \theta}\right)^2 = \left(\dfrac{\partial z}{\partial x}\right)^2 + \left(\dfrac{\partial z}{\partial y}\right)^2$, if $x = r \cos \theta$ and $y = r \sin \theta$.

42. Directional Derivatives. The relation expressed in (39-1) has an important special case when x and y are functions of the distance s along some curve C, which goes through the point (x, y). The curve C may be thought to be represented by a pair of parametric equations

$$x = x(s),$$
$$y = y(s),$$

where x and y are assumed to possess continuous derivatives with respect to the arc parameter s.

Let P (Fig. 30) be any point of the curve C at which $f(x, y)$ is defined and has partial derivatives $\partial f/\partial x$ and $\partial f/\partial y$. Let

$$Q(x + \Delta x, y + \Delta y)$$

be a point close to P on this curve. If Δs is the length of the

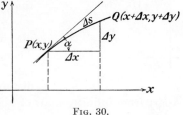

FIG. 30.

arc PQ and Δf is the change in f due to the increments Δx and Δy, then

$$\frac{df}{ds} = \lim_{\Delta s \to 0} \frac{\Delta f}{\Delta s}$$

gives the rate of change of f along C at the point (x, y). But

$$\frac{df}{ds} = \frac{\partial f}{\partial x}\frac{dx}{ds} + \frac{\partial f}{\partial y}\frac{dy}{ds},$$

and

$$\frac{dx}{ds} = \lim_{\Delta s \to 0} \frac{\Delta x}{\Delta s} = \cos \alpha, \qquad \frac{dy}{ds} = \lim_{\Delta s \to 0} \frac{\Delta y}{\Delta s} = \sin \alpha.$$

Therefore,

$$(42\text{-}1) \qquad \frac{df}{ds} = \frac{\partial f}{\partial x} \cos \alpha + \frac{\partial f}{\partial y} \sin \alpha,$$

and it is evident that df/ds depends on the direction of the curve. For this reason, df/ds is called the *directional derivative*. It ⁻epresents the rate of change of f in the direction of the tangent to the particular curve chosen for the point (x, y). If $\alpha = 0$,

$$\frac{df}{ds} = \frac{\partial f}{\partial x},$$

which is the rate of change of f in the direction of the x-axis.   If $\alpha = \pi/2$,

$$\frac{df}{ds} = \frac{\partial f}{\partial y},$$

which is the rate of change of f in the direction of the y-axis.

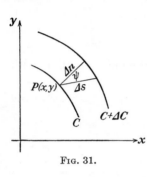

FIG. 31.

Let $z = f(x, y)$, which can be interpreted as the equation of a surface, be represented by drawing the contour lines on the xy-plane for various values of z. Let C (Fig. 31) be the curve in the xy-plane corresponding to the value $z = \gamma$, and let $C + \Delta C$ be the neighboring contour line for $z = \gamma + \Delta\gamma$. Then, $\Delta f/\Delta s \equiv \Delta\gamma/\Delta s$ is the average rate of change of f with respect to the distance Δs between C and $C + \Delta C$.

Apart from infinitesimals of higher order,

$$\frac{\Delta n}{\Delta s} = \cos \psi,$$

where Δn denotes the distance from C to $C + \Delta C$ along the normal to C at (x, y), and ψ is the angle between Δn and Δs; hence, $dn/ds = \cos \psi$.   Therefore,

$$(42\text{-}2) \qquad \frac{df}{ds} = \frac{df}{dn} \cdot \frac{dn}{ds} = \frac{df}{dn} \cos \psi.$$

This relation shows that the derivative of f in any direction may be found by multiplying the derivative along the normal by the cosine of the angle ψ between the particular direction and the normal.   This derivative in the direction of the normal is called the *normal derivative* of f.   Its numerical value obviously is the maximum value that df/ds can take for any direction.   In applied mathematics the vector in the direction of the normal, of magnitude df/dn, is called the *gradient*.

Example.   Using (42-1), find the value of α that makes df/ds a maximum, considering x and y to be fixed.   Find the expression for this maximum value of df/ds.

Since $df/ds = f_x \cos \alpha + f_y \sin \alpha,$

$$\frac{d}{d\alpha}\left(\frac{df}{ds}\right) = -f_x \sin \alpha + f_y \cos \alpha.$$

The condition for a maximum requires that

$$\tan \alpha_1 = \frac{f_y}{f_x}, \quad \text{or} \quad \alpha_1 = \tan^{-1}\frac{f_y}{f_x}.$$

Using this value of α_1,

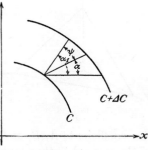

$$\frac{df}{dn} = f_x \frac{f_x}{\sqrt{f_x{}^2 + f_y{}^2}} + f_y \frac{f_y}{\sqrt{f_x{}^2 + f_y{}^2}}$$

$$= \sqrt{f_x{}^2 + f_y{}^2}.$$

The relation (42-2) can be derived directly by use of this expression for df/dn. If α (Fig. 32) gives any direction different from the direction given by α_1, then

Fig. 32.

$$\frac{df}{ds} = f_x \cos \alpha + f_y \sin \alpha.$$

But $\alpha = \alpha_1 - \psi$, so that

$$\frac{df}{ds} = f_x(\cos \alpha_1 \cos \psi + \sin \alpha_1 \sin \psi) + f_y(\sin \alpha_1 \cos \psi - \cos \alpha_1 \sin \psi).$$

Since

$$\cos \alpha_1 = \frac{f_x}{\sqrt{f_x^2 + f_y^2}} \quad \text{and} \quad \sin \alpha_1 = \frac{f_y}{\sqrt{f_x^2 + f_y^2}},$$

$$\frac{df}{ds} = f_x \frac{f_x}{\sqrt{f_x^2 + f_y^2}} \cos \psi + f_x \frac{f_y}{\sqrt{f_x^2 + f_y^2}} \sin \psi$$

$$+ f_y \frac{f_y}{\sqrt{f_x^2 + f_y^2}} \cos \psi - f_y \frac{f_x}{\sqrt{f_x^2 + f_y^2}} \sin \psi$$

$$= \frac{f_x^2 + f_y^2}{\sqrt{f_x^2 + f_y^2}} \cos \psi = \sqrt{f_x^2 + f_y^2} \cos \psi$$

$$= \frac{df}{dn} \cos \psi.$$

PROBLEMS

1. Find the directional derivative of $f(x, y) = x^2y + \sin xy$ at $(1, \pi/2)$, in the direction of the line making an angle of 45° with the x-axis.

2. Find

$$\frac{df}{dn} = \sqrt{\left(\frac{\partial f}{\partial x}\right)^2 + \left(\frac{\partial f}{\partial y}\right)^2},$$

if $x = r \cos \theta$, $y = r \sin \theta$, and f is a function of the variables r and θ.

3. Find the directional derivative of $f(x, y) = x^3y + e^{yx}$ in the direction of the curve which, at the point $(1, 1)$, makes an angle of 30° with the x-axis.

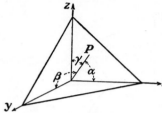

FIG. 33.

4. Find the normal derivative of $f(x, y) = x^2 + y^2$.

43. Tangent Plane and Normal Line to a Surface. It will be recalled that

$$Ax + By + Cz = D$$

is the equation of a plane, where the coefficients A, B, and C are called the direction components of the normal to the plane. If α, β, and γ (Fig. 33) are the direction angles made by the normal to the plane from the origin, then

$$\cos \alpha = \frac{A}{\sqrt{A^2 + B^2 + C^2}}, \qquad \cos \beta = \frac{B}{\sqrt{A^2 + B^2 + C^2}},$$

$$\cos \gamma = \frac{C}{\sqrt{A^2 + B^2 + C^2}}.$$

Therefore,

$$\cos \alpha : \cos \beta : \cos \gamma = A : B : C.$$

If the plane passes through the point (x_0, y_0, z_0), its equation can be written as

$$A(x - x_0) + B(y - y_0) + C(z - z_0) = 0.$$

There is also a normal form for the equation of a plane, entirely analogous to the normal form for the equation of the straight line in the plane. This form is

$$x \cos \alpha + y \cos \beta + z \cos \gamma = p,$$

or

$$\frac{A}{\sqrt{A^2 + B^2 + C^2}} x + \frac{B}{\sqrt{A^2 + B^2 + C^2}} y + \frac{C}{\sqrt{A^2 + B^2 + C^2}} z$$
$$= \frac{D}{\sqrt{A^2 + B^2 + C^2}},$$

in which $p = D/\sqrt{A^2 + B^2 + C^2}$ is the distance from the origin to the plane.

Consider a surface defined by $z = f(x, y)$, in which x and y are considered as the independent variables. Then,

(43-1)
$$dz = \frac{\partial f}{\partial x}\, dx + \frac{\partial f}{\partial y}\, dy$$
$$= \frac{\partial f}{\partial x}\, \Delta x + \frac{\partial f}{\partial y}\, \Delta y.$$

If x_0 and y_0 are chosen, z_0 is determined by $z = f(x, y)$. Let $\Delta x = x - x_0$ and $\Delta y = y - y_0$, and denote dz by $z - z_0$. Then (43-1) becomes

$$(43\text{-}2) \quad z - z_0 = \frac{\partial f}{\partial x}\bigg|_{(x_0, y_0)} (x - x_0) + \frac{\partial f}{\partial y}\bigg|_{(x_0, y_0)} (y - y_0),$$

which is the equation of a plane. If this plane is cut by the plane $x = x_0$, the equation of the line of intersection is

$$z - z_0 = \frac{\partial f}{\partial y}\bigg|_{(x_0, y_0)} (y - y_0),$$

and this is the tangent line to the curve $z = f(x_0, y)$ at the point (x_0, y_0, z_0). Similarly, the line of intersection of the plane defined by (43-2) and the plane $y = y_0$ is the tangent line to the curve $z = f(x, y_0)$ at (x_0, y_0, z_0). The plane defined by (43-2) is called the *tangent plane* to the surface $z = f(x, y)$ at (x_0, y_0, z_0).

The direction cosines of the normal to this plane are proportional to

$$\frac{\partial f}{\partial x}\bigg|_{(x_0, y_0)}, \qquad \frac{\partial f}{\partial y}\bigg|_{(x_0, y_0)}, \qquad -1.$$

The equation of the normal line to the plane (43-2) at (x_0, y_0, z_0) is therefore

$$(43\text{-}3) \qquad \frac{x - x_0}{\dfrac{\partial f}{\partial x}\bigg|_{(x_0, y_0)}} = \frac{y - y_0}{\dfrac{\partial f}{\partial y}\bigg|_{(x_0, y_0)}} = \frac{z - z_0}{-1}.$$

This line is defined as *the normal* to the surface at (x_0, y_0, z_0). Figure 34 shows the difference between $dz = RP'$ and $\Delta z = RQ$. $P(x_0, y_0, z_0)$ is the point of tangency and $R(x_0 + \Delta x, y_0 + \Delta y, z_0)$ is in the plane $z = z_0$. PP' is the tangent plane.

In case the equation of the surface is given in the form

$$F(x, y, z) = 0,$$

the tangent plane and the normal line at (x_0, y_0, z_0) have the respective equations

(43-4) $\left.\dfrac{\partial F}{\partial x}\right|_{(x_0,\ y_0,\ z_0)} (x - x_0) + \left.\dfrac{\partial F}{\partial y}\right|_{(x_0,\ y_0,\ z_0)} (y - y_0)$

$$+ \left.\dfrac{\partial F}{\partial z}\right|_{(x_0,\ y_0,\ z_0)} (z - z_0) = 0$$

and

(43-5) $\qquad \dfrac{x - x_0}{\left.\dfrac{\partial F}{\partial x}\right|_{(x_0,\ y_0,\ z_0)}} = \dfrac{y - y_0}{\left.\dfrac{\partial F}{\partial y}\right|_{(x_0,\ y_0,\ z_0)}} = \dfrac{z - z_0}{\left.\dfrac{\partial F}{\partial z}\right|_{(x_0,\ y_0,\ z_0)}}.$

These equations follow directly from (41-2).

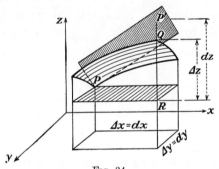

Fɪɢ. 34

Example 1.   At $(6, 2, 3)$ on the surface $x^2 + y^2 + z^2 = 49$, the tangent plane has the equation

$$2x\big|_{(6,\ 2,\ 3)} (x - 6) + 2y\big|_{(6,\ 2,\ 3)} (y - 2) + 2z\big|_{(6,\ 2,\ 3)} (z - 3) = 0$$

or

$$6x + 2y + 3z = 49.$$

The normal line is

$$\frac{x - 6}{12} = \frac{y - 2}{4} = \frac{z - 3}{6}.$$

Example 2.   For $(2, 1, 4)$ on the surface $z = x^2 + y^2 - 1$, the tangent plane is

$$z - 4 = 2x\big|_{(2,\ 1)} (x - 2) + 2y\big|_{(2,\ 1)} (y - 1)$$

or

$$4x + 2y - z = 6.$$

The normal line is

$$\frac{x-2}{4} = \frac{y-1}{2} = \frac{z-4}{-1}.$$

PROBLEMS

1. Find the distance from the origin to the plane $x + y + z = 1$.

2. Find the equations of the tangent plane and the normal line to

(a) $2x^2 + 3y^2 + 4z^2 = 6$ at $(1, 1, \frac{1}{2})$;

(b) $\dfrac{x^2}{4} + \dfrac{y^2}{9} - \dfrac{z^2}{16} = 1$ at $(4, 3, 8)$;

(c) $\dfrac{x^2}{a^2} + \dfrac{y^2}{b^2} + \dfrac{z^2}{c^2} = 1$ at (x_0, y_0, z_0);

(d) $x^2 + 2y^2 - z^2 = 0$ at $(1, 2, 3)$.

3. Referring to (43-4), show that

$$\cos \alpha : \cos \beta : \cos \gamma = \frac{\partial F}{\partial x} : \frac{\partial F}{\partial y} : \frac{\partial F}{\partial z},$$

where $\cos \alpha$, $\cos \beta$, $\cos \gamma$ are direction cosines of the normal line.

4. Show that the sum of the intercepts on the coordinate axes of any tangent plane to $x^{1/2} + y^{1/2} + z^{1/2} = a^{1/2}$ is constant.

44. Space Curves. It will be recalled that a plane curve C whose equation is

(44-1) $y = f(x)$

can be represented in infinitely many ways by a pair of parametric equations

(44-2) $\begin{aligned} x &= x(t), \\ y &= y(t) \end{aligned}$

so chosen that when the independent variable t runs continuously through some set of values $t_1 \leq t \leq t_2$ the corresponding values of x and y, determined by (44-2), satisfy (44-1).

For example, the equation of the upper half of a unit circle with the center at the origin of the cartesian system,

$$y = \sqrt{1 - x^2},$$

can be represented parametrically as

$$\begin{aligned} x &= \cos t, \\ y &= \sin t, \end{aligned} \qquad (0 \leq t \leq \pi),$$

or

$$x = t,$$
$$y = \sqrt{1 - t^2}, \qquad (0 \le t \le 1),$$

or

$$x = 2t,$$
$$y = \sqrt{1 - 4t^2}, \qquad (0 \le t \le \tfrac{1}{2}).$$

Similarly, a space curve C can be represented by means of a set of equations

(44-3)
$$\begin{cases} x = x(t), \\ y = y(t), \\ z = z(t) \end{cases}$$

so selected that when t runs through some set of values the coordinates of the point $P(x, y, z)$, defined by (44-3), trace out the desired curve C.

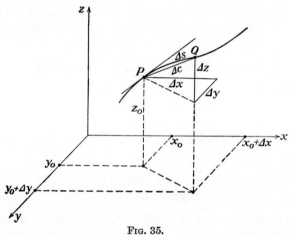

FIG. 35.

It will be assumed that the functions in (44-2) and (44-3) possess continuous derivatives with respect to t, which implies that the curve C has a continuously turning tangent as the point P moves along the curve.

Let $P(x_0, y_0, z_0)$ (Fig. 35) be a point of the curve C defined by (44-3) that corresponds to some value t_0 of the parameter t, and let Q be the point $(x_0 + \Delta x,\ y_0 + \Delta y,\ z_0 + \Delta z)$ that corresponds to $t = t_0 + \Delta t$. The direction ratios of the line PQ

joining P and Q are

$$\frac{\Delta x}{\Delta c} \cdot \frac{\Delta y}{\Delta c} \cdot \frac{\Delta z}{\Delta c} = \frac{\Delta x}{\Delta t} \cdot \frac{\Delta y}{\Delta t} \cdot \frac{\Delta z}{\Delta t}.$$

If Δt is allowed to approach zero, Δx, Δy, and Δz all tend to zero, so that the direction ratios of the tangent line at $P(x_0, y_0, z_0)$ are proportional to $(dx/dt)_{t=t_0} : (dy/dt)_{t=t_0} : (dz/dt)_{t=t_0}$. Hence, the equation of the tangent line to C at P is

$$\frac{x - x_0}{x'(t_0)} = \frac{y - y_0}{y'(t_0)} = \frac{z - z_0}{z'(t_0)},$$

where primes denote derivatives with respect to t.

Example. The equations of the tangent line to the circular helix

$$x = a \cos t,$$
$$y = a \sin t,$$
$$z = at,$$

at $t = \pi/6$, are

$$\frac{x - \frac{\sqrt{3}}{2} a}{-\frac{a}{2}} = \frac{y - \frac{a}{2}}{\frac{\sqrt{3}}{2} a} = \frac{z - \frac{\pi a}{6}}{a}.$$

The element of arc ds is given by

$$(ds)^2 = (dx)^2 + (dy)^2 + (dz)^2,$$

so that the length of a space curve C can be calculated from

$$L = \int_{t_1}^{t_2} \sqrt{\left(\frac{dx}{dt}\right)^2 + \left(\frac{dy}{dt}\right)^2 + \left(\frac{dz}{dt}\right)^2}\, dt.$$

The length of the part of the helix between the points $(a, 0, 0)$ and $(0, a, \pi a/2)$ is

$$L = \frac{\sqrt{2}}{2} \pi a.$$

45. Directional Derivatives in Space. There is no essential difficulty in extending the results of Sec. 42 to any number of variables. Thus, if $u = f(x, y, z)$ is a suitably restricted function of the independent variables x, y, and z, then the directional derivative along a space curve whose tangent line at some point $P(x, y, z)$ (Fig. 35) has the direction cosines $\cos (x, s)$, $\cos (y, s)$, and cos (z, s) is

$$\frac{du}{ds} = \frac{\partial u}{\partial x} \cos (x, s) + \frac{\partial u}{\partial y} \cos (y, s) + \frac{\partial u}{\partial z} \cos (z, s)$$

$$= \frac{\partial u}{\partial x}\frac{dx}{ds} + \frac{\partial u}{\partial y}\frac{dy}{ds} + \frac{\partial u}{\partial z}\frac{dz}{ds}.$$

The magnitude of the normal derivative to the surface $u = $ const. is given by

$$(45\text{-}1) \qquad \frac{du}{dn} = \sqrt{\left(\frac{\partial f}{\partial x}\right)^2 + \left(\frac{\partial f}{\partial y}\right)^2 + \left(\frac{\partial f}{\partial z}\right)^2}.$$

The vector that is normal to the surface $u = $ const. and whose magnitude is du/dn is called the *gradient* of u.

PROBLEM

1. Find the equation of the tangent line to the helix

$$x = a \cos t, \qquad y = a \sin t, \qquad z = at,$$

at the point where $t = \pi/4$. Find the length of the helix between the points $t = 0$ and $t = \pi/4$.

2. Find the directional derivative of $f = xyz$ at $(1, 2, 3)$ in the direction of the line that makes equal angles with the coordinate axes.

3. Find the normal derivative of $f = x^2 + y^2 + z^2$ at $(1, 2, 3)$.

4. Show that the square root of the sum of the squares of the directional derivatives in three perpendicular directions is equal to the normal derivative.

5. Express the normal derivative (45-1) in spherical and cylindrical coordinates, for which the equations of transformation are

(a) $x = r \sin \theta \cos \varphi, \ y = r \sin \theta \sin \varphi, \ z = r \cos \theta$;
(b) $x = r \sin \theta, \ y = r \cos \theta, \ z = z$.

6. What is the direction of the curve $x = t, \ y = t^2, \ z = t^3$ at the point $(1, 1, 1)$?

7. Show that the condition that the surfaces $f(x, y, z) = 0$ and $\varphi(x, y, z) = 0$ intersect orthogonally is that

$$\frac{\partial f}{\partial x}\frac{\partial \varphi}{\partial x} + \frac{\partial f}{\partial y}\frac{\partial \varphi}{\partial y} + \frac{\partial f}{\partial z}\frac{\partial \varphi}{\partial z} = 0.$$

8. Show that the surfaces

$$xyz = 1 \qquad \text{and} \qquad \frac{x^2}{2} + \frac{y^2}{2} - \frac{z^2}{1} = 1$$

intersect at right angles.

9. Find the angle between the normals to the tangent planes to the surfaces $x^2 + y^2 + z^2 = 6$ and $2x^2 + 3y^2 + z^2 = 9$ at the point $(1, 1, 2)$.

10. Show that the direction of the tangent line to the curve of intersection of the surfaces $f(x, y, z) = 0$ and $g(x, y, z) = 0$ is given by

$$\cos \alpha : \cos \beta : \cos \gamma = \begin{vmatrix} f_y & f_z \\ g_y & g_z \end{vmatrix} : \begin{vmatrix} f_z & f_x \\ g_z & g_x \end{vmatrix} : \begin{vmatrix} f_x & f_y \\ g_x & g_y \end{vmatrix}.$$

Hint: Let (x_0, y_0, z_0) be a point on the curve of intersection, and find the line of intersection of the tangent planes to the surfaces at the point (x_0, y_0, z_0).

46. Higher Partial Derivatives. The partial derivatives f_{x_1}, $f_{x_2}, \cdots, f_{x_n}$ of $f(x_1, x_2, \cdots, x_n)$ are functions of $x_1, x_2, \cdots,$ x_n and may have partial derivatives with respect to some or all of these variables. These derivatives are called second partial derivatives of $f(x_1, x_2, \cdots, x_n)$. If there are only two independent variables x and y, then $f(x, y)$ may have the second partial derivatives

$$\frac{\partial}{\partial x} \left(\frac{\partial f}{\partial x} \right) \equiv \frac{\partial^2 f}{\partial x^2} \equiv f_{xx},$$

$$\frac{\partial}{\partial y} \left(\frac{\partial f}{\partial x} \right) \equiv \frac{\partial^2 f}{\partial y\, \partial x} \equiv f_{xy},$$

$$\frac{\partial}{\partial x} \left(\frac{\partial f}{\partial y} \right) \equiv \frac{\partial^2 f}{\partial x\, \partial y} \equiv f_{yx},$$

$$\frac{\partial}{\partial y} \left(\frac{\partial f}{\partial y} \right) \equiv \frac{\partial^2 f}{\partial y^2} \equiv f_{yy}.$$

It should be noticed that f_{xy} means that $\partial f / \partial x$ is first found and then $\dfrac{\partial}{\partial y} \left(\dfrac{\partial f}{\partial x} \right)$ is determined, so that the subscripts indicate the order in which the derivatives are taken. In

$$\frac{\partial^2 f}{\partial y\, \partial x} = \frac{\partial}{\partial y} \left(\frac{\partial f}{\partial x} \right)$$

the order is in keeping with the meaning of the symbol, so that the order appears as the reverse of the order in which the derivatives are taken.

It can be proved* that, if f_{xy} and f_{yx} are continuous functions of x and y, then $f_{xy} = f_{yx}$, so that the order of differentiation is

* See Sokolnikoff, I. S., *Advanced Calculus*, Sec. 31.

immaterial. Similarly, when third partial derivatives are found, $f_{xyx} = f_{xxy} = f_{yxx}$ and $f_{xyy} = f_{yxy} = f_{yyx}$, if these derivatives are continuous.

Example. If $f(x, y) = e^{xy}$, then

$$f_x = ye^{xy}, \qquad f_y = xe^{xy}, \qquad f_{xx} = y^2e^{xy},$$
$$f_{xy} = f_{yx} = e^{xy}(xy + 1), \qquad f_{yy} = x^2e^{xy}.$$

PROBLEMS

1. Verify that $\dfrac{\partial^2 f}{\partial x\, \partial y} = \dfrac{\partial^2 f}{\partial y\, \partial x}$ for

(a) $f = \cos xy^2$, (b) $f = \sin^2 x \cos y$, (c) $f = e^{y/x}$.

2. Prove that if

(a) $f(x, y) = \log (x^2 + y^2) + \tan^{-1} \dfrac{y}{x}$, then $\dfrac{\partial^2 f}{\partial x^2} + \dfrac{\partial^2 f}{\partial y^2} = 0$;

(b) $f(x, y, z) = (x^2 + y^2 + z^2)^{-\frac{1}{2}}$, then $\dfrac{\partial^2 f}{\partial x^2} + \dfrac{\partial^2 f}{\partial y^2} + \dfrac{\partial^2 f}{\partial z^2} = 0$.

3. If $u = x^2 + y^2$ and $\begin{cases} x = s + 3t, \\ y = 2s - t, \end{cases}$ find $\dfrac{\partial^2 u}{\partial s^2}$ and $\dfrac{\partial^2 u}{\partial t^2}$.

4. If $u = f(x, y)$ and $\begin{cases} x = r \cos \theta, \\ y = r \sin \theta, \end{cases}$ find $\dfrac{\partial^2 u}{\partial r^2}$ and $\dfrac{\partial^2 u}{\partial \theta^2}$.

5. Use the results obtained in Prob. 6(b), Sec. 41, in order to show that $\dfrac{\partial^2 u}{\partial x^2} = u(3v^2 - u^2)/(u^2 + v^2)^3$. Find $\dfrac{\partial^2 u}{\partial y\, \partial x}$ and $\dfrac{\partial^2 u}{\partial y^2}$.

6. If $w = w(x, y)$, where $x = x(u, v)$, $y = y(u, v)$, $\partial x/\partial u = \partial y/\partial v$, and $\partial x/\partial v = -\partial y/\partial u$, show that

$$\frac{\partial^2 w}{\partial u^2} + \frac{\partial^2 w}{\partial v^2} = \left(\frac{\partial^2 w}{\partial x^2} + \frac{\partial^2 w}{\partial y^2} \right) \left[\left(\frac{\partial x}{\partial u} \right)^2 + \left(\frac{\partial x}{\partial v} \right)^2 \right].$$

7. Show that the expressions

$$V_1 = \left(\frac{\partial z}{\partial x} \right)^2 + \left(\frac{\partial z}{\partial y} \right)^2 \qquad \text{and} \qquad V_2 = \frac{\partial^2 z}{\partial x^2} + \frac{\partial^2 z}{\partial y^2}$$

upon change of variable by means of $x = r \cos \theta$ and $y = r \sin \theta$ become

$$V_1 = \left(\frac{\partial z}{\partial r} \right)^2 + \frac{1}{r^2} \left(\frac{\partial z}{\partial \theta} \right)^2 \qquad \text{and} \qquad V_2 = \frac{\partial^2 z}{\partial r^2} + \frac{1}{r^2} \frac{\partial^2 z}{\partial \theta^2} + \frac{1}{r} \frac{\partial z}{\partial r}.$$

8. If $V = f(x + ct) + g(x - ct)$, where f and g are any functions possessing continuous second derivatives, show that

$$\frac{\partial^2 V}{\partial t^2} = c^2 \frac{\partial^2 V}{\partial x^2}.$$

9. Show that if $x = e^r \cos \theta$ and $y = e^r \sin \theta$, then

$$\frac{\partial^2 V}{\partial x^2} + \frac{\partial^2 V}{\partial y^2} = e^{-2r} \left(\frac{\partial^2 V}{\partial r^2} + \frac{\partial^2 V}{\partial \theta^2} \right).$$

10. If $V_1(x, y, z)$ and $V_2(x, y, z)$ satisfy the equation

$$\nabla^2 V \equiv \frac{\partial^2 V}{\partial x^2} + \frac{\partial^2 V}{\partial y^2} + \frac{\partial^2 V}{\partial z^2} = 0,$$

show that

$$U \equiv V_1(x, y, z) + (x^2 + y^2 + z^2) V_2(x, y, z)$$

satisfies the equation

$$\nabla^2 \nabla^2 U = 0, \qquad \text{where} \qquad \nabla^2 \equiv \frac{\partial^2}{\partial x^2} + \frac{\partial^2}{\partial y^2} + \frac{\partial^2}{\partial z^2}.$$

47. Taylor's Series for Functions of Two Variables. This section contains a formal development of a function of two variables, $f(x, y)$, in a series analogous to the Taylor's series development of a function of a single variable. It is assumed that the series obtained here converges to the value of the function $f(x, y)$, but the analysis of the conditions under which this convergence will occur is too involved to be discussed in this book.

Consider $f(x, y)$, which is a function of the two variables x and y, and let it have continuous partial derivatives of all orders. Let

(47-1) $x = a + \alpha t$ and $y = b + \beta t,$

where a, b, α, and β are constants and t is a variable. Then

(47-2) $f(x, y) = f(a + \alpha t, b + \beta t) \equiv F(t).$

If $F(t)$ is expanded in Maclaurin's series, there results

(47-3) $F(t) = F(0) + F'(0)t + \dfrac{F''(0)}{2!} t^2 + \dfrac{F'''(0)}{3!} t^3 + \cdots.$

From (47-2) and (47-1), it follows that

$$F'(t) = f_x(x, y) \frac{dx}{dt} + f_y(x, y) \frac{dy}{dt}$$

$$= f_x(x, y)\alpha + f_y(x, y)\beta.$$

Then,

$$F''(t) = [f_{xx}(x, y)\alpha + f_{yx}(x, y)\beta] \frac{dx}{dt} + [f_{xy}(x, y)\alpha + f_{yy}(x, y)\beta] \frac{dy}{dt}$$

$$= f_{xx}(x, y)\alpha^2 + 2f_{xy}(x, y)\alpha\beta + f_{yy}(x, y)\beta^2,$$

and

$$F'''(t) = [f_{xxx}(x, y)\alpha^2 + 2f_{xyx}(x, y)\alpha\beta + f_{yyx}(x, y)\beta^2]\frac{dx}{dt}$$

$$+ [f_{xxy}(x, y)\alpha^2 + 2f_{xyy}(x, y)\alpha\beta + f_{yyy}(x, y)\beta^2]\frac{dy}{dt}$$

$$= f_{xxx}(x, y)\alpha^3 + 3f_{xxy}(x, y)\alpha^2\beta + 3f_{xyy}(x, y)\alpha\beta^2$$

$$+ f_{yyy}(x, y)\beta^3.$$

Higher order derivatives of $F(t)$ can be obtained by continuing this process, but the form is evident from those already obtained. Symbolically expressed,

$$F'(t) = \left(\alpha\frac{\partial}{\partial x} + \beta\frac{\partial}{\partial y}\right)f(x, y) \equiv \alpha\frac{\partial f}{\partial x} + \beta\frac{\partial f}{\partial y},$$

$$F''(t) = \left(\alpha\frac{\partial}{\partial x} + \beta\frac{\partial}{\partial y}\right)^2 f(x, y) \equiv \alpha^2\frac{\partial^2 f}{\partial x^2} + 2\alpha\beta\frac{\partial^2 f}{\partial x\,\partial y} + \beta^2\frac{\partial^2 f}{\partial y^2},$$

$$F'''(t) = \left(\alpha\frac{\partial}{\partial x} + \beta\frac{\partial}{\partial y}\right)^3 f(x, y) \equiv \alpha^3\frac{\partial^3 f}{\partial x^3} + 3\alpha^2\beta\frac{\partial^3 f}{\partial x^2\,\partial y}$$

$$+ 3\alpha\beta^2\frac{\partial^3 f}{\partial x\,\partial y^2} + \beta^3\frac{\partial^3 f}{\partial y^3}.$$

Then,

$$F^{(n)}(t) = \left(\alpha\frac{\partial}{\partial x} + \beta\frac{\partial}{\partial y}\right)^n f(x, y) \equiv \alpha^n\frac{\partial^n f}{\partial x^n} + C_1^n\alpha^{n-1}\beta\frac{\partial^n f}{\partial x^{n-1}\,\partial y}$$

$$+ \cdots + C_{n-1}^n\alpha\beta^{n-1}\frac{\partial^n f}{\partial x\,\partial y^{n-1}} + \beta^n\frac{\partial^n f}{\partial y^n},$$

where

$$C_r^n \equiv \frac{n!}{r!(n-r)!}.$$

Since $t = 0$ gives $x = a$ and $y = b$, it follows that

$$F(0) = f(a, b), \qquad F'(0) = \alpha f_x(a, b) + \beta f_y(a, b), \cdots.$$

Substituting these expressions in (47-3) gives

$$F(t) \equiv f(x, y) = f(a, b) + [\alpha f_x(a, b) + \beta f_y(a, b)]t$$

$$+ [\alpha^2 f_{xx}(a, b) + 2\alpha\beta f_{xy}(a, b) + \beta^2 f_{yy}(a, b)]\frac{t^2}{2!} + \cdots.$$

Since $\alpha t = x - a$ and $\beta t = y - b$, the expansion becomes

$$(47\text{-}4)\quad f(x, y) = f(a, b) + f_x(a, b)(x - a) + f_y(a, b)(y - b)$$

$$+ \frac{1}{2!}[f_{xx}(a, b)(x - a)^2 + 2f_{xy}(a, b)(x - a)(y - b)$$

$$+ f_{yy}(a, b)(y - b)^2] + \cdots.$$

This is Taylor's expansion for a function $f(x, y)$ about the point (a, b).

Another form that is frequently used is obtained by replacing $(x - a)$ by h and $(y - b)$ by k, so that $x = a + h$ and $y = b + k$. Then,

(47-5) $f(a + h, b + k) = f(a, b) + f_x(a, b)h + f_y(a, b)k$

$$+ \frac{1}{2!}[f_{xx}(a, b)h^2 + 2f_{xy}(a, b)hk + f_{yy}(a, b)k^2] + \cdots .$$

This formula is frequently written symbolically as

$$f(a + h, b + k) = f(a, b) + \left(h\frac{\partial}{\partial x} + k\frac{\partial}{\partial y} \right) f(a, b)$$

$$+ \frac{1}{2!} \left(h\frac{\partial}{\partial x} + k\frac{\partial}{\partial y} \right)^2 f(a, b) + \cdots .$$

Example. Obtain the expansion of $\tan^{-1}\frac{y}{x}$ about $(1, 1)$ up to the third-degree terms. Here, $f(x, y) = \tan^{-1}\frac{y}{x}$, so that

$$f(x, y) = \tan^{-1}\frac{y}{x}, \qquad f(1, 1) = \tan^{-1}1 = \frac{\pi}{4};$$

$$f_x(x, y) = -\frac{y}{x^2 + y^2}, \qquad f_x(1, 1) = -\frac{1}{2};$$

$$f_y(x, y) = \frac{x}{x^2 + y^2}, \qquad f_y(1, 1) = \frac{1}{2};$$

$$f_{xx}(x, y) = \frac{2xy}{(x^2 + y^2)^2}, \qquad f_{xx}(1, 1) = \frac{1}{2};$$

$$f_{xy}(x, y) = \frac{y^2 - x^2}{(x^2 + y^2)^2}, \qquad f_{xy}(1, 1) = 0;$$

$$f_{yy}(x, y) = \frac{-2xy}{(x^2 + y^2)^2}, \qquad f_{yy}(1, 1) = -\frac{1}{2}.$$

Then,

$$\tan^{-1}\frac{y}{x} = \frac{\pi}{4} - \frac{1}{2}(x - 1) + \frac{1}{2}(y - 1)$$

$$+ \frac{1}{2!}\left[\frac{1}{2}(x - 1)^2 - \frac{1}{2}(y - 1)^2 \right] + \cdots .$$

PROBLEMS

1. Obtain the expansion for $xy^2 + \cos xy$ about $(1, \pi/2)$ up to the third-degree terms.

2. Expand $f(x, y) = e^{xy}$ at $(1, 1)$, obtaining three terms.
3. Expand $e^x \cos y$ at $(0, 0)$ up to the fourth-degree terms.
4. Show that, for small values of x and y,

$$e^x \sin y = y + xy \text{ (approx.)},$$

and

$$e^x \log (1 + y) = y + xy - \frac{y^2}{2} \text{ (approx.)}.$$

5. Expand $f(x, y) = x^3y + x^2y + 1$ about $(0, 1)$.
6. Expand $(1 - x^2 - y^2)^{\frac{1}{2}}$ about $(0, 0)$ up to the third-degree terms.
7. Show that the development obtained in Prob. 6 is identical with the binomial expansion of $[1 - (x^2 + y^2)]^{\frac{1}{2}}$.

48. Maxima and Minima of Functions of One Variable. A function $f(x)$ is said to have a *maximum* at $x = a$, if

$$\Delta^+ \equiv f(a + h) - f(a) < 0,$$

and

$$\Delta^- \equiv f(a - h) - f(a) < 0,$$

for all sufficiently small positive values of h. If Δ^+ and Δ^- are both positive for all small positive values of h, then $f(x)$ is said to have a *minimum* at $x = a$.

It is shown in the elementary calculus that, if the function $f(x)$ has a derivative at $x = a$, then the necessary condition for a maximum or a minimum is the vanishing of $f'(x)$ at the point $x = a$. Of course, the function $f(x)$ may attain a maximum or a minimum at $x = a$ without having $f'(a) = 0$, but this can occur only if $f'(x)$ ceases to exist at the critical point (see Fig. 36).

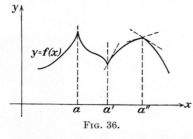

FIG. 36.

Let it be supposed that $f(x)$ has a continuous derivative of order n in some interval about the point $x = a$. Then it follows from Taylor's formula that

$$\Delta^+ \equiv f(a + h) - f(a)$$
$$= f'(a)h + \frac{f''(a)}{2!}h^2 + \cdots + \frac{f^{(n-1)}(a)}{(n - 1)!}h^{n-1} + \frac{f^{(n)}(a + \theta_1 h)}{n!}h^n,$$

where $0 < \theta_1 < 1$, and

$$\Delta^- \equiv f(a - h) - f(a)$$
$$= - f'(a)h + \frac{f''(a)}{2!} h^2 - \cdots + (-1)^{n-1} \frac{f^{(n-1)}(a)}{(n-1)!} h^{n-1}$$
$$+ (-1)^n \frac{f^{(n)}(a - \theta_2 h)}{n!} h^n,$$

where $0 < \theta_2 < 1$. Let it be assumed further that the first $n - 1$ derivatives of $f(x)$ vanish at $x = a$ but that $f^{(n)}(a)$ is not zero. Then

$$\Delta^+ = \frac{f^{(n)}(a + \theta_1 h)}{n!} h^n$$

and

$$\Delta^- = (-1)^n \frac{f^{(n)}(a - \theta_2 h)}{n!} h^n.$$

Since $f^{(n)}(x)$ is assumed to be continuous in some interval about the point $x = a$, $f^{(n)}(a + \theta_1 h)$ and $f^{(n)}(a - \theta_2 h)$ will have the same sign for sufficiently small values of h. Consequently, the signs of Δ^+ and Δ^- will be opposite unless n is an even number. But if $f(x)$ is to have a maximum or a minimum at $x = a$, then Δ^+ and Δ^- must be of the same sign. Accordingly, the necessary condition for a maximum or a minimum of $f(x)$ at $x = a$ is that the first non-vanishing derivative of $f(x)$, at $x = a$, be of even order. Moreover, since both Δ^+ and Δ^- are negative if $f(x)$ is a maximum, it follows that $f^{(n)}(a)$ must be negative. A similar argument shows that, if $f(x)$ has a minimum at $x = a$, then the first non-vanishing derivative of $f(x)$ at $x = a$ must be of even order and positive.

If the first non-vanishing derivative of $f(x)$ at $x = a$ is of odd order and $f''(a) = 0$, then the point $x = a$ is called a *point of inflection*.

Example. Investigate $f(x) = x^5 - 5x^4$ for maxima and minima. Now,

$$f'(x) = 5x^4 - 20x^3,$$

which is zero when $x = 0$ and $x = 4$. Then,

$$f''(x) = 20x^3 - 60x^2, \quad f''(0) = 0, \quad f''(4) = 320;$$
$$f'''(x) = 60x^2 - 120x, \quad f'''(0) = 0;$$
$$f^{IV}(x) = 120x - 120, \quad f^{IV}(0) = -120.$$

Since $f''(4) > 0$, $f(4) = -256$ is a minimum; and since $f^{IV}(0) < 0$, $f(0) = 0$ is a maximum.

PROBLEMS

1. Examine the following for maxima and minima:

(a) $y = x^4 - 4x^3 + 1$;
(b) $y = x^3(x - 5)^2$;
(c) $y = x + \cos x$.

2. Find the minimum of the function $y = x^x$, where $x > 0$.
Hint: Consider the minimum of log y.

3. Show that $x = 0$ gives the minimum value of the function

$$y = e^x + e^{-x} + 2 \cos x.$$

4. Find maxima, minima, and points of inflection, and sketch the curves, for the following:

(a) $y = 3x + 4 \sin x + \sin 2x$;
(b) $y = 3x - 4 \sin x + \sin 2x$;
(c) $y = 6x + 8 \sin x + \sin 2x$.

5. Find the maximum and minimum values of the function

$$y = x \sin x + 2 \cos x.$$

6. Find maxima, minima, and points of inflection, and sketch the curves, for the following:

(a) $y = x \log x$;
(b) $x^5 - (y - x^2)^2 = 0$.

49. Maxima and Minima of Functions of Several Variables.

A function of two variables $f(x, y)$ is said to have a maximum at (a, b), if $f(a + h, b + k) - f(a, b) < 0$ for sufficiently small positive and negative values of h and k, and a minimum, if $f(a + h, b + k) - f(a, b) > 0$.

Geometrically, this means that when the point (a, b, c) on the surface $z = f(x, y)$ is higher than all neighboring points, then (a, b, c) is a maximum; and when (a, b, c) is lower than all neighboring points, it is a minimum point. At a maximum or a minimum point (a, b, c) the curves in which the planes $x = a$ and $y = b$ cut the surface have maxima or minima. Therefore, $f_x(a, b) = 0$ and $f_y(a, b) = 0$. The conditions $f_x = 0$ and $f_y = 0$ can be solved simultaneously to give the critical values.

The testing of the critical values for maxima and minima is more difficult than in the case of functions of one variable. However in many applied problems the physical interpretation will determine whether or not the critical values yield maxima or minima or neither.   An analytical criterion can be established for the case of two variables in a manner analogous to the method used for one variable.   By the use of Taylor's expansion, it can be shown that if $f_x(a, b) = 0$ and $f_y(a, b) = 0$, then $f(a, b)$ is a maximum if

$$D \equiv f_{xy}^2(a, b) - f_{xx}(a, b)f_{yy}(a, b) < 0$$

with

$$f_{xx}(a, b) < 0 \qquad \text{and} \qquad f_{yy}(a, b) < 0,$$

and a minimum if

$$D \equiv f_{xy}^2(a, b) - f_{xx}(a, b)f_{yy}(a, b) < 0$$

with

$$f_{xx}(a, b) > 0 \qquad \text{and} \qquad f_{yy}(a, b) > 0.$$

In case

$$f_{xy}^2(a, b) - f_{xx}(a, b)f_{yy}(a, b) > 0,$$

$f(a, b)$ is neither a maximum nor a minimum.   If

$$f_{xy}^2(a, b) - f_{xx}(a, b)f_{yy}(a, b) = 0,$$

the test gives no information, just as $f''(x) = 0$ gives no criterion in the case of one variable.

These considerations can be extended to functions of more than two variables.   Thus, in the case of a function $f(x, y, z)$ of three variables,

$$\frac{\partial f}{\partial x} = 0, \qquad \frac{\partial f}{\partial y} = 0, \qquad \frac{\partial f}{\partial z} = 0$$

is the necessary condition for a maximum or a minimum.

Example 1.   A long piece of tin 12 in. wide is made into a trough by bending up the sides to form equal angles with the base (Fig. 37).   Find the amount to be bent up and the angle of inclination of the sides that will make the carrying capacity a maximum.

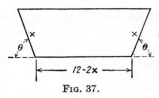

Fig. 37.

The volume will be a maximum if the area of the trapezoidal cross section is a maximum.   The area is

$$A = 12x \sin \theta - 2x^2 \sin \theta + x^2 \sin \theta \cos \theta;$$

for $12 - 2x$ is the lower base, $12 - 2x + 2x \cos \theta$ is the upper base, and $x \sin \theta$ is the altitude. Then,

$$\frac{\partial A}{\partial \theta} = 12x \cos \theta - 2x^2 \cos \theta + x^2 \cos^2 \theta - x^2 \sin^2 \theta$$
$$= x(12 \cos \theta - 2x \cos \theta + x \cos^2 \theta - x \sin^2 \theta)$$

and

$$\frac{\partial A}{\partial x} = 2 \sin \theta (6 - 2x + x \cos \theta).$$

$\partial A/\partial x = 0$ and $\partial A/\partial \theta = 0$, if $\sin \theta = 0$ and $x = 0$, which, from physical considerations, cannot give a maximum.

There remain to be satisfied

$$6 - 2x + x \cos \theta = 0$$

and

$$12 \cos \theta - 2x \cos \theta + x \cos^2 \theta - x \sin^2 \theta = 0.$$

Solving the first equation for x and substituting in the second yield, upon simplification,

$$\cos \theta = \tfrac{1}{2} \quad \text{or} \quad \theta = 60°, \quad \text{and} \quad x = 4.$$

Since physical considerations show that a maximum exists, $x = 4$ and $\theta = 60°$ must give the maximum.

Example 2. Find the maxima and minima of the surface

$$\frac{x^2}{a^2} - \frac{y^2}{b^2} = 2cz.$$

Now,

$$\frac{\partial z}{\partial x} = \frac{1}{c}\frac{x}{a^2}, \qquad \frac{\partial z}{\partial y} = -\frac{1}{c}\frac{y}{b^2},$$

which vanish when $x = y = 0$. But

$$\frac{\partial^2 z}{\partial x^2} = \frac{1}{a^2c}, \qquad \frac{\partial^2 z}{\partial y^2} = -\frac{1}{b^2c}, \qquad \frac{\partial^2 z}{\partial x\,\partial y} = 0.$$

Hence, $D = 1/a^2b^2c^2$ and, consequently, there is no maximum or minimum at $x = y = 0$. The surface under consideration is a saddle-shaped surface called a *hyperbolic paraboloid*. The points for which the first partial derivatives vanish and $D > 0$ are called *minimax*. The reason for this odd name appears from a consideration of the shape of the hyperbolic paraboloid near the origin of the coordinate system. The reader will benefit from sketching it in the vicinity of $(0, 0, 0)$.

PROBLEMS

1. Divide a into three parts such that their product is a maximum. Test by using the second derivative criterion.

2. Find the volume of the largest rectangular parallelepiped that can be inscribed in the ellipsoid

$$\frac{x^2}{a^2} + \frac{y^2}{b^2} + \frac{z^2}{c^2} = 1.$$

3. Find the dimensions of the largest rectangular parallelepiped that has three faces in the coordinate planes and one vertex in the plane

$$\frac{x}{a} + \frac{y}{b} + \frac{z}{c} = 1.$$

4. A pentagonal frame is composed of a rectangle surmounted by an isosceles triangle. What are the dimensions for maximum area of the pentagon if the perimeter is given as P?

5. A floating anchorage is designed with a body in the form of a right-circular cylinder with equal ends that are right-circular cones. If the volume is given, find the dimensions giving the minimum surface area.

6. Given n points P_i whose coordinates are (x_i, y_i, z_i), $(i = 1, 2, \cdots, n)$. Show that the coordinates of the point $P(x, y, z)$, such that the sum of the squares of the distances from P to the P_i is a minimum, are given by

$$\left(\frac{1}{n} \sum_{i=1}^{n} x_i, \frac{1}{n} \sum_{i=1}^{n} y_i, \frac{1}{n} \sum_{i=1}^{n} z_i \right).$$

50. Constrained Maxima and Minima. In a large number of practical and theoretical investigations, it is required that a maximum or minimum value of a function be found when the variables are connected by some relation. Thus, it may be required to find a maximum of $u = f(x, y, z)$, where x, y, and z are connected by the relation $\varphi(x, y, z) = 0$. The resulting maximum is called a *constrained maximum*.

The method of obtaining maxima and minima described in the preceding section can be used to solve a problem of constrained maxima and minima, as follows: If the constraining relation $\varphi(x, y, z) = 0$ can be solved for one of the variables, say z, in terms of the remaining two variables, and if the resulting expression is substituted for z in $u = f(x, y, z)$, there will be obtained a function $u = F(x, y)$. The values of x and y that yield maxima and minima of u can be found by the methods of Sec. 49. However, the solution of $\varphi(x, y, z) = 0$ for any one of the variables may be extremely difficult, and it is desirable to consider an ingenious device used by Lagrange.

To avoid circumlocution the maximum and minimum values of a function of any number of variables will be called its *extremal values*. It follows from Sec. 49 that the necessary condition for the existence of an extremum of a differentiable function $f(x_1, x_2, \cdots, x_n)$ is the vanishing of the first partial derivatives of the function with respect to the independent variables x_1, $x_2, \cdots, x_n$. Inasmuch as the differential of a function is defined as

$$df \equiv \frac{\partial f}{\partial x_1} dx_1 + \frac{\partial f}{\partial x_2} dx_2 + \cdots + \frac{\partial f}{\partial x_n} dx_n,$$

it is clear that df vanishes for those values of $x_1, x_2, \cdots, x_n$ for which the function has extremal values. Conversely, since the variables x_i are assumed to be independent, the vanishing of the differential is the necessary condition for an extremum.

It is not difficult to see that, even when some of the variables are not independent, the vanishing of the total differential is the necessary condition for an extremum. Thus, consider a function

$$(50\text{-}1) \qquad u = f(x, y, z),$$

where one of the variables, say z, is connected with x and y by some constraining relation

$$(50\text{-}2) \qquad \varphi(x, y, z) = 0.$$

Regarding x and y as the independent variables, the necessary conditions for an extremum give $\partial u/\partial x = 0$ and $\partial u/\partial y = 0$, or

$$\frac{\partial u}{\partial x} = \frac{\partial f}{\partial x} + \frac{\partial f}{\partial z}\frac{\partial z}{\partial x} = 0,$$

$$\frac{\partial u}{\partial y} = \frac{\partial f}{\partial y} + \frac{\partial f}{\partial z}\frac{\partial z}{\partial y} = 0.$$

Then the total differential

$$\frac{\partial u}{\partial x} dx + \frac{\partial u}{\partial y} dy = \frac{\partial f}{\partial x} dx + \frac{\partial f}{\partial y} dy + \frac{\partial f}{\partial z}\left(\frac{\partial z}{\partial x} dx + \frac{\partial z}{\partial y} dy\right) = 0;$$

and since the expression in the parenthesis is precisely dz, it follows that

$$(50\text{-}3) \qquad \frac{\partial f}{\partial x} dx + \frac{\partial f}{\partial y} dy + \frac{\partial f}{\partial z} dz = 0.$$

The total differential of the constraining relation (50-2) is

(50-4) $$\frac{\partial \varphi}{\partial x}\, dx + \frac{\partial \varphi}{\partial y}\, dy + \frac{\partial \varphi}{\partial z}\, dz = 0.$$

Let this equation be multiplied by some undetermined multiplier λ and then added to (50-3). The result is

$$\left(\frac{\partial f}{\partial x} + \lambda \frac{\partial \varphi}{\partial x}\right) dx + \left(\frac{\partial f}{\partial y} + \lambda \frac{\partial \varphi}{\partial y}\right) dy + \left(\frac{\partial f}{\partial z} + \lambda \frac{\partial \varphi}{\partial z}\right) dz = 0.$$

Now, if λ is so chosen that

(50-5) $$\begin{cases} \dfrac{\partial f}{\partial x} + \lambda \dfrac{\partial \varphi}{\partial x} = 0, \\[2mm] \dfrac{\partial f}{\partial y} + \lambda \dfrac{\partial \varphi}{\partial y} = 0, \\[2mm] \dfrac{\partial f}{\partial z} + \lambda \dfrac{\partial \varphi}{\partial z} = 0, \\[2mm] \varphi(x,\, y,\, z) = 0, \end{cases}$$

then the necessary condition for an extremum of (50-1) will surely be satisfied.

Thus, in order to determine the extremal values of (50-1), all that is necessary is to obtain the solution of the system of Eqs. (50-5) for the four unknowns x, y, z, and λ. The multiplier λ is called a *Lagrangian multiplier*.

Example 1. Find the maximum and the minimum distances from the origin to the curve

$$5x^2 + 6xy + 5y^2 - 8 = 0.$$

The problem here is to determine the extremal values of

$$f(x,\, y) = x^2 + y^2$$

subject to the condition

$$\varphi(x,\, y) \equiv 5x^2 + 6xy + 5y^2 - 8 = 0.$$

Equations (50-5) in this case become

$$2x + \lambda(10x + 6y) = 0,$$
$$2y + \lambda(6x + 10y) = 0,$$
$$5x^2 + 6xy + 5y^2 - 8 = 0.$$

Multiplying the first of these equations by y and the second by x and then subtracting give

$$6\lambda(y^2 - x^2) = 0,$$

so that $y = \pm x$. Substituting these values of y in the third equation gives two equations for the determination of x, namely,

$$2x^2 = 1 \quad \text{and} \quad x^2 = 2.$$

The first of these gives $f \equiv x^2 + y^2 = 1$, and the second gives $f \equiv x^2 + y^2 = 4$. Obviously, the first value is a minimum, whereas the second is a maximum. The curve is an ellipse of semiaxes 2 and 1 whose major axis makes an angle of 45° with the x-axis.

Example 2. Find the dimensions of the rectangular box, without a top, of maximum capacity whose surface is 108 sq. in.

The function to be maximized is

$$f(x, y, z) \equiv xyz,$$

subject to the condition

(50-6) $$xy + 2xz + 2yz = 108.$$

The first three of Eqs. (50-5) become

(50-7) $$\begin{cases} yz + \lambda(y + 2z) = 0, \\ xz + \lambda(x + 2z) = 0, \\ xy + \lambda(2x + 2y) = 0. \end{cases}$$

In order to solve these equations, multiply the first by x, the second by y, and the last by z, and add. There results

$$\lambda(2xy + 4xz + 4yz) + 3xyz = 0,$$

or

$$\lambda(xy + 2xz + 2yz) + \tfrac{3}{2}xyz = 0.$$

Substituting from (50-6) gives

$$108\lambda + \tfrac{3}{2}xyz = 0,$$

or

$$\lambda = -\frac{xyz}{72}.$$

Substituting this value of λ in (50-7) and dividing out common factors give

$$1 - \frac{x}{72}(y + 2z) = 0,$$

$$1 - \frac{y}{72}(x + 2z) = 0,$$

$$1 - \frac{z}{72}(2x + 2y) = 0.$$

From the first two of these equations, it is evident that $x = y$. The substitution of $x = y$ in the third equation gives $z = 18/y$. Substituting for y and z in the first equation yields $x = 6$. Thus, $x = 6$, $y = 6$, and $z = 3$ give the desired dimensions.

PROBLEMS

1. Work Probs. 1, 2, and 3, Sec. 49, by using Lagrangian multipliers.

2. Prove that the point of intersection of the medians of a triangle possesses the property that the sum of the squares of its distances from the vertices is a minimum.

3. Find the maximum and the minimum of the sum of the angles made by a line from the origin with (*a*) the coordinate axes of a cartesian system; (*b*) the coordinate planes.

4. Find the maximum distance from the origin to the folium of Descartes $x^3 + y^3 - 3axy = 0$.

5. Find the shortest distance from the origin to the plane

$$ax + by + cz = d.$$

51. Differentiation under the Integral Sign. Integrals whose integrands contain a parameter have already occurred in the first chapter. Thus, the length of arc of an ellipse is expressible as a definite integral containing the eccentricity of the ellipse as a parameter.*

Consider a definite integral

$$(51\text{-}1) \qquad \varphi(\alpha) = \int_{u_0}^{u_1} f(x, \alpha) \, dx,$$

in which the integrand contains a parameter α and where u_0 and u_1 are constants. As a specific illustration, let

$$\varphi(\alpha) = \int_0^{\frac{\pi}{2}} \sin \alpha x \, dx.$$

In this case the indefinite integral

$$F(x, \alpha) = \int \sin \alpha x \, dx = -\frac{\cos \alpha x}{\alpha} + C$$

is a function of both x and α; but, upon substitution of the limits, there appears a function of α alone, namely

$$\varphi(\alpha) = \int_0^{\frac{\pi}{2}} \sin \alpha x \, dx = -\frac{\cos \alpha x}{\alpha}\Big|_0^{\frac{\pi}{2}} = \frac{1}{\alpha}\left(1 - \cos \frac{\pi\alpha}{2}\right).$$

* See Sec. 14.

Frequently, it becomes necessary to calculate the derivative of the function $\varphi(\alpha)$ when the indefinite integral is complicated or even cannot be written down explicitly. Inasmuch as the parameter α is independent of x, it appears plausible that in some cases it may be permissible to perform the differentiation under the integral sign, so that one can use the formula

$$\frac{d\varphi}{d\alpha} = \int_{u_0}^{u_1} \frac{\partial f(x, \alpha)}{\partial \alpha} \, dx.$$

This formula turns out to be correct if $f(x, \alpha)$ and $\partial f(x, \alpha)/\partial \alpha$ are continuous functions in both x and α. Thus, forming the difference quotient with the aid of (51-1),

(51-2) $$\frac{\varphi(\alpha + \Delta\alpha) - \varphi(\alpha)}{\Delta\alpha} = \int_{u_0}^{u_1} \frac{f(x, \alpha + \Delta\alpha) - f(x, \alpha)}{\Delta\alpha} \, dx.$$

Now the limit, as $\Delta\alpha \to 0$, of the left-hand member of (51-2) is precisely $d\varphi/d\alpha$, whereas the limit of the expression under the integral sign is $\partial f/\partial \alpha$. Hence, if it is permissible to interchange the order of integration and calculation of the limit, one has

(51-3) $$\frac{d\varphi}{d\alpha} = \int_{u_0}^{u_1} \frac{\partial f(x, \alpha)}{\partial \alpha} \, dx.$$

The restrictions imposed on the function $f(x, \alpha)$ can be shown to be sufficient to justify the inversion of the order of these operations.

Suppose next that the limits of integration u_1 and u_0 are functions of the parameter α, so that

$$\varphi(\alpha) = \int_{u_0(\alpha)}^{u_1(\alpha)} f(x, \alpha) \, dx.$$

In this case, one can proceed as follows: Let

$$\int f(x, \alpha) \, dx = F(x, \alpha)$$

so that

(51-4) $$\frac{\partial F}{\partial x} = f(x, \alpha).$$

Then,

(51-5) $$\varphi(\alpha) = \int_{u_0(\alpha)}^{u_1(\alpha)} f(x, \alpha) \, dx = F(x, \alpha)\Big|_{x=u_0(\alpha)}^{x=u_1(\alpha)}$$
$$= F(u_1, \alpha) - F(u_0, \alpha).$$

Assuming the continuity of all the derivatives involved, one can write*

$$\frac{d\varphi}{d\alpha} = \frac{\partial F(u_1, \alpha)}{\partial u_1} \frac{du_1}{d\alpha} + \frac{\partial F(u_1, \alpha)}{\partial \alpha} - \frac{\partial F(u_0, \alpha)}{\partial u_0} \frac{du_0}{d\alpha} - \frac{\partial F(u_0, \alpha)}{\partial \alpha},$$

which, upon making use of (51-4) and (51-5), becomes

$$\frac{d\varphi}{d\alpha} = f(u_1, \alpha) \frac{du_1}{d\alpha} - f(u_0, \alpha) \frac{du_0}{d\alpha} + \frac{\partial}{\partial \alpha} [F(u_1, \alpha) - F(u_0, \alpha)]$$

$$= f(u_1, \alpha) \frac{du_1}{d\alpha} - f(u_0, \alpha) \frac{du_0}{d\alpha} + \frac{\partial}{\partial \alpha} \int_{u_0(\alpha)}^{u_1(\alpha)} f(x, \alpha) \, dx.$$

The partial derivative appearing in this expression means that the differentiation is to be performed with respect to α, treating u_0 and u_1 as constants. Hence, making use of (51-3),

(51-6) $$\frac{d\varphi}{d\alpha} = f(u_1, \alpha) \frac{du_1}{d\alpha} - f(u_0, \alpha) \frac{du_0}{d\alpha} + \int_{u_0(\alpha)}^{u_1(\alpha)} \frac{\partial f(x, \alpha)}{\partial \alpha} \, dx.$$

This formula is known as the formula of Leibnitz, and it specializes to (51-3) when u_1 and u_0 are independent of α. The validity of this formula can be established under somewhat less restrictive hypotheses,† but the limitations imposed on the function $f(x, \alpha)$ in the foregoing discussion are usually met in problems arising in applied mathematics.

Example 1.   Find $\frac{d\varphi}{d\alpha}$, if $\varphi(\alpha) = \int_{-\alpha^2}^{2\alpha} e^{-\frac{x^2}{\alpha^2}} \, dx$.

Then

$$\frac{d\varphi}{d\alpha} = \int_{-\alpha^2}^{2\alpha} \frac{2x^2}{\alpha^3} e^{-\frac{x^2}{\alpha^2}} \, dx - e^{-\alpha^2}(-2\alpha) + e^{-4}(2)$$

$$= \int_{-\alpha^2}^{2\alpha} \frac{2x^2}{\alpha^3} e^{-\frac{x^2}{\alpha^2}} \, dx + 2\alpha e^{-\alpha^2} + 2e^{-4}.$$

Example 2.   Formula (51-3) is frequently used for evaluating definite integrals. Thus, if

$$\varphi(\alpha) = \int_0^\pi \log (1 + \alpha \cos x) \, dx,$$

---

* See Sec. 39.

† See SOKOLNIKOFF, I. S., *Advanced Calculus*, Sec. 39, p. 121.

then

$$\varphi'(\alpha) = \int_0^\pi \frac{\cos x}{1 + \alpha \cos x}\, dx = \frac{1}{\alpha}\int_0^\pi \left(1 - \frac{1}{1 + \alpha \cos x}\right) dx$$

$$= \frac{1}{\alpha}\left(x + \frac{1}{\sqrt{1 - \alpha^2}}\, \sin^{-1}\frac{\alpha + \cos x}{1 + \alpha \cos x}\right)\Bigg|_0^\pi$$

$$= \frac{1}{\alpha}\left[\pi + \frac{1}{\sqrt{1 - \alpha^2}}\left(\sin^{-1}\frac{\alpha - 1}{1 - \alpha} - \sin^{-1}\frac{\alpha + 1}{1 + \alpha}\right)\right]$$

$$= \frac{1}{\alpha}\left(\pi + \frac{-\pi}{\sqrt{1 - \alpha^2}}\right) = \frac{\pi}{\alpha} - \frac{\pi}{\alpha\sqrt{1 - \alpha^2}}.$$

Therefore,

$$\varphi(\alpha) = \pi \int \left(\frac{1}{\alpha} - \frac{1}{\alpha\sqrt{1 - \alpha^2}}\right) d\alpha$$

$$= \pi \left(\log \alpha + \log\frac{1 + \sqrt{1 - \alpha^2}}{\alpha}\right) + c$$

or

$$\varphi(\alpha) = \pi \log (1 + \sqrt{1 - \alpha^2}) + c.$$

But, when $\alpha = 0$,

$$\varphi(0) = \int_0^\pi \log 1 \, dx = 0.$$

Hence,

$$0 = \pi \log 2 + c \qquad \text{and} \qquad c = -\pi \log 2,$$

and

$$\varphi(\alpha) = \pi \log \left(\frac{1 + \sqrt{1 - \alpha^2}}{2}\right).$$

PROBLEMS

1. Find $d\varphi/d\alpha$ if $\varphi(\alpha) = \int_0^{\pi/2} \sin \alpha x \, dx$ by using the Leibnitz formula, and check your result by direct calculation.

2. Find $d\varphi/d\alpha$, if $\varphi(\alpha) = \int_0^\pi (1 - \alpha \cos x)^2 \, dx$.

3. Find $d\varphi/d\alpha$, if $\varphi(\alpha) = \int_0^{\alpha^2} \tan^{-1}\frac{x}{\alpha^2} \, dx$.

4. Find $d\varphi/d\alpha$, if $\varphi(\alpha) = \int_0^\alpha \tan (x - \alpha) \, dx$.

5. Find $d\varphi/dx$, if $\varphi(x) = \int_0^{x^2} \sqrt{x} \, dx$.

6. Differentiate under the sign and thus evaluate $\displaystyle\int_0^\pi \frac{dx}{(\alpha - \cos x)^2}$ by using $\displaystyle\int_0^\pi \frac{dx}{\alpha - \cos x} = \frac{\pi}{(\alpha^2 - 1)^{1/2}}$, if $\alpha^2 > 1$.

7. Show that

$$\int_0^\pi \log (1 - 2\alpha \cos x + \alpha^2) \, dx = 0, \qquad \text{if } \alpha^2 \leq 1$$

$$= \pi \log \alpha^2, \quad \text{if } \alpha^2 \geq 1.$$

8. Verify that

$$y = \frac{1}{k} \int_0^x f(\alpha) \sin k(x - \alpha)\, d\alpha$$

is a solution of the differential equation

$$\frac{d^2y}{dx^2} + k^2y = f(x),$$

where k is a constant.

CHAPTER V

MULTIPLE INTEGRALS

It is assumed that the reader is somewhat familiar with the problem of calculating the volumes of solids with the aid of double and triple integrals and has some facility in setting up such integrals. The first three sections of this chapter contain a brief summary of some basic facts concerning double and triple integrals, preparatory to the development of the expressions for the volume elements in spherical and cylindrical coordinates. These expressions are used frequently in applied mathematics and are seldom included in the first course in calculus. A brief discussion of surface integrals is also given here.

First, it may be well to recall the definition of the simple integral $\int_a^b f(x)\,dx$. Let the function $f(x)$ be continuous and single valued for $a \leq x \leq b$. The interval (a, b) of the x-axis is divided into n parts by the points $a \equiv x_0, x_1, x_2, \cdots,$ $x_n \equiv b$. Let $\Delta x_i = x_i - x_{i-1}$, and let ξ_i be a value of x such that $x_{i-1} < \xi_i \leq x_i$. Form the sum $\sum_{i=1}^{n} f(\xi_i)\,\Delta x_i$, and take the limit of this sum as $n \to \infty$ and all the $\Delta x_i \to 0$. Under the given assumptions on $f(x)$, this limit will exist, and it is defined as the definite integral of $f(x)$ over the interval (a, b) of the x-axis. Thus,

$$\lim_{n \to \infty} \sum_{i=1}^{n} f(\xi_i)\,\Delta x_i \equiv \int_a^b f(x)\,dx.$$

Geometrically, this integral can be interpreted as the area between the curve $y = f(x)$ and the x-axis included between the lines $x = a$ and $x = b$. The evaluation of the integral can often be accomplished by the use of the following theorem.

FUNDAMENTAL THEOREM OF INTEGRAL CALCULUS. *If $f(x)$ is continuous in the interval $a \leq x \leq b$ and $G(x)$ is a function such that $dG/dx = f(x)$ for all values of x in this interval, then*

$$\int_a^b f(x)\,dx = G(b) - G(a).$$

52. Definition and Evaluation of the Double Integral. The double integral is defined and geometrically interpreted in a manner entirely analogous to that sketched above for the simple integral. Let $f(x, y)$ be a continuous and single-valued function within a region R (Fig. 38), bounded by a closed curve C, and upon the boundary C. Let the region R be subdivided in any manner into n sub-regions $\Delta R_1, \Delta R_2, \cdots, \Delta R_n$ of areas $\Delta A_1, \Delta A_2, \cdots, \Delta A_n$. Let (ξ_i, η_i) be any point in the subregion ΔR_i, and form the sum

$$\sum_{i=1}^{n} f(\xi_i, \eta_i)\, \Delta A_i.$$

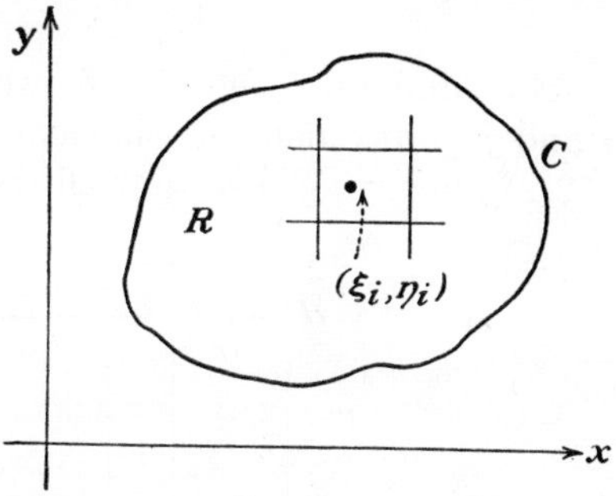

FIG. 38.

The limit of this sum, as $n \to \infty$ and all $\Delta A_i \to 0$, is defined as the double integral of $f(x, y)$ over the region R. Thus,

$$(52\text{-}1) \qquad \lim_{n \to \infty} \sum_{i=1}^{n} f(\xi_i, \eta_i)\, \Delta A_i \equiv \int_R f(x, y)\, dA.$$

The region R is called the region of integration, corresponding to the interval of integration (a, b) in the case of the simple integral. The integral (52-1) is sometimes written as

$$\iint_R f(x, y)\, dx\, dy.$$

In order to evaluate the double integral, it will be simpler to consider first the case in which the region R (Fig. 39) is a rectangle bounded by the lines $x = a$, $x = b$, $y = c$, $y = d$. The extension to other types of regions will be indicated later. Subdivide R into mn rectangles by drawing the lines $x = x_1$, $x = x_2, \cdots, \ x = x_{n-1}$, $y = y_1$, $y = y_2, \cdots, \ y = y_{m-1}$. Define $\Delta x_i \equiv x_i - x_{i-1}$, where $x_0 = a$ and $x_n = b$, and define $\Delta y_j \equiv y_j - y_{j-1}$, where $y_0 = c$ and $y_m = d$. Let ΔR_{ij} be the rectangle bounded by the lines $x = x_{i-1}$, $x = x_i$, $y = y_{j-1}$, $y = y_j$. Then, if the area of ΔR_{ij} is denoted by ΔA_{ij},

$$\Delta A_{ij} = \Delta x_i\, \Delta y_j.$$

Let (ξ_{ij}, η_{ij}) be any point of ΔR_{ij}. The sum $\displaystyle\sum_{i=1,\,j=1}^{i=n,\,j=m} f(\xi_{ij}, \eta_{ij})\,\Delta A_{ij}$ can be written as

(52-2) $$\sum_{i=1,\,j=1}^{i=n,\,j=m} f(\xi_{ij}, \eta_{ij})\,\Delta x_i\,\Delta y_j.$$

This summation sign signifies that the terms can be summed for i and j in any manner whatsoever. Suppose that the terms of (52-2) are arranged so that all the rectangles ΔR_{i1} are used first,

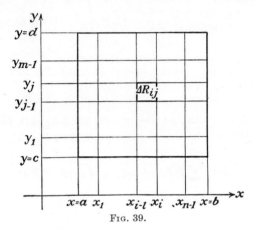

Fig. 39.

then all the rectangles ΔR_{i2}, then all the rectangles ΔR_{i3}, etc. This is equivalent to taking the sum of the terms for each row of rectangles and then adding these sums. Then (52-2) can be written

(52-3) $$\sum_{j=1}^{m} \Delta y_j \left[\sum_{i=1}^{n} f(\xi_{ij}, \eta_{ij})\,\Delta x_i \right].$$

But

$$\lim_{n\to\infty} \sum_{i=1}^{n} f(\xi_{ij}, \eta_{ij})\,\Delta x_i = \int_a^b f(x, \eta_j)\,dx,$$

so that

$$\sum_{i=1}^{n} f(\xi_{ij}, \eta_{ij})\,\Delta x_i = \int_a^b f(x, \eta_j)\,dx + \epsilon_j,$$

where $\displaystyle\lim_{n\to\infty} \epsilon_j = 0$. Moreover, $\displaystyle\int_a^b f(x, \eta_j)\,dx$ is a function of η_j, say $\varphi(\eta_j)$. Thus (52-3) becomes

$$\sum_{j=1}^{m} [\varphi(\eta_j) + \epsilon_j] \, \Delta y_j = \int_c^d [\varphi(y) + \epsilon] \, dy + \epsilon'$$

$$= \int_c^d \varphi(y) \, dy + \epsilon(d - c) + \epsilon'$$

$$= \int_c^d \int_a^b f(x, y) \, dx \, dy + \epsilon(d - c) + \epsilon',$$

in which $\lim\limits_{n \to \infty} \epsilon = 0$ and $\lim\limits_{m \to \infty} \epsilon' = 0$.   Taking the limit as $n \to \infty$ and $m \to \infty$ gives

$$(52\text{-}4) \qquad \int_R f(x, y) \, dA = \int_c^d \int_a^b f(x, y) \, dx \, dy.$$

The double integral is, therefore, evaluated by considering $f(x, y)$ as a function of x alone, but containing y as a parameter, and integrating it between $x = a$ and $x = b$ and then integrating the resulting function of y between $y = c$ and $y = d$.   The right member of (52-4) is known as an iterated integral, and (52-4) establishes the relation between the double integral over the rectangle R and an iterated integral over the same rectangle.

Similarly, by taking the sum of the terms in each column and then adding these sums,

$$(52\text{-}5) \qquad \int_R f(x, y) \, dA = \int_a^b \int_c^d f(x, y) \, dy \, dx.$$

In case (52-5) is used, $f(x, y)$ is first considered as a function of y alone and integrated between $y = c$ and $y = d$, and then the resulting function of x is integrated between $x = a$ and $x = b$.   Either (52-4) or (52-5) can be used, but one of them is frequently simpler in the case of a particular function $f(x, y)$.

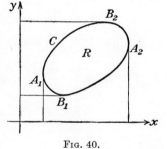

Fig. 40.

Suppose R is, not a rectangle, but a region bounded by a closed curve C (Fig. 40) that is cut by any line parallel to one of the axes in, at most, two points. Let B_1 and B_2 be the points of C having the minimum and maximum ordinates, and let A_1 and A_2 be the points of C having the minimum and maximum abscissas. Let $x = \varphi_1(y)$ be the equation of $B_1A_1B_2$, and $x = \varphi_2(y)$ be the equation of $B_1A_2B_2$. Then, in taking the sum of the terms by rows and adding these sums, the limits for the first integration will be $\varphi_1(y)$ and $\varphi_2(y)$, instead of the constants a and b. The limits for the second integration will be β_1 and β_2, in which β_1 is the y-coordinate of B_1 and β_2 is the y-coordinate of B_2. Then (52-4) is replaced by

$$(52\text{-}6) \qquad \int_R f(x, y) \, dA = \int_{\beta_1}^{\beta_2} \int_{\varphi_1(y)}^{\varphi_2(y)} f(x, y) \, dx \, dy.$$

Similarly, if $y = f_1(x)$ is the equation of $A_1B_1A_2$, $y = f_2(x)$ is the equation of $A_1B_2A_2$, α_1 is the abscissa of A_1, and α_2 is the abscissa of A_2, (52-5) is replaced by

$$(52\text{-}7) \qquad \int_R f(x, y) \, dA = \int_{\alpha_1}^{\alpha_2} \int_{f_1(x)}^{f_2(x)} f(x, y) \, dy \, dx.$$

In case R is a region bounded by a closed curve C that is cut

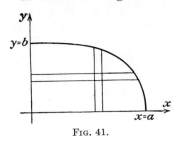

in more than two points by some parallel to one of the axes, the previous results can be applied to subregions of R whose boundaries satisfy the previous conditions. By adding algebraically the integrals over these subregions, the double integral over R is obtained.

Fig. 41.

Example 1. Compute the value of $I_1 = \int_R y \, dA$ where R is the region in the first quadrant bounded by the ellipse

$$\frac{x^2}{a^2} + \frac{y^2}{b^2} = 1 \qquad \text{(Fig. 41).}$$

Upon using (52-6) and summing first by rows,

$$I_1 = \int_0^b \int_0^{\frac{a}{b}\sqrt{b^2 - y^2}} y \, dx \, dy = \int_0^b \left(xy \Big|_0^{\frac{a}{b}\sqrt{b^2 - y^2}} \right) dy$$

$$= \frac{a}{b} \int_0^b y \sqrt{b^2 - y^2} \, dy = -\frac{a}{3b} (b^2 - y^2)^{3/2} \Big|_0^b$$

$$= \frac{ab^2}{3}.$$

Using (52-7), one has

$$I_1 = \int_0^a \int_0^{\frac{b}{a}\sqrt{a^2 - x^2}} y \, dy \, dx = \int_0^a \left(\frac{y^2}{2} \Big|_0^{\frac{b}{a}\sqrt{a^2 - x^2}} \right) dx$$

$$= \frac{b^2}{2a^2} \int_0^a (a^2 - x^2) \, dx = \frac{b^2}{2a^2} \left(a^2 x - \frac{x^3}{3} \right) \Big|_0^a = \frac{ab^2}{3}.$$

It may be remarked that the value of I_1 is equal to $\bar{y}A$, in which $\bar{y}$ is the y-coordinate of the center of gravity of this quadrant of the ellipse and A is its area. Since $A = \pi ab/4$,

$$\bar{y} = \frac{I_1}{A} = \frac{ab^2/3}{\pi ab/4} = \frac{4b}{3\pi}.$$

Similarly, by evaluating $I_2 = \int_R x \, dA = a^2b/3$,

$$\bar{x} = \frac{I_2}{A} = \frac{a^2b/3}{\pi ab/4} = \frac{4a}{3\pi},$$

which is the x-coordinate of the center of gravity.

Example 2. Moment of Inertia. It will be recalled that the moment of inertia of a particle about an axis is the product of its mass by the square of its distance from the axis. If it is desired to find the moment of inertia of a plane region about an axis perpendicular to the plane of the region, the method of Sec. 52 can be applied, where $f(x, y)$ is the square of the distance from the point (x, y) of the region to the axis.   Then

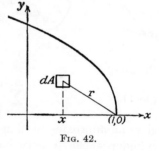

$$M = \int_R r^2 \, dA.$$

For example, let it be required to find the moment of inertia of the area in the first quadrant (Fig. 42), bounded by the parabola $y^2 = 1 - x$ and the coordinate axes, about an axis perpendicular to the xy-plane at $(1, 0)$.   The distance from any point $P(x, y)$ to $(1, 0)$ is $r = \sqrt{(x - 1)^2 + y^2}$. Therefore,

Fig. 42.

$$M = \int_R [(x - 1)^2 + y^2] \, dA.$$

Evaluating this integral by means of (52-6) gives

$$M = \int_0^1 \int_0^{1-y^2} [(x - 1)^2 + y^2] \, dx \, dy = \int_0^1 \left[\frac{(x - 1)^3}{3} + xy^2 \right]_0^{1-y^2} dy$$

$$= \int_0^1 \left(-\frac{y^6}{3} + y^2 - y^4 + \frac{1}{3} \right) dy = \frac{44}{105}.$$

53. Geometric Interpretation of the Double Integral. If $f(x, y)$ is a continuous and single-valued function defined over the region R (Fig. 43) of the xy-plane, then $z = f(x, y)$ is the equation of a surface.   Let C be the closed curve that is the boundary of R.   Using R as a base, construct a cylinder having its elements parallel to the z-axis. This cylinder intersects $z = f(x, y)$ in a curve Γ, whose projection on the xy-plane is C. Denote by S the portion of $z = f(x, y)$ that is enclosed by Γ. Let R be subdivided as in Sec. 52 by the lines $x = x_i$, $(i = 1, 2, \cdots, n - 1)$, and $y = y_j$, $(j = 1, 2, \cdots, m - 1)$.

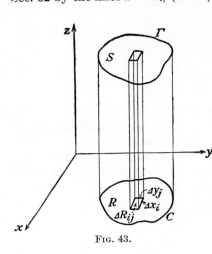

Through each line $x = x_i$ pass a plane parallel to the yz-plane; and through each line $y = y_j$ pass a plane parallel to the xz-plane. The rectangle ΔR_{ij}, whose area is $\Delta A_{ij} = \Delta x_i\, \Delta y_j$, will be the base of a rectangular prism of height $f(\xi_{ij},\ \eta_{ij})$, whose volume is approximately equal to the volume enclosed between the surface and the xy-plane by the planes $x = x_{i-1}$, $x = x_i$, $y = y_{j-1}$, and $y = y_j$. Then the sum

Fig. 43.

(53-1)
$$\sum_{i=1, j=1}^{i=n, j=m} f(\xi_{ij}, \eta_{ij})\, \Delta x_i\, \Delta y_j$$

gives an approximate value for the volume V of the portion of the cylinder enclosed between $z = f(x, y)$ and the xy-plane. As $n \to \infty$ and $m \to \infty$, the sum (53-1) approaches V, so that

(53-2)
$$V = \int_R f(x, y)\, dA.$$

The integral in (53-2) can be evaluated by (52-6) in which the prisms are added first in the x-direction or by (52-7) in which the prisms are added first in the y-direction.

It should be noted that formulas (52-6) and (52-7) give the value of the area of the region R if the function $f(x, y) = 1$; for the left member becomes

$$\int_R dA = \int \int_R dx\, dy,$$

which is A. A can be evaluated by

$$\int_{\beta_1}^{\beta_2} \int_{\varphi_1(y)}^{\varphi_2(y)} dx\, dy \qquad \text{or} \qquad \int_{\alpha_1}^{\alpha_2} \int_{f_1(x)}^{f_2(x)} dy\, dx.$$

Example. Find the volume of the tetrahedron bounded by the plane $\dfrac{x}{a} + \dfrac{y}{b} + \dfrac{z}{c} = 1$ and the coordinate planes (Fig. 44). Here,

$$z = c\left(1 - \frac{x}{a} - \frac{y}{b}\right).$$

If the prisms are summed first in the x-direction, they will be summed from $x = 0$ to the line ab, whose equation is

$$\frac{x}{a} + \frac{y}{b} = 1.$$

Therefore,

$$
\begin{aligned}
V &= \int_0^b \int_0^{a\left(1-\frac{y}{b}\right)} c\left(1 - \frac{x}{a} - \frac{y}{b}\right) dx\, dy \\
&= c \int_0^b \left(x - \frac{x^2}{2a} - \frac{xy}{b}\right)\Big|_0^{a\left(1-\frac{y}{b}\right)} dy \\
&= ac \int_0^b \left(\frac{1}{2} - \frac{y}{b} + \frac{y^2}{2b^2}\right) dy \\
&= \frac{abc}{6}.
\end{aligned}
$$

This result was obtained by using (52-6) for the evaluation of V, but (52-7) could be used equally well.

54. Triple Integrals. The triple integral is defined in a manner entirely analogous to the definition of the double integral. The function

$$f(x, y, z)$$

is to be continuous and single valued over the region of space R enclosed by the surface S. Let R be subdivided into subregions ΔR_{ijk}. If ΔV_{ijk} is the volume of ΔR_{ijk}, the triple integral of $f(x, y, z)$ over R is defined by

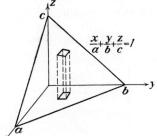

Fig. 44.

$$(54\text{-}1) \quad \int_R f(x, y, z)\, dV \equiv \lim_{n,m,p\to\infty} \sum_{i=1,j=1,k=1}^{i=n,j=m,k=p} f(\xi_{ijk}, \eta_{ijk}, \zeta_{ijk})\, \Delta V_{ijk}$$

by exactly the same argument as that used in Sec. 52.

In order to evaluate the triple integral, R is considered to be subdivided by planes parallel to the three coordinate planes, the case of the rectangular parallelepiped being treated first.   In this case,

$$\Delta V_{ijk} = \Delta x_i \, \Delta y_j \, \Delta z_k.$$

By suitably arranging the terms of the sum

$$\sum_{i=1, j=1, k=1}^{i=n, j=m, k=p} f(\xi_{ijk}, \eta_{ijk}, \zeta_{ijk}) \, \Delta x_i \, \Delta y_j \, \Delta z_k,$$

it can be shown, as in Sec. 52, that

$$(54\text{-}2) \quad \int_R f(x, y, z) \, dV = \int_{z_0}^{z_1} \int_{y_0}^{y_1} \int_{x_0}^{x_1} f(x, y, z) \, dx \, dy \, dz.$$

By other arrangements of the terms of the sum, the triple integral can be expressed by means of iterated integrals in which the order of integration is any permutation of that given in (54-2).

If R is not a rectangular parallelepiped, the triple integral over R will be evaluated by iterated integrals in which the limits for the first two integrations will be functions instead of constants.   By extending the method of Sec. 53, it can be shown that

$$(54\text{-}3) \quad \int_R f(x, y, z) \, dV = \int_{z_1}^{z_2} \int_{f_1(z)}^{f_2(z)} \int_{\varphi_1(y,z)}^{\varphi_2(y,z)} f(x, y, z) \, dx \, dy \, dz.$$

Similarly, the triple integral can be evaluated by interchanging the order of integration in the iterated integral and suitably choosing the limits.

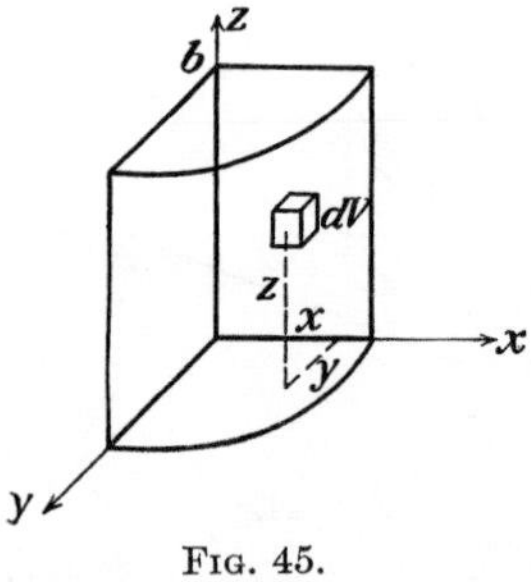

The expression (54-3), or the similar expressions obtained by a different choice of the order of integration, gives the formula for the volume of R in case $f(x, y, z) \equiv 1$.   Therefore,

$$V = \int_{z_1}^{z_2} \int_{f_1(z)}^{f_2(z)} \int_{\varphi_1(y,z)}^{\varphi_2(y,z)} dx \, dy \, dz.$$

Fig. 45.   Also, the formula (54-3) may be considered as giving the total mass of the volume V that has variable density $f(x, y, z)$.

Example.   Let it be required to find the moment of inertia I_x of the solid bounded by the cylinder $x^2 + y^2 = a^2$ and the planes $z = 0$ and $z = b$ about the x-axis (Fig. 45).   Assume uniform density σ.   The function $f(x, y, z)$ is the square of the distance of any point $P(x, y, z)$ from the x-axis.   Therefore,

$$f(x, y, z) = y^2 + z^2.$$

Hence,

$$
\begin{aligned}
I_x &= \int_R (y^2 + z^2)\sigma \, dV \\
&= 4\sigma \int_0^a \int_0^{\sqrt{a^2-x^2}} \int_0^b (y^2 + z^2) \, dz \, dy \, dx \\
&= 4\sigma \int_0^a \int_0^{\sqrt{a^2-x^2}} \left(by^2 + \frac{b^3}{3} \right) dy \, dx = 4\sigma \int_0^a \left(\frac{by^3}{3} + \frac{b^3 y}{3} \right)\Big|_0^{\sqrt{a^2-x^2}} dx \\
&= \frac{4\sigma b}{3} \int_0^a (a^2 + b^2 - x^2) \sqrt{a^2 - x^2} \, dx \\
&= \frac{4\sigma a^2 b}{3} \int_0^{\frac{\pi}{2}} (a^2 + b^2 - a^2 \sin^2 \theta) \cos^2 \theta \, d\theta \\
&= \frac{4\sigma a^2 b}{3} \left[(a^2 + b^2) \frac{\pi}{4} - \frac{a^2 \pi}{16} \right] = \frac{\sigma a^2 b \pi}{12} (3a^2 + 4b^2).
\end{aligned}
$$

PROBLEMS

1. Evaluate

(a) $\int_0^1 \int_x^{\sqrt{x}} (x^2 + y^2) \, dy \, dx$;

(b) $\int_{-1}^2 \int_{x^2}^{x+2} dy \, dx$;

(c) $\int_0^\pi \int_0^{a(1 - \cos \theta)} \rho \, d\rho \, d\theta$,

and describe the regions of integration in (a) and (b).

2. Verify that $\int_R (x^2 + y^2) \, dy \, dx = \int_R (x^2 + y^2) \, dx \, dy$, where the region R is a triangle formed by the lines $y = 0$, $y = x$, and $x = 1$.

3. Evaluate and describe the regions of integration for

(a) $\int_0^a \int_{a-x}^{\sqrt{a^2-x^2}} y \, dy \, dx$;

(b) $\int_0^a \int_{-\sqrt{a^2-x^2}}^{\sqrt{a^2-x^2}} dy \, dx$;

(c) $\int_0^1 \int_x^{\sqrt{x}} (1 + x^2 + y^2) \, dy \, dx$;

(d) $\int_{-1}^2 \int_x^{x+2} dy \, dx$;

(e) $\int_1^2 \int_2^5 xy \, dx \, dy$.

4. Find the areas enclosed by the following pairs of curves:

(a) $y = x$, $y = x^2$;

(b) $y = 2 - x$, $y^2 = 2(2 - x)$;

(c) $y = 4 - x^2$, $y = 4 - 2x$;

(d) $y^2 = 5 - x$, $y = x + 1$;

(e) $y = \sqrt{a^2 - x^2}$, $y = a - x$.

5. Find by double integration the volume of one of the wedges cut off from the cylinder $x^2 + y^2 = a^2$ by the planes $z = 0$ and $z = x$.

6. Find the volume of the solid bounded by the paraboloid $y^2 + z^2 = 4x$ and the plane $x = 5$.

7. Find the volume of the solid bounded by the plane $z = 0$, the surface $z = x^2 + y^2 + 2$, and the cylinder $x^2 + y^2 = 4$.

8. Find the smaller of the areas bounded by $y = 2 - x$ and $x^2 + y^2 = 4$.

9. Find the volume bounded by the cylinders $y = x^2$, $y^2 = x$ and the planes $z = 0$ and $z = 1$.

10. Find the volume of the solid bounded by the cylinders $x^2 + y^2 = a^2$ and $y^2 + z^2 = a^2$.

11. Find the coordinates of the center of gravity of the area enclosed by $y = 4 - x^2$ and $y = 4 - 2x$.

12. Find the moments of inertia about the x- and y- axes of the smaller of the areas enclosed by $y = a - x$ and $x^2 + y^2 = a^2$.

13. Evaluate the following:

(a) $\int_0^2 \int_1^3 \int_1^2 xy^2z \, dz \, dy \, dx$;

(b) $\int_0^a \int_0^{\sqrt{a^2-y^2}} \int_0^{\sqrt{a^2-x^2}} dz \, dx \, dy$;

(c) $\int_0^2 \int_0^{\sqrt{2x-x^2}} \int_0^{\frac{x^2+y^2}{4}} dz \, dy \, dx$.

14. Find by triple integration

(a) The volume in the first octant bounded by the coordinate planes and the plane $x + 2y + 3z = 4$.

(b) The volume of one of the wedges cut off from the cylinder $x^2 + y^2 = a^2$ by the planes $z = 0$ and $z = x$.

(c) The volume enclosed by the cylinder $x^2 + y^2 = 1$ and the planes $z = 0$ and $z = 2 - x$.

(d) The volume enclosed by the cylinders $y^2 = z$ and $x^2 + y^2 = a^2$ and by the plane $z = 0$.

(e) The volume enclosed by the cylinders $y^2 + z^2 = a^2$ and $x^2 + y^2 = a^2$.

(f) The volume enclosed by $y^2 + 2z^2 = 4x - 8$, $y^2 + z^2 = 4$, and $x = 0$.

(g) The volume in the first octant bounded by the coordinate planes and $x + 3y + 2z = 6$.

(h) The volume enclosed by the cylinder $x^2 + y^2 = 9$ and the planes $z = 5 - x$ and $z = 0$.

(i) The volume of the cap cut off from $y^2 + z^2 = 4x$ by the plane $z = x$.

15. Find the moments of inertia about the coordinate axes of the solids in Prob. 14

16. Find the coordinates of the center of gravity of each of the volumes in Prob. 14.

17. Find by triple integration the moment of inertia of the volume of a hemisphere about a diameter.

18. Find the coordinates of the center of gravity of the volume of the solid in Prob. 17.

19. Find by triple integration the moment of inertia of the volume of the cone $y^2 + z^2 = a^2x^2$ about its axis.

20. Find the moment of inertia of the cone in Prob. 19 about a diameter of its base.

21. Find the volume in the first octant bounded by $z = x + 1$, $x = 0$, $y = 0$, $x = 2z$, and $x^2 + y^2 = 4$.

22. Find the coordinates of the center of gravity of the volume bounded by $z = 2(2 - x - y)$, $z = 0$, and $z = 4 - x^2 - y^2$.

55. Jacobians. Change of Variable. If it is desired to make a change of variable in a double or triple integral, the method is not so simple as in the case of the simple integral. It is probably already familiar to the reader that the element of area dA, which is equal to $dx\,dy$ in rectangular coordinates, is not equal to $d\rho\,d\theta$ in polar coordinates. In order to obtain a general method for transforming the element of area or the element of volume from one set of coordinates to another, it is necessary to introduce the definition of the Jacobian, or functional determinant.

Let $u = u(x, y)$ and $v = v(x, y)$ be two continuous functions of the independent variables x and y, such that $\partial u/\partial x$, $\partial u/\partial y$, $\partial v/\partial x$, and $\partial v/\partial y$ are also continuous in x and y. Then

$$(55\text{-}1) \qquad \frac{\partial u}{\partial x}\frac{\partial v}{\partial y} - \frac{\partial u}{\partial y}\frac{\partial v}{\partial x} \equiv \begin{vmatrix} \dfrac{\partial u}{\partial x} & \dfrac{\partial v}{\partial x} \\[2mm] \dfrac{\partial u}{\partial y} & \dfrac{\partial v}{\partial y} \end{vmatrix}$$

is called the Jacobian, or functional determinant, of u, v with respect to x, y. It is usually denoted by

$$J\left(\frac{u, v}{x, y}\right) \qquad \text{or} \qquad \frac{\partial(u, v)}{\partial(x, y)}.$$

In the case of three variables, let $u = u(x, y, z)$, $v = v(x, y, z)$, and $w = w(x, y, z)$ be continuous together with their first partial derivatives. The Jacobian, or functional determinant, of u, v, w

with respect to x, y, z is defined by

(55-2)
$$\begin{vmatrix} \dfrac{\partial u}{\partial x} & \dfrac{\partial v}{\partial x} & \dfrac{\partial w}{\partial x} \\[2mm] \dfrac{\partial u}{\partial y} & \dfrac{\partial v}{\partial y} & \dfrac{\partial w}{\partial y} \\[2mm] \dfrac{\partial u}{\partial z} & \dfrac{\partial v}{\partial z} & \dfrac{\partial w}{\partial z} \end{vmatrix}.$$

The usual symbols for it are

$$J\left(\frac{u,\, v,\, w}{x,\, y,\, z}\right) \quad \text{or} \quad \frac{\partial(u,\, v,\, w)}{\partial(x,\, y,\, z)}.$$

The Jacobian of any number of functions u_1, u_2, $\cdots$, u_n, with respect to the variables x_1, x_2, $\cdots$, x_n, is defined by an obvious extension of (55-1) and (55-2).   It is denoted by

$$J\left(\frac{u_1,\, u_2,\, \cdots,\, u_n}{x_1,\, x_2,\, \cdots,\, x_n}\right) \quad \text{or} \quad \frac{\partial(u_1,\, u_2,\, \cdots,\, u_n)}{\partial(x_1,\, x_2,\, \cdots,\, x_n)}.$$

The Jacobian is of great importance in mathematics.*   It is used here in connection with the change of variable in multiple integrals.   If it is desired to change the variable in $\int_R f(x, y)\, dA$ by making $x = x(u, v)$ and $y = y(u, v)$. the expression† for dA in terms of u and v is given by

(55-3)
$$dA = \left| J\left(\frac{x,\, y}{u,\, v}\right) \right| du\, dv.$$

Thus, in transforming to polar coordinates by means of $x = \rho \cos \theta$, $y = \rho \sin \theta$,

$$J\left(\frac{x,\, y}{\rho,\, \theta}\right) = \begin{vmatrix} \cos \theta & \sin \theta \\ -\rho \sin \theta & \rho \cos \theta \end{vmatrix} = \rho \cos^2 \theta + \rho \sin^2 \theta = \rho.$$

Therefore,

$$dA = \rho\, d\rho\, d\theta,$$

a result that is already familiar from elementary calculus.

---

* Note that the Jacobian appeared in Sec. 41 in connection with the differentiation of implicit functions.

† See SOKOLNIKOFF, I. S., Advanced Calculus, Sec. 46.

It follows from (55-3) that

(55-4) $\displaystyle\int_R f(x, y)\, dA = \int \int_R f[x(u, v), y(u, v)]\left|J\left(\frac{x, y}{u, v}\right)\right| du\, dv.$

The right-hand member of (55-4) can be written as

$$\int \int_R F(u, v)\, du\, dv,$$

where

$$F(u, v) \equiv f[x(u, v), y(u, v)] \cdot \left|J\left(\frac{x, y}{u, v}\right)\right|.$$

If it is desired to evaluate this double integral by means of an iterated integral, the limits for u and v must be determined from a consideration of the region R.

Similarly, if $x = x(u, v, w)$, $y = y(u, v, w)$, and $z = z(u, v, w)$, then

(55-5) $\displaystyle dV = \left|J\left(\frac{x, y, z}{u, v, w}\right)\right| du\, dv\, dw$

and

(55-6) $\displaystyle\int_R f(x, y, z)\, dV$

$$= \int \int \int_R f[x(u, v, w), y(u, v, w), z(u, v, w)]\left|J\left(\frac{x, y, z}{u, v, w}\right)\right| du\, dv\, dw.$$

56. Spherical and Cylindrical Coordinates.   Corresponding to the system of polar coordinates in the plane, there are two systems of space coordinates that are frequently used in practical problems.   The first of these is the system of spherical, or polar, coordinates.   Let $P(x, y, z)$ (Fig. 46) be any point whose projection on the xy-plane is $Q(x, y)$.   Then the spherical coordinates of P are ρ, φ, θ, in which ρ is the distance OP, φ is the angle between OQ and the positive x-axis, and θ is the angle between OP and the positive z-axis.   Then, from Fig. 46, it is seen that

$x = OQ \cos \varphi = OP \cos (90° - \theta) \cos \varphi = \rho \sin \theta \cos \varphi,$
$y = OQ \sin \varphi = \rho \sin \theta \sin \varphi,$
$z = \rho \cos \theta.$

The element of volume in spherical coordinates can be obtained by means of (55-5).   Since

$$J\left(\frac{x, y, z}{\rho, \varphi, \theta}\right) = \begin{vmatrix} \sin\theta\cos\varphi & \sin\theta\sin\varphi & \cos\theta \\ -\rho\sin\theta\sin\varphi & \rho\sin\theta\cos\varphi & 0 \\ \rho\cos\theta\cos\varphi & \rho\cos\theta\sin\varphi & -\rho\sin\theta \end{vmatrix}$$

$$= -\rho^2 \sin\theta,$$

it follows that

(56-1) $$dV = \rho^2 \sin\theta \, d\rho \, d\varphi \, d\theta.$$

This element of volume is the volume of the solid bounded by the

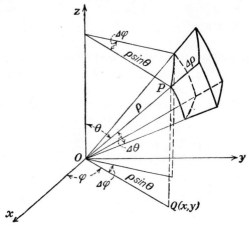

Fig. 46.

two concentric spheres of radii ρ and $\rho + d\rho$, the two planes

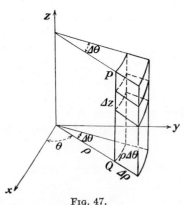

Fig. 47.

through the z-axis that make angles of φ and $\varphi + d\varphi$ with the xz-plane, and the two cones of revolution whose common axis is the z-axis and whose vertical angles are 2θ and $2(\theta + d\theta)$.

The second space system corresponding to polar coordinates in the plane is the system of cylindrical coordinates. Any point $P(x, y, z)$, whose projection on the xy-plane is Q (Fig. 47), has the cylindrical coordinates ρ, θ, z,

where θ is the angle between OQ and the positive x-axis, ρ is the distance OQ, and z is the distance QP. From Fig. 47, it is evident that $x = \rho \cos \theta$, $y = \rho \sin \theta$, and $z = z$.   Since

$$J\left(\frac{x, y, z}{\rho, \theta, z}\right) = \begin{vmatrix} \cos \theta & \sin \theta & 0 \\ -\rho \sin \theta & \rho \cos \theta & 0 \\ 0 & 0 & 1 \end{vmatrix} = \rho,$$

it follows that

(56-2) $dV = \rho \, d\rho \, d\theta \, dz.$

This element of volume is the volume of the solid bounded by the two cylinders whose radii are ρ and $\rho + d\rho$, the two planes through the z-axis that make angles θ and $\theta + d\theta$ with the xz-plane, and the two planes parallel to the xy-plane at distances z and $z + dz$.

Example 1.   Find the x-coordinate of the center of gravity of the solid of uniform density σ lying in the first octant and bounded by the three coordinate planes and the sphere $x^2 + y^2 + z^2 = a^2$.
   Since

$$\bar{x} = \frac{\sigma \int_R x \, dV}{\sigma \int_R dV} = \frac{\int_R x \, dV}{\pi a^3/6},$$

it is necessary to compute $\int_R x \, dV$.   This integral can be calculated by evaluating the iterated integral

$$\int_0^a \int_0^{\sqrt{a^2 - z^2}} \int_0^{\sqrt{a^2 - y^2 - z^2}} x \, dx \, dy \, dz,$$

but it is easier to transform to spherical coordinates.   Then,

$$\int_R x \, dV = \int_0^{\frac{\pi}{2}} \int_0^{\frac{\pi}{2}} \int_0^a \rho \sin \theta \cos \varphi \cdot \rho^2 \sin \theta \, d\rho \, d\theta \, d\varphi$$

$$= \int_0^{\frac{\pi}{2}} \int_0^{\frac{\pi}{2}} \frac{\rho^4}{4}\bigg|_0^a \sin^2 \theta \cos \varphi \, d\theta \, d\varphi$$

$$= \frac{a^4\pi}{16} \int_0^{\frac{\pi}{2}} \cos \varphi \, d\varphi = \frac{a^4\pi}{16}.$$

Therefore,

$$\bar{x} = \frac{a^4\pi/16}{\pi a^3/6} = \frac{3a}{8}.$$

Example 2.   In the example of Sec. 54, find I_z by transforming the integral into cylindrical coordinates.   Then,

$$I_x = \int_R (y^2 + z^2)\sigma \, dV = \sigma \int_0^a \int_0^{2\pi} \int_0^b (\rho^2 \sin^2 \theta + z^2)\rho \, dz \, d\theta \, d\rho$$

$$= \sigma \int_0^a \int_0^{2\pi} \left(\rho^3 \sin^2 \theta \, z + \frac{\rho}{3} z^3 \right)\Big|_0^b d\theta \, d\rho$$

$$= \sigma \int_0^a \int_0^{2\pi} \left(b\rho^3 \sin^2 \theta + \frac{b^3\rho}{3} \right) d\theta \, d\rho$$

$$= \sigma \int_0^a b \left(\frac{\rho^3\theta}{2} - \frac{\rho^3 \sin 2\theta}{4} + \frac{b^2\rho\theta}{3} \right)\Big|_0^{2\pi} d\rho$$

$$= \sigma \int_0^a \left(\pi b\rho^3 + \frac{2\pi b^3}{3}\rho \right) d\rho$$

$$= \sigma b\pi \left(\frac{\rho^4}{4} + \frac{b^2\rho^2}{3} \right)\Big|_0^a = \frac{\sigma a^2 b\pi}{12} (3a^2 + 4b^2).$$

57. Surface Integrals. Another important application of multiple integrals occurs in the problem of defining the area of a surface. Let $z = f(x, y)$ be the equation of a surface S (Fig. 48).

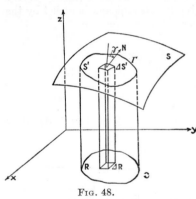

FIG. 48.

Let S' be a portion of this surface bounded by a closed curve Γ, and such that any line parallel to the z-axis cuts S' in only one point. If C is the projection of Γ on the xy-plane, let the region R, of which C is the boundary, be subdivided by lines parallel to the axes into subregions ΔR_i. Through these subdividing lines pass planes parallel to the z-axis. These planes cut from S' small regions $\Delta S'_i$ of area $\Delta\sigma_i$. Let ΔA_i be the area of ΔR_i. Then, except for infinitesimals of higher order,

$$\Delta A_i = \cos \gamma_i \Delta\sigma_i,$$

where $\cos \alpha_i$, $\cos \beta_i$, and $\cos \gamma_i$ represent the direction cosines of the normal to S at any point (x_i, y_i, z_i) of $\Delta S'_i$. Since (see Sec. 43)

$$\cos \alpha_i : \cos \beta_i : \cos \gamma_i = \frac{\partial z}{\partial x}\Big|_i : \frac{\partial z}{\partial y}\Big|_i : -1,$$

it follows that

$$\cos \gamma_i = \frac{-1}{\pm \sqrt{(\partial z/\partial x)_i^2 + (\partial z/\partial y)_i^2 + 1}}.$$

Upon using the positive value for cos γ_i,

$$\Delta\sigma_i = \sec \gamma_i \, \Delta A_i = \sqrt{\left(\frac{\partial z}{\partial x}\right)_i^2 + \left(\frac{\partial z}{\partial y}\right)_i^2 + 1} \; \Delta A_i.$$

Then,

$$\lim_{n \to \infty} \sum_{i=1}^{n} \sqrt{\left(\frac{\partial z}{\partial x}\right)_i^2 + \left(\frac{\partial z}{\partial y}\right)_i^2 + 1} \; \Delta A_i$$

is defined as the area of the surface S'. Since this limit is

$$\int_R \sqrt{\left(\frac{\partial z}{\partial x}\right)^2 + \left(\frac{\partial z}{\partial y}\right)^2 + 1} \; dA,$$

the value of σ is given by

$$(57\text{-}1) \quad \sigma = \int_R \sec \gamma \, dA = \int \int_R \sqrt{\left(\frac{\partial z}{\partial x}\right)^2 + \left(\frac{\partial z}{\partial y}\right)^2 + 1} \; dx \, dy.$$

Similarly, by projecting S' on the other coordinate planes, it can be shown that

$$\sigma = \int_{R_1} \sec \alpha \, dA$$

$$= \int_{R_2} \sec \beta \, dA.$$

The integral of a function $\varphi(x, y, z)$ over the surface $z = f(x, y)$ can now be defined by the equation

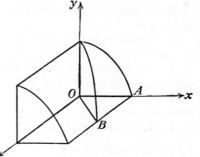

Fig. 49.

$$(57\text{-}2) \quad \int_S \varphi(x, y, z) \, d\sigma$$

$$= \int \int_R \varphi[x, y, f(x, y)] \sqrt{\left(\frac{\partial f}{\partial x}\right)^2 + \left(\frac{\partial f}{\partial y}\right)^2 + 1} \; dx \, dy.$$

It is assumed that $\varphi(x, y, z)$ is continuous and single valued for all points of some region T that contains S.

Example. Find the area of that portion of the surface of the cylinder $x^2 + y^2 = a^2$ which lies in the first octant between the planes $z = 0$ and $z = mx$ (Fig. 49).

This surface can be projected on the xz-plane or on the yz-plane but not on the xy-plane (since any perpendicular to the xy-plane that meets the surface at all will lie on the surface). The projection on the xz-plane is the triangle OAB. Hence,

$$\sigma = \int_{OAB} \sec \beta \, dA.$$

But

$$\sec \beta = \sqrt{\left(\frac{\partial y}{\partial x}\right)^2 + 1 + \left(\frac{\partial y}{\partial z}\right)^2}$$

$$= \sqrt{\left(\frac{-x}{\sqrt{a^2 - x^2}}\right)^2 + 1 + 0} = a(a^2 - x^2)^{-\frac{1}{2}}.$$

Therefore,

$$\sigma = \int_0^a \int_0^{mx} a(a^2 - x^2)^{-\frac{1}{2}} \, dz \, dx$$

$$= \int_0^a amx(a^2 - x^2)^{-\frac{1}{2}} \, dx = a^2 m.$$

PROBLEMS

1. Find the coordinates of the center of gravity of the area bounded by $x^{\frac{1}{2}} + y^{\frac{1}{2}} = a^{\frac{1}{2}}$, $x = 0$, and $y = 0$.

2. Find the moment of inertia of the area of one loop of $\rho^2 = a^2 \sin 2\theta$ about an axis perpendicular to its plane at the pole.

3. (a) Find the expression for dA in terms of u and v, if $x = u(1 - v)$ and $y = uv$.

(b) Find the expression for dV in terms of u, v, and w, if $x = u(1 - v)$, $y = uv(1 - w)$, and $z = uvw$.

4. Find the center of gravity of one of the wedges of uniform density cut from the cylinder $x^2 + y^2 = a^2$ by the planes $z = mx$ and $z = -mx$.

5. Find the volume enclosed by the circular cylinder $\rho = 2a \cos \theta$, the cone $z = \rho$, and the plane $z = 0$ (use cylindrical coordinates).

6. Find the center of gravity of the solid of uniform density bounded by the four planes $\frac{x}{a} + \frac{y}{b} + \frac{z}{c} = 1$, $x = 0$, $y = 0$, and $z = 0$.

7. Find the moment of inertia of the solid of uniform density bounded by the cylinder $x^2 + y^2 = a^2$ and the planes $z = 0$ and $z = b$ about the z-axis.

8. Find, by the method of Sec. 57, the area of the surface of the sphere $x^2 + y^2 + z^2 = a^2$ that lies in the first octant.

9. Prove that

$$J\left(\frac{u, v}{x, y}\right) \cdot J\left(\frac{x, y}{u, v}\right) = 1.$$

Hint: Write out the Jacobians, and multiply.

10. Prove that

$$J\left(\frac{u, v}{x, y}\right) \cdot J\left(\frac{x, y}{\xi, \eta}\right) = J\left(\frac{u, v}{\xi, \eta}\right),$$

where $u = u(x, y)$, $v = v(x, y)$, $x = x(\xi, \eta)$, and $y = y(\xi, \eta)$.

11. Find the surface of the sphere $x^2 + y^2 + z^2 = a^2$ cut off by the cylinder $x^2 - ax + y^2 = 0$.

12. Find the volume bounded by the cylinder and the sphere of Prob. 11.

13. Find the surface of the cylinder $x^2 + y^2 = a^2$ cut off by the cylinder $y^2 + z^2 = a^2$.

14. Find the coordinates of the center of gravity of the portion of the surface of the sphere cut off by the right-circular cone whose vertex is at the center of the sphere.

15. Use cylindrical coordinates to find the moment of inertia of the volume of a right-circular cylinder about its axis.

16. Find the moments of inertia of the volume of the ellipsoid

$$\frac{x^2}{a^2} + \frac{y^2}{b^2} + \frac{z^2}{c^2} = 1$$

about its axes.

17. Kinetic energy T is defined as $T = \frac{1}{2}Mv^2$, where M is the mass and v is the velocity of a particle. If the body is rotating with a constant angular velocity ω, show that

$$T = \int_V \tfrac{1}{2} r^2 \omega^2 \, \rho \, dV = \tfrac{1}{2} I \omega^2,$$

where ρ is the density and I is the moment of inertia of the body about the axis of rotation.

58. Green's Theorem in Space.

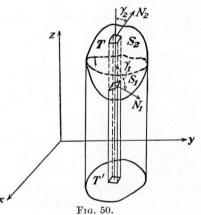

FIG. 50.

An important theorem that establishes the connection between the integral over the volume and the integral over the surface enclosing the volume is given next. This theorem has wide applicability in numerous physical problems* and is frequently termed the *divergence theorem*.

THEOREM. *If* $P(x, y, z)$, $Q(x, y, z)$, $R(x, y, z)$ *and* $\partial P/\partial x,\ \partial Q/\partial y,\ \partial R/\partial z$ *are continuous and single-valued functions in a region* T *bounded by a closed surface* S, *then*

$$\int_S (P \cos \alpha + Q \cos \beta + R \cos \gamma) \, d\sigma = \int_T \left(\frac{\partial P}{\partial x} + \frac{\partial Q}{\partial y} + \frac{\partial R}{\partial z} \right) dV.$$

It will be assumed that S (Fig. 50) is cut by any line parallel to

---

* See, in this connection, Secs. 125, 130, 131.

one of the coordinate axes in at most two points. If S is not such a surface, then T is subdivided into regions each of which satisfies this condition, and the extension to more general types of regions is immediate.

A parallel to the z-axis may cut S in two points (x_i, y_i, z_i) and $(x_i, y_i, \bar{z}_i)$, in which $z_i \leq \bar{z}_i$. Let $z = f_1(x, y)$ be the equation satisfied by (x_i, y_i, z_i) and $z = f_2(x, y)$ be the equation satisfied by $(x_i, y_i, \bar{z}_i)$. Thus, S is divided into two parts, S_1, whose equation is $z = f_1(x, y)$, and S_2, whose equation is $z = f_2(x, y)$. Then,

$$\int_S R(x, y, z) \cos \gamma \, d\sigma,$$

taken over the exterior of S, is equal to

$$\int_{S_2} R(x, y, z) \cos \gamma \, d\sigma + \int_{S_1} R(x, y, z) \cos \gamma \, d\sigma,$$

taken over the exteriors of the surfaces S_1 and S_2. But, from (57-2), these surface integrals are equal to double integrals taken over the projection T' of T on the xy-plane. Therefore,*

$$\int_S R(x, y, z) \cos \gamma \, d\sigma = \int_{T'} \{R[x, y, f_2(x, y)] - R[x, y, f_1(x, y)]\} \, dA$$

$$= \int \int_{T'} R(x, y, z) \Big|_{z=f_1(x,y)}^{z=f_2(x,y)} dy \, dx$$

$$= \int \int \int_T \frac{\partial R}{\partial z} \, dz \, dy \, dx$$

or

$$\int_S R(x, y, z) \cos \gamma \, d\sigma = \int_T \frac{\partial R}{\partial z} \, dV.$$

Similarly, it can be shown that

$$\int_S P(x, y, z) \cos \alpha \, d\sigma = \int_T \frac{\partial P}{\partial x} \, dV$$

and

$$\int_S Q(x, y, z) \cos \beta \, d\sigma = \int_T \frac{\partial Q}{\partial y} \, dV.$$

* The negative sign appears in the right-hand member of the equation because

$$\cos \gamma \leq 0 \text{ for } S_1,$$

where the subscripts refer to S_2 and S_1.

Therefore,

$$(58\text{-}1) \quad \int_S (P \cos \alpha + Q \cos \beta + R \cos \gamma)\, d\sigma = \int_T \left(\frac{\partial P}{\partial x} + \frac{\partial Q}{\partial y} + \frac{\partial R}{\partial z} \right) dV.$$

Since $\cos \alpha\, d\sigma = dy\, dz$, $\cos \beta\, d\sigma = dz\, dx$, and $\cos \gamma\, d\sigma = dx\, dy$, (58-1) can be written in the form

$$(58\text{-}2) \quad \int \int_S (P\, dy\, dz + Q\, dz\, dx + R\, dx\, dy)$$

$$= \int \int \int_T \left(\frac{\partial P}{\partial x} + \frac{\partial Q}{\partial y} + \frac{\partial R}{\partial z} \right) dx\, dy\, dz.$$

The formula (58-2) bears the name of Green.*

Example. By transforming to a triple integral, evaluate

$$I = \int \int_S (x^3\, dy\, dz + x^2 y\, dz\, dx + x^2 z\, dx\, dy),$$

where S is the surface bounded by $z = 0$, $z = b$, and $x^2 + y^2 = a^2$.

Calculating the right-hand member with the aid of (58-2) and making use of the symmetry, one finds

$$I = 4 \int_0^a \int_0^{\sqrt{a^2 - x^2}} \int_0^b (3x^2 + x^2 + x^2)\, dz\, dy\, dx$$

$$= 4 \cdot 5b \int_0^a x^2 \sqrt{a^2 - x^2}\, dx$$

$$= \tfrac{5}{4}\pi a^4 b.$$

A direct calculation of the integral I may prove to be instructive. The evaluation of the integral can be carried out by calculating the sum of the integrals evaluated over the projections of the surface S on the coordinate planes. Thus,

$$I = \int_{-a}^a \int_0^b (\sqrt{a^2 - y^2})^3\, dz\, dy - \int_{-a}^a \int_0^b (-\sqrt{a^2 - y^2})^3\, dz\, dy$$

$$+ \int_{-a}^a \int_0^b x^2 \sqrt{a^2 - x^2}\, dz\, dx - \int_{-a}^a \int_0^b x^2(-\sqrt{a^2 - x^2})\, dz\, dx$$

$$+ \int_{-a}^a \int_{-\sqrt{a^2-y^2}}^{\sqrt{a^2-y^2}} x^2 \cdot b\, dx\, dy - \int_{-a}^a \int_{-\sqrt{a^2-y^2}}^{\sqrt{a^2-y^2}} x^2 \cdot 0\, dx\, dy,$$

which upon evaluation is seen to check with the result obtained above. It should be noted that the angles α, β, γ are made by the exterior normal with the positive direction of the coordinate axes.

---

* The names of Gauss and Ostrogradsky are also associated with this theorem.

59. Symmetrical Form of Green's Theorem. One of the most widely used formulas in the applications of analysis to a great variety of problems is a form of Green's theorem obtained by setting

$$P = u\frac{\partial v}{\partial x}, \qquad Q = u\frac{\partial v}{\partial y}, \qquad R = u\frac{\partial v}{\partial z}$$

in (58-1). The result of the substitution is

$$\int_S u\left(\frac{\partial v}{\partial x}\cos\alpha + \frac{\partial v}{\partial y}\cos\beta + \frac{\partial v}{\partial z}\cos\gamma\right)d\sigma$$

$$= \int_T u\left(\frac{\partial^2 v}{\partial x^2} + \frac{\partial^2 v}{\partial y^2} + \frac{\partial^2 v}{\partial z^2}\right)dV$$

$$+ \int_T \left(\frac{\partial u}{\partial x}\frac{\partial v}{\partial x} + \frac{\partial u}{\partial y}\frac{\partial v}{\partial y} + \frac{\partial u}{\partial z}\frac{\partial v}{\partial z}\right)dV.$$

But the direction cosines of the exterior normal n to the surface are

$$\cos\alpha = \frac{dx}{dn}, \qquad \cos\beta = \frac{dy}{dn}, \qquad \cos\gamma = \frac{dz}{dn},$$

so that the foregoing integral reads

$$(59\text{-}1) \qquad \int_S u\frac{dv}{dn}\,d\sigma = \int_T u\,\nabla^2 v\,dV$$

$$+ \int_T \left(\frac{\partial u}{\partial x}\frac{\partial v}{\partial x} + \frac{\partial u}{\partial y}\frac{\partial v}{\partial y} + \frac{\partial u}{\partial z}\frac{\partial v}{\partial z}\right)dV,$$

where

$$\nabla^2 v \equiv \frac{\partial^2 v}{\partial x^2} + \frac{\partial^2 v}{\partial y^2} + \frac{\partial^2 v}{\partial z^2}.$$

Interchanging the roles of u and v in (59-1) and subtracting the result from (59-1) give the desired formula

$$\int_S \left(u\frac{dv}{dn} - v\frac{du}{dn}\right)d\sigma = \int_T (u\,\nabla^2 v - v\,\nabla^2 u)\,dV.$$

A reference to the conditions imposed upon P, Q, and R in the theorem of Sec. 58 shows that, in order to ensure the validity of this formula, it is sufficient to require the continuity of the functions u and v and their first and second space derivatives throughout a closed region T.

PROBLEMS

1. Evaluate, by using Green's theorem,

$$\int\int_S (xy\,dy\,dz + y^2\,dz\,dx + yz\,dx\,dy),$$

where S is the surface $x^2 + y^2 + z^2 = a^2$.

2. Show from geometrical considerations that the angle $d\theta$ subtended at the origin by an element ds of a plane curve C is

$$d\theta = \cos(n, r)\,\frac{ds}{r},$$

where r is the radius vector of the curve, and (n, r) is the angle between the radius vector and the normal to the curve. Hence, show that

$$\theta = \int_C \frac{\cos(n, r)\,ds}{r} = \int_C \frac{1}{r}\frac{dr}{dn}\,ds,$$

where the integral is a line integral along the curve C.

3. A solid angle is defined as the angle subtended at the vertex of a cone. The area cut out from a unit sphere by the cone, with its vertex at the center, is called the measure of the solid angle. The measure of the solid angle is clearly equal to the area cut out by the cone from any sphere concentric with the unit sphere divided by the square of the radius of this sphere. In a manner analogous to that employed in Prob. 2, show that the element of solid angle is

$$d\omega = \frac{\cos(n, r)\,d\sigma}{r^2},$$

where the angle between the radius vector and the exterior normal to the surface S is (n, r). Also, show that

$$\omega = \int_S \frac{\cos(n, r)\,d\sigma}{r^2} = \int_S \frac{1}{r^2}\frac{dr}{dn}\,d\sigma,$$

where the integral is extended over the surface S.

4. By transforming to a triple integral, evaluate

$$\int\int_S (x^3\,dy\,dz + y^3\,dz\,dx + z^3\,dx\,dy),$$

where S is the spherical surface $x^2 + y^2 + z^2 = a^2$. Also, attempt to calculate this integral directly.

5. Set $v = 1$ in Green's symmetrical formula, and assume that u satisfies the equation of Laplace, $\nabla^2 u = 0$. What is the value of $\int_S \frac{du}{dn}\,d\sigma$ if S is an arbitrary closed surface?

6. The density of a square plate varies directly as the square of the distance from one vertex. Find the center of gravity and the moment of inertia of the plate about an axis perpendicular to the plate and passing through the center of gravity.

7. Find the volume of a rectangular hole cut through a sphere if a diameter of the sphere coincides with the axis of the hole.

8. Show that the attraction of a homogeneous sphere at a point exterior to the sphere is the same as though all the mass of the sphere were concentrated at the center of the sphere. Assume the inverse square law of force.

9. The Newtonian potential V due to a body T at a point P is defined by the equation $V(P) = \int_T dm/r$, where dm is the element of mass of the body and r is the distance from the point P to the element of mass dm. Show that the potential of a homogeneous spherical shell of inner radius b and outer radius a is

$$V = 2\pi\sigma(a^2 - b^2), \qquad \text{if } \rho < b,$$

and

$$= \frac{4}{3}\pi\sigma \frac{a^3 - b^3}{\rho}, \qquad \text{if } \rho > a,$$

where σ is the density and ρ is the distance to P from the center of the shell.

10. Find the Newtonian potential on the axis of a homogeneous circular cylinder of radius a.

11. Show that the force of attraction of a right-circular cone upon a point at its vertex is $2\pi\sigma h(1 - \cos\alpha)$, where h is the altitude of the cone and 2α is the angle at the vertex.

12. Show that the force of attraction of a homogeneous right-circular cylinder upon a point on its axis is

$$2\pi\sigma[h + \sqrt{R^2 + a^2} - \sqrt{(R + h)^2 + a^2}\,];$$

here h is altitude, a is radius, and R is the distance from the point to one base of the cylinder.

13. Set up the integral representing the part of the surface of the sphere $x^2 + y^2 + z^2 = 100$ intercepted by the planes $x = 1$ and $x = 4$.

14. Find the mass of a sphere whose density varies as the square of the distance from the center.

15. Find the moment of inertia of the sphere in Prob. 14 about a diameter.

CHAPTER VI

LINE INTEGRAL

The line integral, to be considered in this chapter, is as useful in many theoretical and practical problems as the ordinary definite integral defined in Chap. V. The discussion of the line integral will be followed by several illustrations of its use in applied mathematics.

60. Definition of Line Integral. Let C be a continuous curve (Fig. 51), joining $A(a, b)$ and $B(c, d)$. Let $M(x, y)$ and $N(x, y)$ be two functions that are single-valued and continuous functions of x and y for all points of C. Choose $n - 1$ points $P_i(x_i, y_i)$ on the curve C, which is thus divided into n parts. Let $\Delta x_i = x_i - x_{i-1}$ and $\Delta y_i = y_i - y_{i-1}$, where $x_0 = a, y_0 = b, x_n = c, y_n = d$. Let ξ_i and η_i be defined by $x_{i-1} \leq \xi_i < x_i, \; y_{i-1} \leq \eta_i < y_i$ and form

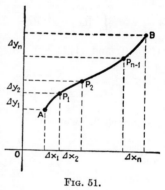

FIG. 51.

$$\sum_{i=1}^{n} [M(\xi_i, \eta_i)\, \Delta x_i + N(\xi_i, \eta_i)\, \Delta y_i].$$

The limit of this sum as $n \to \infty$ and all $\Delta x_i \to 0$ and $\Delta y_i \to 0$ simultaneously is defined as a line integral along C.
Thus,

(60-1)
$$\lim_{n \to \infty} \sum_{i=1}^{n} [M(\xi_i, \eta_i)\, \Delta x_i + N(\xi_i, \eta_i)\, \Delta y_i]$$
$$\equiv \int_{C} [M(x, y)\, dx + N(x, y)\, dy].$$

Obviously, the value of this integral depends, in general, on the particular choice of the curve C. If the equation of C is known in one of the forms $y = f(x)$, $x = \varphi(y)$ or $x = f_1(t)$, $y = f_2(t)$, the

197

line integral may be reduced to a definite integral in one variable by substitution, as is indicated in the following examples. However, it is frequently inconvenient to make this reduction, and thus it is desirable to consider the properties and uses of (60-1).

Example 1. Let the points $(0, 0)$ and $(1, 1)$ be connected by the line $y = x$. Let $M(x, y) = x - y^2$ and $N(x, y) = 2xy$. Then the line integral along $y = x$,

$$I \equiv \int_{(0,0)}^{(1,1)} [(x - y^2) \, dx + 2xy \, dy],$$

becomes, on substitution of $y = x$,

$$\int_0^1 [(x - x^2) \, dx + 2x^2 \, dx] = \int_0^1 (x + x^2) \, dx = \tfrac{5}{6}.$$

If $(0, 0)$ and $(1, 1)$ are connected by the parabola $y = x^2$, I along $y = x^2$ is

$$\int_0^1 [(x - x^4) \, dx + 2x^3(2x \, dx)] = \int_0^1 (x + 3x^4) \, dx = 1\tfrac{1}{10}.$$

Example 2.   Consider

$$M(x, y) = 2x^2 + 4xy$$

and

$$N(x, y) = 2x^2 - y^2,$$

with the curve $y = x^2$ connecting the points $(1, 1)$ and $(2, 4)$.   Then

$$\int_{(1,1)}^{(2,4)} (M \, dx + N \, dy) = \int_1^2 (2x^2 + 4x \cdot x^2) \, dx + \int_1^4 (2y - y^2) \, dy = 13\tfrac{2}{3}.$$

Inasmuch as $dy = 2x \, dx$, this integral can be written as

$$\int_1^2 (2x^2 + 4x^3) \, dx + \int_1^2 (2x^2 - x^4)2x \, dx = 13\tfrac{2}{3}.$$

If the equation of the parabola in this example is written in a parametric form as

$$x = t,$$
$$y = t^2, \qquad (1 \leq t \leq 2),$$

then the integrand of the line integral can be expressed in terms of the parameter t.   Substituting for x, y, dx, and dy in terms of t gives

$$\int_{(1,1)}^{(2,4)} [M \, dx + N \, dy)] = \int_1^2 [(2t^2 + 4t^3) + (2t^2 - t^4)2t] \, dt$$
$$= \int_1^2 (2t^2 + 8t^3 - 2t^5) \, dt = 13\tfrac{2}{3}.$$

The reader will readily verify that the value of this integral over a rectilinear path C joining the points $(1, 1)$ and $(2, 4)$ is also $13\frac{2}{3}$. In fact, the value of this integral depends only on the end points and not upon the curve joining them. The reason for this remarkable behavior will appear in Sec. 63.

PROBLEMS

1. Find the value of $\int_{(0,0)}^{(1,1)} [\sqrt{y}\, dx + (x - y)\, dy]$ along the following curves:

    (a) Straight line $x = t$, $y = t$.
    (b) Parabola $x = t^2$, $y = t$.
    (c) Parabola $x = t$, $y = t^2$.
    (d) Cubical parabola $x = t$, $y = t^3$.

2. Find the value of $\int_{(0,0)}^{(1,3)} [x^2 y\, dx + (x^2 - y^2)\, dy]$ along (a) $y = 3x^2$; (b) $y = 3x$.

3. Find the value of $\int_{(0,0)}^{(1,1)} (x^2\, dx + y^2\, dy)$ along the curves of Prob. 1 above.

4. Find the value of $\int_{(0,0)}^{(1,1)} [(x^2 + y^2)\, dx - 2xy\, dy]$ along (a) $y = x$; (b) $x = y^2$; (c) $y = x^2$.

5. Find the value of $\int_{(0,0)}^{(x,y)} (y \sin x\, dx - x \cos y\, dy)$ along $y = x$.

6. Find the value of $\int_{(-a,0)}^{(a,0)} (x\, dy + y\, dx)$ along the upper half of the circle $x^2 + y^2 = a^2$.

7. Evaluate the integral of Prob. 6 over the path formed by the lines $x = -a$, $y = a$, $x = a$. What is the value of this integral if the path is a straight line joining the points $(-a, 0)$ and $(a, 0)$?

8. Find the value of $\int_{(1,0)}^{(0,1)} (x^2\, dx + y^2\, dy)$ along the path given by $x = \sin t$, $y = \cos t$.

9. Evaluate the integral of Prob. 8 if the path is a straight line joining $(0, 1)$ and $(1, 0)$.

10. What is the value of the integral of Prob. 8 if the path is the curve $y = 1 - x^2$?

61. Area of a Closed Curve.

Let C be a continuous closed curve which nowhere crosses itself. The equation of such a curve, in parametric form, can be given as

$$(61\text{-}1) \qquad \begin{cases} x = f_1(t), \\ y = f_2(t), \end{cases}$$

where the parameter t varies continuously from some value

$t = t_0$ to $t = t_1$ and the functions $f_1(t)$ and $f_2(t)$ are continuous and single-valued in the interval $t_0 \leq t \leq t_1$. Inasmuch as the curve is assumed to be closed, the initial and the final points of the curve coincide, so that

$$f_1(t_0) = f_1(t_1)$$

and

$$f_2(t_0) = f_2(t_1).$$

The statement that the curve C does not cut itself implies that there is no other pair of values of the parameter t for which

$$f_1(t') = f_1(t'')$$

and

$$f_2(t') = f_2(t'').$$

A closed curve satisfying the condition stated above will be called *simple*.

As t varies continuously from t_0 to t_1, the points (x, y) determined by (61-1) will trace out the curve C in a certain sense. If C is described so that a man walking along the curve in the direction of the description has the enclosed area always to his left, the curve C is said to be described in the *positive direction*, and the enclosed area will be considered positive; but if C is described so that the enclosed area is to the right, then C is described in the *negative direction*, and the area is regarded as negative.

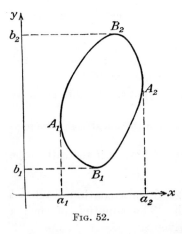

Fig. 52.

Consider at first a simple closed curve C such that no line parallel to one of the coordinate axes, say the y-axis, intersects C in more than two points. Let C be bounded by the lines $x = a_1$, $x = a_2$, $y = b_1$, $y = b_2$, which are tangent to C at A_1, A_2, B_1, and B_2, respectively. Clearly, C cannot be the graph of a single-valued function. Therefore, let the equation of $A_1B_1A_2$ be given by $y_1 = f_1(x)$, and the equation of $A_1B_2A_2$ by $y_2 = f_2(x)$, where $f_1(x)$ and $f_2(x)$ are single-valued functions. Then the area enclosed by C (Fig. 52) is given by

$$(61\text{-}2) \qquad A = \int_{a_1}^{a_2} y_2 \, dx - \int_{a_1}^{a_2} y_1 \, dx$$

$$= - \int_{a_2}^{a_1} y_2 \, dx - \int_{a_1}^{a_2} y_1 \, dx,$$

or

$$(61\text{-}3) \qquad A = - \int_C y \, dx,$$

in which the last integral is to be taken around C in a counter-clockwise direction.

Similarly, if $x_1 = \varphi_1(y)$ is the equation of $B_1A_1B_2$ and $x_2 = \varphi_2(y)$ is the equation of $B_1A_2B_2$,

$$A = \int_{b_1}^{b_2} x_2 \, dy - \int_{b_1}^{b_2} x_1 \, dy$$

$$= \int_{b_1}^{b_2} x_2 \, dy + \int_{b_2}^{b_1} x_1 \, dy$$

or

$$(61\text{-}4) \qquad A = \int_C x \, dy.$$

Again, the last integral is to be taken around C in a counter-clockwise direction. It may be noted that (61-3) and (61-4) both require that the area be to the left as C is described if the value of A is to be positive.

By adding (61-3) and (61-4), a new formula for A is obtained, namely,

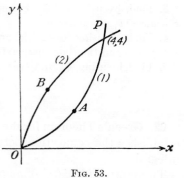

FIG. 53.

$$(61\text{-}5)$$

$$A = \tfrac{1}{2} \int_C (-y \, dx + x \, dy).$$

This formula gives a line-integral expression for A.

To illustrate the application of (61-5), the area between (1) $x^2 = 4y$ and (2) $y^2 = 4x$ (Fig. 53) will be determined.

Then,

$$A = \frac{1}{2} \int_C (-y\,dx + x\,dy) = \frac{1}{2} \int_{(1)} (-y\,dx + x\,dy)$$

$$+ \frac{1}{2} \int_{(2)} (-y\,dx + x\,dy)$$

$$= \frac{1}{2} \int_0^4 \left(-\frac{x^2}{4}\,dx + x \cdot \frac{x}{2}\,dx \right) + \frac{1}{2} \int_4^0 \left(-y \cdot \frac{y}{2}\,dy + \frac{y^2}{4}\,dy \right)$$

$$= \frac{x^3}{24}\Big|_0^4 - \frac{y^3}{24}\Big|_4^0 = \frac{16}{3}.$$

For convenience the first integral was expressed in terms of x, whereas the second integral is simpler in terms of y.

The restriction that the curve C be such that no line parallel to one of the coordinate axes cuts it in more than two points can be removed if it is possible to draw a finite number of lines connecting pairs of points on C, so that the area enclosed by the curve is subdivided into regions each of which is of the type considered in the foregoing.   This extension is indicated in detail in the following section.

PROBLEMS

1. Find, by using (61-5), the area of the ellipse $x = a \cos \varphi$, $y = b \sin \varphi$.

2. Find, by using (61-5), the area between $y^2 = 9x$ and $y = 3x$.

3. Find, by using (61-5), the area of the hypocycloid of four cusps $x = a \cos^3 \theta$, $y = a \sin^3 \theta$.

4. Find, by using (61-5), the area of the triangle formed by the line $x + y = a$ and the coordinate axes.

5. Find, by using (61-5), the area enclosed by the loop of the strophoid

$$x = \frac{1 - t^2}{1 + t^2}, \qquad y = \frac{t(1 - t^2)}{1 + t^2}.$$

62. Green's Theorem for the Plane.   This remarkable theorem establishes the connection between a line integral and a double integral.

THEOREM.   *If $M(x, y)$ and $N(x, y)$, $\partial M/\partial y$ and $\partial N/\partial x$ are continuous single-valued functions over a closed region R, bounded by the curve C, then*

$$\int \int_R \left(\frac{\partial M}{\partial y} - \frac{\partial N}{\partial x} \right) dx\,dy = - \int_C (M\,dx + N\,dy).$$

The double integral is taken over the given region, and the curve C is described in the positive direction.

The theorem will be proved first for a simple closed curve of the type considered in Sec. 61 (see Fig. 52).

Again, let $y_1 = f_1(x)$ be the equation of $A_1B_1A_2$ and $y_2 = f_2(x)$ be the equation of $A_1B_2A_2$. Then,

$$\int\int_R \frac{\partial M}{\partial y}\,dx\,dy = \int_{a_1}^{a_2} dx \int_{y_1}^{y_2} \frac{\partial M}{\partial y}\,dy$$

$$= \int_{a_1}^{a_2} [M(x, y_2) - M(x, y_1)]\,dx$$

$$= -\int_{a_2}^{a_1} M(x, y_2)\,dx - \int_{a_1}^{a_2} M(x, y_1)\,dx,$$

or

$$(62\text{-}1) \qquad \int\int_R \frac{\partial M}{\partial y}\,dx\,dy = -\int_C M(x, y)\,dx.$$

Similarly, if $x_1 = \varphi_1(y)$ is the equation of $B_1A_1B_2$ and $x_2 = \varphi_2(y)$ is the equation of $B_1A_2B_2$,

$$\int\int_R \frac{\partial N}{\partial x}\,dx\,dy = \int_{b_1}^{b_2} dy \int_{x_1}^{x_2} \frac{\partial N}{\partial x}\,dx = \int_{b_1}^{b_2} [N(x_2, y) - N(x_1, y)]\,dy$$

$$= \int_{b_1}^{b_2} N(x_2, y)\,dy + \int_{b_2}^{b_1} N(x_1, y)\,dy,$$

or

$$(62\text{-}2) \qquad \int\int_R \frac{\partial N}{\partial x}\,dx\,dy = \int_C N(x, y)\,dy.$$

Therefore, if (62-2) is subtracted from (62-1),

$$(62\text{-}3) \quad \int\int_R \left(\frac{\partial M}{\partial y} - \frac{\partial N}{\partial x}\right) dx\,dy = -\int_C [M(x, y)\,dx + N(x, y)\,dy].$$

It will be observed that setting $M = -\dfrac{y}{2}$ and $N = \dfrac{x}{2}$ gives the formula (61-5).

Now, let the region have any continuous boundary curve C, so long as it is possible to draw a finite number of lines that divide the region into subregions each of the type considered in the first part of this section; that is, the subregions must have boundary curves that are cut by any parallel to one of the coordinate axes in at most two points. Such a region R is shown in Fig. 54.

By drawing the lines A_1A_2 and A_3A_4, the region R is divided into three subregions R_1, R_2, and R_3. The boundary curve of each region is of the simple type. The positive direction of each boundary curve is indicated by the arrows. The theorem can be applied to each subregion separately. When the three equations are added, the left-hand members add to give the double integral over the entire region R. The right-hand members give

$$- \int_{C_1} (M \ dx + N \ dy) - \int_{C_2} (M \ dx + N \ dy) - \int_{C_3} (M \ dx + N \ dy),$$

where

$$C_1 = A_1B_1A_2 + A_2A_1,$$
$$C_2 = A_1A_2 + A_2B_2A_3 + A_3A_4 + A_4A_1,$$
$$C_3 = A_4A_3 + A_3B_3A_4.$$

Since each of the lines A_1A_2 and A_3A_4 is traversed once in each direction, the line integrals that arise from them will cancel. The remaining line integrals, taken over the arcs of C, add to give the line integral over C. Therefore,

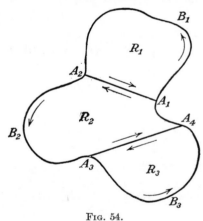

Fig. 54.

$$\int \int_R \left(\frac{\partial M}{\partial y} - \frac{\partial N}{\partial x} \right) dx \ dy$$
$$= - \int_C (M \ dx + N \ dy)$$

holds for regions of the type R.

Another type of region in which an auxiliary line is introduced is the region whose boundary is formed by two or more distinct curves. Thus, if R (Fig. 55) is the region between C_1 and C_2, the line A_1A_2 is drawn in order to make the total boundary

$$C_1 + A_2A_1 + C_2 + A_1A_2$$

a single curve. The theorem can be applied, and the line integrals over A_2A_1 and A_1A_2 will cancel, leaving only the line integrals over C_1 and C_2.

If the region R is such that any closed curve drawn in it can, by a continuous deformation, be shrunk to a point without crossing the boundary of the region, then the latter is called *simply connected*. Thus, regions bounded by a circle, a rectangle, or an ellipse are simply connected. The region R exterior to C_2 and interior to C_1 (Fig. 55) is not simply connected because a circle drawn within R and enclosing C_2 cannot be shrunk to a point without crossing C_2. In ordinary parlance, regions that have holes are not simply connected regions; they are called

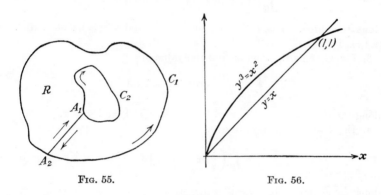

FIG. 55.   FIG. 56.

multiply connected regions. The importance of this classification will appear in the next two sections.

Example. Evaluate by using Green's theorem

$$\int_C (x^2 y\ dx + y^3\ dy),$$

where C is the closed path formed by $y = x$ and $y^3 = x^2$ from $(0, 0)$ to $(1, 1)$ (Fig. 56). Since $M = x^2 y$ and $N = y^3$,

$$\frac{\partial M}{\partial y} = x^2 \quad \text{and} \quad \frac{\partial N}{\partial x} = 0.$$

Then,

$$\int_C (x^2 y\ dx + y^3\ dy) = -\int\int_R \left(\frac{\partial M}{\partial y} - \frac{\partial N}{\partial x}\right) dx\ dy$$

$$= -\int_0^1 \int_{y^{3/2}}^{y} x^2\ dx\ dy = -\int_0^1 \frac{x^3}{3}\Big|_{y^{3/2}}^{y}\ dy$$

$$= \int_0^1 \left(\frac{y^{9/2}}{3} - \frac{y^3}{3}\right) dy = -\frac{1}{44}.$$

PROBLEMS

1. Find, by Green's theorem, the value of

$$\int_C (x^2 y \, dx + y \, dy)$$

along the closed curve C formed by $y^2 = x$ and $y = x$ between $(0, 0)$ and $(1, 1)$.

2. Find, by Green's theorem, the value of

$$\int_C [(x^2 + y) \, dx + (x - y^2) \, dy]$$

along the closed curve C formed by $y^3 = x^2$ and $y = x$ between $(0, 0)$ and $(1, 1)$.

3. Use Green's theorem to find the value of

$$\int_C [(xy - x^2) \, dx + x^2 y \, dy]$$

along the closed curve C formed by $y = 0$, $x = 1$, and $y = x$.

4. Use Green's theorem to evaluate

$$\int_C \left(\frac{1}{y} \, dx + \frac{1}{x} \, dy \right)$$

along the closed path formed by $y = 1$, $x = 4$, and $y = + \sqrt{x}$.

5. Check the answers of the four preceding problems by evaluating the line integrals directly.

63. Properties of Line Integrals. THEOREM 1. *Let M and N be two functions of x and y, such that M, N, $\partial M/\partial y$, and $\partial N/\partial x$ are continuous and single-valued at every point of a simply connected region R. The necessary and sufficient condition that $\int_C (M \, dx + N \, dy) = 0$ around every closed curve C drawn in R is that*

$$\frac{\partial M}{\partial y} = \frac{\partial N}{\partial x},$$

for every point of R.

Since

$$- \int_C (M \, dx + N \, dy) = \int \int_A \left(\frac{\partial M}{\partial y} - \frac{\partial N}{\partial x} \right) dx \, dy.$$

where A is the region enclosed by C, it follows that

$$\frac{\partial M}{\partial y} = \frac{\partial N}{\partial x}$$

makes the double integral, and consequently the line integral. have the value zero. Conversely, let $\int_C (M\,dx + N\,dy) = 0$ around every closed curve C drawn in R. Suppose that

$$\frac{\partial M}{\partial y} - \frac{\partial N}{\partial x} \neq 0$$

at some point P of R. Since $\partial M/\partial y$ and $\partial N/\partial x$ are continuous functions of x and y,

$$\frac{\partial M}{\partial y} - \frac{\partial N}{\partial x}$$

is also a continuous function of x and y. Therefore, there must exist some region S, about P, in which $\dfrac{\partial M}{\partial y} - \dfrac{\partial N}{\partial x}$ has the same sign as at P. Then,

$$\int\int_S \left(\frac{\partial M}{\partial y} - \frac{\partial N}{\partial x}\right) dx\,dy \neq 0,$$

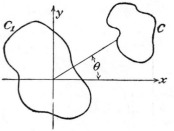

and hence $\int (M\,dx + N\,dy) \neq 0$ around the boundary of this region. This contradicts the hypothesis that

$$\int_C (M\,dx + N\,dy) = 0$$

Fig. 57.

around every closed curve C drawn in R. It follows that

$$\frac{\partial M}{\partial y} = \frac{\partial N}{\partial x}$$

at all points of R.

Example 1. Let

$$M = \frac{-y}{x^2 + y^2} \qquad \text{and} \qquad N = \frac{x}{x^2 + y^2}.$$

Then,

$$\frac{\partial M}{\partial y} = \frac{\partial N}{\partial x} = \frac{y^2 - x^2}{(x^2 + y^2)^2}.$$

M, N, $\partial M/\partial y$, and $\partial N/\partial x$ are continuous and single-valued for all points of the xy-plane except $(0, 0)$. Hence, $\int_C (M\,dx + N\,dy) = 0$ around any closed curve C (Fig. 57) that does not enclose $(0, 0)$. In polar coordinates, obtained by the change of variables

$$x = \rho \cos \theta, \qquad y = \rho \sin \theta,$$

$$\int_C \left(\frac{-y}{x^2 + y^2} \, dx + \frac{x}{x^2 + y^2} \, dy \right) = \int_C d\theta.$$

If C does not enclose the origin, θ varies along C from its original value θ_0 back to θ_0.   Therefore, $\int_C d\theta = 0$.   If C_1 encloses the origin, θ varies along C_1 from θ_0 to $\theta_0 + 2\pi$, so that $\int_{C_1} d\theta = 2\pi$.

Example 2.   Find, by Green's theorem, the value of

$$I = \int_C [(x^2 + xy) \, dx + (y^2 + x^2) \, dy],$$

where C is the square formed by the lines $y = \pm 1$ and $x = \pm 1$.   Since

$$\frac{\partial M}{\partial y} = x, \qquad \frac{\partial N}{\partial x} = 2x,$$

$$I = \int_{-1}^{1} \int_{-1}^{1} x \, dy \, dx = 0.$$

Note that the line integral has the value zero, but $\partial M / \partial y \neq \partial N / \partial x$. This does not contradict Theorem 1. Why?

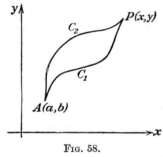

FIG. 58.

THEOREM 2.   *Let M and N satisfy the conditions of Theorem 1. The necessary and sufficient condition that $\int_{(a,b)}^{(x,y)} (M \, dx + N \, dy)$ be independent of the curve connecting (a, b) and (x, y) is that $\partial M / \partial y = \partial N / \partial x$ at all points of the region R. In this case the line integral is a function of the end points only.*

Suppose $\partial M / \partial y = \partial N / \partial x$.   Let C_1 and C_2 (Fig. 58) be any two curves from A to P, and let

$$I_1 \equiv \int_{C_1} (M \, dx + N \, dy)$$

and

$$I_2 \equiv \int_{C_2} (M \, dx + N \, dy)$$

be the values of the line integral from A to P along C_1 and C_2, respectively.   Then $I_1 - I_2$ is the value of the integral around the closed path formed by C_1 and C_2.   By Theorem 1,

$$I_1 - I_2 = 0.$$

Therefore, $I_1 = I_2$, so that the line integral taken over any two paths from A to P has the same value.

Conversely, suppose that $\int (M\,dx + N\,dy)$ is independent of the path from A to P. Then, for any two curves C_1 and C_2, $I_1 = I_2$. It follows that $\int (M\,dx + N\,dy) = 0$ for the closed path formed by C_1 and C_2. Hence, by Theorem 1, $\partial M/\partial y = \partial N/\partial x$.

Example. Consider

$$\int_{(1,1)}^{(2,2)} \left(\frac{1 + y^2}{x^3}\,dx - \frac{1 + x^2}{x^2}\,y\,dy \right).$$

Since $\partial M/\partial y = 2y/x^3$ and $\partial N/\partial x = 2y/x^3$ and both functions are continuous except at $(0, 0)$, the line integral is independent of the path so long as it does not enclose the origin. Choose $y = 1$ from $(1, 1)$ to $(2, 1)$ and $x = 2$ from $(2, 1)$ to $(2, 2)$ as the path of integration. Then,

$$I = \int_1^2 \frac{2}{x^3}\,dx - \int_1^2 \frac{5}{4}\,y\,dy = -\left.\frac{1}{x^2}\right|_1^2 - \left.\frac{5}{8}\,y^2\right|_1^2 = -\frac{9}{8}.$$

THEOREM 3. *Let M and N satisfy the conditions of Theorem 1. The necessary and sufficient condition that there exist a function $F(x, y)$ such that $\partial F/\partial x = M$ and $\partial F/\partial y = N$ is that $\partial M/\partial y = \partial N/\partial x$ at all points of the region R.*

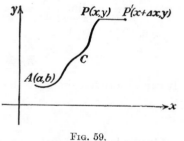

FIG. 59.

If $\partial M/\partial y = \partial N/\partial x$, Theorem 2 proves that

$$\int_{(a,b)}^{(x,y)} (M\,dx + N\,dy)$$

is independent of the path. Therefore,

(63-1) $$\int_{(a,b)}^{(x,y)} (M\,dx + N\,dy) = F(x, y),$$

and this function $F(x, y)$ depends only on the coordinates of the end points of the path. Hence,

$$F(x + \Delta x, y) = \int_{(a,b)}^{(x+\Delta x,y)} (M\,dx + N\,dy).$$

Let the path of integration be chosen as a curve C (Fig. 59) from A to P and the straight line PP' from $P(x, y)$ to $P'(x + \Delta x,$

y). Then,

$$F(x + \Delta x, y) = \int_{(a,b)}^{(x,y)} (M\,dx + N\,dy) + \int_{(x,y)}^{(x+\Delta x,y)} (M\,dx + N\,dy)$$

or

$$(63\text{-}2) \qquad F(x + \Delta x, y) = F(x, y) + \int_{x}^{x+\Delta x} M(x, y)\,dx.$$

The second integral reduces to the simpler form given in (63-2) since y is constant along PP', and therefore $dy = 0$. From (63-2),

$$\frac{\partial F}{\partial x} \equiv \lim_{\Delta x \to 0} \left[\frac{F(x + \Delta x, y) - F(x, y)}{\Delta x} \right]$$

$$= \lim_{\Delta x \to 0} \left[\frac{1}{\Delta x} \int_{x}^{x+\Delta x} M(x, y)\,dx \right].$$

Application of the first mean-value theorem* gives

$$\int_{x}^{x+\Delta x} M(x, y)\,dx = \Delta x\, M(\xi, y), \qquad (x \le \xi \le x + \Delta x).$$

Therefore,

$$\frac{\partial F}{\partial x} = \lim_{\Delta x \to 0} \left[\frac{1}{\Delta x} \cdot \Delta x\, M(\xi, y) \right] = \lim_{\Delta x \to 0} M(\xi, y).$$

Hence,

$$\frac{\partial F}{\partial x} = M(x, y).$$

It can be proved similarly that

$$\frac{\partial F}{\partial y} = N(x, y).$$

---

* It may be recalled that

$$\int_{a}^{b} f(x)\,dx = (b - a)f(\xi), \qquad (a \le \xi \le b),$$

is the first mean-value theorem for definite integrals. If $\int f(x)dx = F(x)$, then $f(x) = F'(x)$. From these relations, the mean-value theorem for definite integrals can be transformed into

$$F(b) - F(a) = (b - a)F'(\xi),$$

where $a \le \xi \le b$, or

$$F'(\xi) = \frac{F(b) - F(a)}{b - a},$$

which is the mean-value theorem of the differential calculus.

The function F is really a function of both end points. Multiplying $\partial F/\partial x = M(x, y)$ by dx and $\partial F/\partial y = N(x, y)$ by dy gives

$$dF = \frac{\partial F}{\partial x}\,dx + \frac{\partial F}{\partial y}\,dy = M(x, y)\,dx + N(x, y)\,dy.$$

Thus, if

$$\frac{\partial M}{\partial y} = \frac{\partial N}{\partial x},$$

the integrand in $\int_C (M\,dx + N\,dy)$ is the exact differential of the function $F(x, y)$, which is determined by the formula (63-1).

The most general expression for a function $\Phi(x, y)$, whose total differential is $d\Phi = M\,dx + N\,dy$, is

$$\Phi(x, y) = F(x, y) + C,$$

where C is an arbitrary constant. Indeed, since dI and $d\Phi$ are equal,

$$d(F - \Phi) = 0,$$

so that

$$F - \Phi = \text{const.}$$

To prove the necessity of the condition of the theorem, note that if there exists a function $F(x, y)$ such that

$$\frac{\partial F}{\partial x} = M(x, y) \qquad \text{and} \qquad \frac{\partial F}{\partial y} = N(x, y),$$

then

$$\frac{\partial^2 F}{\partial y\,\partial x} = \frac{\partial M}{\partial y} \qquad \text{and} \qquad \frac{\partial^2 F}{\partial x\,\partial y} = \frac{\partial N}{\partial x}.$$

Since $\partial M/\partial y$ and $\partial N/\partial x$ are both continuous, $\dfrac{\partial^2 F}{\partial x\,\partial y}$ and $\dfrac{\partial^2 F}{\partial y\,\partial x}$ are also continuous; hence,*

$$\frac{\partial^2 F}{\partial x\,\partial y} = \frac{\partial^2 F}{\partial y\,\partial x}.$$

Therefore,

$$\frac{\partial M}{\partial y} = \frac{\partial N}{\partial x}.$$

* See Sec. 46.

As a corollary to Theorem 3, one can state the following: *The necessary and sufficient condition that $M(x, y)\, dx + N(x, y)\, dy$ be an exact differential is that $\partial M/\partial y = \partial N/\partial x$.*

PROBLEMS

1. Show that

$$\int_{(0,1)}^{(1,2)} [(x^2 + y^2)\, dx + 2xy\, dy]$$

is independent of the path, and determine its value.

2. Test the following for independence of path:

    (a) $\int (y \cos x\, dx + \sin x\, dy)$;

    (b) $\int [(x^2 - y^2)\, dx + 2xy\, dy]$;

    (c) $\int [(x - y^2)\, dx + 2xy\, dy]$;

    (d) $\int [(x^3 - y^2)\, dx - 2(x - 1)y\, dy]$.

3. Show that $\int_{(0,0)}^{(1,1)} \left[\dfrac{(1 - y^2)}{(1 + x)^3}\, dx + \dfrac{y}{(1 + x)^2}\, dy \right]$ is independent of the path, and find its value.

4. Show that the line integral

$$\int_C \left[\frac{-y\, dx}{x^2 + y^2} + \frac{x\, dy}{x^2 + y^2} \right]$$

evaluated along a square 2 units on the side and with center at the origin has the value 2π. Give the reason for failure of this integral to vanish along this closed path.

5. Find the values of the following line integrals:

    (a) $\int_{(0,0)}^{\left(\frac{\pi}{2}, \frac{\pi}{2}\right)} (y \cos x\, dx + \sin x\, dy)$;

    (b) $\int_{(0,0)}^{\left(\frac{1}{2}, \frac{1}{2}\right)} \left(\dfrac{xy\, dx}{\sqrt{1 - x^2}} - \sqrt{1 - x^2}\, dy \right)$;

    (c) $\int_{(1,1)}^{(2,3)} [(x + 1)\, dx + (y + 1)\, dy]$.

64. Multiply Connected Regions. It was shown that the necessary and sufficient condition for the vanishing of the line integral $\int_C [M(x, y)\, dx + N(x, y)\, dy]$ around the closed path C is the equality of $\partial M/\partial y$ and $\partial N/\partial x$ at every point of the region enclosed by C. It was assumed that C was drawn in a simply connected region R and that the functions $M(x, y)$ and $N(x, y)$, together with their first partial derivatives, were continuous on and in the interior of C. The latter condition was imposed in order to ensure the integrability of the functions involved. The reason for imposing the restriction on the connectivity of the region essentially lies in the type of regions permitted by Green's theorem.

Thus, consider a region R containing one hole (Fig. 60). The region R will be assumed to consist of the exterior of C_2 and the interior of C_1. Let a closed contour C be drawn, which lies entirely in R and encloses C_2. Now, even though the functions $M(x, y)$ and $N(x, y)$ together with their derivatives may be continuous in R, the integral

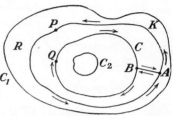

$$\int_C [M(x, y)\, dx + N(x, y)\, dy]$$

FIG. 60.

may not vanish. For let K be any other closed curve lying in R and enclosing C_2, and suppose that the points A and B of K and C are joined by a straight line AB. Consider the integrals

$$\int_{APA} + \int_{AB} + \int_{BQB} + \int_{BA},$$

where the subscripts on the integrals indicate the direction of integration along the curves K, C, and along the straight line AB, as is indicated in Fig. 60. Since the path AB is traversed twice, in opposite directions, the second and the last of the integrals above will annul each other, so that there will remain only the integral along K, traversed in the counterclockwise direction, and the integral along C, in the clockwise direction. Now, if M and N satisfy the conditions of Theorem 1, Sec. 63, then

$$\int_{\circlearrowleft K} (M\, dx + N\, dy) + \int_{\circlearrowright C} (M\, dx + N\, dy) = 0,$$

where the arrows on the circles indicate the direction of integration. Thus,

(64-1) $$\int_{\circlearrowleft K} (M\, dx + N\, dy) = \int_{\circlearrowleft C} (M\, dx + N\, dy),$$

both integrals being taken in the counterclockwise direction.

The important statement embodied in (64-1) is that the magnitude of the line integral evaluated over a closed path in R, surrounding the hole, has the same constant value whatever be the path enclosing C_2. This value need not be zero, as is seen from a simple example already mentioned in Sec. 63. Thus, let the region R consist of the exterior of the circle of radius unity and with center at the origin and of the interior of a concentric circle of radius 3 (Fig. 61).

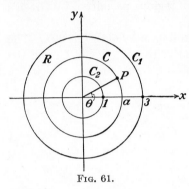

FIG. 61.

The functions $M = \dfrac{-y}{x^2 + y^2}$ and $N = \dfrac{x}{x^2 + y^2}$, and their derivatives, obviously satisfy the conditions of continuity in R and on C_1 and C_2. Also, $\partial M/\partial y = \partial N/\partial x$. But

$$\int_C \left(\frac{-y\,dx}{x^2 + y^2} + \frac{x}{x^2 + y^2}\,dy \right),$$

where C is the circle

$$x = a \cos \theta,$$
$$y = a \sin \theta, \qquad (1 < a < 3),$$

gives

$$\int_0^{2\pi} \frac{a^2 \sin^2 \theta + a^2 \cos^2 \theta}{a^2}\,d\theta = 2\pi.$$

The function $F(x, y)$, of which $M(x, y)\,dx + N(x, y)\,dy$ is an exact differential, is $F(x, y) = \tan^{-1} \dfrac{y}{x}$, which is a multiple-valued function.

The function

$$F(x, y) = \int_{(a,b)}^{(x,y)} [M(x, y)\,dx + N(x, y)\,dy],$$

where M and N satisfy the conditions of Theorem 1, Sec. 63, will be single-valued if the region R is simply connected (as is required in Theorem 1) but not necessarily so if the region is multiply connected.

65. Line Integrals in Space. The line integral over a space curve C is defined in a way entirely analogous to that described in Sec. 63.

Let C be a continuous space curve joining the points A and B, and let $P(x, y, z)$, $Q(x, y, z)$, and $R(x, y, z)$ be three continuous, single-valued functions of the variables x, y, z. Divide the curve C into n arcs Δs_i, $(i = 1, 2, \cdots, n)$, whose projections on the coordinate axes are Δx_i, Δy_i, Δz_i, and form the sum

$$\sum_{i=1}^{n} [P(\xi_i, \eta_i, \zeta_i)\, \Delta x_i + Q(\xi_i, \eta_i, \zeta_i)\, \Delta y_i + R(\xi_i, \eta_i, \zeta_i)\, \Delta z_i],$$

where (ξ_i, η_i, ζ_i) is a point chosen at random on the arc Δs_i. The limit of this sum as n increases indefinitely in such a way that all $\Delta s_i \rightarrow 0$ is called the *line integral* of $P\,dx + Q\,dy + R\,dz$, taken along C between the points A and B. It is denoted by the symbol

$$(65\text{-}1) \quad \int_C [P(x, y, z)\, dx + Q(x, y, z)\, dy + R(x, y, z)\, dz].$$

The conditions imposed upon the functions P, Q, and R are sufficient to ensure the existence of the limit, provided that the curve C is suitably restricted.

If the equation of the space curve C is given in parametric form as

$$(65\text{-}2) \qquad \begin{cases} x = f_1(t), \\ y = f_2(t), \\ z = f_3(t), \end{cases} \qquad (t_0 \le t \le t_1),$$

where $f_1(t)$, $f_2(t)$, and $f_3(t)$ possess continuous derivatives in the interval $t_0 \le t \le t_1$, the line integral (65-1) can be expressed as a definite integral

$$\int_{t_0}^{t_1} [P \cdot f_1'(t) + Q \cdot f_2'(t) + R \cdot f_3'(t)]\, dt,$$

where P, Q, and R are expressed in terms of t with the aid of (65-2).

It is possible to derive three theorems analogous to those given in Sec. 63 for line integrals in the plane. They are as follows:

THEOREM 1. *Let a simply connected region of space be one in which* $P(x, y, z)$, $Q(x, y, z)$, *and* $R(x, y, z)$ *and their partial derivatives are continuous and single-valued functions of* x, y, *and* z. *Then the necessary and sufficient condition that*

$$\int (P \, dx + Q \, dy + R \, dz) = 0$$

around every closed curve in the region is that

$$\frac{\partial P}{\partial y} = \frac{\partial Q}{\partial x}, \qquad \frac{\partial Q}{\partial z} = \frac{\partial R}{\partial y}, \qquad \frac{\partial R}{\partial x} = \frac{\partial P}{\partial z},$$

for every point of the region.

THEOREM 2. *Let the functions considered satisfy the conditions of Theorem 1. Then the necessary and sufficient condition that*

$$\int_{(a,b,c)}^{(x,y,z)} (P \, dx + Q \, dy + R \, dz)$$

be independent of the path from (a, b, c) *to* (x, y, z) *is that*

$$\frac{\partial P}{\partial y} = \frac{\partial Q}{\partial x}, \qquad \frac{\partial Q}{\partial z} = \frac{\partial R}{\partial y}, \qquad \frac{\partial R}{\partial x} = \frac{\partial P}{\partial z},$$

for every point of the region.

THEOREM 3. *Let the functions* P, Q, *and* R *satisfy the conditions of Theorem 1. Then, the necessary and sufficient condition that there exist a function* $F(x, y, z)$ *such that*

$$\frac{\partial F}{\partial x} = P, \qquad \frac{\partial F}{\partial y} = Q, \qquad \frac{\partial F}{\partial z} = R$$

is that

$$\frac{\partial P}{\partial y} = \frac{\partial Q}{\partial x}, \qquad \frac{\partial Q}{\partial z} = \frac{\partial R}{\partial y}, \qquad \frac{\partial R}{\partial x} = \frac{\partial P}{\partial z},$$

for every point of the region. The function $F(x, y, z)$ *is given by the formula*

$$F(x, y, z) = \int_{(a,b,c)}^{(x,y,z)} (P \, dx + Q \, dy + R \, dz).$$

COROLLARY. *The necessary and sufficient condition that*

$$P \, dx + Q \, dy + R \, dz$$

be an exact differential of some function $\Phi(x, y, z)$ *is that*

$$\frac{\partial P}{\partial y} = \frac{\partial Q}{\partial x}, \qquad \frac{\partial Q}{\partial z} = \frac{\partial R}{\partial y}, \qquad \frac{\partial R}{\partial x} = \frac{\partial P}{\partial z},$$

for every point of the region. The function $\Phi(x, y, z)$ *is determined from the formula*

$$\Phi(x, y, z) = \int_{(a,b,c)}^{(x,y,z)} (P \, dx + Q \, dy + R \, dz) + \text{const.}$$

These results are of particular importance in hydrodynamics and the theory of electromagnetism. The vector derivation and interpretation of these results are given in Chap. IX on Vector Analysis.

66. Illustrations of the Application of the Line Integrals.

1. *Work.* It will be assumed that a force $F(x, y)$ acts at every point of the xy-plane (Fig. 62). This force varies from point to point in magnitude and direction.

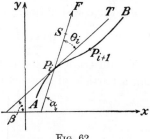

FIG. 62.

An example of such conditions is the case of an electric field of force. The problem is to determine the work done on a particle moving from the point $A(a, b)$ to the point $B(c, d)$ along some curve C. Divide the arc AB of C into n segments by the points $P_1, P_2, \cdots, P_{n-1}$, and let $\Delta s_i = P_i P_{i+1}$. Then the force acting at P_i is $F(x_i, y_i)$. Let it be directed along the line $P_i S$, and let $P_i T$ be the tangent to C at P_i, making an angle θ_i with $P_i S$.

The component of $F(x_i, y_i)$ along $P_i T$ is $F \cos \theta_i$ and the element of work done on the particle in moving through the distance Δs_i is approximately $F(x_i, y_i) \cos \theta_i \, \Delta s_i$. The smaller Δs_i, the better this approximation will be. Therefore, the work done in moving the particle from A to B along C is

$$W = \lim_{n \to \infty} \sum_{i=0}^{n-1} F(x_i, y_i) \cos \theta_i \, \Delta s_i \equiv \int_C F(x, y) \cos \theta \, ds.$$

If α is the inclination of $P_i S$ and β is the inclination of $P_i T$, then $\theta = \alpha - \beta$ and $\cos \theta = \cos \alpha \cos \beta + \sin \alpha \sin \beta$, so that

$$(66\text{-}1) \quad W = \int_C F(x, y) \, (\cos \alpha \cos \beta + \sin \alpha \sin \beta) \, ds.$$

From the definition of α, it is evident that

$$F \cos \alpha = x\text{-component of } F \equiv X,$$
$$F \sin \alpha = y\text{-component of } F \equiv Y.$$

Moreover, since $dx/ds = \cos \beta$ and $dy/ds = \sin \beta$,

$$\cos \beta \, ds = dx \quad \text{and} \quad \sin \beta \, ds = dy.$$

Therefore, (66-1) becomes

$$W = \int_C (X \, dx + Y \, dy),$$

which is a line integral of the form (60-1).

If C is a space curve, then an argument in every respect similar to the foregoing shows that the work done in producing a displacement along a curve C in a field of force where the components along the coordinate axes are X, Y, and Z is

$$W = \int_C (X \, dx + Y \, dy + Z \, dz).$$

To illustrate the use of this formula, the work done in displacing a particle of mass m along some curve C, joining the points

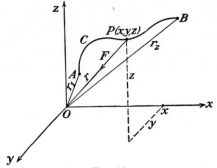

Fig. 63.

A and B, will be calculated. It will be assumed that the particle is moving under the Newtonian law of attraction

$$F = \frac{km}{r^2},$$

where k is the gravitational constant and r is the distance from the center of attraction O (containing a unit mass) to a position of the particle (Fig. 63).

The component of force in the direction of the positive x-axis is

$$X = F \cos (x, r) = - \frac{km}{r^2} \cdot \frac{x}{r}.$$

Similarly,

$$Y = - \frac{km}{r^2} \cdot \frac{y}{r} \quad \text{and} \quad Z = - \frac{km}{r^2} \cdot \frac{z}{r}.$$

The work done in displacing the particle from A to B is

$$W = -\int_A^B \frac{km}{r^3}\,(x\,dx + y\,dy + z\,dz).$$

But

$$r = \sqrt{x^2 + y^2 + z^2} \quad \text{and} \quad dr = \frac{x\,dx + y\,dy + z\,dz}{r}.$$

Therefore,

$$W = -km\int_A^B \frac{dr}{r^2} = km\left[\frac{1}{r}\right]_A^B,$$

which depends only on the coordinates of the points A and B and not on the path C. Denoting the distances from O to A and B by r_1 and r_2, respectively, gives

$$W = km\left(\frac{1}{r_2} - \frac{1}{r_1}\right).$$

The quantity $\Phi \equiv km/r$ is known as the gravitational potential of the mass m. It is easily checked that

$$X = \frac{\partial\Phi}{\partial x}, \qquad Y = \frac{\partial\Phi}{\partial y}, \qquad Z = \frac{\partial\Phi}{\partial z},$$

so that the partial derivatives of the potential function Φ give the components of force along the coordinate axes. Moreover, the directional derivative of Φ in any direction s is

$$\begin{aligned}
\frac{d\Phi}{ds} &= \frac{\partial\Phi}{\partial x}\frac{dx}{ds} + \frac{\partial\Phi}{\partial y}\frac{dy}{ds} + \frac{\partial\Phi}{\partial z}\frac{dz}{ds}\\
&= X\cos(x, s) + Y\cos(y, s) + Z\cos(z, s)\\
&= F_s,
\end{aligned}$$

where F_s is the component of force in the direction s.

A conservative field of force is defined as a field of force in which the work done in producing a displacement between two fixed points is independent of the path. It is clear that in a conservative field the integral

$$\int_C (X\,dx + Y\,dy + Z\,dz)$$

along every closed path is zero, so that the integrand is an **exact** differential.

2. *Flow of a Liquid.* Let C be a curve on a plane surface across which a liquid is flowing. The xy-plane will be chosen to coincide with the surface. The lines of flow are indicated in Fig. 64 by the curved arrows. It will be assumed that the flow of the liquid takes place in planes parallel to the xy-plane and that the depth of the liquid is unity. The problem is to determine the amount of liquid that flows across C in a unit of time.

If v_i is the velocity of the liquid and α_i is the inclination of the tangent to the line of flow at P_i, then $v_x|_i = v_i \cos \alpha_i$ is the x-component of v_i and $v_y|_i = v_i \sin \alpha_i$ is the y-component of v_i. Let Δs_i denote the segment $P_i P_{i+1}$ of C. A particle at P_i will move in time Δt to P'_i, while a particle at P_{i+1} will move to P'_{i+1}. Therefore, the amount of liquid crossing $P_i P_{i+1}$ in time Δt is equal to the volume of the cylinder whose altitude is unity and whose base is $P_i P_{i+1} P'_{i+1} P'_i$. Aside from infinitesimals of higher order, this volume is

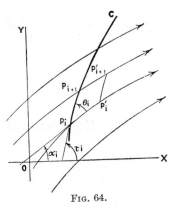

FIG. 64.

$$\Delta V_i = P_i P'_i \cdot P_i P_{i+1} \sin \theta_i,$$

in which θ_i denotes the angle between $P_i P'_i$ and $P_i P_{i+1}$. But $P_i P_{i+1} = \Delta s_i$ and, except for infinitesimals of higher order, $P_i P'_i = v_i \Delta t$. Therefore, $\Delta V_i = v_i \Delta t \cdot \Delta s_i \sin \theta_i$. The volume of liquid crossing C in a unit of time is

$$V = \lim_{n \to \infty} \sum_{i=1}^{n} v_i \sin \theta_i \, \Delta s_i.$$

If τ_i denotes the inclination of the tangent to C at P_i, then $\tau_i = \theta_i + \alpha_i$. Therefore,

$$\begin{aligned}
v_i \sin \theta_i \, \Delta s_i &= v_i(\sin \tau_i \cos \alpha_i - \cos \tau_i \sin \alpha_i) \, \Delta s_i \\
&= v_i \cos \alpha_i \sin \tau_i \, \Delta s_i - v_i \sin \alpha_i \cos \tau_i \, \Delta s_i \\
&= v_x|_i \, \Delta y_i - v_y|_i \, \Delta x_i.
\end{aligned}$$

Hence,

(66-2)
$$V = \int_C (-v_y \, dx + v_x \, dy)$$

is the line integral which gives the amount of liquid that crosses C in a unit of time.

If the contour C is a closed one and the liquid is incompressible, then the net amount of liquid crossing C is zero, since as much liquid enters the region as leaves it. This is on the assumption, of course, that the interior of C contains no sources or sinks. Thus, a steady flow of incompressible liquid is characterized by the equation

$$\int_C (-v_y \, dx + v_x \, dy) = 0,$$

over any closed contour not containing sources or sinks. This implies that (see Sec. 63)

$$(66\text{-}3) \qquad\qquad -\frac{\partial v_y}{\partial y} = \frac{\partial v_x}{\partial x},$$

which is an important equation of hydrodynamics known as the *equation of continuity*. Moreover, from Theorem 3, Sec. 63, it is known that there exists a function Ψ such that

$$(66\text{-}4) \qquad\qquad \frac{\partial \Psi}{\partial x} = -v_y \qquad \text{and} \qquad \frac{\partial \Psi}{\partial y} = v_x.$$

This function Ψ is called the *stream function*, and it has a simple physical meaning, for

$$\Psi(x, y) = \int_{(a,b)}^{(x,y)} (-v_y \, dx + v_x \, dy)$$

represents the amount of liquid crossing, per unit time, any curve joining (a, b) with (x, y).

The function defined by the integral

$$(66\text{-}5) \qquad\qquad \Phi(x, y) = \int_{(a,b)}^{(x,y)} (v_x \, dx + v_y \, dy)$$

is called the *velocity potential*. It is readily shown that

$$(66\text{-}6) \qquad\qquad \frac{\partial \Phi}{\partial x} = v_x \qquad \text{and} \qquad \frac{\partial \Phi}{\partial y} = v_y.$$

Upon comparing (66-4) with (66-6), it is seen that

$$\frac{\partial \Phi}{\partial x} = \frac{\partial \Psi}{\partial y} \qquad \text{and} \qquad \frac{\partial \Phi}{\partial y} = -\frac{\partial \Psi}{\partial x}.$$

These are the celebrated Cauchy-Riemann differential equations.

If the integral (66-2) around a closed curve C does not vanish, then the region bounded by C may contain sources (if V is positive) or sinks (if V is negative). The presence of sources or sinks is characterized by the singularities of the function Ψ, that is, those points for which Ψ is not continuous or where its derivatives may cease to be continuous.*

The foregoing discussion is readily generalized to a steady flow of liquids in space. Instead of the integral (66-5), one will have

$$\Phi(x, y, z) = \int_{(a,b,c)}^{(x,y,z)} (v_x \, dx + v_y \, dy + v_z \, dz),$$

and if the integral is independent of the path C drawn in a simply connected region, the equations corresponding to (66-3) are

$$\frac{\partial v_x}{\partial y} - \frac{\partial v_y}{\partial x} = 0, \qquad \frac{\partial v_z}{\partial y} - \frac{\partial v_y}{\partial z} = 0, \qquad \frac{\partial v_x}{\partial z} - \frac{\partial v_z}{\partial x} = 0.$$

In such a case the integrand is an exact differential, and the velocity potential $\Phi(x, y, z)$ gives

$$\frac{\partial \Phi}{\partial x} = v_x, \qquad \frac{\partial \Phi}{\partial y} = v_y, \qquad \frac{\partial \Phi}{\partial z} = v_z.$$

3. *Thermodynamics.* A thermodynamical state of any substance is found to be characterized by the following physical quantities: (1) pressure p, (2) volume v, and (3) absolute temperature T. The pressure, volume, and temperature are connected by the equation

(66-7) $$F(p, v, T) = 0,$$

so that any two of the three quantities p, v, and T will suffice to determine completely the state of the substance.

In the case of an ideal gas enclosed in a receptacle, Eq. (66-7) has the form

$$pv - RT = 0,$$

where R is a constant. Let p and v be chosen to determine the state of the gas, and consider p and v as the coordinates of a point P in the pv-plane. As the state of the gas changes, the point P, which characterizes the state, will describe some curve C in the pv-plane. If the process is cyclic, so that the substance returns to its original state, then the curve C will be a closed one.

It is important to know the amount Q of heat lost or absorbed by the gas while the gas in the receptacle (for example, steam in

---

* See in this connection Sec. 64.

an engine cylinder) changes its state. Let Δp, Δv, and ΔT be small changes in the pressure, volume, and temperature, respectively. Now if any two of these quantities, say p and v, do not change, then the amount of heat supplied is nearly proportional to the change in the remaining quantity. If all three quantities change, then the total change ΔQ in the amount of heat supplied is approximately equal to the sum of the quantities ΔQ_1, ΔQ_2, and ΔQ_3, due to changes Δp, Δv, and ΔT, respectively.*
Thus,

$$\Delta Q = \Delta Q_1 + \Delta Q_2 + \Delta Q_3$$
$$\doteq c_1 \Delta p + c_2 \Delta v + c_3 \Delta T,$$

where c_1, c_2, and c_3 are constants of proportionality. Then, the total amount of heat supplied in the process is given by the equation

$$(66\text{-}8) \qquad Q = \int_C (c_1 \, dp + c_2 \, dv + c_3 \, dT).$$

Solving (66-7) for T in terms of p and v gives $T = f(p, v)$, so that

$$dT = \frac{\partial f}{\partial p} \, dp + \frac{\partial f}{\partial v} \, dv.$$

If this expression is substituted in (66-8), one obtains

$$(66\text{-}9) \quad Q = \int_C \left[\left(c_1 + c_3 \frac{\partial f}{\partial p} \right) dp + \left(c_2 + c_3 \frac{\partial f}{\partial v} \right) dv \right],$$

where the integration is performed over the curve C in the pv-plane, which is called the pv diagram.

Consider the state of the gas in the cylinder of a steam engine, and let the piston be displaced through a distance Δs. Then, if the area of the piston is A, the work ΔW performed by the piston is given by

$$\Delta W = pA \, \Delta s = p \, \Delta v,$$

and the total work W performed during one cycle is

$$W = \int_C p \, dv.$$

It follows from (61-4) that this is precisely equal to the **area of** the pv diagram.

---

* This principle is called the principle of superposition of effects.

In deriving (66-9), it was assumed that p and v were the independent variables, and it followed, upon making use of (66-7), that the increment of heat is given by*

$$dQ = \left(c_1 + c_3 \frac{\partial f}{\partial p}\right) dp + \left(c_2 + c_3 \frac{\partial f}{\partial v}\right) dv$$
$$\equiv P(p, v) \, dp + V(p, v) \, dv,$$

where P and V are known functions of p and v. The expression for dQ is not, in general, an exact differential (that is, $\partial P/\partial v \neq \partial V/\partial p$), for the line integral (66-9) need not vanish for a cyclic process. However, it is possible to state that the difference between dQ and the work $p \, dv$ is an exact differential, namely,

(66-10) $$dU \equiv dQ - p \, dv,$$

where the function U is called the internal energy of the gas.

It is also possible to state† that the ratio of dQ to the absolute temperature, namely,

(66-11) $$dS \equiv \frac{dQ}{T}$$

is likewise an exact differential. The function S is called the entropy, and it plays a fundamental role in all investigations in thermodynamics.

The formulas (66-10) and (66-11) can be used to show that for an isothermal process (that is, when $dT = 0$)

$$dQ = p \, dv,$$

so that all the heat absorbed by the gas goes into the performance of the work $p \, dv$. If the process is adiabatic (that is, such that there is no gain or loss of heat), then $dQ = 0$ and, therefore, $dS = 0$. It follows that the entropy S is constant during such a process.

* By making use of T and v, or T and p, as the independent variables, it is possible to write down two other important expressions for dQ.

† These assertions follow from the first and second laws of thermodynamics.

CHAPTER VII

ORDINARY DIFFERENTIAL EQUATIONS

67. Preliminary Remarks. The great usefulness of mathematics in the natural sciences derives from the fact that it is possible to formulate many laws governing natural phenomena with the aid of the unambiguous language of mathematics. Some of the natural laws, for example those dealing with the rates of change, are best expressed by means of equations involving derivatives or differentials.

Any function containing variables and their derivatives (or differentials) is called a *differential expression*, and every equation involving differential expressions is called a *differential equation*. Differential equations are divided into two classes, *ordinary* and *partial*. The former contain only one independent variable and derivatives with respect to it. The latter contain more than one independent variable.

The order of the highest derivative contained in a differential equation is called the *order* of the differential equation. Thus,

$$\left(\frac{d^2y}{dx^2}\right)^4 + 3\frac{dy}{dx} + 5y^2 = 0$$

is an ordinary differential equation of order 2, and

$$\left(\frac{\partial^3 y}{\partial t^3}\right)^2 + 3\frac{\partial^2 y}{\partial x\,\partial t} + yxt = 0$$

is a partial differential equation of order 3.

When a differential equation can be expressed as a polynomial in all the derivatives involved, the exponent of the highest derivative is called the *degree* of the equation. In the foregoing examples the degree of the ordinary equation is 4 and that of the partial differential equation is 2. It should be observed that the degree of

$$\frac{d^3y}{dx^3} + \sqrt{\frac{dy}{dx} + y^4} = 0$$

is 2, when this equation is rationalized

225

If an ordinary differential equation is of the first degree in the dependent variable and all its derivatives, it is called a *linear differential equation.* The general form for a linear differential equation of the nth order is

$$p_0(x) \frac{d^n y}{dx^n} + p_1(x) \frac{d^{n-1}y}{dx^{n-1}} + \cdots + p_{n-1}(x) \frac{dy}{dx} + p_n(x)y = f(x),$$

where the $p_i(x)$ and $f(x)$ are functions of x only.

An explicit function $y = f(x)$, or an equation $\varphi(x, y) = 0$ which defines y as an implicit function of x, is said to be a solution of the differential equation

(67-1) $$F[x, y, y', y'', \cdots, y^{(n)}] = 0,$$

provided that, whenever the values of y, y', y'', $\cdots$, $y^{(n)}$ are substituted in the left-hand member of (67-1), the latter vanishes identically.

For example,

(67-2) $$\frac{dy}{dx} + y \cos x = 0$$

has a solution

$$y = e^{-\sin x}, \quad \text{or} \quad \log y + \sin x = 0,$$

because the substitution of y and y' calculated from either one of these expressions reduces (67-2) to an identity $0 = 0$. Thus, differentiation of the second equation gives $\frac{1}{y}\frac{dy}{dx} + \cos x = 0$, so that $y' = -y \cos x$, and substitution in (67-2) gives $0 = 0$.

The graph of a solution of an ordinary differential equation is called an *integral curve* of the equation.

PROBLEM

Classify the following differential equations, and determine their orders and degrees:

(a) $\dfrac{d^4 y}{dx^4} + \left(\dfrac{dy}{dx}\right)^3 - y^2 = 0;$

(b) $\dfrac{\partial^4 z}{\partial x^4} + 2 \dfrac{\partial^2 z}{\partial x\, \partial y} + \dfrac{\partial^4 z}{\partial y^4} = 0;$

(c) $\dfrac{dy}{dx} + \sin y + x = 0;$

(d) $\dfrac{d^2 y}{dx^2} - \sqrt{1 - y^2}\, \dfrac{dy}{dx} = 0;$

(e) $y'' - \sqrt{1 - x^2}\, y' + 5y = 0;$

(f) $\dfrac{\partial^2 y}{\partial t^2} = k^2 \dfrac{\partial^2 y}{\partial x^2};$

(g) $y'' + x^2 y' + xy = \sin x;$

(h) $\dfrac{\partial z}{\partial t} = a^2 \left(\dfrac{\partial^2 z}{\partial x^2} + \dfrac{\partial^2 z}{\partial y^2} \right).$

68. Remarks on Solutions.   Consider a differential equation of the first order,

(68-1) $$\frac{dy}{dx} = f(x, y),$$

where $f(x, y)$ is a single-valued and continuous function of the variables x and y. If a point (x_0, y_0) is chosen in the xy-plane and its coordinates are substituted in (68-1), then

$$\frac{dy}{dx} = f(x_0, y_0)$$

determines a direction associated with the point (x_0, y_0), since dy/dx can be interpreted geometrically as the slope of an integral curve. If a second point (x_1, y_1) is chosen and its coordinates are substituted in (68-1), a direction is associated with (x_1, y_1). Continuing in this way, it is possible to find a direction associated with every point of the plane for which $f(x, y)$ is defined. Now, suppose that a point (x_0, y_0) is chosen in the plane (Fig. 65) and the direction associated with this point is determined. Let (x_1, y_1) be a point very near to (x_0, y_0) and in the direction specified by

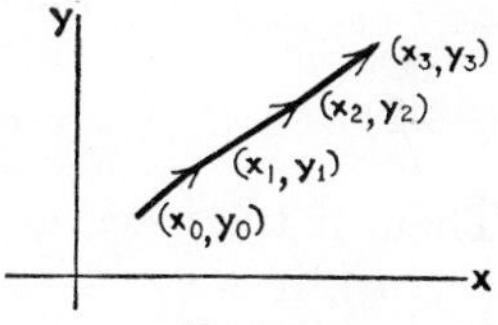

Fig. 65.

$$\frac{dy}{dx} = f(x_0, y_0).$$

Then,

$$\frac{dy}{dx} = f(x_1, y_1)$$

determines a new direction. Upon proceeding a short distance in this new direction, a third direction given by

$$\frac{dy}{dx} = f(x_2, y_2)$$

is determined by the selection of a point (x_2, y_2) which is close to (x_1, y_1). If this process is continued, there will be built up a curve made up of short straight-line segments. If the points (x_0, y_0), (x_1, y_1), (x_2, y_2), $\cdots$, (x_n, y_n) are chosen very close together, it becomes intuitively clear that this series of straight-line segments approximates a smooth curve associated with the initial point (x_0, y_0). Evidently, the equation of this curve will be a solution of the differential equation (68-1), for the slope of the curve is

$$\frac{dy}{dx} = f(x, y).$$

In general, a different choice of (x_0, y_0) will lead to a different integral curve and thus to a different solution of (68-1).

The foregoing discussion forms the basis of one method of graphical solution of differential equations of the first order. Another important method of approximate solution of differential equations is the method of infinite series, which is outlined next.

Let it be supposed that the function $f(x, y)$ in (68-1) can be expanded in Taylor's series about the point (x_0, y_0); then the solution of (68-1) can be obtained in the form of a power series in $x - x_0$. Indeed, denote the solution of (68-1) by

(68-2) $$y = F(x).$$

Then, if the integral curve defined by (68-2) is to pass through (x_0, y_0), it is necessary that

$$y = F(x_0) = y_0.$$

Substituting the coordinates of (x_0, y_0) in (68-1) gives

$$\frac{dy}{dx} = f(x_0, y_0) = F'(x_0).$$

Differentiating (68-1) yields

(68-3) $$\frac{d^2y}{dx^2} = \frac{\partial f(x, y)}{\partial x} + \frac{\partial f(x, y)}{\partial y}\frac{dy}{dx},$$

so that the value of the second derivative of (68-2) at x_0 is

$$F''(x_0) = \left(\frac{d^2y}{dx^2}\right)_{x_0, y_0} = \frac{\partial f(x_0, y_0)}{\partial x} + \frac{\partial f(x_0, y_0)}{\partial y}F'(x_0).$$

The formula (68-3) can be used to calculate d^3y/dx^3, and its value at the point (x_0, y_0) can be obtained, for the values of the first and second derivatives of $F(x)$ at $x = x_0$ are already known.

In this manner, one can attempt to find the solution of (68-1) in the form of the series

$$y = F(x_0) + F'(x_0)(x - x_0) + \frac{F''(x_0)}{2!}(x - x_0)^2 + \cdots.$$

In essence, this method of solution is the same as the method of undetermined coefficients that is discussed in Sec. 98. Another important method, due to the French mathematician E. Picard, is discussed in Sec. 103.

Next consider a family of curves

$$(68\text{-}4) \qquad\qquad y = x^2 + c,$$

where c is an arbitrary constant. Differentiation of (68-4) gives

$$\frac{dy}{dx} = 2x,$$

which is the differential equation of the family of curves (68-4), and which is free from arbitrary constants. If the given functional relation contains two arbitrary constants, as, for example,

$$y = c_1 \sin^{-1} x + c_2,$$

then it is possible to eliminate these constants c_1 and c_2 by two differentiations. The first differentiation gives

$$\frac{dy}{dx} = \frac{c_1}{\sqrt{1 - x^2}}.$$

Solving for c_1 yields

$$c_1 = \sqrt{1 - x^2}\,\frac{dy}{dx},$$

and differentiation of this equation gives

$$\frac{d^2y}{dx^2} - \frac{x}{1 - x^2}\frac{dy}{dx} = 0.$$

This is a differential equation of the second order, and clearly it has $y = c_1 \sin^{-1} x + c_2$ as a solution. It should be observed that two differentiations were necessary in order to eliminate two arbitrary constants.

In general, if $f(x, y, c_1, c_2, \cdots, c_n) = 0$ is a functional relation involving n arbitrary constants and defining y as a function of x, then n successive differentiations will produce n equations involving derivatives up to and including those of the nth order. These n equations together with the given equation $f(x, y, c_1, c_2, \cdots, c_n) = 0$ can be used to eliminate the n constants $c_1, c_2, \cdots, c_n$, and the result will be a differential equation of the nth order whose solution is $f(x, y, c_1, c_2, \cdots, c_n) = 0$. It can be shown that, in general, a differential equation of the nth order has a solution which contains n arbitrary constants. Moreover, no solution of a differential equation of the nth order can contain more than n arbitrary constants. A solution that contains n arbitrary constants is called the *general solution* of the differential equation.

The foregoing discussion does not prove these facts. It merely suggests that a functional relation containing n arbitrary constants leads to a differential equation of order n. For the proof of this theorem and its converse, any advanced treatise on differential equations* can be consulted.

Any solution that is obtained from the general solution by specifying the values of the arbitrary constants is called a *particular solution*. Particular solutions are usually the ones that are of interest in applications of differential equations. It should be remarked, however, that some differential equations possess solutions which cannot be obtained from the general solution by specifying the values of the arbitrary constants. Some examples illustrating the existence of such solutions are given in Sec. 83.

PROBLEMS

Find the differential equations of the following families of curves:

1. $x^2 + cx + y = c^2$.

2. $c_1 \sin x + c_2 \cos x = y$.

3. $c_1 x + c_2 e^x + c_3 e^{-x} = y$.

4. $ce^x - xy + e^{-x} = 0$.

5. $(x - c_1)^2 + (y - c_2)^2 = 1$.

6. $y = c_1 e^x \sin x + c_2 e^x \cos x$.

7. $c^2 x + cy + 1 = 0$.

8. $c_1^2 x + c_1 y + c_2 = 0$.

9. $y = c_1 x^3 + c_2 x^2 + c_3 x$.

* See INCE, E. L. Ordinary Differential Equations.

10. $y^2 - 4cx = 0.$

11. $y = c_1 e^{2x} + c_2 e^{3x} + x.$

69. Newtonian Laws. In order to illustrate the prominence of the subject of differential equations in a study of various phenomena, the next four sections are primarily concerned with the task of setting up the differential equations from the basic physical principles. A systematic treatment of the problem of solving various types of differential equations frequently occurring in practice will be given in the subsequent sections.

The formulation of the basic principles from which many differential equations arise rests on the following fundamental laws of dynamics, which were enunciated by Sir Isaac Newton.

1. Every particle persists in its state of rest or moves in a straight line with constant speed unless it is compelled by some force to change that state.

2. The rate of change of momentum of a particle is proportional to the force acting on it and is in the direction of the force.

3. Action and reaction are equal and opposite.

The first law merely states that any change of velocity of a particle (that is, acceleration) is the result of some external force. The second law postulates that the resultant force f acting on a particle is proportional to the product of the mass m by its acceleration a; for momentum is defined as the product of mass m and velocity v, and the rate of change of momentum is

$$\frac{d}{dt}(mv) = m\frac{dv}{dt} = ma.$$

Thus,

$$ma = kf,$$

where k is the proportionality constant, which can be made equal to unity by a proper choice of units.

Obviously, the second law includes the first; for if the force acting on a particle is zero, then its acceleration is zero and the particle must either remain at rest or move with constant velocity.

The third law asserts that, if two particles exert forces on each other, then the force exerted by the first on the second is equal to the force exerted by the second on the first. This law can be used to define the mass of a body.

Frequent use of these laws will be made in the following page. There is one more law, formulated by Newton, that will be found of cardinal importance in this study. It is the law of gravitation. Newton was led to it by his attempts to explain the motions of the planets. This law states that two bodies attract each other with a force proportional to the product of their masses and inversely proportional to the square of the distance between them, the distance being large compared with the dimensions of the bodies. If the force of attraction is denoted by F, the masses of the two bodies by m_1 and m_2, and the distance between them by r, then

(69-1) $$F = \frac{Km_1m_2}{r^2},$$

where K is the proportionality constant, called the gravitational constant. In the c.g.s. system the value of K is 6.664×10^{-8}.

The three fundamental principles formulated by Newton in reality form the postulates of dynamics and furnish a definition of force, and the law of gravitation permits one to compare masses with the aid of the beam balance.

The law of attraction (69-1) assumes a simpler form in the case of a small body of mass m falling to the earth from heights that are not too great. It can be established that a sphere attracts a particle at an external point as if the whole mass of the sphere were collected at its center.* If the height of the particle above the earth's surface is small compared with the radius of the earth, the law of attraction becomes, since r in (69-1) is sensibly constant and equal to the radius of the earth,

(69-2) $$F = mg,$$

where g is a new constant called the acceleration due to gravity. Its value in the c.g.s. system is approximately 980 cm. per second per second and in the f.p.s. system 32.2 ft. per second per second.

Thus, the differential equation of the falling body can be written as

(69-3) $$\frac{d^2s}{dt^2} = g,$$

where s is the distance traveled by the body and t is the time in seconds. Integration of (69-3) gives

* In this connection, see Secs. 16 and 66.

(69-4) $$\frac{ds}{dt} = gt + v_0;$$

and, since the velocity v is equal to ds/dt, (69-4) may be written

$$v = gt + v_0,$$

where v_0 is the constant of integration so chosen as to equal the initial velocity, that is, the value of v at the time $t = 0$.

Integrating (69-4) gives

(69-5) $$s = \tfrac{1}{2}gt^2 + v_0 t + s_0,$$

where s_0 is the distance of the body from the point of reference at the time $t = 0$. Equation (69-5) furnishes all the desired information about the freely falling body.

70. Simple Harmonic Motion. Simple harmonic motion is the most important form of periodic motion. It represents a linear vibration of such a sort that the vibrating particle is accelerated toward the center of its path in such a way that the acceleration is proportional to the displacement of the particle from the center. If the displacement of the particle from its central position is denoted by x, the definition of simple harmonic motion demands that

(70-1) $$\frac{d^2x}{dt^2} = -\omega^2 x,$$

where ω^2 is a constant of proportionality and the negative sign signifies that the acceleration is directed oppositely to the displacement x.

In order to find the equation of motion, that is, the displacement of the particle in terms of the time t, multiply both sides of (70-1) by $2\dfrac{dx}{dt}$ and obtain

(70-2) $$2\,\frac{dx}{dt} \cdot \frac{d^2x}{dt^2} = -2\,\frac{dx}{dt}\,\omega^2 x.$$

The left-hand side of (70-2) is the derivative of $(dx/dt)^2$, and integration yields

$$\left(\frac{dx}{dt}\right)^2 = -\omega^2 x^2 + c^2,$$

where the constant of integration is written for convenience in the form c^2, for it must be positive; otherwise, the velocity dx/dt will be imaginary.

Extracting the square root and solving for dt give

$$dt = \frac{dx}{\sqrt{c^2 - \omega^2 x^2}},$$

which upon integration becomes

$$\frac{1}{\omega} \sin^{-1} \frac{\omega x}{c} = t + c_1$$

or

(70-3) $$x = A \sin (\omega t + B),$$

where $A = c/\omega$ and $B = c_1 \omega$. The period of the motion, $T = 2\pi/\omega$, is independent of the amplitude A.

It will be seen in the next section that (70-3) approximately represents the behavior of a simple pendulum.

71. Simple Pendulum. Let P be a position of the bob of a simple pendulum of mass m and of length l (Fig. 66), and let θ be the angle, measured in radians, made by OP with the position of equilibrium OQ. Denote the tangential acceleration by d^2s/dt^2, where s represents the displacement, considered positive to the right of OQ.

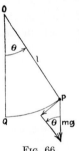

Fig. 66.

The acceleration d^2s/dt^2 along the path of the bob is produced by the tangential component of the force of gravity mg, so that its magnitude is $mg \sin \theta$. Since the velocity of the bob is decreasing when the bob is moving to the right of its position of equilibrium OQ, the acceleration will be negative. Hence, since force is equal to the product of mass and acceleration, one can write

(71-1) $$m \frac{d^2s}{dt^2} = -mg \sin \theta.$$

The normal component of the force of gravity acts along OP and is balanced by the reaction of the string (Newton's third law of motion) and centrifugal force.

Remembering that $s = l\theta$, (71-1) can be written as

(71-2) $$\frac{d^2\theta}{dt^2} = -\frac{g}{l} \sin \theta;$$

and if the angle θ is so small that* $\sin \theta$ can be replaced by θ,

(71-3)
$$\frac{d^2\theta}{dt^2} = -\frac{g}{l}\,\theta.$$

This equation is precisely of the form (70-1), and its general solution is

(71-4)
$$\theta = c_1 \sin\,(\omega t + c_2),$$

where c_1 and c_2 are arbitrary constants and $\omega^2 = g/l$.

However, from physical considerations it is clear that there is nothing arbitrary in the behavior of the pendulum. Moreover, it is known that, if the pendulum bob is held initially at an angle α and then released without receiving any impulse, the pendulum will vibrate in a perfectly definite manner, so that it must be possible to calculate the position of the bob at any later time t.

These remarks concerning the initial position of the pendulum bob and the fact that the bob was released with zero velocity can be stated mathematically as follows: If the time at which the pendulum was released is denoted by $t = 0$, then

(71-5)
$$\begin{cases} \theta = \alpha & \text{when } t = 0, \\ \dfrac{d\theta}{dt} = 0 & \text{when } t = 0. \end{cases}$$

Therefore, the general solution (71-4) of (71-3) must satisfy the initial conditions (71-5). Substituting the first of these initial conditions in (71-4) gives

(71-6)
$$\alpha = c_1 \sin c_2.$$

Differentiation of (71-4) with respect to t shows that

$$\frac{d\theta}{dt} = c_1\omega \cos\,(\omega t + c_2),$$

and therefore the second initial condition yields

$$0 = c_1\omega \cos c_2,$$

which is satisfied if $c_2 = \pi/2$. Substituting this value of c_2 in (71-6) gives $c_1 = \alpha$. Thus, the particular solution of (71-3) that satisfies the initial conditions is

$$\theta = \alpha \sin\left(\omega t + \frac{\pi}{2}\right) = \alpha \cos \omega t.$$

* See Prob. 11, Sec. 13.

Naturally, a different choice of the initial conditions would lead to different values for c_1 and c_2.

The solution of the problem of a simple pendulum that was just obtained was based on the assumption that θ was sufficiently small to permit the replacement of $\sin \theta$ by θ. If this is not the case, the problem is somewhat more difficult. In order to solve (71-2), multiply both sides by $2\dfrac{d\theta}{dt}$, obtaining

$$2\frac{d\theta}{dt}\frac{d^2\theta}{dt^2} = -\frac{2g}{l}\sin\theta\,\frac{d\theta}{dt}.$$

Integration gives

$$\left(\frac{d\theta}{dt}\right)^2 = \frac{2g}{l}\cos\theta + C.$$

If $d\theta/dt = 0$ when $\theta = \alpha$,

$$0 = \frac{2g}{l}\cos\alpha + C$$

and

(71-7) $$\left(\frac{d\theta}{dt}\right)^2 = \frac{2g}{l}(\cos\theta - \cos\alpha).$$

The angular velocity is given by $d\theta/dt$; and since the linear velocity is $l\dfrac{d\theta}{dt}$, the velocity in the path at the lowest point is

$$\sqrt{\frac{2g}{l}(\cos\theta - \cos\alpha)}\;l\Big|_{\theta=0} = \sqrt{2gl(1-\cos\alpha)}.$$

It may be observed that this is the same velocity that would have been acquired if the bob had fallen freely under the force of gravity through the same difference in level, for $v = \sqrt{2gh}$ and $h = l(1 - \cos\alpha)$.

Integrating (71-7) yields

(71-8) $$t = \sqrt{\frac{l}{2g}}\int \frac{d\theta}{\sqrt{\cos\theta - \cos\alpha}},$$

which gives the formula for determining the time required for the bob to move from the initial position to any other.

If the lowest position of the bob is chosen as the initial position, then $\theta = 0$ when $t = 0$, and (71-8) becomes

$$(71\text{-}9) \qquad t = \sqrt{\frac{l}{2g}} \int_0^{\theta_1} \frac{d\theta}{\sqrt{\cos\theta - \cos\alpha}},$$

where $0 \leq \theta_1 \leq \alpha$.

In order to evaluate (71-9), first reduce the integral to a more convenient form by means of the relation $\cos\theta = 1 - 2\sin^2\frac{\theta}{2}$. Then,

$$(71\text{-}10) \qquad t = \sqrt{\frac{l}{2g}} \int_0^{\theta_1} \frac{d\theta}{\sqrt{2\left(\sin^2\frac{\alpha}{2} - \sin^2\frac{\theta}{2}\right)}}.$$

Let

$$\sin\frac{\theta}{2} = \sin\frac{\alpha}{2}\sin\varphi;$$

then

$$\cos\frac{\theta}{2} \cdot \frac{1}{2}\,d\theta = \sin\frac{\alpha}{2}\cos\varphi\,d\varphi$$

and

$$d\theta = \frac{2\sin\frac{\alpha}{2}\cos\varphi\,d\varphi}{\cos\frac{\theta}{2}} = \frac{2\sin\frac{\alpha}{2}\cos\varphi\,d\varphi}{\sqrt{1 - \sin^2\frac{\alpha}{2}\sin^2\varphi}}.$$

Substitution of these expressions in (71-10) gives

$$t = \sqrt{\frac{l}{2g}} \int_0^{\varphi_1} \frac{2\sin\frac{\alpha}{2}\cos\varphi\,d\varphi}{\sqrt{2\left(\sin^2\frac{\alpha}{2} - \sin^2\frac{\alpha}{2}\sin^2\varphi\right)}\sqrt{1 - \sin^2\frac{\alpha}{2}\sin^2\varphi}},$$

or

$$t = \sqrt{\frac{l}{g}} \int_0^{\varphi_1} \frac{d\varphi}{\sqrt{1 - \sin^2\frac{\alpha}{2}\sin^2\varphi}}.$$

If the time involved is the time required for the completion of one-quarter of the vibration, then $\theta_1 = \alpha$ and hence $\varphi_1 = \pi/2$.

The entire period is then

$$T = 4 \sqrt{\frac{l}{g}} \int_0^{\frac{\pi}{2}} \frac{d\varphi}{\sqrt{1 - \sin^2 \frac{\alpha}{2} \sin^2 \varphi}} \equiv 4 \sqrt{\frac{l}{g}} \int_0^{\frac{\pi}{2}} \frac{d\varphi}{\sqrt{1 - k^2 \sin^2 \varphi}},$$

where $k^2 \equiv \sin^2 \frac{\alpha}{2}$.

If $(1 - k^2 \sin^2 \varphi)^{-\frac{1}{2}}$ is expanded by the binomial theorem, so that

$$T = 4 \sqrt{\frac{l}{g}} \int_0^{\frac{\pi}{2}} d\varphi \left(1 + \frac{1}{2} k^2 \sin^2 \varphi + \frac{3}{8} k^4 \sin^4 \varphi + \cdots \right),$$

term-by-term integration* gives

$$T = 2\pi \sqrt{\frac{l}{g}} \left(1 + \frac{1}{4} k^2 + \frac{9}{64} k^4 + \cdots \right).$$

It may be noted that the period is a function of the amplitude, which was not true in the case of simple harmonic motion.

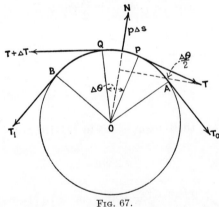

FIG. 67.

A reference to Sec. 14 shows that the period of a simple pendulum is expressible as an elliptic integral of the first kind.

* Note Wallis's formula

$$\int_0^{\frac{\pi}{2}} \sin^n \theta \, d\theta = \int_0^{\frac{\pi}{2}} \cos^n \theta \, d\theta = \frac{(n-1)(n-3) \cdots 2 \text{ or } 1}{n(n-2) \cdots 2 \text{ or } 1} \alpha,$$

where $\alpha = 1$ when n is odd, $\alpha = \pi/2$ when n is even.

72. Further Examples of Derivation of Differential Equations.

1. *The Slipping of a Belt on a Pulley.* Let T_0 and T_1 be the tensions of the belt (Fig. 67) at the points A and B. Consider an element of the belt of length Δs, which has end points P and Q and subtends an angle $\Delta\theta$ at O. Let the tension at P be T and at Q be $T + \Delta T$, and let the normal pressure per unit of length of the arc be p, so that the total normal force on the element of arc Δs is $p \, \Delta s$. If the angle $\Delta\theta$ is assumed to be small, the normal pressure may be thought of as acting in the direction of the line ON, which bisects the angle $\Delta\theta$. From the definition of the coefficient of friction μ, it follows that the frictional force is equal to the product of μ by the normal pressure, so that the frictional force on PQ is $\mu p \, \Delta s$, and, since $\Delta\theta$ is small, this frictional force may be assumed to act at right angles to ON. If it is assumed that the belt is at the point of slipping, the components of force along ON must balance. Hence,

$$T \sin \frac{\Delta\theta}{2} + (T + \Delta T) \sin \frac{\Delta\theta}{2} = p \, \Delta s$$

or

(72-1) $$(2T + \Delta T) \sin \frac{\Delta\theta}{2} = p \, \Delta s.$$

Similarly, by equating the forces acting at right angles to ON,

$$(T + \Delta T) \cos \frac{\Delta\theta}{2} - T \cos \frac{\Delta\theta}{2} = \mu p \, \Delta s$$

or

(72-2) $$\Delta T \cos \frac{\Delta\theta}{2} = \mu p \, \Delta s.$$

Eliminating $p \, \Delta s$ between (72-1) and (72-2) leads to

(72-3) $$\frac{2T + \Delta T}{\Delta T} \tan \frac{\Delta\theta}{2} = \frac{1}{\mu}.$$

Solving (72-3) for ΔT gives

$$\Delta T = \tan \frac{\Delta\theta}{2} \cdot \frac{2T\mu}{1 - \mu \tan \frac{\Delta\theta}{2}},$$

and dividing both members of this equation by $\Delta\theta$ leads to

$$\frac{\Delta T}{\Delta \theta} = \frac{\tan \frac{\Delta \theta}{2}}{\frac{\Delta \theta}{2}} \cdot \frac{T \mu}{1 - \mu \tan \frac{\Delta \theta}{2}}.$$

The limit of this expression as $\Delta \theta \to 0$ is

(72-4) $$\frac{dT}{d\theta} = \mu T,$$

since

$$\lim_{\alpha \to 0} \frac{\tan \alpha}{\alpha} = 1.$$

Separating the variables in (72-4) yields

$$\frac{dT}{T} = \mu \, d\theta,$$

which, upon integration, becomes

$$\log T = \mu \theta + c$$

or

(72-5) $$T = c_1 e^{\mu \theta}.$$

The arbitrary constant c_1 that enters into the solution of the differential equation can be determined from the initial condition $T = T_0$ when $\theta = 0$. Substituting these values in (72-5) gives

$$T = T_0 e^{\mu \theta},$$

so that the tension T_1 corresponding to the angle of lap α is

$$T_1 = T_0 e^{\mu \alpha}.$$

PROBLEM

Find the tensions T_1 in the foregoing illustration when $T_0 = 100$, $\mu = \frac{1}{2}$, and the angles of lap are $\pi/2$, $\frac{3}{4}\pi$, and π radians.

2. *Elastic Curve.* Consider a horizontal beam under the action of vertical loads. It is assumed that all the forces acting on the beam lie in the plane containing the central axis of the beam. Choose the x-axis along the central axis of the beam in undeformed state and the positive y-axis down (Fig. 68). Under the action of external forces F_i the beam will be bent and its central axis deformed. The deformed central axis, shown in the figure by the dotted line, is known as the *elastic curve*, and it is an important problem in the theory of elasticity to determine its shape.

It can be shown* that a beam made of elastic material that obeys Hooke's law is deformed in such a way that the curvature K of the elastic curve is proportional to the bending moment M. In fact,

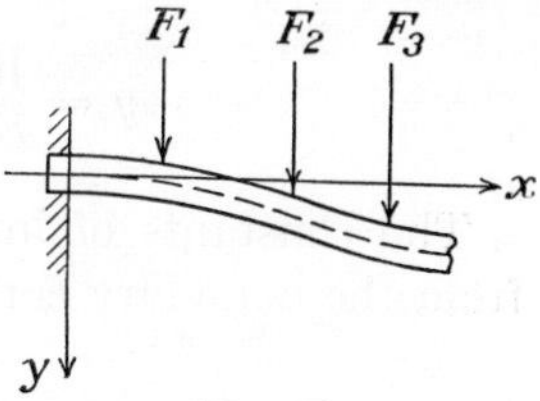

$$(72\text{-}6) \quad K = \frac{d^2y/dx^2}{\left[1 + \left(\dfrac{dy}{dx}\right)^2\right]^{3/2}} = \frac{M}{EI},$$

FIG. 68.

where E is Young's modulus, I is the moment of inertia of the cross section of the beam about a horizontal line passing through the centroid of the section and lying in the plane of the cross section, and y is the ordinate of the elastic curve. The important relation (72-6) bears the name of the *Bernoulli-Euler law*.

The bending moment M in any cross section of the beam is equal to the algebraic sum of the moments of all the forces F_i acting on one side of the section. The moments of the forces F_i are taken about a horizontal line lying in the cross section in question.

If the deflection of the beam is small, the slope of the elastic curve is also small, so that one may neglect the square of dy/dx in the formula for curvature. Thus, for small deflections the formula (72-6) can be written as

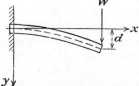

FIG. 69.

$$(72\text{-}7) \qquad \frac{d^2y}{dx^2} = \frac{M}{EI}.$$

As an illustration of the application of this formula, consider a cantilever beam of length l, which is built in at the left end and which carries a load W on its free end (Fig. 69). The weight of the beam is assumed negligible in comparison with the magnitude of the load W, so that the moment M in any cross section at a distance x from the built-in end is

$$M = W(l - x).$$

* See TIMOSHENKO, S., *Theory of Elasticity*, p. 41; LOVE, A. E. H., *A Treatise on the Mathematical Theory of Elasticity*, 4th ed., pp. 129–130.

When this expression is substituted in (72-7), there results

$$\frac{d^2y}{dx^2} = \frac{W}{EI}(l - x),$$

and integrating gives

$$y = \frac{W}{EI}\left(\frac{lx^2}{2} - \frac{x^3}{6}\right) + c_1 x + c_2.$$

The constants of integration, c_1 and c_2, are easily evaluated from the boundary conditions

$$y = 0, \qquad \text{when } x = 0,$$
$$\frac{dy}{dx} = 0, \qquad \text{when } x = 0,$$

the first of which expresses the fact that the displacement at the built-in end is zero and the second that the slope of the elastic curve is zero when $x = 0$. It is easily checked that these boundary conditions require that

$$y = \frac{W}{2EI}\left(lx^2 - \frac{x^3}{3}\right),$$

so that the displacement d at the free end is

$$d = \frac{Wl^3}{3EI}.$$

PROBLEM

A beam of length l is freely supported at its ends and is loaded in the middle by a concentrated vertical load W, which is large in comparison with the weight of the beam. Show that the maximum deflection is one-sixteenth of that of the cantilever beam discussed above. *Hint:* From symmetry, it is clear that the behavior of this beam is the same as that of the cantilever beam of length $l/2$ which is loaded by a concentrated load of magnitude $W/2$ at its free end (Fig. 70).

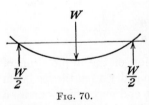

Fig. 70.

3. *Cable Supporting a Horizontal Roadway.* Let a cable that supports a horizontal roadway be suspended from two points A and B (Fig. 71). It will be assumed that the load on the roadway is so large compared with the weight of the cable that

the weight of the cable can be neglected.   The problem is to determine the shape assumed by the cable.

Denote the tension at the point P of the cable by T and that at the point Q by $T + \Delta T$, and let w be the load per foot run. Since the cable is in equilibrium, the horizontal and vertical components of the forces acting on any portion Δs of the cable must balance.   Thus, equating the horizontal and vertical components gives a system of two equations

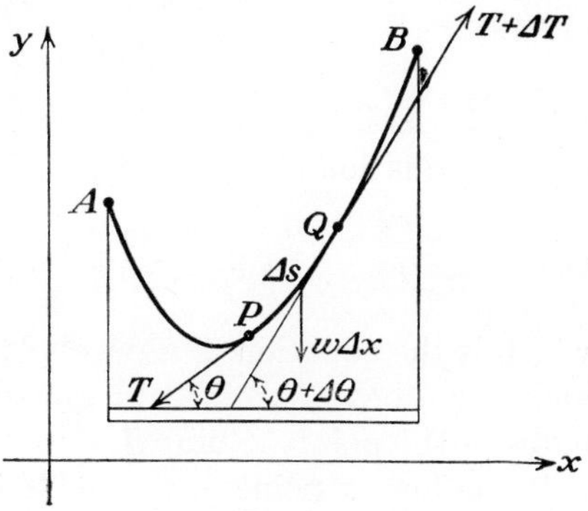

(72-8) $T \cos \theta$
$= (T + \Delta T) \cos (\theta + \Delta \theta)$

and

(72-9) $T \sin \theta = -w \, \Delta x$
$+ (T + \Delta T) \sin (\theta + \Delta \theta)$.

Dividing (72-9) by (72-8) gives

Fig. 71.

(72-10) $\tan \theta = \tan (\theta + \Delta \theta) - \dfrac{w \, \Delta x}{(T + \Delta T) \cos (\theta + \Delta \theta)}$.

But (72-8) does not depend on the magnitude of Δs and, since Δs is arbitrary in size, it appears that the horizontal component of the tension at any point of the cable is a constant, say T_0. Substituting this value in the right-hand member of (72-10) and rearranging give

$$\tan (\theta + \Delta \theta) - \tan \theta = \frac{w \, \Delta x}{T_0},$$

or

(72-11) $$\frac{\tan (\theta + \Delta \theta) - \tan \theta}{\Delta \theta} = \frac{w}{T_0} \frac{\Delta x}{\Delta \theta}.$$

The left-hand member of (72-11) is the difference quotient, and its limit as $\Delta \theta$ is made to approach zero is the derivative of $\tan \theta$.   Hence, passing to the limit gives

(72-12) $$\sec^2 \theta = \frac{w}{T_0} \frac{dx}{d\theta}.$$

Recalling that $\tan \theta = \dfrac{dy}{dx}$, so that $\theta = \tan^{-1} \dfrac{dy}{dx}$, it follows that

$$\frac{d\theta}{dx} = \frac{d^2y/dx^2}{1 + (dy/dx)^2}.$$

Moreover,

$$\sec^2 \theta = 1 + \left(\frac{dy}{dx}\right)^2.$$

Substituting from these two expressions in (72-12) leads to the differential equation of the curve assumed by the cable, namely,

(72-13) $$\frac{d^2y}{dx^2} = \frac{w}{T_0}.$$

If (72-13) is integrated twice with respect to x, one obtains the desired equation of the curve,

(72-14) $$y = \frac{w}{2T_0} x^2 + c_1 x + c_2,$$

which is the equation of a parabola. The arbitrary constants c_1 and c_2 can be determined by substituting in (72-14) the coordinates of the points A and B.

If the lowest point of the cable is chosen as the origin of the coordinate system, the equation of the parabola becomes

(72-15) $$y = \frac{w}{2T_0} x^2.$$

The length of any portion of the cable can easily be calculated with the aid of (72-15).

PROBLEMS

1. Find the length of the parabolic cable when the latter supports a roadway which is l ft. long. Express the length of the cable in an infinite series in powers of l. *Hint:* Expand the integrand in the expression for the length of the cable.

2. Find an approximate expression for the sag d in terms of the length l by using the first two terms of the infinite series expansion that was obtained in Prob. 1.

4. *Uniform Flexible Cable Hanging under Its Own Weight.* Let a flexible cable (Fig. 72) be suspended from two points A and B. Denote the weight per unit length of the cable by w, and consider the forces acting on the element of cable Δs. As in the preceding example, the horizontal and vertical components of force must balance, for the cable is in equilibrium. If the tension at P is denoted by T and that at Q by $T + \Delta T$, it follows that

$$T \cos \theta = (T + \Delta T) \cos (\theta + \Delta \theta)$$

and

$$T \sin \theta = (T + \Delta T) \sin (\theta + \Delta \theta) - w \, \Delta s.$$

Dividing the second of these equations by the first gives

$$\tan \theta = \tan (\theta + \Delta \theta) - \frac{w \, \Delta s}{(T + \Delta T) \cos (\theta + \Delta \theta)}.$$

This equation has the structure of Eq. (72-10), and an analysis in every respect similar to that outlined in the preceding illus-

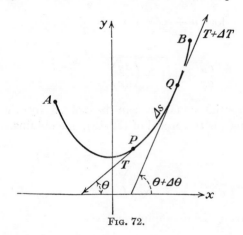

FIG. 72.

tration leads to the equation

$$(72\text{-}16) \qquad\qquad \sec^2 \theta = \frac{w}{T_0} \frac{ds}{d\theta},$$

where T_0 is the tension at the lowest point of the cable.   Since

$$\frac{ds}{d\theta} = \frac{ds/dx}{d\theta/dx},$$

where

$$\frac{ds}{dx} = \sqrt{1 + \left(\frac{dy}{dx}\right)^2} \qquad \text{and} \qquad \frac{d\theta}{dx} = \frac{d^2y/dx^2}{1 + (dy/dx)^2},$$

and since $\sec^2 \theta = 1 + (dy/dx)^2$, it follows upon substitution in (72-16) that the differential equation of the curve assumed by the cable is

$$(72\text{-}17) \qquad\qquad \frac{d^2y}{dx^2} = \frac{w}{T_0} \sqrt{1 + \left(\frac{dy}{dx}\right)^2}.$$

If dy/dx is replaced by u, (72-17) becomes

$$\frac{du}{dx} = \frac{w}{T_0} \sqrt{1 + u^2},$$

or

$$\frac{du}{\sqrt{1 + u^2}} = \frac{w}{T_0} dx.$$

Integrating this equation gives

$$\log (u + \sqrt{1 + u^2}) = \frac{w}{T_0} x + c_1,$$

or

(72-18) $$\frac{dy}{dx} + \sqrt{1 + \left(\frac{dy}{dx}\right)^2} = e^{\frac{w}{T_0}x + c_1} .$$

This differential equation can be solved by the following device: Taking the reciprocal of (72-18), one obtains

$$\frac{1}{\dfrac{dy}{dx} + \sqrt{1 + \left(\dfrac{dy}{dx}\right)^2}} = e^{-\left(\frac{w}{T_0}x + c_1\right)},$$

and rationalizing the denominator gives

(72-19) $$-\frac{dy}{dx} + \sqrt{1 + \left(\frac{dy}{dx}\right)^2} = e^{-\left(\frac{w}{T_0}x + c_1\right)}.$$

When (72-19) is subtracted from (72-18), there results

$$\frac{dy}{dx} = \frac{1}{2}\left[e^{\frac{w}{T_0}x + c_1} - e^{-\left(\frac{w}{T_0}x + c_1\right)} \right]$$

and integration gives

$$y = \frac{T_0}{2w}\left[e^{\frac{w}{T_0}x + c_1} + e^{-\left(\frac{w}{T_0}x + c_1\right)} \right] + c_2.$$

The constants c_1 and c_2 can be determined from the condition that the curve passes through the points A and B, whose coordinates are assumed to be known.

If the constants c_1 and c_2 are chosen to be equal to zero, then the lowest point of the curve is at $(0, T_0/w)$, and the equation of the curve assumed by the cable has the form

(72-20) $$y = \frac{a}{2}\left(e^{\frac{x}{a}} + e^{-\frac{x}{a}}\right).$$

A curve whose equation has the form (72-20) is called a catenary

PROBLEM

Find the length of the catenary between the limits 0 and x.

73. Hyperbolic Functions. Combinations of exponential functions analogous to the one that appears in (72-20) are of such frequent occurrence in applied mathematics that it has been found convenient to give them a special name. The function $\frac{1}{2}(e^x + e^{-x})$ is called the hyperbolic cosine of x and is denoted by

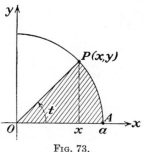

(73-1) $\cosh x \equiv \frac{1}{2}(e^x + e^{-x}).$

The derivative of $\cosh x$ is equal to $\frac{1}{2}(e^x - e^{-x})$ and is called the hyperbolic sine of x. Thus,

(73-2) $\sinh x \equiv \frac{1}{2}(e^x - e^{-x})$

FIG. 73.

These functions are called hyperbolic because they bear relations to the rectangular hyperbola $x^2 - y^2 = a^2$ that are very similar to those borne by the circular functions to the circle $x^2 + y^2 = a^2$. Thus, consider the equation of a circle (Fig. 73)

$$x^2 + y^2 = a^2$$

whose parametric equations are

$$x = a \cos t$$

and

$$y = a \sin t.$$

The equation of a rectangular hyperbola (Fig. 74) is

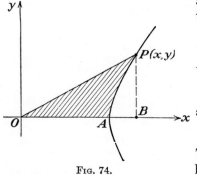

FIG. 74.

(73-3) $x^2 - y^2 = a^2,$

and the reader can readily show with the aid of the definitions

(73-1) and (73-2) that (73-3) can be written in a parametric form as

$$(73\text{-}4) \qquad \begin{cases} x = a \cosh t, \\ y = a \sinh t. \end{cases}$$

It will be shown next that the parameter t can be interpreted for the circle and the hyperbola in a similar way.

The area u of the circular sector OAP (Fig. 73) is

$$u = \tfrac{1}{2}a^2 t,$$

so that

$$t = \frac{2u}{a^2}.$$

On the other hand, the area of the hyperbolic sector OAP (Fig. 74) is given by

$$(73\text{-}5) \qquad u = \tfrac{1}{2}xy - \int_a^x \sqrt{x^2 - a^2}\, dx,$$

where the first term in (73-5) represents the area of the triangle OBP.

Integrating (73-5) gives

$$u = \frac{a^2}{2} \log \frac{x + \sqrt{x^2 - a^2}}{a} = \frac{a^2}{2} \log \frac{x + y}{a},$$

so that

$$\log \frac{x + y}{a} = \frac{2u}{a^2},$$

and

$$(73\text{-}6) \qquad \frac{x + y}{a} = e^{\frac{2u}{a^2}}.$$

Also, since $x^2 - y^2 = a^2$, it follows that

$$(73\text{-}7) \qquad \frac{x - y}{a} = e^{-\frac{2u}{a^2}}.$$

Adding and subtracting (73-6) and (73-7) lead to

$$(73\text{-}8) \qquad \begin{cases} x = a \dfrac{e^{\frac{2u}{a^2}} + e^{-\frac{2u}{a^2}}}{2} = a \cosh \dfrac{2u}{a^2}, \\[2ex] y = a \dfrac{e^{\frac{2u}{a^2}} - e^{-\frac{2u}{a^2}}}{2} = a \sinh \dfrac{2u}{a^2}, \end{cases}$$

which are precisely Eqs. (73-4) with $t = 2u/a^2$.

From (73-8), it is clear that

$$\frac{x}{a} = \cosh \frac{2u}{a^2} \quad \text{and} \quad \frac{y}{a} = \sinh \frac{2u}{a^2}$$

and a reference to Fig. 73 shows that

$$\frac{x}{a} = \cos \frac{2u}{a^2} \quad \text{and} \quad \frac{y}{a} = \sin \frac{2u}{a^2}.$$

Therefore, the circular functions may be defined by means of certain ratios involving the coordinates of the point $P(x, y)$ on the circle $x^2 + y^2 = a^2$, whereas the hyperbolic functions are expressed as ratios involving the coordinates of the point $P(x, y)$ on the hyperbola $x^2 - y^2 = a^2$.

The definitions of the hyperbolic tangent, hyperbolic cotangent, hyperbolic secant, and hyperbolic cosecant are as follows:

$$\tanh x = \frac{\sinh x}{\cosh x},$$

$$\coth x = \frac{1}{\tanh x},$$

$$\operatorname{sech} x = \frac{1}{\cosh x},$$

$$\operatorname{csch} x = \frac{1}{\sinh x}.$$

The inverse hyperbolic functions are defined in a way similar to that used in defining the inverse circular functions. Thus, if

$$y = \tanh x,$$

then

$$x = \tanh^{-1} y,$$

which is read "*the inverse hyperbolic tangent of y.*" The definition of the remaining inverse hyperbolic functions is similar. There are some interesting relations that connect these inverse hyperbolic functions with the logarithmic functions.*

It will be recalled that the expansion in Maclaurin's series for e^u is

(73-9) $$e^u = 1 + u + \frac{u^2}{2!} + \frac{u^3}{3!} + \cdots,$$

---

* See Probs. 5 and 7 at the end of this section.

so that

(73-10) $$e^x = 1 + x + \frac{x^2}{2!} + \frac{x^3}{3!} + \cdots$$

and

(73-11) $$e^{-x} = 1 - x + \frac{x^2}{2!} - \frac{x^3}{3!} + \cdots .$$

Subtracting (73-11) from (73-10) gives

$$e^x - e^{-x} = 2\left(x + \frac{x^3}{3!} + \frac{x^5}{5!} + \cdots \right),$$

so that

(73-12) $$\sinh x \equiv \frac{e^x - e^{-x}}{2} = x + \frac{x^3}{3!} + \frac{x^5}{5!} + \cdots .$$

On the other hand, addition of (73-10) and (73-11) shows that

(73-13) $$\cosh x \equiv \frac{e^x + e^{-x}}{2} = 1 + \frac{x^2}{2!} + \frac{x^4}{4!} + \cdots .$$

Moreover, if it is assumed that (73-9) holds for complex numbers as well as for real numbers, then

(73-14) $$e^{ix} = 1 + ix + \frac{(ix)^2}{2!} + \frac{(ix)^3}{3!} + \cdots$$

and

(73-15) $$e^{-ix} = 1 - ix + \frac{(-ix)^2}{2!} + \frac{(-ix)^3}{3!} + \cdots ,$$

where $i \equiv \sqrt{-1}$. Adding (73-14) and (73-15) and simplifying show that

$$e^{ix} + e^{-ix} = 2\left(1 - \frac{x^2}{2!} + \frac{x^4}{4!} - \frac{x^6}{6!} + \cdots \right),$$

which is recognized to be the series for cos x multiplied by 2. Thus,

(73-16) $$\cos x = \frac{e^{ix} + e^{-ix}}{2}.$$

It is readily verified that subtraction of (73-15) from (73-14) leads to the formula

(73-17) $$\sin x = \frac{e^{ix} - e^{-ix}}{2i}.$$

By combining (73-16) with (73-17) there result two interesting relations,

$$\cos x + i \sin x = e^{ix} \quad \text{and} \quad \cos x - i \sin x = e^{-ix},$$

which are frequently used in various investigations in applied mathematics. These relations are known as the *Euler formulas*.

The following table exhibits the formal analogy that exists between the circular and hyperbolic functions. The relations that are given for hyperbolic functions can be established readily from the definitions for the hyperbolic sine and the hyperbolic cosine.

Circular Functions	Hyperbolic Functions
$\sin x = \dfrac{1}{2i}(e^{ix} - e^{-ix})$	$\sinh x = \dfrac{1}{2}(e^{x} - e^{-x})$
$\cos x = \dfrac{1}{2}(e^{ix} + e^{-ix})$	$\cosh x = \dfrac{1}{2}(e^{x} + e^{-x})$
$\tan x = \dfrac{e^{ix} - e^{-ix}}{i(e^{ix} + e^{-ix})}$	$\tanh x = \dfrac{e^{x} - e^{-x}}{e^{x} + e^{-x}}$
$\cot x = \dfrac{1}{\tan x}$	$\coth x = \dfrac{1}{\tanh x}$
$\sin x = x - \dfrac{x^3}{3!} + \dfrac{x^5}{5!} - \cdots$	$\sinh x = x + \dfrac{x^3}{3!} + \dfrac{x^5}{5!} + \cdots$
$\cos x = 1 - \dfrac{x^2}{2!} + \dfrac{x^4}{4!} - \cdots$	$\cosh x = 1 + \dfrac{x^2}{2!} + \dfrac{x^4}{4!} + \cdots$
$\sin^2 x + \cos^2 x = 1$	$\cosh^2 x - \sinh^2 x = 1$
$1 + \tan^2 x = \sec^2 x$	$1 - \tanh^2 x = \operatorname{sech}^2 x$
$\sin 2x = 2 \sin x \cos x$	$\sinh 2x = 2 \sinh x \cosh x$
$\cos 2x = \cos^2 x - \sin^2 x$	$\cosh 2x = \cosh^2 x + \sinh^2 x$
$\sin (x \pm y) = \sin x \cos y$ $\pm \cos x \sin y$	$\sinh (x \pm y) = \sinh x \cosh y \pm \cosh x \sinh y$
$\dfrac{d \sin x}{dx} = \cos x$	$\dfrac{d \sinh x}{dx} = \cosh x$
$\dfrac{d \cos x}{dx} = - \sin x$	$\dfrac{d \cosh x}{dx} = \sinh x$
$\dfrac{d \tan x}{dx} = \sec^2 x$	$\dfrac{d \tanh x}{dx} = \operatorname{sech}^2 x$

Example 1. A telephone wire (Fig. 75) weighing 8 lb. per 100 ft. is stretched between two poles 200 ft. apart. If the sag is 1 ft., find the tension in the wire.

Note that

$$y = a \cosh \frac{x}{a} = a \left(1 + \frac{x^2}{2! \, a^2} + \frac{x^4}{4! \, a^4} + \cdots \right),$$

where $a = T_0/w$.

The vertical component of the tension is clearly equal to ws, where s is the length of the wire. But the length of the catenary between the points whose abscissas are 0 and x is

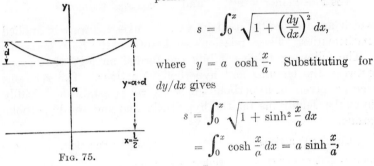

FIG. 75.

$$s = \int_0^x \sqrt{1 + \left(\frac{dy}{dx}\right)^2}\, dx,$$

where $y = a \cosh \frac{x}{a}$. Substituting for dy/dx gives

$$s = \int_0^x \sqrt{1 + \sinh^2 \frac{x}{a}}\, dx$$

$$= \int_0^x \cosh \frac{x}{a}\, dx = a \sinh \frac{x}{a},$$

so that the vertical component of tension is

$$T_y = ws = wa \sinh \frac{x}{a},$$

and the total tension at any point is

$$T = \sqrt{T_0{}^2 + T_y{}^2} = wa \sqrt{1 + \sinh^2 \frac{x}{a}}$$

$$= wa \cosh \frac{x}{a}$$

$$= wy.$$

At the point of support, $y = a + d$, so that $T = w(a + d)$. Since d is usually small, the tension in the wire is nearly constant and approximately equal to T_0.

If the wire is very taut and the distance between the poles is not large,

$$y \doteq a + \frac{x^2}{2a}*$$

or

$$y - a \doteq \frac{x^2}{2a}.$$

When $x = l/2$, where l is the distance between the poles, and d is the sag, $y - a = d$ and

$$d \doteq \frac{(l/2)^2}{2a} = \frac{l^2}{8a},$$

so that

$$a = \frac{l^2}{8d} = \frac{T_0}{w},$$

* The symbol $a \doteq b$ is used to signify that a is approximately equal to b.

or

$$T_0 = \frac{wl^2}{8d}.$$

Substituting the numerical values for w, l, and d gives for the value of the tension at the lowest point

$$T_0 = \frac{(0.08)(200)^2}{(8) \cdot (1)} = 400 \text{ lb.}$$

Example 2. A parachute, supporting a mass m, is falling from a distance h above the ground. Determine the velocity with which it strikes the ground if the air resistance is proportional to the square of the velocity.

If the air resistance be denoted by R, then

$$R = kv^2,$$

where k is a proportionality constant depending upon the design of the parachute. The force acting downward is

$$m \frac{d^2s}{dt^2} = m \frac{dv}{dt},$$

which is equal to $mg - kv^2$. Hence,

$$m \frac{dv}{dt} = mg - kv^2$$

or

$$\frac{dv}{dt} = g(1 - a^2v^2),$$

where $a^2 = k/gm$. Integrating

$$\int \frac{dv}{1 - a^2v^2} = g \int dt$$

gives

$$\frac{1}{2a} \log \frac{1 + av}{1 - av} = gt + c_1.$$

If $v = 0$ when $t = 0$, it follows that $c_1 = 0$. The integrated expression then simplifies to

$$\frac{1 + av}{1 - av} = e^{2agt}$$

or

$$v = \frac{1}{a} \frac{e^{2agt} - 1}{e^{2agt} + 1} = \frac{1}{a} \tanh agt$$

$$= \sqrt{\frac{gm}{k}} \tanh \sqrt{\frac{kg}{m}} t.$$

It is easily shown that

$$\lim_{t \to \infty} \tanh t = 1,$$

and it follows that the terminal velocity is $v_t = \sqrt{gm/k}$.
But $ds/dt = v$, so that

$$s = \frac{1}{a} \int \tanh agt \, dt$$

$$= \frac{1}{a^2 g} \log \cosh agt + c_2;$$

and since $s = 0$ when $t = 0$, $c_2 = 0$. Hence,

$$s = \frac{m}{k} \log \cosh \sqrt{\frac{kg}{m}} t.$$

PROBLEMS

1. A wire is stretched between two supports 100 ft. apart. If
the weight of the wire is 10 lb. per 100 ft. and the tension in the wire is
300 lb., find the amount of sag at the middle.

2. Newton's law of cooling states that the rate of decrease of the
difference in temperature of a body surrounded by a medium of constant temperature is proportional to the difference between the temperature of the body and that of the medium, that is,

$$\frac{d\theta}{dt} = -k(\theta - \theta_0).$$

Find the temperature θ of the body at any time t, if the initial temperature is θ_1.

3. If a wire weighing w lb. per unit of length is stretched between two
supports l units apart, show that the length of the wire is approximately

$$s = l \left(1 + \frac{w^2 l^2}{24 T^2} \right),$$

where T is the tension.

4. Show that any complex number $a + bi$ can be put in the form

$$a + bi = re^{\theta i}, \text{ where } r = \sqrt{a^2 + b^2} \text{ and } \theta = \tan^{-1} \frac{b}{a}.$$

5. If $y = \sinh x$, then x is called the inverse hyperbolic sine and is denoted by $x \equiv \sinh^{-1} y$. Prove that $x = \sinh^{-1} y = \log (y + \sqrt{y^2 + 1})$.

6. Establish the formulas for hyperbolic functions given in the table of Sec. 73.

7. Establish the following formulas:

(a) $d \sinh u = \cosh u \, du$;

(b) $d \cosh u = \sinh u \, du$;

(c) $d \tanh u = \mathrm{sech}^2 u \, du$;

(d) $d \coth u = - \, \mathrm{csch}^2 u \, du$;

(e) $d \, \mathrm{sech} \, u = - \, \mathrm{sech} \, u \tanh u \, du$;

(f) $d \, \mathrm{csch} \, u = - \, \mathrm{csch} \, u \coth u \, du$;

(g) $d \sinh^{-1} u = \dfrac{du}{\sqrt{u^2 + 1}}$;

(h) $d \cosh^{-1} u = \dfrac{du}{\sqrt{u^2 - 1}}$;

(i) $d \tanh^{-1} u = \dfrac{du}{1 - u^2}$;

(j) $d \coth^{-1} u = \dfrac{du}{1 - u^2}$;

(k) $d \, \mathrm{sech}^{-1} u = - \dfrac{du}{u \sqrt{1 - u^2}}$;

(l) $d \, \mathrm{csch}^{-1} u = - \dfrac{du}{u \sqrt{1 + u^2}}$;

(m) $\cosh^{-1} y = \log (y + \sqrt{y^2 - 1}) = \sinh^{-1} \sqrt{y^2 - 1}$;

(n) $\sinh^{-1} y = \log (y + \sqrt{y^2 + 1}) = \cosh^{-1} \sqrt{y^2 + 1}$;

(o) $\tanh^{-1} y = \dfrac{1}{2} \log \dfrac{1 + y}{1 - y}$ if $y^2 < 1$;

(p) $\coth^{-1} y = \dfrac{1}{2} \log \dfrac{y + 1}{y - 1}$ if $y^2 > 1$;

(q) $\mathrm{sech}^{-1} y = \log \dfrac{1 + \sqrt{1 - y^2}}{y}$ if $0 < y \leq 1$;

(r) $\mathrm{csch}^{-1} y = \log \dfrac{1 \pm \sqrt{y^2 + 1}}{y}$ $\begin{cases} +, \text{ if } y > 0 \\ -, \text{ if } y < 0. \end{cases}$

8. Plot the graphs of the hyperbolic functions.

9. A man and a parachute, weighing w lb., fall from rest under the force of gravity. If the resistance of the air is assumed to be proportional to the speed v and if the limiting speed is v_0, find the expression for the speed as a function of the time t.

Hint:

$$\frac{w}{g} \frac{dv}{dt} = w - kv.$$

10. A man and a parachute are falling with the speed of 100 ft. per second at the instant the parachute is opened. What is the speed of the man at the end of t sec. if the air resistance is proportional to the square of the speed?

11. It can be established that the steady flow of heat across a large wall is proportional to the space rate of decrease of temperature θ across the wall and to the area A of the wall, that is,

$$Q = -kA \frac{d\theta}{dx},$$

where x is the distance from one of the faces of the wall and Q is the constant quantity of heat passing through the wall. The constant k (thermal conductivity) depends on the properties of the material. Integrate this equation and calculate the amount of heat per square centimeter passing through a refrigerator wall, if the thickness of the wall is 6 cm. and the temperature inside the refrigerator is 0°C., while outside it is 20°C. Assume $k = 0.0002$.

12. A tank contains initially v gal. of brine holding x_0 lb. of salt in solution. A salt solution containing w lb. of salt per gallon enters the tank at the rate of r gal. per minute; and the mixture, which is kept uniform by stirring, leaves the tank at the same rate. What is the concentration of the brine at the end of t min.?

Hint: Let x denote the amount of salt present at the end of t min.; then, at a later instant $t + \Delta t$, the change in the quantity of salt is $\Delta x = wr\, \Delta t - (x/v)r\, \Delta t$. Hence, $dx/dt = wr - xr/v = (r/v)(wv - x)$.

74. First-order Differential Equations.

Generally speaking, the problem of solving differential equations is a very difficult one. There are very few types of equations whose solutions can be written down at once; in practice, special methods of solution, suitable to the particular problem under consideration, have to be depended upon. Seeking special methods of solution is a difficult task, and the mathematician, at present at least, is almost entirely restricted to a consideration of linear differential equations. Very little is known concerning the solution of non-linear differential equations. Even such a simple-appearing first-order equation as

$$\frac{dy}{dx} = f(x, y)$$

cannot be solved in general; that is, there are no formulas available for solving a non-linear differential equation of the first order. However, it is possible to classify some of the first-order non-linear differential equations according to several types and to indicate the special methods of solution suitable for each of these types.   The next ten sections will be concerned with the solutions of the special types of non-linear differential equations that are of common occurrence in practice.   The remainder of the chapter will be devoted to the general methods of solution of the important types of linear differential equations.

75. Equations with Separable Variables.   If the given differential equation

$$F\left(\frac{dy}{dx}, x, y\right) = 0$$

can be put in the form

$$f_1(x)\, dx + f_2(y)\, dy = 0,$$

where $f_1(x)$ is a function of x only and $f_2(y)$ is a function of y only, the equation is said to be an equation with separable variables.   Such an equation is easily integrable, and its general solution is

$$\int f_1(x)\, dx + \int f_2(y)\, dy = c,$$

where c is an arbitrary constant.   In order to obtain an explicit solution, all that is necessary is to perform the indicated integrations.

Example.   Solve

$$\frac{dy}{dx} + e^x y = e^x y^2.$$

This can be written as

$$\frac{dy}{dx} + e^x(y - y^2) = 0$$

or

$$\frac{dy}{y - y^2} + e^x\, dx = 0.$$

Integration gives

$$\log \frac{y}{1 - y} + e^x = c,$$

which is the general solution required.

PROBLEMS

Solve the following differential equations:

1. $\sqrt{1 - x^2}\, dy + \sqrt{1 - y^2}\, dx = 0.$

2. $\dfrac{dy}{dx} - xy^2 + x = 0.$

3. $\dfrac{dy}{dx} = \dfrac{\sin^2 x}{\sin y}.$

4. $\sin x \cos^2 y\, dx + \cos^2 x\, dy = 0.$

5. $\sqrt{1 + x}\, dy - (1 + y^2)\, dx = 0.$

6. $e^x \sqrt{1 - y^2}\, dx + \dfrac{y}{x}\, dy = 0.$

7. $\dfrac{dy}{dx} = \dfrac{1 + y}{1 + x}.$

8. $e^x \dfrac{dy}{dx} + y - y^2 = 0.$

9. $\sinh x\, dy + \cosh y\, dx = 0.$

10. $x^2 \dfrac{dy}{dx} - y^2 = x^2 y \dfrac{dy}{dx}.$

11. $\dfrac{dy}{dx} = \log y \dfrac{dy}{dx} + \tan x \sec^2 x.$

12. $x^2(1 + 4y^2)\, dx + 3yx^3\, dy = 0.$

13. $\dfrac{\sin^{-1} x}{y}\, dx + (1 - e^y)\, dy = 0.$

14. $\dfrac{dy}{dx} + \dfrac{xy}{1 - x^2} = 0.$

15. $\dfrac{dy}{dx} = \dfrac{y(x + 1)}{x(y - 1)}.$

16. $(1 + x^2)\, dy - (1 + y^2)\, dx = 0.$

17. $\dfrac{dy}{dx} = \dfrac{y^2 + 2y + 1}{x^2 - 2x + 1}.$

18. $x^2(1 + y)\, dy + y^2(x - 1)\, dx = 0.$

19. $y(1 - y)\, dx - (x + 1)\, dy = 0.$

20. $\dfrac{dy}{dx} = \dfrac{x(1 + y^2)}{y(1 + x^2)}.$

21. $(y - xy)\, dx + x^2\, dy = 0.$

22. Let A be the amount of a substance at the beginning of a chemical reaction, and let x be the amount of the substance entered in the reaction after t sec. Then, the simple law of chemical reaction states that the rate of change of the substance is proportional to the amount of the substance remaining; that is, $dx/dt = c(A - x)$, where c is a constant depending on the reaction. Show that $x = A(1 - e^{-ct})$.

23. Let a solution contain two substances whose amounts expressed in gram molecules, at the beginning of a reaction, are A and B. If an equal amount x of both substances has changed at the time t, then the amounts of the substances remaining are $A - x$ and $B - x$. The basic law of chemical reactions states that the rate of change is proportional to the amounts of the substances remaining; that is,

$$\frac{dx}{dt} = k(A - x)(B - x).$$

Solve this equation under the hypothesis that $x = 0$ when $t = 0$. Discuss the case when $A = B$.

76. Homogeneous Differential Equations.

It will be recalled* that a function $f(x, y)$, of the two variables x and y, is said to be homogeneous of degree n provided that

$$f(\lambda x, \lambda y) \equiv \lambda^n f(x, y).$$

Thus,

$$f(x, y) = x^3 + x^2 y + y^3$$

is a homogeneous function of degree 3, and

$$f(x, y) = x^2 \sin \frac{x}{y} + xy$$

is a homogeneous function of degree 2.

If the differential equation is of the form

(76-1) $$f_1(x, y)\, dx + f_2(x, y)\, dy = 0,$$

where $f_1(x, y)$ and $f_2(x, y)$ are homogeneous functions of the same degree, then (76-1) can be written in the form

(76-2) $$\frac{dy}{dx} = -\frac{f_1(x, y)}{f_2(x, y)} \equiv \varphi(x, y),$$

where $\varphi(x, y)$ is a homogeneous function of degree zero, that is,

$$\varphi(\lambda x, \lambda y) \equiv \lambda^0\, \varphi(x, y) \equiv \varphi(x, y).$$

If λ is set equal to $1/x$, then

$$\varphi(x, y) \equiv \varphi(\lambda x, \lambda y) = \varphi\left(1, \frac{y}{x}\right),$$

which shows that a homogeneous function of degree zero can always be expressed as a function of y/x. This suggests making

*See Sec. 40.

the substitution $y/x = v$. Then, since $y = vx$,

$$\frac{dy}{dx} = \frac{dv}{dx}\, x + v.$$

Substituting this value of dy/dx in (76-2) gives

$$x\frac{dv}{dx} + v = \varphi(1, v).$$

This equation is of the type considered in Sec. 75. Separating the variables leads to

$$\frac{dv}{\varphi(1, v) - v} = \frac{dx}{x},$$

which can be integrated at once to give

$$F(v, x, c) = 0.$$

Since $v = y/x$, the general solution of (76-1) is

$$F\left(\frac{y}{x}, x, c\right) = 0.$$

An equation of the form

$$\frac{dy}{dx} = \frac{a_1x + a_2y + a_3}{b_1x + b_2y + b_3}$$

can be reduced to the solution of a homogeneous equation by a change of variable. This is indicated in detail in Prob. 11 at the end of this section.

Example. Solve

$$y^2 + x^2\frac{dy}{dx} = xy\frac{dy}{dx}.$$

This equation can be put in the form

$$y^2dx + (x^2 - xy)\, dy = 0,$$

which is of the type (76-1). By setting $y = vx$ and $dy = v\, dx + x\, dv$, the equation becomes

$$(vx)^2\, dx + (x^2 - vx^2)(v\, dx + x\, dv) = 0.$$

This reduces to

$$v\, dx + x(1 - v)\, dv = 0$$

and, upon separation of the variables, to

$$\frac{dx}{x} + \frac{1-v}{v}\, dv = 0.$$

Integration yields

$$\log x + \log v - v = c$$

or

$$\log x + \log \frac{y}{x} - \frac{y}{x} = c,$$

which simplifies to

$$\log y - \frac{y}{x} = c.$$

PROBLEMS

Solve the following differential equations:

1. $(x^2 + y^2)\, dy + 2xy\, dx = 0.$

2. $x\dfrac{dy}{dx} - y = \sqrt{x^2 - y^2}.$

3. $x\cos\dfrac{y}{x}\dfrac{dy}{dx} = y\cos\dfrac{y}{x} - x.$

4. $(x + y)\dfrac{dy}{dx} = x - y.$

5. $x^2 y\, dx - (x^3 - y^3)\, dy = 0.$

6. $\dfrac{dy}{dx} = \dfrac{xy - y^2}{x^2}.$

7. $\dfrac{dy}{dx} = \dfrac{y}{x - \sqrt{xy}}.$

8. $x(\sqrt{xy} + y)\, dx - x^2\, dy = 0.$

9. $x\dfrac{dy}{dx} = y + xe^{\frac{y}{x}}.$

10. $\dfrac{dy}{dx} = \dfrac{y^2 - x\sqrt{x^2 - y^2}}{xy}.$

11. Discuss the problem of transforming the differential equation

$$\frac{dy}{dx} = \frac{a_1 x + a_2 y + a_3}{b_1 x + b_2 y + b_3}$$

into a homogeneous equation by the change of variable $x = x' + h$ and $y = y' + k$. Determine the values of h and k for which the original equation is transformed into

$$\frac{dy'}{dx'} = \frac{a_1 x' + a_2 y'}{b_1 x' + b_2 y'}$$

and solve this equation. If $a_1 b_2 - a_2 b_1 = 0$, set $a_1 x + a_2 y = z$.

12. $(x^2 - xy)\, dy + y^2\, dx = 0.$

13. $(y^2 - x^2)\, dy + 2xy\, dx = 0.$

14. $\dfrac{dy}{dx} = \dfrac{1 + 2x + y}{1 - 2x - y}.$

15. $(x - y + 1)\, dx + (x + y - 1)\, dy = 0.$

16. $y^2\, dx + (xy + x^2)\, dy = 0.$

17. $(2x^3 y - y^4)\, dx + (2xy^3 - x^4)\, dy = 0.$

18. $(x^2 + y^2)\, dx + 3xy\, dy = 0.$

19. $(x^2 + y^2)\, dx - xy\, dy = 0.$

20. $(x + y)\, dy - (x - y)\, dx = 0.$

77. Exact Differential Equations. It was shown in Sec. 63 that the necessary and sufficient condition that the expression

$$P(x, y)\, dx + Q(x, y)\, dy$$

be an exact differential of some function $F(x, y)$ is that

(77-1) $$\frac{\partial P}{\partial y} = \frac{\partial Q}{\partial x},$$

where these partial derivatives are continuous functions.

Consider now the differential equation

(77-2) $$P(x, y)\, dx + Q(x, y)\, dy = 0,$$

and suppose that the functions $P(x, y)$ and $Q(x, y)$ satisfy the condition (77-1), so that there exists a function $F(x, y)$ such that

$$\begin{aligned} dF &= \frac{\partial F}{\partial x}\, dx + \frac{\partial F}{\partial y}\, dy \\ &= P(x, y)\, dx + Q(x, y)\, dy. \end{aligned}$$

Such a differential equation is called an *exact differential equation.* It is clear that the function

$$F(x, y) = c,$$

where c is an arbitrary constant, will be a solution of (77-2). An explicit form of the function $F(x, y)$ will be obtained next.

By hypothesis the condition (77-1) is satisfied so that one can write

(77-3) $\dfrac{\partial F}{\partial x} = P(x, y)$ and $\dfrac{\partial F}{\partial y} = Q(x, y).$

Now, the first of these equations will surely be satisfied by the expression

(77-4) $F(x, y) = \displaystyle\int P(x, y)\, dx + f(y),$

where the y appearing under the integral sign is treated as a parameter and $f(y)$ is an arbitrary function of y alone. The function $f(y)$ will be determined next, in such a way that (77-4) satisfies the second of Eqs. (77-3).

Differentiating (77-4) with respect to y and equating the result to $Q(x, y)$ give

$$\frac{\partial F}{\partial y} = \frac{\partial}{\partial y} \int P(x, y)\, dx + \frac{df}{dy} = Q(x, y),$$

so that

(77-5) $\dfrac{df}{dy} = Q(x, y) - \dfrac{\partial}{\partial y} \displaystyle\int P(x, y)\, dx.$

Hence,

(77-6) $f(y) = \displaystyle\int \left[Q(x, y) - \frac{\partial}{\partial y} \int P(x, y)\, dx \right] dy.$

Substitution of (77-6) in (77-4) gives the explicit formula

(77-7) $F(x, y) = \displaystyle\int P(x, y)\, dx + \int \left[Q(x, y) \right.$

$$\left. - \frac{\partial}{\partial y} \int P(x, y)\, dx \right] dy.$$

To illustrate the use of this formula, consider

$$(2xy + 1)\, dx + (x^2 + 4y)\, dy = 0.$$

Here,

$$\frac{\partial P}{\partial y} = \frac{\partial Q}{\partial x} = 2x,$$

so that the formula (77-7) is applicable. The reader will verify that the substitution of the expressions for P and Q in (77-7) gives

$$F(x, y) = x^2 y + x + 2y^2 + c.$$

Hence, the solution is

$$x^2y + x + 2y^2 = c.$$

Instead of using the formula (77-7), one frequently proceeds as follows: Since $\partial P/\partial y = \partial Q/\partial x$, the existence of a function $F(x, y)$ such that

$$\frac{\partial F}{\partial x} = 2xy + 1 \quad \text{and} \quad \frac{\partial F}{\partial y} = x^2 + 4y$$

is assured. Now, if

$$\frac{\partial F}{\partial x} = 2xy + 1$$

is integrated with respect to x, y being treated as a constant, there results

$$F(x, y) = x^2y + x + c_1(y),$$

where $c_1(y)$ is not a function of x but may be a function of y, since y was treated as a constant. Similarly, the second condition

$$\frac{\partial F}{\partial y} = x^2 + 4y,$$

upon integration with respect to y, gives

$$F(x, y) = x^2y + 2y^2 + c_2(x).$$

Comparison of the two expressions for $F(x, y)$ shows that if

$$F(x, y) = x^2y + x + 2y^2,$$

then

$$\frac{\partial F}{\partial x} = 2xy + 1 \quad \text{and} \quad \frac{\partial F}{\partial y} = x^2 + 4y.$$

Thus, the general solution of the given equation is

$$x^2y + x + 2y^2 = c.$$

PROBLEMS

Integrate the following equations if they are exact:

1. $(y \cos xy + 2x)\, dx + x \cos xy\, dy = 0.$
2. $(y^2 + 2xy + 1)\, dx + (2xy + x^2)\, dy = 0.$
3. $(e^x + 1)\, dx + dy = 0.$
4. $(3x^2y - y^3)\, dx + (x^3 - 3y^2x)\, dy = 0.$

5. $(3x^2y - y^3) \, dx - (x^3 + 3y^2x) \, dy = 0.$

6. $\dfrac{y}{x^2} \cos \dfrac{y}{x} \, dx - \dfrac{1}{x} \cos \dfrac{y}{x} \, dy = 0.$

7. $2x \log y \, dx + \dfrac{x^2}{y} \, dy = 0.$

8. $\dfrac{x \sqrt{1 - y^2}}{\sqrt{1 - x^2}} \, dx + y \dfrac{\sqrt{1 - x^2}}{\sqrt{1 - y^2}} \, dy = 0.$

9. $(2x + e^x \log y) \, dx + \dfrac{e^x}{y} \, dy = 0.$

10. $2x \sin y \, dx - x^2 \cos y \, dy = 0.$

11. $(2x + yx^3) \, dx + 5(x - 3x^2y) \, dy = 0.$

12. $\left(2x + \dfrac{1}{y} e^{x/y}\right) dx - \dfrac{1}{y^2} e^{x/y} \, dy = 0.$

13. $\sin 2y \, dx + 2x \cos 2y \, dy = 0.$

14. $x^2(y + 1) \, dx - y^2(x - 1) \, dy = 0.$

15. $y(1 + x^2)^{-1} \, dx - \tan^{-1} x \, dy = 0.$

78. Integrating Factors.   It is not difficult to see that every differential equation of the type

$$(78\text{-}1) \qquad M(x, y) \, dx + N(x, y) \, dy = 0,$$

which has a solution $F(x, y) = c$, can be made exact by multiplying both members by a suitable function of x and y.   For since $F(x, y) = c$ is a solution of (78-1),

$$(78\text{-}2) \qquad \frac{\partial F}{\partial x} \, dx + \frac{\partial F}{\partial y} \, dy = 0,$$

and it follows from a comparison of (78-1) and (78-2) that

$$\frac{\partial F}{\partial x} = \mu(x, y)M \qquad \text{and} \qquad \frac{\partial F}{\partial y} = \mu(x. y)N.$$

Therefore,

$$\mu(x, y)(M \, dx + N \, dy) = 0$$

is an exact equation.   The function $\mu(x, y)$ is termed an *integrating factor*.   Moreover, it is clear that there is an unlimited number of such functions for each equation.   Despite this fact, it must not be concluded that an integrating factor can always be found easily.   In simpler cases, however, the integrating factor can be found by inspection.

Thus, in order to solve

$$x \, dy - y \, dx = 0,$$

which is not exact as it stands, multiply both sides by $1/xy$. Then the equation becomes

$$\frac{dy}{y} - \frac{dx}{x} = 0,$$

which is exact. Another integrating factor for this same equation is $1/x^2$. Similarly, multiplication by $1/y^2$ makes the equation exact.

In Prob. 1 at the end of this section will be found a few of the integrable combinations that frequently occur in practice.

Example. The differential equation

$$(y^2 - x^2)\, dy + 2xy\, dx = 0$$

is not an exact equation, but on rearrangement it becomes

$$y^2\, dy + 2xy\, dx - x^2\, dy = 0,$$

which can be made exact with the aid of the integrating factor $1/y^2$. The resulting equation is

$$dy + \frac{2xy\, dx - x^2\, dy}{y^2} = 0,$$

which integrates to

$$y + \frac{x^2}{y} = c.$$

PROBLEMS

1. Verify the following:

(a) $d\left(\tan^{-1}\dfrac{y}{x}\right) = \dfrac{x\, dy - y\, dx}{x^2 + y^2}$;

(b) $d\left(\log\dfrac{y}{x}\right) = \dfrac{x\, dy - y\, dx}{xy}$;

(c) $d\left(\dfrac{x}{y}\right) = -\dfrac{x\, dy - y\, dx}{y^2}$;

(d) $d\left(\dfrac{y}{x}\right) = \dfrac{x\, dy - y\, dx}{x^2}$;

(e) $\tfrac{1}{2}d(x^2 + y^2) = x\, dx + y\, dy$;

(f) $d(xy) = x\, dy + y\, dx$.

2. Solve the following equations by finding a suitable integrating factor:

(a) $x\, dy - y\, dx + x^2\, dx = 0$;

(b) $(xy^2 + y)\, dx + (x - x^2 y)\, dy = 0$;

(c) $x \, dy + 3y \, dx = xy \, dy$;

(d) $(x^2 + y^2 + 2x) \, dy - 2y \, dx = 0$;

(e) $x \, dy - y \, dx = xy \, dy$;

(f) $(x^2 - y^2) \, dy - 2xy \, dx = 0$;

(g) $x \, dy - (y + \log x) \, dx = 0$.

79. Equations of the First Order in Which One of the Variables Does Not Occur Explicitly. Suppose that the dependent variable y does not occur explicitly in the equation. The form of the equation is then

$$F\left(\frac{dy}{dx}, x\right) = 0.$$

If this equation is solved for dy/dx to obtain

$$\frac{dy}{dx} = f(x),$$

then y is obtained by a simple quadrature as

$$y = \int f(x) \, dx + c.$$

Example. Consider

$$\left(\frac{dy}{dx}\right)^2 - 4x \frac{dy}{dx} + x^2 = 0.$$

Solving for dy/dx gives

$$\frac{dy}{dx} = (2 \pm \sqrt{3})x$$

and

$$y = \frac{2 \pm \sqrt{3}}{2} x^2 + c.$$

Hence, the solutions are

$$y - \frac{2 + \sqrt{3}}{2} x^2 - c = 0$$

and

$$y - \frac{2 - \sqrt{3}}{2} x^2 - c = 0.$$

These solutions can be combined into one equation by multiplying one by the other to give

$$(y - c)^2 - 2x^2(y - c) + \tfrac{1}{4}x^4 = 0.$$

If the independent variable is missing, the equation is of the form

$$F\left(\frac{dy}{dx}, y\right) = 0.$$

Solving for dy/dx gives

$$\frac{dy}{dx} = f(y)$$

or

$$\frac{dx}{dy} = \frac{1}{f(y)}.$$

Integration of this equation yields

$$x = \int \frac{dy}{f(y)} + c.$$

Occasionally, the differential equation can be solved easily by factoring. For example, consider

$$2\left(\frac{dy}{dx}\right)^2 - (2y^2 + x)\frac{dy}{dx} + xy^2 = 0.$$

This equation can be written in the form

$$\left(\frac{dy}{dx} - y^2\right)\left(2\frac{dy}{dx} - x\right) = 0,$$

so that one is led to the solution of the differential equations

$$\frac{dy}{dx} - y^2 = 0 \qquad \text{and} \qquad 2\frac{dy}{dx} - x = 0.$$

It follows that the general solution of the given equation can be written as

$$\left(x + \frac{1}{y} + c\right)\left(2y - \frac{x^2}{2} + c\right) = 0.$$

PROBLEMS

Solve the following differential equations:

1. $\left(\dfrac{dy}{dx}\right)^2 + y^2 = 1.$

2. $\left(\dfrac{dy}{dx}\right)^2 + x^2 = 1.$

3. $\dfrac{dy}{dx} - \dfrac{1}{1 + y^2}\dfrac{dy}{dx} + 1 = 0.$

4. $\left(\dfrac{dy}{dx}\right)^2 - 2y\dfrac{dy}{dx} - 3y^2 = 0.$

5. $\left(\dfrac{dy}{dx}\right)^2 - 2\dfrac{dy}{dx} + 1 = 0.$ *Hint:* Factor.

6. $\left(\dfrac{dy}{dx}\right)^3 - (x + 1) = 0.$

7. $\left(\dfrac{dy}{dx}\right)^2 + (2x - y)\dfrac{dy}{dx} - 2xy = 0.$

8. $\left(\dfrac{dy}{dx}\right)^2 + (x - e^x)\dfrac{dy}{dx} - xe^x = 0.$

9. $\left(\dfrac{dy}{dx}\right)^2 - y^2 + 1 = 0.$

10. $xy\left(\dfrac{dy}{dx}\right)^2 + (x - y)\dfrac{dy}{dx} - 1 = 0.$

80. Differential Equations of the Second Order. Occasionally, it is possible to solve a differential equation of the second order by reducing the problem to that of solving first-order equations. Thus, if the given equation is of the form

$$F\left(\dfrac{d^2y}{dx^2}, \dfrac{dy}{dx}\right) = 0,$$

the substitution of $p = dy/dx$ reduces it to

$$F\left(\dfrac{dp}{dx}, p\right) = 0,$$

which is an equation of the first order of the type treated in Sec. 79. If this equation is solved for p to give

$$p = f(x, c),$$

the solution for y can be obtained at once, since $p = dy/dx$.

No general rules can be given for solving non-linear differential equations, and the task must be left to the skill and ingenuity of the student. An example of the solution of a non-linear differential equation by means of an artifice was given in Sec. 72 in dealing with the equation of a flexible cable. Another example may prove interesting and useful.

Example. Consider the equation

$$y\dfrac{d^2y}{dx^2} - 2\left(\dfrac{dy}{dx}\right)^2 + y^2 = 0.$$

If dy/dx is replaced by p, the resulting equation is

$$y\dfrac{dp}{dx} - 2p^2 + y^2 = 0.$$

Since

$$\frac{dp}{dx} = p\,\frac{dp}{dy},$$

the equation can be written as

$$py\,\frac{dp}{dy} - 2p^2 + y^2 = 0,$$

or

$$\frac{dp}{dy} = \frac{2p^2 - y^2}{py},$$

which is a homogeneous equation. Setting $p = vy$ gives

$$v + y\,\frac{dv}{dy} = \frac{2y^2v^2 - y^2}{y^2v} = \frac{2v^2 - 1}{v},$$

which reduces to

$$\frac{dy}{y} = \frac{v\,dv}{v^2 - 1}.$$

Therefore,

$$\log y = \log (v^2 - 1)^{1/2} + \log c_1$$

and

$$y = c_1 \sqrt{v^2 - 1}.$$

But $v = p/y$, so that

$$y = c_1 \sqrt{\frac{p^2}{y^2} - 1}$$

and

$$p = \pm \frac{y}{c_1} \sqrt{y^2 + c_1^2}.$$

Since $p = dy/dx$, the last equation becomes

$$\frac{dy}{dx} = \pm \frac{y}{c_1} \sqrt{y^2 + c_1^2}$$

or

$$\frac{dy}{\pm \dfrac{y}{c_1} \sqrt{y^2 + c_1^2}} = dx.$$

Therefore,

$$\pm \log \frac{c_1 + \sqrt{y^2 + c_1^2}}{y} = x + c_2.$$

Combining these two solutions by multiplication gives the solution

$$(x + c_2)^2 - \left(\log \frac{c_1 + \sqrt{y^2 + c_1^2}}{y} \right)^2 = 0,$$

which can be written, also, as

$$(x + c_2)^2 - \left(\operatorname{csch}^{-1} \frac{y}{c_1} \right)^2 = 0.$$

It is seen from this example that if the given differential equation is of the form

(80-1) $F(y, y', \cdots, y^{(n)}) = 0,$

then one can introduce the new variable

$$p \equiv y'$$

and calculate the successive derivatives as follows:

$$y'' = \frac{dp}{dx} = \frac{dp}{dy} p,$$

$$y''' = \frac{d}{dx} \left(\frac{dp}{dy} p \right) = \frac{d}{dy} \left(\frac{dp}{dy} p \right) p = \frac{d^2p}{dy^2} p^2 + \left(\frac{dp}{dy} \right)^2 p,$$

. . . .

The substitution of these derivatives in (80-1) leads to a differential equation of order $n - 1$. It may be possible to solve this differential equation and obtain the general solution in the form

$$p = F(y, c_1, \cdots, c_{n-1}),$$

so that

(80-2) $\dfrac{dy}{dx} = F(y, c_1, \cdots, c_{n-1}).$

Equation (80-2) is one with separable variables.

PROBLEMS

Solve the following differential equations:

1. $\dfrac{d^2y}{dx^2} + y = 0.$ Solve by substituting $dy/dx = p$, and also by using the integrating factor $2\,dy/dx$.

2. $(x^2 - 1) \dfrac{d^2y}{dx^2} + x \dfrac{dy}{dx} = 0.$

3. $\dfrac{d^4y}{dx^4} - k^2 \dfrac{d^2y}{dx^2} = 0.$

4. $\dfrac{d^2y}{dx^2} + e^y = 0.$

5. $x^2 \dfrac{d^2y}{dx^2} + (x - 1) = 0.$

6. $\dfrac{d^2y}{dx^2} - \left(\dfrac{dy}{dx}\right)^2 - 1 = 0.$

7. $\dfrac{d^2y}{dx^2} + y \dfrac{dy}{dx} = 0.$

81. Gamma Functions. Consider a particle of mass m that is moving in a straight line under the influence of an attractive force whose intensity varies inversely as the distance of the particle from the center of attraction. The equation of such a motion is obtainable immediately from the definition of force (Newton's second law). Denoting the distance from the center of attraction by y, it follows that

$$m \frac{d^2y}{dt^2} = -\frac{k}{y}$$

or

$$\frac{d^2y}{dt^2} = -\frac{a}{y},$$

where $a = k/m$.

This is a non-linear equation of the type

$$\frac{d^2y}{dt^2} = F(y),$$

which can always be solved by multiplying both sides of the equation by $2\,dy/dt$ and integrating. Thus,

$$2 \frac{dy}{dt} \frac{d^2y}{dt^2} = -2 \frac{dy}{dt} \frac{a}{y}$$

and integrating with respect to t gives

$$\left(\frac{dy}{dt}\right)^2 = -2a \log y + c.$$

If the velocity of the particle is zero when $y = y_0$, then $c = 2a \log y_0$ and

$$\frac{dy}{dt} = -\sqrt{2a \log \frac{y_0}{y}}.$$

The negative sign was chosen for the square root because y is a decreasing function of t. Solving for dt and integrating yield

$$t = -\frac{1}{\sqrt{2a}} \int_{y_0}^{y} \frac{dy}{\sqrt{\log \dfrac{y_0}{y}}}.$$

The integral can be put in a simpler form by making the obvious transformation $\log (y_0/y) = x$, or $y = y_0 e^{-x}$. If T is the time required to reach the center of attraction, $y = 0$, the integral becomes

$$(81\text{-}1) \qquad T = \frac{y_0}{\sqrt{2a}} \int_0^{\infty} x^{-\frac{1}{2}} e^{-x}\, dx.$$

This integral cannot be evaluated in terms of a finite number of the elementary functions. In fact, an integral of this type led Euler to the discovery of the so-called Gamma functions.

The remainder of this section will be concerned with the study of the improper integral

$$(81\text{-}2) \qquad \Gamma(\alpha) = \int_0^{\infty} x^{\alpha-1} e^{-x}\, dx, \qquad \text{where } \alpha > 0,$$

which is the generalization of (81-1). It will be shown that (81-2) defines an interesting function, called the Gamma function, which provides a generalization of the factorial and which will prove useful in the study of Bessel functions.

It is not difficult to prove* that (81-2) converges for all positive values of α and diverges whenever $\alpha \le 0$. However, it is possible to define the function $\Gamma(\alpha)$ for negative values of α with the aid of the recursion formula which will be developed next.

If $\alpha > 0$, then it follows from (81-2) that

$$(81\text{-}3) \qquad \Gamma(\alpha + 1) = \int_0^{\infty} x^{\alpha} e^{-x}\, dx.$$

Integrating the right-hand member of (81-3) by parts gives

$$\int_0^{\infty} x^{\alpha} e^{-x}\, dx = -x^{\alpha} e^{-x} \Big|_0^{\infty} + \alpha \int_0^{\infty} x^{\alpha-1} e^{-x}\, dx$$

$$= \alpha \int_0^{\infty} x^{\alpha-1} e^{-x}\, dx$$

$$= \alpha \Gamma(\alpha).$$

Thus,

$$(81\text{-}4) \qquad \Gamma(\alpha + 1) = \alpha \Gamma(\alpha).$$

*See Sokolnikoff, I. S., *Advanced Calculus*, p. 373.

But

$$\Gamma(1) = \int_0^\infty e^{-x}\, dx = 1,$$

so that when $\alpha = 1$ the formula (81-4) becomes

$$\Gamma(2) = 1 \cdot \Gamma(1) = 1.$$

Setting $\alpha = 2, 3, \cdots, n$ gives

$$\Gamma(3) = 2\Gamma(2) = 1 \cdot 2,$$
$$\Gamma(4) = 3\Gamma(3) = 1 \cdot 2 \cdot 3,$$
$$\cdots \cdots \cdots \cdots \cdots \cdots,$$
$$\Gamma(n) = (n-1)\Gamma(n-1) = (n-1)!,$$
$$\Gamma(n+1) = n\Gamma(n) = n!.$$

Hence, the formula (81-4) enables one to compute the values of $\Gamma(\alpha)$ for all positive integral values of the argument α.

If by some means (for example, by using infinite series) the values of $\Gamma(\alpha)$ are obtained for all values of α between 1 and 2, then, with the aid of the recursion formula (81-4), the values of $\Gamma(\alpha)$ are readily obtained when α lies between 2 and 3. These values being known, it is easy to obtain $\Gamma(\alpha)$ where $3 < \alpha < 4$, etc. The values of $\Gamma(\alpha)$ for α lying between 1 and 2 have been computed* to a high degree of accuracy, so that it is possible to find the value of $\Gamma(\alpha)$ for all $\alpha > 0$.

It remains to define $\Gamma(\alpha)$ for negative values of α. The recursion formula (81-4) can be written as

$$(81\text{-}5) \qquad\qquad \Gamma(\alpha) = \frac{\Gamma(\alpha+1)}{\alpha}.$$

The formula (81-5) becomes meaningless when α is set equal to zero, for

$$\lim_{\alpha \to 0+} \Gamma(\alpha) = +\infty \qquad \text{and} \qquad \lim_{\alpha \to 0-} \Gamma(\alpha) = -\infty.$$

It follows from (81-5) that the function $\Gamma(-\alpha)$ is discontinuous when α is a positive integer.

If any number $-1 < \alpha < 0$ is substituted in the left-hand side of (81-5), the right-hand side gives the value of $\Gamma(\alpha)$; for the values of $\alpha + 1$ lie between 0 and 1, and $\Gamma(\alpha)$ is known

* A small table is found in B. O. Peirce, A Short Table of Integrals, p. 140.

for these values of α. Thus,

$$\Gamma\left(-\frac{1}{2}\right) = \frac{\Gamma(\frac{1}{2})}{-\frac{1}{2}}, \qquad \Gamma(-0.9) = \frac{\Gamma(0.1)}{-0.9}, \text{ etc.}$$

In this manner the values of $\Gamma(\alpha)$ for $-1 < \alpha < 0$ can be computed. If these values are known and the recursion formula (81-5) is used, the values of $\Gamma(\alpha)$ for $-2 < \alpha < -1$ can be obtained, etc. The adjoining figure represents the graph of $\Gamma(\alpha)$ (Fig. 76).

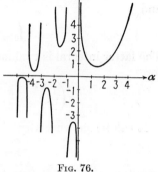

It was observed that

$$\Gamma(\alpha + 1) = \alpha!$$

when α is a positive integer. This formula may serve as the definition of factorials of fractional numbers. Thus,

$$\Gamma(\tfrac{3}{2}) = \tfrac{1}{2}!,$$
$$\Gamma(\tfrac{1}{2}) = (-\tfrac{1}{2})!,$$
$$\Gamma(1) = 0! = 1.$$

Fig. 76.

This section will be concluded with an ingenious method of evaluating $\frac{1}{2}!$. Now,

$$\tfrac{1}{2}! = \Gamma(\tfrac{3}{2}) = \int_0^\infty e^{-x} x^{\frac{1}{2}}\, dx.$$

If the variable in this integral be changed by the transformation $x = y^2$, the integral becomes

$$(81\text{-}6) \qquad \tfrac{1}{2}! = 2 \int_0^\infty e^{-y^2} y^2\, dy.$$

Since the definite integral is independent of the variable of integration and is a function of the limits,

$$(81\text{-}7) \qquad \tfrac{1}{2}! = 2 \int_0^\infty e^{-z^2} z^2\, dz.$$

Multiplying (81-6) by (81-7) gives

$$(\tfrac{1}{2}!)^2 = 4 \int_0^\infty e^{-z^2} z^2\, dz \int_0^\infty e^{-y^2} y^2\, dy,$$

which can be written as a double integral

$$(81\text{-}8) \qquad (\tfrac{1}{2}!)^2 = 4 \int_0^\infty \int_0^\infty e^{-(y^2+z^2)} y^2 z^2\, dy\, dz.$$

In order to evaluate (81-8), transform it into polar coordinates by setting $z = r \cos \theta$ and $y = r \sin \theta$. The element of area $dy \, dz$ becomes $r \, dr \, d\theta$, and (81-8) becomes

$$(\tfrac{1}{2}!)^2 = 4 \int_0^\infty dr \int_0^{\frac{\pi}{2}} r^5 e^{-r^2} \sin^2 \theta \cos^2 \theta \, d\theta.$$

But

$$\int_0^{\frac{\pi}{2}} \sin^2 \theta \cos^2 \theta \, d\theta = \frac{\pi}{16}$$

and

$$\int_0^\infty e^{-r^2} r^5 \, dr = 1.$$

The latter integral is evaluated by integration by parts. Therefore

$$\left(\frac{1}{2}!\right)^2 = \frac{\pi}{4} \qquad \text{or} \qquad \frac{1}{2}! = \frac{\sqrt{\pi}}{2}.$$

It can be shown with the aid of the recursion formula that

$$(-\tfrac{1}{2})! = \sqrt{\pi}.$$

It follows that (81-1) has the value $y_0 \sqrt{\pi/(2a)}$ sec.

PROBLEMS

1. Compute the values of $\Gamma(\alpha)$ for every integer and half integer from 0 to 5 by using the relations $\Gamma(1) = 1$ and $\Gamma(\tfrac{1}{2}) = \sqrt{\pi}$. Plot the curve $y = \Gamma(\alpha)$ with the aid of these values.

2. The Beta function $B(m, n)$ is defined by the integral

$$B(m, n) = \int_0^1 x^{m-1}(1 - x)^{n-1} \, dx.$$

If x is replaced by y^2 in $\Gamma(n) = \int_0^\infty x^{n-1} e^{-x} \, dx$, there results

$$\Gamma(n) = 2 \int_0^\infty e^{-y^2} y^{2n-1} \, dy.$$

Using this integral, form

$$\Gamma(m)\Gamma(n) = 4 \int_0^\infty x^{2n-1} e^{-x^2} \, dx \int_0^\infty y^{2m-1} e^{-y^2} \, dy.$$

Express this product as a double integral, transform to polar coordinates, and show that

$$B(m, n) = B(n, m) = \frac{\Gamma(m)\Gamma(n)}{\Gamma(m + n)}.$$

3. Show, by a suitable change of variable, that (81-2) reduces to

$$\int_0^1 \left(\log \frac{1}{y}\right)^{\alpha-1} dy.$$

4. Show that

$$\frac{d^n \Gamma(\alpha)}{d\alpha^n} = \int_0^\infty x^{\alpha-1} e^{-x} (\log x)^n \, dx.$$

82. Orthogonal Trajectories. In a variety of practical investigations, it is desirable to determine the equation of a family of curves that intersect the curves of a given family at right angles. For example, it is known that the lines of equal potential, due to a distribution of steady current flowing in a homogeneous conducting medium, intersect the lines of current flow at right angles. Again, the stream lines of a steady flow of liquid intersect the lines of equal velocity potential (see Sec. 66) at right angles.

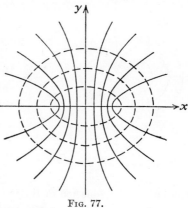

Fig. 77.

Let the equation of the given family of curves be

(82-1) $f(x, y, c) = 0,$

where c is an arbitrary parameter. By specifying the values of the parameter c, one obtains a family of curves (see solid curves in Fig. 77). Let it be required to determine the equation of a family of curves orthogonal to the family defined by (82-1).

The differential equation of the family of curves (82-1) can be obtained by eliminating the parameter c from (82-1) and its derivative,

(82-2) $\dfrac{\partial f}{\partial x} + \dfrac{\partial f}{\partial y}\dfrac{dy}{dx} = 0.$

Let the resulting differential equation be

$$F\left(x, y, \frac{dy}{dx}\right) = 0.$$

Now, by definition, the orthogonal family of curves cuts the curves of the given family (82-1) at right angles. Hence, the slope at any point of a curve of the orthogonal family is the negative reciprocal of the slope of the curves of the given family. Thus, the differential equation of the desired family of curves is

$$F\left(x, y, -\frac{dx}{dy}\right) = 0.$$

This is a differential equation of the first order, and its general solution has the form

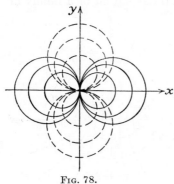

(82-3) $\varphi(x, y, c) = 0.$

The family of curves defined by (82-3) is the desired family of curves orthogonal to the curves of the given family (82-1). It is called the family of orthogonal trajectories.

Example. Let it be required to find the family of curves orthogonal to the family of circles (Fig. 78)

Fig. 78.

(82-4) $x^2 + y^2 - cx = 0.$

The differential equation of the family (82-4) can be obtained by differentiating (82-4) with respect to x and eliminating the parameter c between (82-4) and the equation that results from the differentiation.

The reader will check that the differential equation of the family (82-4) is

$$2xy\frac{dy}{dx} + x^2 - y^2 = 0.$$

Hence, the differential equation of the family of curves orthogonal to (82-4) is

$$2xy\frac{dx}{dy} - x^2 + y^2 = 0.$$

This is a homogeneous differential equation whose solution is easily found to be

$$x^2 + y^2 - cy = .0.$$

Thus, the desired family of curves is the family of circles with centers on the y-axis (see Fig. 78).

PROBLEMS

1. Find the orthogonal trajectories of the family of concentric circles $x^2 + y^2 = a^2$.

2. Find the orthogonal trajectories of the family of hyperbolas $xy = c$.

3. Find the orthogonal trajectories of the family of curves $y = cx^n$. Sketch the curves of the given and the desired families for $n = 1, -1, 2$.

4. If the equation of a family of curves is given in polar coordinates as $f(r, \theta, c) = 0$, show that the tangent of the angle made by the radius vector and the tangent line at any point (r, θ) of a curve of the family is equal to $r\dfrac{d\theta}{dr}$. Hence, show that the differential equation of the orthogonal trajectories of the given family of curves is obtained by replacing $r\dfrac{d\theta}{dr}$ by $-\dfrac{1}{r}\dfrac{dr}{d\theta}$ in the differential equation of the given family of curves.

5. Using the results of Prob. 4, show that the orthogonal trajectories of the family of cardioids $r = c(1 - \cos\theta)$ is another family of cardioids.

6. Find the orthogonal trajectories of the family of spirals $r = e^{c\theta}$.

7. Find the orthogonal trajectories of the family of similar ellipses $x^2/4 + y^2/9 = c^2$.

8. Find the orthogonal trajectories of the family of parabolas $y^2 = 4px$.

9. Find the equation of the curve such that the area bounded by the curve, the x-axis, and an ordinate is proportional to the ordinate.

83. Singular Solutions. It was remarked in Sec. 68 that a differential equation may possess solutions which cannot be obtained from the general solution by specifying the values of the arbitrary constants. Such solutions are called *singular solutions.*

Consider a family of integral curves defined by

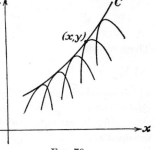

FIG. 79.

$$(83\text{-}1) \qquad \varphi(x, y, c) = 0,$$

where (83-1) is the general solution of the differential equation

$$(83\text{-}2) \qquad f\left(x, y, \frac{dy}{dx}\right) = 0.$$

Assume that the family of curves defined by (83-1) is such that it has an envelope* (Fig. 79). Since the slope of the envelope at any point (x, y) is the same as that of the integral curve which is

* It will be recalled that an envelope of a family of curves is a fixed curve C such that every curve of the family is tangent to C.

tangent to the envelope at (x, y), it follows that the equation of the envelope must satisfy (83-2). In general, the envelope is not a curve belonging to the family of curves defined by (83-1), and hence its equation cannot be obtained from (83-1) by specifying the value of the arbitrary constant c. It will be recalled that the equation of the envelope is obtained by eliminating the parameter c between the equations

$$\varphi(x, y, c) = 0 \quad \text{and} \quad \frac{\partial \varphi}{\partial c} = 0.$$

Example. It is readily verified that the family of integral curves associated with the equation

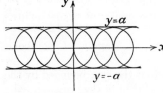

$$(83\text{-}3) \qquad y^2 \left(\frac{dy}{dx}\right)^2 + y^2 = a^2$$

is the family of circles

$$(83\text{-}4) \qquad (x - c)^2 + y^2 = a^2.$$

Fig. 80.

The equation of the envelope of the family (83-4) is obtained by eliminating c between (83-4) and

$$\frac{\partial \varphi}{\partial c} \equiv -2(x - c) = 0.$$

There results

$$(83\text{-}5) \qquad y = \pm a,$$

which represents the equation of a pair of lines tangent to the family of circles (83-4) (Fig. 80). Obviously, (83-5) is a singular solution of (83-3), for it cannot be obtained from (83-4) by any choice of the constant c.

Inasmuch as the problem of determining the singular solutions of a given differential equation is relatively rare in applied work, the subject will not be pursued here any further.

REVIEW PROBLEMS

1. A particle slides down an inclined plane making an angle θ with the horizontal. If the initial velocity is zero and gravity is the only force acting, what are the velocity of the particle and the distance traveled during the time t? Compare the time of descent and the terminal velocity with those of a particle falling freely from the same height as that of the inclined plane.

2. A particle falls in a liquid under the action of the force of gravity. If the resistance to the motion is proportional to the velocity of the particle, what is the distance traveled in t seconds when the particle starts from rest?

3. A bullet is projected upward with an initial velocity of v_0 ft. per second. If the force of gravity and a resistance that is proportional to the velocity are the only forces acting, find the velocity at the end of t sec. and the distance traveled by the bullet in t sec.

4. The rate of decomposition of a certain chemical substance is proportional to the amount of the substance still unchanged. If the amount of the substance at the end of t hr. is x and x_0 is the initial amount, show that $x = x_0 e^{-kt}$, where k is the constant of proportionality. What is the constant of proportionality if x changes from 1000 g. to 500 g. in 2 hr.?

5. A torpedo moving in still water is retarded with a force proportional to the velocity. Find the speed at the end of t sec. and the distance traveled in t sec., if the initial speed is 30 miles per hour.

6. A disk is rotating about a vertical axis in an oil bath. If the retardation due to friction of the oil is proportional to the angular velocity ω, find ω after t sec. The initial velocity is ω_0.

7. Water is flowing out through a circular hole in the side of a cylindrical tank 2 ft. in diameter. The velocity of the water in the jet is $\sqrt{2gh}$, where h is the height in feet of the surface of the water above the center of the orifice. How long will it take the water to fall from a height of 25 ft. to a height of 9 ft. above the orifice, if the orifice is 1 in. in diameter?

8. Water is flowing out from a 2-in. horizontal pipe running full. Find the discharge in cubic feet per second if the jet of water strikes the ground 4 ft. beyond the end of the pipe when the pipe is 2 ft. above the ground.

9. A projectile is fired, with an initial velocity v_0, at an angle α with the horizontal. Find the equation of the path under the assumption that the force of gravity is the only force acting on the projectile.

10. A cylindrical tumbler containing liquid is rotated with a constant angular velocity about the axis of the tumbler. Show that the surface of the liquid assumes the shape of a paraboloid of revolution. *Hint:* The resultant force acting on a particle of the liquid is directed normally to the surface. This resultant is compounded of the force of gravity and the centrifugal force.

11. Two chemical substances combine in such a way as to produce a compound. If the rate of combination is proportional to the product of the unconverted amounts of the parent substances, find the amount of the compound produced at the end of time t. The initial amounts of the parent substances are a and b, and the converted amounts are equal.

Hint: $dx/dt = k(a - x)(b - x)$.

12. Assume that the pressure p of the air at any height h is equal to the weight of the vertical column of air above it. If the density of the air is proportional to the pressure, what is the law connecting the pressure p with the height h?

13. A particle of mass m is sliding down a rough inclined plane (the coefficient of friction $\mu = 0.2$), whose height is 300 ft. and whose angle of inclination is 30°. If the particle starts from rest, how long will it take to reach the foot of the plane? With what velocity will it be traveling then?

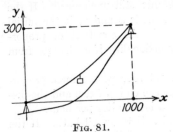

FIG. 81.

Hint: The differential equation of motion is

$$\frac{d^2s}{dt^2} = g(\sin \alpha - \mu \cos \alpha),$$

where α is the angle of inclination of the plane.

14. A runaway carrier in an aerial tramway is moving along the arc of a second-degree parabola joining the points whose coordinates are (0, 0) and (1000, 300) (Fig. 81). How long will it take the carrier to reach the lowest point if the frictional resistance is neglected and if the carrier starts from the top with initial velocity zero? See in this connection the *Engineers' Bulletin of the Colorado Society of Engineers,* June, 1935.

15. A brick is set moving in a straight line over the ice with an initial velocity of 20 ft. per second. If the coefficient of friction between the brick and the ice is 0.2, how long will it be before the brick stops?

16. A certain radioactive salt decomposes at a rate proportional to the amount present at any instant t. How much of the salt will be left 300 years hence, if 100 mg. that was set aside 50 years ago has been reduced to 90 mg.?

17. A skier weighing 150 lb. is coasting down a 10° incline. If the force of friction opposing the motion is 5 lb. and the air resistance is two times the speed in feet per second, what is the skier's speed after t sec.?

18. A tank contains 1000 gal. of brine holding 1 lb. of salt per gallon. If salt water containing 2 lb. of salt per gallon is allowed to enter the tank at the rate of 1 gal. per minute and the mixture, which is kept uniform by stirring, is permitted to flow out at the same rate, what is the amount of salt in the tank at any time t?

Hint: Let the amount of salt present at any time t be x; then, the rate at which x changes is equal to the rate of gain, in pounds per minute, diminished by the rate of loss. Thus,

$$\frac{dx}{dt} = 2 - \frac{x}{1000}.$$

19. A 100-gal. tank contains pure water. If 50 per cent alcohol is allowed to enter the tank at the rate of 2 gal. per minute and the mixture of alcohol and water, which is kept uniform by stirring, leaves the tank at the same rate, what is the amount of alcohol in the tank at the end of 10 min.?

20. The rate at which two chemical substances are combining is proportional to the amount of the first substance remaining unchanged. If initially there are 20 lb. of this substance and 2 hr. later there are only 10 lb., how much of the substance will be left at the end of 4 hr.?

21. A series circuit consists of a condenser whose capacity is c farads and the resistance is R ohms. Before the circuit was closed the condenser contained a charge of q_0 coulombs. What is the charge on the condenser t sec. later?   (The differential equation is $R\frac{dq}{dt} + \frac{q}{c} = 0$.)

22. The rate at which a body is cooling is proportional to the difference in the temperatures of the body and the surrounding medium. It is known that the temperature of a body fell from 120° to 70°C. in 1 hr., when it was placed in air at 20°C. How long will it take the body to cool to 40°C.?   30°C.?   20°C.?

23. A bullet is fired vertically down from a balloon that is 2 miles above the surface of the earth. On the assumption that the resistance is proportional to the square of the velocity, find the velocity with which the bullet strikes the earth if the initial velocity is 1800 ft. per second.

84. Linear Differential Equations. The remainder of this chapter will be restricted to the treatment of linear differential equations, that is, equations of the type

$$(84\text{-}1) \quad p_0(x)\frac{d^n y}{dx^n} + p_1(x)\frac{d^{n-1}y}{dx^{n-1}} + \cdots + p_{n-1}(x)\frac{dy}{dx} + p_n(x)y = f(x),$$

where the $p_i(x)$ and $f(x)$ are either functions of x or constants.   It is extremely fortunate that a large number of physical phenomena are successfully described with the aid of linear differential equations. It will be shown in the succeeding sections that it is possible to give a more detailed account of the treatment and solution of linear differential equations than has been furnished for non-linear equations.

85. Linear Equations of the First Order. A linear differential equation of the first order has the form

$$(85\text{-}1) \qquad \frac{dy}{dx} + f_1(x)y = f_2(x).$$

In order to solve this equation, set $y = uv$, where u and v are functions of x that are to be determined later. With this substitution, (85-1) becomes

$$u\frac{dv}{dx} + v\frac{du}{dx} + f_1(x)uv = f_2(x)$$

or

$$(85\text{-}2) \qquad v\left[\frac{du}{dx} + f_1(x)u\right] + u\frac{dv}{dx} = f_2(x).$$

If u is suitably chosen, the bracket in (85-2) can be made equal to zero, thus reducing (85-2) to a simple form. In order to choose u so that the expression in the bracket is equal to zero, set

$$\frac{du}{dx} + f_1(x)u = 0$$

or

$$\frac{du}{u} + f_1(x)\,dx = 0.$$

Integrating gives

$$\log u + \int f_1(x)\,dx = c,$$

and choosing the simplest expression for u, by setting $c = 0$, produces

$$u = e^{-\int f_1(x)\,dx}.$$

With this choice of u, (85-2) becomes

$$e^{-\int f_1(x)\,dx}\frac{dv}{dx} = f_2(x)$$

or

$$\frac{dv}{dx} = e^{\int f_1(x)\,dx}f_2(x),$$

which integrates into

$$v = \int e^{\int f_1(x)\,dx}f_2(x)\,dx + c.$$

By hypothesis, $y = uv$, so that

(85-3) $y = e^{-\int f_1(x)\,dx} \int e^{\int f_1(x)\,dx} f_2(x)\,dx + ce^{-\int f_1(x)\,dx}$.

This is the general solution of (85-1).

Example 1. Solve

$$\frac{dy}{dx} + y\cos x = \sin 2x.$$

Upon using formula (85-3),

$$y = e^{-\int \cos x\,dx} \int e^{\int \cos x\,dx} \sin 2x\,dx + ce^{-\int \cos x\,dx}$$

$$= e^{-\sin x} \int e^{\sin x} \sin 2x\,dx + ce^{-\sin x},$$

which is easily evaluated by replacing $\sin 2x$ by $2\sin x\cos x$.

Example 2. Solve

$$\frac{dy}{dx} + \frac{2y}{x+1} = (x+1)^3.$$

Here,

$$y = e^{-\int \frac{2\,dx}{x+1}} \int e^{\int \frac{2\,dx}{x+1}} (x+1)^3\,dx + ce^{-\int \frac{2\,dx}{x+1}}$$

$$= \frac{1}{(x+1)^2} \int (x+1)^5\,dx + \frac{c}{(x+1)^2},$$

which is easily evaluated.

PROBLEMS

Solve the following equations:

1. $(1 + x^2)\,dy + \left(xy - \dfrac{1}{x}\right) dx = 0.$

2. $(x^2 + 1)\dfrac{dy}{dx} + 2xy = x^2.$

3. $\dfrac{dy}{dx} = e^{-x^2} - 2xy.$

4. $\dfrac{dy}{dx} + xy - x = 0.$

5. $\dfrac{dy}{dx} + y\cos x = \cos^3 x.$

6. $x\dfrac{dy}{dx} + y - x^2\sin x = 0.$

7. $\dfrac{dy}{dx} = \dfrac{y-1}{x^2+1}.$

8. $L\dfrac{dI}{dt} + RI = E,$ given that $I = 0$ when $t = 0$; L. R, and E are constants.

9. $\dfrac{dy}{dx} = y + \cos x - \sin x.$

10. $\dfrac{dy}{dx} - y \sec x \csc x = e^x (1 - \sec x \csc x).$

11. $\dfrac{dx}{dy} + yx = y.$

12. $dx + 2x\,dy - y\,dy = 0.$

13. $\dfrac{dy}{dx} + y \sec^2 x = \tan x \sec^2 x.$

14. $(x + 1)\dfrac{dy}{dx} - y = e^x (x + 1)^2.$

15. $\dfrac{dy}{dx} - 2y - e^{3x} = 0.$

86. A Non-linear Equation Reducible to Linear Form (Bernoulli's Equation). An equation of the type

$$(86\text{-}1) \qquad \frac{dy}{dx} + f_1(x)y = f_2(x)y^n,$$

in which n may be regarded different from zero and unity, can be reduced to linear form by the substitution $z = y^{1-n}$. Then,

$$\frac{dz}{dx} = (1 - n)y^{-n}\frac{dy}{dx}$$

and (86-1) becomes

$$\frac{dz}{dx} - (n - 1)f_1(x)z = -(n - 1)f_2(x),$$

which is a linear equation in z.

Example. Solve

$$\frac{dy}{dx} + y = xy^3.$$

Setting $z = 1/y^2$, the equation becomes

$$\frac{dz}{dx} - 2z = -2x,$$

whose general solution is

$$z = ce^{2x} + x + \tfrac{1}{2},$$

so that

$$y^{-2} = ce^{2x} + x + \tfrac{1}{2}.$$

PROBLEMS

Solve the following equations:

1. $y^3 \dfrac{dy}{dx} + \dfrac{y^4}{x} = \sin x.$

2. $\dfrac{dy}{dx} + y = xy^3.$

3. $\dfrac{1}{y^6} \dfrac{dy}{dx} + \dfrac{1}{xy^5} = x^2.$

4. $\dfrac{dy}{dx} - x^{-1}y + x^{-2}y^2 = 0.$

5. $x \dfrac{dy}{dx} + y = y^2 \log x.$

6. $\dfrac{dy}{dx} + xy = x^3y^3.$

7. $\dfrac{dx}{dy} + x - yx^3 = 0.$

8. $\dfrac{dy}{dx} - \dfrac{x}{1 - x^2}\, y = \dfrac{xy^2}{1 - x^2}.$

87. Linear Differential Equations of the *n*th Order. No formulas are available for the solution of the linear differential equation, with variable coefficients, of order greater than 1. This section contains some interpretations of the symbolic notation that will be found useful in the solution of the linear differential equation

$$(87\text{-}1) \quad \frac{d^n y}{dx^n} + a_1 \frac{d^{n-1}y}{dx^{n-1}} + a_2 \frac{d^{n-2}y}{dx^{n-2}} + \cdots + a_{n-1}\frac{dy}{dx} + a_n y = f(x),$$

in which the a_i are constants.

It will be convenient to introduce the new notation

$$\frac{dy}{dx} \equiv Dy \qquad \text{and} \qquad \frac{d^n y}{dx^n} \equiv D^n y.$$

In this notation, (87-1) becomes

$$D^n y + a_1 D^{n-1}y + a_2 D^{n-2}y + \cdots + a_{n-1} Dy + a_n y = f(x)$$

or

$$(87\text{-}2) \quad (D^n + a_1 D^{n-1} + a_2 D^{n-2} + \cdots + a_{n-1}D + a_n)y = f(x).$$

The expression in the parentheses in (87-2) is known as a linear differential operator of order n. Obviously, it is not an algebraic expression multiplying y but is a symbol signifying that certain operations of differentiation are to be performed on the function y. Thus, $D^2 - 2D + 5$ operating on $\log x$ gives

$$
\begin{aligned}
(D^2 - 2D + 5) \log x &\equiv D^2 \log x - 2D \log x + 5 \log x \\
&\equiv \frac{d^2 \log x}{dx^2} - 2\frac{d \log x}{dx} + 5 \log x \\
&\equiv -\frac{1}{x^2} - \frac{2}{x} + 5 \log x.
\end{aligned}
$$

The gain in simplicity in using the operational notation results from the fact that linear differential operators *with constant coefficients* formally obey the laws which are valid for polynomials. Thus

$$
D(y + z) \equiv \frac{d}{dx}(y + z) = \frac{dy}{dx} + \frac{dz}{dx} \equiv Dy + Dz
$$

so that the operator D is distributive. If the symbol

$$
(D + a_1)(D + a_2),
$$

where a_1 and a_2 are constants, is interpreted to mean that the operator $D + a_1$ is applied to $(D + a_2)y$, then

$$
\begin{aligned}
(D + a_1)(D + a_2)y &\equiv (D + a_1)[(D + a_2)y] \\
&= (D + a_1)\left(\frac{dy}{dx} + a_2 y\right) \\
&= \frac{d}{dx}\left(\frac{dy}{dx} + a_2 y\right) + a_1\left(\frac{dy}{dx} + a_2 y\right) \\
&= D^2 y + (a_1 + a_2) Dy + a_1 a_2 y \\
&= [D^2 + (a_1 + a_2)D + a_1 a_2]y.
\end{aligned}
$$

It is readily established that operating on y with

$$
(D + a_2)(D + a_1)
$$

produces precisely the same result. Hence, the commutative law holds, or

$$
\begin{aligned}
(D + a_1)(D + a_2)y &\equiv (D + a_2)(D + a_1)y \\
&\equiv [D^2 + (a_1 + a_2)D + a_1 a_2]y.
\end{aligned}
$$

It is readily established that the law of exponents also holds, namely,

$$
D(D^n y) = D^{n+1} y,
$$

so that linear operators can be multiplied like ordinary algebraic quantities, where the powers of D in the result are to be interpreted as successive differentiations.

The solution of (87-2) can be written in the symbolic form

$$y = \frac{1}{D^n + a_1 D^{n-1} + \cdots + a_{n-1} D + a_n} f(x).$$

The meaning of this symbol will be investigated next.

Consider a simple differential equation

$$(87\text{-}3) \qquad \frac{dy}{dx} = f(x) \qquad \text{or} \qquad Dy = f(x).$$

The solution of (87-3), in symbolic form, is

$$y = \frac{1}{D} f(x),$$

so that the symbol $1/D$ must be interpreted as integration* with respect to x. Thus,

$$y = \frac{1}{D} f(x) = \int f(x)\, dx.$$

The meaning of a more complicated symbol can be obtained from a consideration of the first-order equation

$$(87\text{-}4) \qquad \frac{dy}{dx} + ay = f(x),$$

where a is a constant. Writing this equation in the operational notation, it becomes

$$(D + a)y = f(x).$$

The symbolic solution in this case is

$$(87\text{-}5) \qquad y = \frac{1}{D + a} f(x).$$

It was established in Sec. 85 that the general solution of (87-4) is

$$(87\text{-}6) \qquad y = ce^{-ax} + e^{-ax} \int e^{ax} f(x)\, dx,$$

---

* In order to make the definition of the operator $1/D$ unambiguous, one could agree that the constant of integration should be selected so that $y = 0$ when x assumes some specific value. However, in order to avoid complication, the constant that arises from the integration of $f(x)$ will be suppressed.

and it is desirable to give the symbolic solution (87-5) an interpretation that is consistent with the actual solution (87-6). Now, the solution (87-6) consists of two parts, the first of which, ce^{-ax}, if taken alone, obviously does not satisfy (87-4). The second part

$$e^{-ax} \int e^{ax} f(x) \, dx$$

is a solution of (87-4), for (87-6) represents the general solution which reduces to

$$e^{-ax} \int e^{ax} f(x) \, dx$$

when the arbitrary constant is taken as zero. The part of the solution (87-6) containing $f(x)$ is called a *particular integral* of (87-4), and the part containing the arbitrary constant is called the *complementary function*. It may be observed that the complementary function ce^{-ax} satisfies the homogeneous linear differential equation*

$$\frac{dy}{dx} + ay = 0.$$

It is convenient to associate with the symbol (87-5) the particular integral of (87-4), namely,

(87-7) $$\frac{1}{D + a} f(x) \equiv e^{-ax} \int e^{ax} f(x) \, dx.$$

The arbitrary constant arising from the integration in (87-7) may be taken as zero, for the addition of this constant of integration will give rise to a term that can be merged with the complementary function. The integral operator

$$\frac{1}{D + a} f(x),$$

as defined by (87-7), is of fundamental importance in the following sections. The meaning of a more complicated symbolic solution will be given later.

Example 1. To interpret the symbol

$$\frac{1}{D + a} x^m,$$

---

* The term *homogeneous linear differential equation* should not be confused with the homogeneous equation discussed in Sec. 76. The homogeneous linear differential equation is one of the type (84-1), where $f(x) \equiv 0$.

write out its meaning with the aid of (87-7). Then,

$$\frac{1}{D+a} x^m \equiv e^{-ax} \int e^{ax} x^m \, dx$$

$$= \frac{x^m}{a} - \frac{mx^{m-1}}{a^2} + \frac{m(m-1)x^{m-2}}{a^3} - \cdots , \text{ if } m \geqq 0,$$

except when $a = 0$. If $a = 0$ and $m \neq -1$, then

$$\frac{1}{D} x^m \equiv \int x^m \, dx = \frac{x^{m+1}}{m+1}.$$

Example 2.

$$\frac{1}{D+a} \sin mx \equiv e^{-ax} \int e^{ax} \sin mx \, dx = \frac{a \sin mx - m \cos mx}{a^2 + m^2}.$$

PROBLEMS

1. Show that

$$\frac{1}{D+a} [f_1(x) + f_2(x)] = \frac{1}{D+a} f_1(x) + \frac{1}{D+a} f_2(x).$$

2. What is the meaning of $\dfrac{1}{D+a} e^{mx}$?

3. What is the meaning of $\dfrac{1}{D+a} \cos mx$?

88. Some General Theorems. In Sec. 87, it was found that the general solution of the non-homogeneous linear differential equation of the first order contained as part of itself the solution of the homogeneous equation

$$\frac{dy}{dx} + ay = 0.$$

It will be shown next that a similar statement can be made concerning the general solution of the nth-order linear equation.

Consider first a homogeneous linear differential equation of the nth order with constant coefficients,

$$(88\text{-}1) \quad \frac{d^n y}{dx^n} + a_1 \frac{d^{n-1} y}{dx^{n-1}} + \cdots + a_{n-1} \frac{dy}{dx} + a_n y = 0.$$

If $y = e^{mx}$ is substituted in this equation, the result is

$$(m^n + a_1 m^{n-1} + \cdots + a_{n-1} m + a_n) e^{mx} = 0.$$

If m is chosen so that it satisfies the equation

$$(88\text{-}2) \quad m^n + a_1 m^{n-1} + \cdots + a_{n-1} m + a_n = 0,$$

which is called the *auxiliary*, or *characteristic, equation*, then $y = e^{mx}$ will be a solution of (88-1). But (88-2) has, in general, n distinct roots, $m_1, m_2, \cdots, m_n$, so that there will be n distinct solutions

$$y_1 = e^{m_1 x}, \qquad y_2 = e^{m_2 x}, \cdots, \qquad y_n = e^{m_n x}.$$

Because of the linear character of (88-1), it is clear that, if $y = e^{m_i x}$ is a solution, then

$$y = c_i e^{m_i x},$$

where c_i is an arbitrary constant, is also a solution. Moreover, it is readily verified that the sum of the solutions of a homogeneous linear differential equation is also a solution of the equation. Thus,

$$(88\text{-}3) \qquad y = c_1 e^{m_1 x} + c_2 e^{m_2 x} + \cdots + c_n e^{m_n x}$$

will be a solution; and since it contains n arbitrary constants (all roots m_i are assumed to be distinct), it is the general solution of (88-1).

Let

$$(88\text{-}4) \quad \frac{d^n y}{dx^n} + a_1 \frac{d^{n-1} y}{dx^{n-1}} + \cdots + a_{n-1} \frac{dy}{dx} + a_n y = f(x),$$

where $f(x) \neq 0$; and assume that, by inspection or otherwise, a solution $y = u(x)$ of (88-4) has been found. Then, if (88-3) is the general solution of the homogeneous equation (88-1),

$$(88\text{-}5) \quad y = c_1 e^{m_1 x} + c_2 e^{m_2 x} + \cdots + c_n e^{m_n x} + u(x)$$

will be the general solution of (88-4). This fact can be verified by direct substitution of (88-5). That (88-5) is the general solution follows from the fact that it contains n arbitrary constants. The part of (88-5) that is denoted by $u(x)$ is called a *particular integral* of (88-4), and the part containing the arbitrary constants **is** called the *complementary function*.

Example 1. Solve

$$\frac{d^3 y}{dx^3} - \frac{d^2 y}{dx^2} - 2\frac{dy}{dx} = e^{-x}.$$

The auxiliary equation is

$$m^3 - m^2 - 2m = 0,$$

and its roots are $m_1 = 0$, $m_2 = -1$, $m_3 = 2$. Then the complementary

function is
$$Y \equiv c_1 + c_2 e^{-x} + c_3 e^{2x}.$$
A particular integral $u(x)$ is
$$u(x) \equiv \tfrac{1}{3} x e^{-x}.$$
Therefore, the general solution is given by
$$y = Y + u(x).$$

If (88-1) is written in symbolic form as

(88-6) $(D^n + a_1 D^{n-1} + \cdots + a_{n-1} D + a_n)y = 0$

and the differential operator (which is of precisely the same form as the auxiliary equation defined above) is treated as an algebraic expression, then (88-6) can be written as

(88-7) $(D - m_1)(D - m_2) \cdots (D - m_n)y = 0.$

Consider the n first-order linear homogeneous equations

$$(D - m_1)y = 0,$$
$$(D - m_2)y = 0,$$
$$\ldots\ldots\ldots\ldots\ldots,$$
$$(D - m_n)y = 0,$$

whose solutions can be obtained at once by recalling that the meaning of the symbol is given by

$$(D - m)y \equiv \frac{dy}{dx} - my.$$

These solutions are $e^{m_1 x}$, $e^{m_2 x}$, $\cdots$, $e^{m_n x}$, which are precisely the same as the solutions obtained for (88-1) by a different method.

The general solution of (88-7) was found to be (88-3) under the assumption that all the roots m_i were distinct. If some of the roots are equal, the number of arbitrary constants c_i in (88-3) is less than n and the solution given there is not the general solution. Suppose that the equation

$$\frac{d^2 y}{dx^2} + a_1 \frac{dy}{dx} + a_2 y = 0$$

is such that its auxiliary equation has a double root, that is, $m_1 = m_2 = m$. Then this equation can be written as

$$(D - m)(D - m)y = 0.$$

If $(D - m)y$ is set equal to v, the equation becomes

$$(D - m)v = 0$$

and $v = c_1 e^{mx}$ is its solution. Since $(D - m)y = v$, it follows that

$$(D - m)y = c_1 e^{mx},$$

which is a linear equation whose solution can be found, with the aid of (87-6), to be

$$y = e^{mx}(c_2 + c_1 x).$$

Thus, if the auxiliary equation has a double root, the solution corresponding to that root is

$$y = e^{mx}(c_2 + c_1 x).$$

By an entirely similar argument, it can be established that, if the auxiliary equation possesses a root m of multiplicity r, then the solution corresponding to that root is

$$y = e^{mx}(c_1 + c_2 x + \cdots + c_r x^{r-1}).$$

Example 2.   Find the solution of

$$(D^3 - 3D^2 + 4)y = 0.$$

The auxiliary equation is

$$m^3 - 3m^2 + 4 = 0 \qquad \text{or} \qquad (m + 1)(m - 2)^2 = 0.$$

Therefore the general solution is

$$y = c_1 e^{-x} + (c_2 + c_3 x)e^{2x}.$$

Example 3.   Find the solution of

$$(D^2 + 1)y = 0.$$

The auxiliary equation is

$$m^2 + 1 = 0 \qquad \text{or} \qquad (m - i)(m + i) = 0.$$

Therefore, the general solution is

$$y = c_1 e^{ix} + c_2 e^{-ix} = A \cos x + B \sin x.$$

PROBLEMS

1. Find the general solutions of

(a) $\dfrac{d^2y}{dx^2} + 3\dfrac{dy}{dx} - 54y = 0.$

(b) $\dfrac{d^2y}{dx^2} - 5\dfrac{dy}{dx} + 6y = 0.$

(c) $\dfrac{d^2y}{dx^2} + 2\dfrac{dy}{dx} + y = 0.$

(d) $(D^3 - 2D^2 + D)y = 0.$

(e) $(D^4 + 3D^3 + 3D^2 + D)y = 0.$

(f) $(D^4 - k^4)y = 0.$

(g) $(D^3 - 3D^2 + 4)y = 0.$

(h) $(D^3 - 13D + 12)y = 0.$

(i) $(D^3 + D^2 - D - 1)y = 0.$

(j) $(D^4 + 2D^3 + D^2)y = 0.$

89. The Meaning of the Operator

$$\frac{1}{D^n + a_1D^{n-1} + \cdots + a_{n-1}D + a_n}\, f(x).$$

In Sec. 87 the meaning of the operator $\dfrac{1}{D + a}f(x)$ was given. Now, consider a second-order linear differential equation with constant coefficients,

$$\frac{d^2y}{dx^2} + a_1\frac{dy}{dx} + a_2y = f(x)$$

or

(89-1) $(D^2 + a_1D + a_2)y = f(x).$

It was remarked in Sec. 87 that linear operators with constant coefficients obey the ordinary laws of algebra and can be treated as polynomials. Therefore, (89-1) can be factored to read

$$(D - m_1)(D - m_2)y = f(x)$$

or

$$(D - m_2)y = \frac{1}{D - m_1}f(x)$$

$$= e^{m_1x}\int e^{-m_1x}f(x)\,dx,$$

in accordance with (87-7). Hence,

(89-2) $y = \dfrac{1}{D - m_2}\, e^{m_1x}\displaystyle\int e^{-m_1x}f(x)\,dx$

$$\equiv e^{m_2x}\int\left[e^{(m_1-m_2)x}\int e^{-m_1x}f(x)\,dx\right]dx.$$

For $m_1 = m_2$, (89-2) reduces to

$$(89\text{-}3) \qquad y = e^{m_1 x} \int \int e^{-m_1 x} f(x) \, dx \, dx.$$

By direct substitution in (89-1), it is easy to establish the fact that (89-2) is a particular solution of (89-1). The general solution, according to Sec. 88, is made up of the sum of (89-2) and the general solution of the homogeneous equation

$$\frac{d^2 y}{dx^2} + a_1 \frac{dy}{dx} + a_2 y = 0,$$

which is known to be

$$y = c_1 e^{m_1 x} + c_2 e^{m_2 x}, \qquad m_1 \neq m_2,$$

or

$$y = (c_1 + c_2 x) e^{m_1 x}, \qquad m_1 = m_2.$$

The interpretation of the symbol

$$\frac{1}{D^n + a_1 D^{n-1} + \cdots + a_{n-1} D + a_n} f(x)$$

which represents the symbolic solution of the differential equation

$$\frac{d^n y}{dx^n} + a_1 \frac{d^{n-1} y}{dx^{n-1}} + \cdots + a_{n-1} \frac{dy}{dx} + a_n y = f(x),$$

or

$$(89\text{-}4) \qquad (D^n + a_1 D^{n-1} + \cdots + a_{n-1} D + a_n) y = f(x),$$

can now be made easily. Write the operator in (89-4) in factored form,

$$D^n + a_1 D^{n-1} + \cdots + a_{n-1} D + a_n$$
$$= (D - m_1)(D - m_2) \cdots (D - m_n),$$

so that (89-4) becomes

$$y = \frac{1}{(D - m_n)(D - m_{n-1}) \cdots (D - m_1)} f(x)$$

$$= \frac{1}{D - m_n} \cdot \frac{1}{D - m_{n-1}} \cdots \frac{1}{D - m_1} f(x).$$

Successive operations on $f(x)$ with $\dfrac{1}{D - m_i}$ give

$$(89\text{-}5) \qquad y = e^{m_1 x} \int e^{(m_2 - m_1) x} \int e^{(m_3 - m_2) x} \cdots \int e^{-m_n x} f(x) \, (dx)^n,$$

and the result is a particular integral of (89-4).

It can be shown that if the operator

$$\frac{1}{D^n + a_1 D^{n-1} + \cdots + a_{n-1}D + a_n}$$

is decomposed into partial fractions (the denominator being treated as a polynomial in D), then

$$y = \frac{1}{D^n + a_1 D^{n-1} + \cdots + a_{n-1}D + a_n} f(x)$$

$$= \left(\frac{A_1}{D - m_1} + \frac{A_2}{D - m_2} + \cdots + \frac{A_n}{D - m_n} \right) f(x),$$

which gives, by (87-7),

$$(89\text{-}6) \quad y = A_1 e^{m_1 x} \int e^{-m_1 x} f(x) \, dx + A_2 e^{m_2 x} \int e^{-m_2 x} f(x) \, dx$$

$$+ \cdots + A_n e^{m_n x} \int e^{-m_n x} f(x) \, dx,$$

which is also a particular integral of (89-4).

Thus, there are available two methods for the determination of the particular integral. The first method of finding the particular integral, (89-5), is known as the method of iteration, and the second, (89-6), as the method of partial fractions. Generally speaking, formula (89-6) is easier to apply. However, if the roots of the auxiliary equation are not all distinct, the decomposition of the operator into partial fractions, of the type considered, cannot be effected and formula (89-5) must be used.

Example 1.   Solve

$$\frac{d^2 y}{dx^2} - 5 \frac{dy}{dx} + 6y = e^{4x}$$

or

$$(D^2 - 5D + 6)y = e^{4x}$$

or

$$(D - 3)(D - 2)y = e^{4x}.$$

The particular integral, as obtained by the method of iteration, is

$$y = \frac{1}{D - 3} \cdot \frac{1}{D - 2} e^{4x} = \frac{1}{D - 3} e^{2x} \int e^{2x} \, dx$$

$$= e^{3x} \int \left(e^{-x} \int e^{2x} \, dx \right) dx = \frac{e^{4x}}{2}.$$

If the method of partial fractions is used, then

$$y = \frac{1}{D-3} \cdot \frac{1}{D-2} e^{4x} = \left(\frac{1}{D-3} - \frac{1}{D-2} \right) e^{4x}$$
$$= e^{3x} \int e^{-3x} e^{4x} \, dx - e^{2x} \int e^{-2x} e^{4x} \, dx = \frac{e^{4x}}{2}.$$

The complementary function is

$$c_1 e^{3x} + c_2 e^{2x};$$

therefore, the general solution is

$$y = c_1 e^{3x} + c_2 e^{2x} + \frac{e^{4x}}{2}.$$

Example 2.   Solve

$$\frac{d^2 y}{dx^2} + 2 \frac{dy}{dx} + y = x \qquad \text{or} \qquad (D+1)(D+1)y = x.$$

The particular integral is

$$y = \frac{1}{(D+1)(D+1)} x = e^{-x} \int \int e^x x \, (dx)^2 = x - 2,$$

and the general solution is given by

$$y = (c_1 + c_2 x)e^{-x} + x - 2.$$

PROBLEMS

1. Solve $\dfrac{dy}{dx} + 3y = x^3$.

2. Solve $\dfrac{d^2 y}{dx^2} + 5 \dfrac{dy}{dx} + 6y = e^x$.

3. Solve $\dfrac{d^2 y}{dx^2} - 2 \dfrac{dy}{dx} + y = x$.

4. The flexure y for end thrust P is given by

$$EI \frac{d^2 y}{dx^2} = \frac{wl}{2} x - \frac{wx^2}{2} + Py,$$

where E is Young's modulus, w is the load, and I is the moment of inertia.   Solve this equation.

5. Solve $(D^3 - 2D^2 - D + 2)y = 1 - 2x$.

6. Solve $(D^2 + \frac{1}{2}D - \frac{1}{2})y = \cos x - 3 \sin x$.

7. Solve $(D^3 - 3D + 2)y = 2 \sin x - 4 \cos x$.

8. Solve $(D^2 - 1)y = 5x - 2$.

9. Solve $(D^3 - D^2 - 8D + 12)y = 1$.

10. Solve $(D^4 - 1)y = e^x \cos x$.

11. Solve $(D^2 - 2D + 1)y = xe^x$.

12. Solve $(D^2 + D - 2)y = \sin 2x$.

13. The differential equation of the deflection y of the truss of a suspension bridge has the form

$$EI \frac{d^4y}{dx^4} - (H + h) \frac{d^2y}{dx^2} = p - q \frac{h}{H},$$

where H is the horizontal tension in the cable under dead load q, h is the tension due to the live load p, E is Young's modulus, and I is the moment of inertia of the cross section of the truss about the horizontal axis of the truss through the center of gravity of the section and perpendicular to the direction of the length of the truss. Solve this equation under the assumption that $p - qh/H$ is a constant.

14. The differential equation of the deflection y of a rotating shaft has the form

$$EI \frac{d^4y}{dx^4} = \rho\omega^2 y,$$

where EI is the flexural rigidity of the shaft, ρ is the mass per unit length of the shaft, and ω is the angular velocity of rotation. Solve this equation.

15. The differential equation of the buckling of an elastically supported beam under an axial load P has the form

$$\frac{d^4y}{dx^4} + \frac{P}{EI} \frac{d^2y}{dx^2} + \frac{k}{EI} y = 0,$$

where EI is the flexural rigidity and k is the modulus of the foundation. Solve this equation.

90. Oscillation of a Spring and Discharge of a Condenser.

The foregoing discussion gives all the essential facts for solving an nth-order linear differential equation with constant coefficients. At this point, it is desirable to apply the methods of solution, outlined above, to a group of important practical problems.

Suppose that it is required to determine the position of the end of a helical spring at any time t. It is assumed that the spring is set vibrating in a vacuum so that considerations of damping do not enter here. If a mass M (Fig. 82) is applied to the end of the spring, it produces an elongation s which, according to Hooke's law, is proportional to the applied force. Thus,

$$F = ks,$$

where $F = Mg$ from the second law of motion and k represents the stiffness of the spring. Then,

$$Mg = ks.$$

If at any later time t an additional force is applied to produce an extension y, after which this additional force is removed, the spring will start oscillating. The problem is to determine the position of the end point of the spring at any subsequent time.

The forces acting on the mass M are the force of gravity Mg downward, which will be taken as the positive direction for

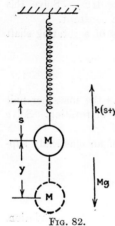

FIG. 82.

the displacement y, and the tension T in the spring, which acts in the direction opposite to that of the force of gravity. Hence, from Newton's second law of motion,

$$M \frac{d^2y}{dt^2} = Mg - T.$$

Since T is the tension in the spring when its elongation is $s + y$, Hooke's law states that $T = k(s + y)$, so that

$$M \frac{d^2y}{dt^2} = Mg - k(s + y).$$

But $Mg = ks$, and therefore the foregoing equation becomes

$$M \frac{d^2y}{dt^2} + ky = 0.$$

Setting $k/M = a^2$ reduces this to

(90-1) $\dfrac{d^2y}{dt^2} + a^2y = 0$ or $(D^2 + a^2)y = 0.$

Factoring gives $(D - ai)(D + ai)y = 0$, from which it is clear that the general solution is

$$y = c_1 e^{-ait} + c_2 e^{ait}.$$

Recalling that $e^{ix} = \cos x + i \sin x$ (Sec. 73), the solution can be written as

$$y = c_1(\cos at - i \sin at) + c_2(\cos at + i \sin at)$$
$$= A \cos at + B \sin at,$$

where $A = c_1 + c_2$ and $B = (c_2 - c_1)i$. The arbitrary constants A and B can be determined from the initial conditions. The solution reveals the fact that the spring vibrates with a simple harmonic motion whose period is

$$T = \frac{2\pi}{a} = 2\pi \sqrt{\frac{M}{k}}.$$

The period depends on the stiffness of the spring as would be expected—the stiffer the spring, the greater the frequency of vibration.

It is instructive to compare the solution just obtained with that of the corresponding electrical problem. It will be seen that a striking analogy exists between the mechanical and electrical systems. This analogy is responsible for many recent improvements in the design of telephone equipment.

Let a condenser (Fig. 83) be discharged through an inductive coil of negligible resistance. It is known that the charge Q on a condenser plate is proportional to the potential difference of the plates, that is,

$$Q = CV,$$

where C is the capacity of the condenser. Moreover, the current I flowing through the coil is

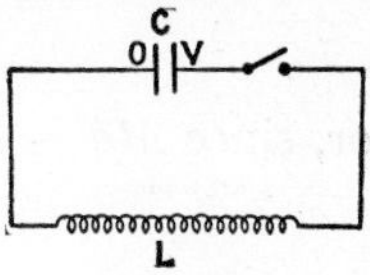

Fig. 83.

$$I = -\frac{dQ}{dt},$$

and, if the inductance be denoted by L, the e.m.f. opposing V is $L\, dI/dt$, since the IR drop is assumed to be negligible. Thus,

$$V - L\frac{dI}{dt} = 0$$

or

$$\frac{Q}{C} - L\left[\frac{d}{dt}\left(-\frac{dQ}{dt}\right)\right] = 0.$$

Simplifying gives

$$\frac{d^2Q}{dt^2} + \frac{1}{CL}\,Q = 0,$$

which is of precisely the same form as (90-1), where $a^2 = 1/CL$, and the general solution is then

$$Q = A \cos \frac{t}{\sqrt{CL}} + B \sin \frac{t}{\sqrt{CL}}.$$

The period of oscillation is

$$T = 2\pi \sqrt{CL}.$$

Note that the inductance L corresponds to the mass M of the mechanical example and that $1/C$ corresponds to the stiffness k of the spring.

91. Viscous Damping. Let the spring of the mechanical example of Sec. 90 be placed in a resisting medium in which the damping force is proportional to the velocity. This kind of damping is termed viscous damping.

Since the resisting medium opposes the displacement, the damping force $r \dfrac{dy}{dt}$ acts in the direction opposite to that of the displacement of the mass M. The force equation, in this case, becomes

$$M \frac{d^2y}{dt^2} = Mg - k(y + s) - r \frac{dy}{dt}$$

or, since $Mg = ks$,

$$\frac{d^2y}{dt^2} + \frac{r}{M} \frac{dy}{dt} + \frac{k}{M} y = 0.$$

In order to solve this equation, write it in the more convenient form

(91-1) $$\frac{d^2y}{dt^2} + 2b \frac{dy}{dt} + a^2y = 0.$$

In this case the auxiliary equation is

$$m^2 + 2bm + a^2 = 0$$

and its roots are

$$m = -b \pm \sqrt{b^2 - a^2},$$

so that the general solution is

(91-2) $$y = c_1 e^{(-b + \sqrt{b^2 - a^2})t} + c_2 e^{(-b - \sqrt{b^2 - a^2})t}.$$

It will be instructive to interpret the physical significance of the solution (91-2) corresponding to the three distinct cases that arise when $b^2 - a^2 > 0$, $b^2 - a^2 = 0$, and $b^2 - a^2 < 0$. If $b^2 - a^2$ is positive, the roots of the auxiliary equation are real and distinct. Denote them by m_1 and m_2, so that (91-2) is

(91-3) $$y = c_1 e^{m_1 t} + c_2 e^{m_2 t}.$$

The arbitrary constants c_1 and c_2 are determined from the initial conditions. Thus, let the spring be stretched so that $y = d$ and then released without giving the mass M an initial velocity. The conditions are then

$$y = d$$

when $t = 0$ and

$$\frac{dy}{dt} = 0$$

when $t = 0$.

Substituting these values into (91-3) and the derivative of (91-3) gives the two equations

$$d = c_1 + c_2 \quad \text{and} \quad 0 = m_1 c_1 + m_2 c_2.$$

These determine

$$c_1 = -\frac{m_2 d}{m_1 - m_2} \quad \text{and} \quad c_2 = \frac{m_1 d}{m_1 - m_2}.$$

Hence, the solution of (91-3) is

$$y = \frac{d}{m_1 - m_2} (m_1 e^{m_2 t} - m_2 e^{m_1 t}).$$

The graph of the displacement represented as a function of t is of the type shown in Fig. 84. Theoretically, y never becomes zero, although it comes arbitrarily close to it. This is the so-called o v e r d a m p e d case. The retarding force is so great in this case that no vibration can occur.

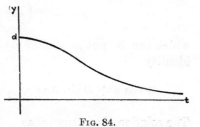

Fig. 84.

If $b^2 - a^2 = 0$, the two roots of the auxiliary equation are equal and the general solution of (91-1) becomes

$$y = e^{-bt}(c_1 + c_2 t).$$

If the initial conditions are

$$y = d$$

when $t = 0$ and

$$\frac{dy}{dt} = 0$$

when $t = 0$, the solution is

$$y = de^{-bt}(1 + bt).$$

This type of motion of the spring is called dead-beat. If the retarding force is decreased by an arbitrarily small amount, the motion will become oscillatory.

The most interesting case occurs when $b^2 < a^2$, so that the roots of the auxiliary equation are imaginary. Denote $b^2 - a^2$ by $-\alpha^2$, so that

$$m = -b \pm i\alpha$$

and

$$y = c_1 e^{(-b+i\alpha)t} + c_2 e^{(-b-i\alpha)t}$$
$$= e^{-bt}(A \cos \alpha t + B \sin \alpha t).$$

If the initial conditions are chosen as before,

$$y = d$$

when $t = 0$ and

$$\frac{dy}{dt} = 0$$

when $t = 0$, the arbitrary constants A and B can be evaluated. The result is

$$y = de^{-bt}\left(\cos \alpha t + \frac{b}{\alpha} \sin \alpha t\right),$$

which can be put in a more convenient form by the use of the identity

$$A \cos \theta + B \sin \theta \equiv \sqrt{A^2 + B^2} \cos \left(\theta - \tan^{-1} \frac{B}{A}\right).$$

The solution then appears as

$$(91\text{-}4) \qquad y = \frac{d}{\alpha} \sqrt{\alpha^2 + b^2}\, e^{-bt} \cos \left(\alpha t - \tan^{-1} \frac{b}{\alpha}\right).$$

The nature of the motion as described by (91-4) is seen from Fig. 85. It is an oscillatory motion with the amplitude decreasing exponentially. The period of the motion is $T = 2\pi/\alpha$. In the undamped case the period is $T = 2\pi/a$; and since

$$\alpha = \sqrt{a^2 - b^2} < a,$$

it follows that

$$\frac{2\pi}{\alpha} > \frac{2\pi}{a}.$$

Thus the period of oscillation is increased by the damping.

An electrical problem corresponding to the example of the viscous damping of a spring is the following: A condenser (Fig. 86) of capacity C is discharged through an inductive coil whose resistance is not negligible. Referring to Sec. 90 and remember-

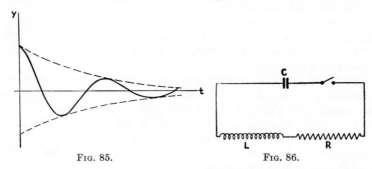

FIG. 85.   FIG. 86.

ing that the IR drop is not negligible, the voltage equation is found to be

$$V - L\frac{dI}{dt} - IR = 0$$

or

$$\frac{Q}{C} + L\frac{d^2Q}{dt^2} + R\frac{dQ}{dt} = 0.$$

Simplifying gives

$$\frac{d^2Q}{dt^2} + \frac{R}{L}\frac{dQ}{dt} + \frac{Q}{CL} = 0,$$

and this equation is of the same form as that in the mechanical example. The mass corresponds to the inductance L, r corresponds to the electrical resistance R, and the stiffness k corresponds to $1/C$. Its solution is the same as that of the corresponding mechanical example and is obtained by setting $2b = R/L$ and $a^2 = 1/CL$.

PROBLEMS

1. The force of 1000 dynes will stretch a spring 1 cm. A mass of 100 g. is suspended at the end of the spring and set vibrating. Find the equation of motion and the frequency of vibration if the mass is pulled down 2 cm. and then released. What will be the solution if the mass is projected down from rest with a velocity of 10 cm. per second?

2. Two equal masses are suspended at the end of an elastic spring of stiffness k. One mass falls off. Describe the motion of the remaining mass.

3. The force of 98,000 dynes extends a spring 2 cm. A mass of 200 g. is suspended at the end, and the spring is pulled down 10 cm. and released. Find the position of the mass at any instant t, if the resistance of the medium is neglected.

4. Solve Prob. 3 under the assumption that the spring is viscously damped. It is given that the resistance is 2000 dynes for a velocity of 1 cm. per second. What must the resistance be in order that the motion be a dead-beat?

5. A condenser of capacity 4 microfarads is charged so that the potential difference of the plates is 100 volts. The condenser is then discharged through a coil of resistance 500 ohms and inductance 0.5 henry. Find the potential difference at any later time t. How large must the resistance be in order that the discharge just fails to be oscillatory? Determine the potential difference for this case. Note that the equation in this case is

$$L \frac{d^2V}{dt^2} + R \frac{dV}{dt} + \frac{V}{C} = 0.$$

6. Solve Prob. 5 if $R = 100$ ohms, $C = 0.5$ microfarad, and $L = 0.001$ henry.

7. A simple pendulum of length l is oscillating through a small angle θ in a medium in which the resistance is proportional to the velocity. Show that the differential equation of the motion is

$$\frac{d^2\theta}{dt^2} + 2k \frac{d\theta}{dt} + \frac{g}{l} \theta = 0.$$

Discuss the motion, and show that the period is $2\pi/\sqrt{\omega^2 - k^2}$ where $\omega^2 = g/l$.

8. An iceboat weighing 500 lb. is driven by a wind that exerts a force of 25 lb. Five pounds of this force are expended in overcoming frictional resistance. What speed will this boat acquire at the end of 30 sec. if it starts from rest?

Hint: The force producing the motion is $F = (25 - 5) = 20$. Hence, $500 \, dv/dt = 20g$.

9. A body is set sliding down an inclined plane with an initial velocity of v_0 ft. per second. If the angle made by the plane with the horizontal is θ and the coefficient of friction is μ, show that the distance traveled in t sec. is

$$s = \tfrac{1}{2}g(\sin\theta - \mu\cos\theta)t^2 + v_0 t.$$

Hint: $m\, d^2s/dt^2 = mg\sin\theta - \mu mg\cos\theta$.

10. One end of an elastic rubber band is fastened at a point P, and the other end supports a mass of 10 lb. When the mass is suspended freely, its weight doubles the length of the band. If the original length of the band is 1 ft. and the weight is dropped from the point P, how far will the band extend? What is the equation of motion?

11. It is shown in books on strength of materials and elasticity that the deflection of a long beam lying on an elastic base, the reaction of which is proportional to the deflection y, satisfies the differential equation

$$EI\,\frac{d^4y}{dx^4} = -ky.$$

Set $a^4 = k/(4EI)$, and show that the characteristic equation corresponding to the resulting differential equation is $m^4 + 4a^4 = 0$, whose roots are $m = \pm\, a \pm ai$. Thus show that the general solution is

$$y = c_1 e^{ax}\cos ax + c_2 e^{ax}\sin ax + c_3 e^{-ax}\cos ax \\ + c_4 e^{-ax}\sin ax.$$

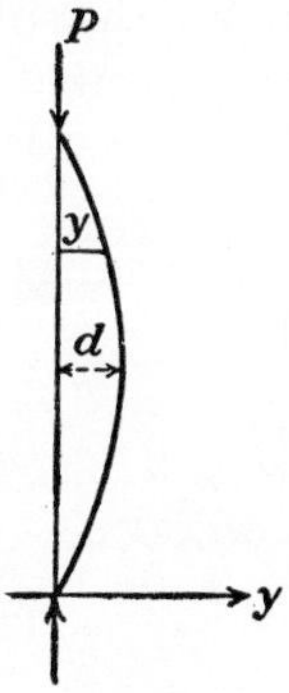

Fig. 87.

12. If a long column is subjected to an axial load P and the assumption that the curvature is small is not made, then the Bernoulli-Euler law gives (see Sec. 72)

$$\frac{\dfrac{d^2y}{dx^2}}{\left[1 + \left(\dfrac{dy}{dx}\right)^2\right]^{3/2}} = \frac{M}{EI}.$$

Since the moment M is equal to $-Py$ (Fig. 87), it follows upon setting $dy/dx = p$ that the differential equation of the deformed central axis is

$$\frac{p\,\dfrac{dp}{dy}}{(1 + p^2)^{3/2}} = -\frac{Py}{EI}.$$

Solve this differential equation for p, and show that the length of the central line is given by the formula

$$s = 2\sqrt{\frac{EI}{P}}\,F\left(k, \frac{\pi}{2}\right),$$

where $k^2 = d^2P/4EI$, d is the maximum deflection, and $F(k, \pi/2)$ is the elliptic integral of the first kind. The equation of the elastic curve, in this case, cannot be expressed in terms of the elementary functions, for the formula for y leads to an elliptic integral.

92. Forced Vibrations. In the discussion of Sec. 91, it was supposed that the vibrations were free. Thus, in the case of the mechanical example, it was assumed that the point of support of the spring was stationary and, in the electrical example, that there was no source of e.m.f. placed in series with the coil.

Now, suppose that the point of support of the spring is vibrating in accordance with some law which gives the displacement of the top of the spring as a function of the time t, say $x = f(t)$, where x is measured positively downward. Just as before, the spring is supposed to be supporting a mass M, which produces an elongation s of the spring. If the displacement of the mass M from its position of rest is y, it is clear that, when the top of the spring is displaced through a distance x, the actual extension of the spring is $y - x$. If the resistance of the medium is neglected, the force equation is

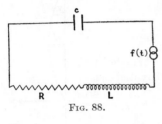

FIG. 88.

$$M \frac{d^2y}{dt^2} = Mg - k(s + y - x) = -k(y - x),$$

whereas, if the spring is viscously damped, it is

$$M \frac{d^2y}{dt^2} = Mg - k(s + y - x) - r \frac{dy}{dt}.$$

Upon simplifying this last equation, it becomes

(92-1) $$M \frac{d^2y}{dt^2} + r \frac{dy}{dt} + ky = kx,$$

where x is supposed to be a known function of t.

The corresponding electrical example is that of a condenser (Fig. 88) placed in series with the source of e.m.f. and that discharges through a coil containing inductance and resistance. The voltage equation is

$$-RI - L \frac{dI}{dt} + V = f(t),$$

where $f(t)$ is the impressed e.m.f. given as a function of t. Since

$$-I = \frac{dQ}{dt} = C \frac{dV}{dt},$$

the equation becomes

$$(92\text{-}2) \qquad CL\,\frac{d^2V}{dt^2} + CR\,\frac{dV}{dt} + V = f(t).$$

An interesting case arises when the impressed e.m.f. is sinusoidal, for example,

$$f(t) = E_0 \sin \omega t.$$

Then the equation takes the form

$$\frac{d^2V}{dt^2} + \frac{R}{L}\,\frac{dV}{dt} + \frac{1}{CL}\,V = \frac{1}{CL}\,E_0 \sin \omega t.$$

Both (92-1) and (92-2) are non-homogeneous linear equations with constant coefficients of the type

$$(92\text{-}3) \qquad \frac{d^2y}{dt^2} + 2b\,\frac{dy}{dt} + a^2y = a^2f(t).$$

The solution of this equation is the sum of the complementary function and the particular integral (see Sec. 88). The complementary function has the form shown by (91-2), namely

$$c_1 e^{m_1 t} + c_2 e^{m_2 t},$$

where

$$m_1 = -b + \sqrt{b^2 - a^2} \qquad \text{and} \qquad m_2 = -b - \sqrt{b^2 - a^2}.$$

The particular integral, by (89-5), is

$$(92\text{-}4) \qquad Y = a^2 e^{m_2 t} \int e^{(m_1 - m_2)t} \left[\int e^{-m_1 t} f(t) \, dt \right] dt.$$

From the discussion of Sec. 91, it is clear that the part of the solution which is due to free vibrations is a decreasing function of t and will become negligibly small after sufficient time has elapsed. Thus the "steady-state solution" is given by the particular integral (92-4).

Let it be assumed that the impressed force, x in (92-1) and $f(t)$ in (92-2), is simply harmonic of period $2\pi/\omega$ and of amplitude a_0. Then,

$$f(t) = a_0 \sin \omega t,$$

and (92-4) becomes

$$Y \equiv a^2 e^{m_2 t} \int e^{(m_1 - m_2)t} \left(\int e^{-m_1 t} a_0 \sin \omega t \, dt \right) dt.$$

The result of integration* is

(92-5)
$$Y = \frac{a^2 a_0}{\sqrt{(a^2 - \omega^2)^2 + 4b^2\omega^2}} \sin(\omega t - \epsilon),$$

where

$$\epsilon = \tan^{-1} \frac{2b\omega}{a^2 - \omega^2}.$$

This is the steady-state solution.

The remainder of this section will be devoted to the physical interpretation of the solution (92-5). It is observed that if the impressed frequency is very high (large ω), then the amplitude of the sinusoid (92-5) is small, so that the effect of the impressed force is small. When $\omega = a$, the amplitude is $a_0 a/2b$, which may be dangerously large if b (and hence the resistance of the medium) is small. For a fixed b (resistance of the medium) and a (natural frequency of the system), the maximum amplitude occurs when $(a^2 - \omega^2)^2 + 4b^2\omega^2$ is a minimum, that is, when

$$\frac{d}{d\omega}[(a^2 - \omega^2)^2 + 4b^2\omega^2] = 0.$$

This is readily found to be when

$$\omega^2 = a^2 - 2b^2.$$

Upon recalling the physical significance of a and b, these results can be interpreted immediately in terms of the physical quantities.

93. Resonance. It was remarked in Sec. 92 that if the impressed frequency is equal to the natural frequency of vibration, then the amplitude of (92-5) may be abnormally large. Stated in terms of the physical quantities of the electrical and mechanical examples, this means that the maximum voltage of the electrical system may be dangerously large or that the maximum displacement of the spring may be so great as to produce rupture.

The phenomenon of forced vibration is of profound importance in many engineering problems. Not so many years ago the collapse of a building in one of the larger American cities was

---

* Integration in this case is a little tedious. For actual integration, it is convenient to replace sin ωt by the equivalent exponential expression

$$\frac{e^{i\omega t} - e^{-i\omega t}}{2i}.$$

attributed to the rhythmic swaying of the dancing couples, who happened to strike the natural frequency of the beam supporting the structure. Again, the failure of the Tacoma bridge was explained by some on the basis of forced vibration. It is also well known that soldiers are commanded to break step in crossing a bridge, for fear that they may strike the note of the cables. The walls of Jericho are reported to have fallen after seven priests with seven trumpets blew a long blast.

The phenomenon of resonance occurs when the impressed frequency is equal to the natural frequency. Consider Eq. (92-3) in which b (resistance) is zero and $f(t) = a_0 \sin at$, so that

$$(93\text{-}1) \qquad \frac{d^2y}{dt^2} + a^2y = a^2a_0 \sin at.$$

The particular integral in this case is

$$(93\text{-}2) \qquad Y = a_0a^2e^{-ait} \int \left(e^{2ait} \int e^{-ait} \sin at \, dt \right) dt,$$

since $m_1 = ai$ and $m_2 = -ai$. If $\sin at$ is replaced by $\dfrac{e^{ait} - e^{-ait}}{2i}$, (93-2) integrates into

$$Y = -a_0a^2 \left(\frac{t \cos at}{2a} + \frac{1}{8a^2} \sin at + \frac{i}{8a^2} \cos at \right).$$

If Y is added to the complementary function $c_1 \cos at + c_2 \sin at$, the general solution is given by

$$(93\text{-}3) \qquad y = A \cos at + B \sin at - \frac{a_0a}{2} t \cos at,$$

where the last two terms of Y have been combined with the complementary function. Let the initial conditions be $y = 0$ when $t = 0$, and $dy/dt = 0$ when $t = 0$. Then $A = 0$ and $B = a_0/2$, and (93-3) will be

$$(93\text{-}4) \qquad y = \frac{a_0}{2} (\sin at - at \cos at).$$

This equation represents a vibration whose amplitude increases with time; for the amplitude of the first term is the constant $a_0/2$, and the amplitude of the second term is proportional to the time t. In fact, if sufficient time is allowed, the amplitude may become greater than any preassigned number. This remark ought not to stimulate the student to design an apparatus to produce an infinite amplification or an infinite force. In any physical case, there is some resistance b present, and a brief reference to (92-5) will show that b prevents the oscillations from becoming arbitrarily large.

PROBLEMS

Show that a particular integral of

1. $\dfrac{d^2y}{dt^2} + a^2y = \sin at$ is $y = -\dfrac{1}{2a}\,t\cos at$.

2. $\dfrac{d^2y}{dt^2} + a^2y = \cos at$ is $y = \dfrac{1}{2a}\,t\sin at$.

94. Simultaneous Differential Equations. In many investigations, it is necessary to consider systems of differential equations involving several dependent variables and one independent variable. For example, the motion of a particle in the plane can be described with the aid of the variables x and y, representing the coordinates of the particle, each of which may depend on time. It will be indicated in this section how a system of n ordinary differential equations involving n dependent variables may be reduced to a study of a single differential equation of higher order.

Let two dependent variables x and y be functions of an independent variable t, and let it be required to determine x and y from the simultaneous equations

$$(94\text{-}1) \qquad \begin{cases} \dfrac{dx}{dt} + ax + by = f_1(t), \\[2mm] \dfrac{dy}{dt} + cx + dy = f_2(t), \end{cases}$$

where a, b, c, and d are constants. If these equations are written in operational form, they are

$$(D + a)x + by = f_1(t),$$
$$cx + (D + d)y = f_2(t).$$

Operating on the second of these equations with $\dfrac{1}{c}(D + a)$ gives

$$(D + a)x + \frac{1}{c}(D + a)(D + d)y = \frac{1}{c}(D + a)f_2(t)$$

and, if the first equation is subtracted from this result,

$$\frac{1}{c}(D + a)(D + d)y - by = \frac{1}{c}(D + a)f_2(t) - f_1(t).$$

This is a second-order linear differential equation which can be solved for y. In order to determine x, solve the second equation of (94-1) for x,

$$x = \frac{1}{c}\left[f_2(t) - \frac{dy}{dt} - dy\right],$$

and substitute the value of y in terms of t.

The reader may show in the same way that the solution of a system of two second-order linear differential equations can be reduced to the solution of a linear differential equation of the fourth order (see Example 2 below).

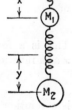

Example 1. Consider

$$\frac{dx}{dt} + 2x - 2y = t,$$

$$\frac{dy}{dt} - 3x + y = e^t$$

or

$$(D + 2)x - 2y = t,$$
$$-3x + (D + 1)y = e^t.$$

Operate on the second of these equations with $\frac{1}{3}(D + 2)$ to obtain

$$-(D + 2)x + \frac{1}{3}(D + 2)(D + 1)y = \frac{1}{3}(D + 2)e^t,$$

and add this result to the first equation. The result is

FIG. 89.

$$\frac{1}{3}(D + 2)(D + 1)y - 2y = \frac{1}{3}(D + 2)e^t + t,$$

which simplifies to

$$(D^2 + 3D - 4)y = 3e^t + 3t.$$

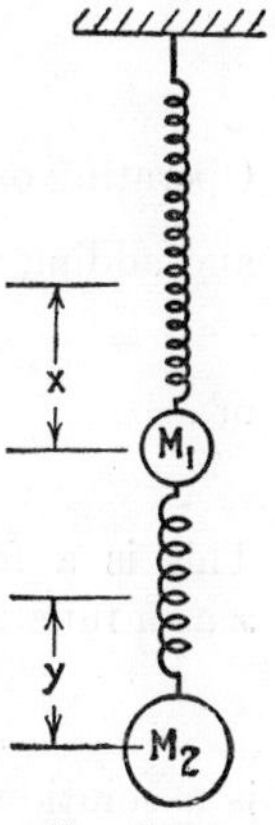

This equation can be solved for y as a function of t, and the result can be substituted in the second of the given equations to obtain x.

Example 2. Let the two masses M_1 and M_2 be suspended from two springs, as indicated in Fig. 89, and assume that the coefficients of stiffness of the springs are k_1 and k_2, respectively. Denote the displacements of the masses from their positions of equilibrium by x and y. Then it can be established that the following equations must hold:

$$M_2 \frac{d^2y}{dt^2} = -k_2(y - x),$$

$$M_1 \frac{d^2x}{dt^2} = k_2(y - x) - k_1x.$$

These equations can be simplified to read

$$\frac{d^2y}{dt^2} + \frac{k_2}{M_2} y - \frac{k_2}{M_2} x = 0,$$

$$\frac{d^2x}{dt^2} - \frac{k_2}{M_1} y + \frac{k_1 + k_2}{M_1} x = 0.$$

By setting

$$\frac{k_1}{M_1} = a^2, \qquad \frac{k_2}{M_2} = b^2, \qquad \frac{M_2}{M_1} = m,$$

the equations reduce to

$$(D^2 + b^2)y - b^2x = 0,$$
$$-b^2my + (D^2 + a^2 + b^2m)x = 0.$$

Operating on the second of these reduced equations with $\frac{1}{b^2m} (D^2 + b^2)$ and adding the result to the first of the equations give

$$(D^2 + b^2)(D^2 + a^2 + b^2m)x - b^4mx = 0$$

or

$$[D^4 + (a^2 + b^2 + b^2m)D^2 + a^2b^2]x = 0.$$

This is a fourth-order differential equation which can be solved for x as a function of t. It is readily checked that

$$x = A \sin (\omega t - \epsilon)$$

is a solution, provided that ω is suitably chosen. There will be two positive values of ω which will satisfy the conditions. The motion of the spring is a combination of two simple harmonic motions of different frequencies.

PROBLEMS

1. Solve Examples 1 and 2, Sec. 94.

2. The equations of motion of a particle of mass m are

$$m \frac{d^2x}{dt^2} = X, \qquad m \frac{d^2y}{dt^2} = Y, \qquad m \frac{d^2z}{dt^2} = Z,$$

where x, y, z are the coordinates of the particle and X, Y, Z are the components of force in the directions of the x-, y-, and z-axes, respectively. If the particle moves in the xy-plane under a central attractive force, proportional to the distance of the particle from the origin, find the differential equations of motion of the particle.

3. Find the equation of the path of a particle whose coordinates x and y satisfy the differential equations

$$m\frac{d^2x}{dt^2} + He\frac{dy}{dt} = Ee,$$

$$m\frac{d^2y}{dt^2} - He\frac{dx}{dt} = 0,$$

where H, E, e, and m are constants. Assume that $x = y = dx/dt = dy/dt = 0$ when $t = 0$. This system of differential equations occurs in the determination of the ratio of the charge to the mass of an electron.

4. The currents I_1 and I_2 in the two coupled circuits shown in Fig. 90 satisfy the following differential equations:

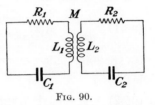

FIG. 90.

$$M\frac{d^2I_1}{dt^2} + L_2\frac{d^2I_2}{dt^2} + R_2\frac{dI_2}{dt} + \frac{I_2}{C_2} = 0,$$

$$M\frac{d^2I_2}{dt^2} + L_1\frac{d^2I_1}{dt^2} + R_1\frac{dI_1}{dt} + \frac{I_1}{C_1} = 0.$$

Reduce the solution of this system to that of a single fourth-order differential equation. Solve the resulting equation under the assumption that the resistances R_1 and R_2 are negligible.

95. Linear Equations with Variable Coefficients. With the exception of linear equations with constant coefficients and such equations with variable coefficients as are reducible to those with constant coefficients by a change of variable, there are no general methods for solving linear differential equations of order higher than the first. In general, solutions of differential equations with variable coefficients cannot be expressed in terms of a finite number of elementary functions, and it was seen in a number of specific examples that the solutions of such equations lead to new functions which are defined either by definite integrals or by infinite series. Some of these functions are of such frequent occurrence in applied mathematics that it has been expedient to calculate their values and tabulate them, precisely as the values of logarithms and trigonometric functions are tabulated. It must be borne in mind that the term *elementary function* as applied to logarithmic and circular functions is, in a sense, a misnomer and that such functions as Gamma functions, Bessel functions, and Legendre polynomials become just as "elementary" after their values have been tabulated. The elementariness of any given function is measured by the ease with which its value can be ascertained.

The remainder of this chapter contains a brief treatment of those linear differential equations which are of common occurrence in practice. An attempt will be made to express the solutions in convergent power series in x. This involves the tacit assumption that the solutions are capable of being expanded in Maclaurin's series, which, of course, is not true in general, and it is therefore not surprising that occasionally this method fails to give a solution. The method consists in assuming that a solution of the differential equation

$$(95\text{-}1) \quad \frac{d^n y}{dx^n} + p_1(x) \frac{d^{n-1} y}{dx^{n-1}} + \cdots + p_{n-1}(x) \frac{dy}{dx} + p_n(x)y = f(x)$$

is expressible in a convergent infinite series in powers of x, of the type

$$(95\text{-}2) \quad y = a_0 + a_1 x + a_2 x^2 + \cdots + a_n x^n + \cdots,$$

where the coefficients a_i are to be determined so that the series will satisfy the differential equation. If the coefficients of the derivatives in (95-1) are polynomials in x, then the obvious mode of procedure is to substitute the infinite series (95-2) into the equation (95-1), expand $f(x)$ in Maclaurin's series, combine the like powers of x, and equate to zero the coefficient of each power of x. This leads to an infinite set of algebraic equations in the a_i, which can sometimes be determined by algebraic means.

It is stated without proof that a homogeneous linear differential equation of order n,

$$(95\text{-}3) \quad \frac{d^n y}{dx^n} + p_1(x) \frac{d^{n-1} y}{dx^{n-1}} + \cdots + p_{n-1}(x) \frac{dy}{dx} + p_n(x)y = 0,$$

where the p_i are continuous one-valued functions of x, possesses n linearly independent solutions, and only n. If these solutions are $y_1(x)$, $y_2(x)$, $\cdots$, $y_n(x)$, then the general solution of the equation is given by

$$(95\text{-}4) \quad y = c_1 y_1 + c_2 y_2 + \cdots + c_n y_n.$$

This fact can be immediately verified by substituting (95-4) in (95-3). It is also clear that, if $u(x)$ is any particular solution of

(95-1), then its general solution is $y = c_1y_1 + c_2y_2 + \cdots + c_ny_n + u(x)$, where $c_1y_1 + c_2y_2 + \cdots + c_ny_n$ is the solution of the related homogeneous equation (95-3).

Frequently, it is of practical importance to know whether a given set of functions is linearly independent. Inasmuch as the definition for linear independence that is given in Sec. 34 is difficult to apply, a test for the linear independence of the solutions will be stated.*

THEOREM. *The necessary and sufficient condition that a given set of solutions y_1, y_2, $\cdots$, y_n of the nth order differential equation* (95-3) *be linearly independent is that the determinant*

$$W \equiv \begin{vmatrix} y_1 & y_2 & \cdots & y_n \\ y_1' & y_2' & \cdots & y_n' \\ y_1'' & y_2'' & \cdots & y_n'' \\ \cdots\cdots\cdots\cdots\cdots\cdots\cdots\cdots \\ y_1^{(n-1)} & y_2^{(n-1)} & \cdots & y_n^{(n-1)} \end{vmatrix} \neq 0.$$

This determinant is called the Wronskian.

Example. By substitution, it can be verified that $y_1 = \sin x$, $y_2 = \cos x$, and $y_3 = e^{ix}$ are solutions of the differential equation

$$\frac{d^3y}{dx^3} - \frac{d^2y}{dx^2} + \frac{dy}{dx} - y = 0.$$

But the Wronskian is

$$W \equiv \begin{vmatrix} \sin x & \cos x & e^{ix} \\ \cos x & -\sin x & ie^{ix} \\ -\sin x & -\cos x & -e^{ix} \end{vmatrix} = 0,$$

and therefore this set of solutions is not linearly independent. In other words, at least one of them can be expressed as a linear combination of the other two. It is known that

$$e^{ix} = \cos x + i \sin x.$$

It is readily verified that a linearly independent set of solutions is $y_1 = \sin x$, $y_2 = \cos x$, and $y_3 = e^x$, so that the general solution is

$$y = c_1 \sin x + c_2 \cos x + c_3e^x.$$

PROBLEMS

Determine whether or not the following sets of functions are linearly independent:

* See INCE, E. L., Ordinary Differential Equations.

1. $y_1 = \sin x + x$, $y_2 = e^x$, $y_3 = 3e^x - 2x - 2 \sin x$.
2. $y_1 = x^2 - 2x + 5$, $y_2 = 3x - 7$, $y_3 = \sin x$.
3. $y_1 = e^{ix} + x$, $y_2 = \cos x + x$, $y_3 = \sin x$.
4. $y_1 = (x + 1)^2$, $y_2 = (x - 1)^2$, $y_3 = 3x$.
5. $y_1 = \log x$, $y_2 = \sinh x$, $y_3 = e^x$, $y_4 = e^{-x}$.

96. Variation of Parameters.

Two methods of determining a particular integral of a linear differential equation with constant coefficients were discussed and illustrated in Sec. 89. Another important method that is applicable to linear equations with either constant or variable coefficients will be described here. This method, due to the great French mathematician Lagrange (1736–1813), permits one to determine a particular integral of

$$(96\text{-}1) \quad \frac{d^n y}{dx^n} + p_1(x)\frac{d^{n-1}y}{dx^{n-1}} + \cdots + p_{n-1}(x)\frac{dy}{dx} + p_n(x)y = f(x),$$

when the general solution of the related homogeneous equation

$$(96\text{-}2) \quad \frac{d^n y}{dx^n} + p_1(x)\frac{d^{n-1}y}{dx^{n-1}} + \cdots + p_{n-1}(x)\frac{dy}{dx} + p_n(x)y = 0$$

is known.

Let the general solution of (96-2) be

$$(96\text{-}3) \qquad y = c_1 y_1 + c_2 y_2 + \cdots + c_n y_n,$$

in which the c_i are arbitrary constants, and assume that a set of n functions $v_1(x)$, $v_2(x)$, $\cdots$, $v_n(x)$ can be so chosen that

$$(96\text{-}4) \qquad y = v_1 y_1 + v_2 y_2 + \cdots + v_n y_n$$

will satisfy (96-1). Since $y_1(x)$, $y_2(x)$, $\cdots$, $y_n(x)$ are known functions of x, (96-1) imposes only one condition upon the v_i in (96-4). Inasmuch as there are n functions v_i, it is clear that $n - 1$ further independent conditions can be imposed upon the v_i, provided that these conditions are consistent.

Differentiating (96-4) gives

$$y' = (v_1 y_1' + v_2 y_2' + \cdots + v_n y_n') + (v_1' y_1 + v_2' y_2 + \cdots + v_n' y_n).$$

As one condition to be imposed on the v_i, let

$$v_1' y_1 + v_2' y_2 + \cdots + v_n' y_n = 0,$$

so that

$$y' = v_1 y_1' + v_2 y_2' + \cdots + v_n y_n'.$$

Then,

$$y'' = (v_1 y_1'' + v_2 y_2'' + \cdots + v_n y_n'') + (v_1' y_1' + v_2' y_2' + \cdots + v_n' y_n');$$

and if the second condition to be satisfied by the v_i is

$$v_1' y_1' + v_2' y_2' + \cdots + v_n' y_n' = 0,$$

it follows that

$$y'' = v_1 y_1'' + v_2 y_2'' + \cdots + v_n y_n''.$$

By continuing this process a set of $n - 1$ conditions is imposed on the v_i, namely,

$$(96\text{-}5) \quad \begin{cases} v_1' y_1 + v_2' y_2 + \cdots + v_n' y_n = 0, \\ v_1' y_1' + v_2' y_2' + \cdots + v_n' y_n' = 0, \\ \cdots\cdots\cdots\cdots\cdots\cdots\cdots\cdots\cdots\cdots\cdots\cdots\cdots, \\ v_1' y_1^{(n-2)} + v_2' y_2^{(n-2)} + \cdots + v_n' y_n^{(n-2)} = 0, \end{cases}$$

as a consequence of which

$$y' = v_1 y_1' + v_2 y_2' + \cdots + v_n y_n',$$
$$y'' = v_1 y_1'' + v_2 y_2'' + \cdots + v_n y_n'',$$
$$\cdots\cdots\cdots\cdots\cdots\cdots\cdots\cdots\cdots\cdots\cdots\cdots\cdots,$$
$$y^{(n-1)} = v_1 y_1^{(n-1)} + v_2 y_2^{(n-1)} + \cdots + v_n y_n^{(n-1)}.$$

Calculating $y^{(n)}$ yields

$$y^{(n)} = v_1 y_1^{(n)} + v_2 y_2^{(n)} + \cdots + v_n y_n^{(n)} + v_1' y_1^{(n-1)} + v_2' y_2^{(n-1)} + \cdots + v_n' y_n^{(n-1)}.$$

Substituting y, y', $\cdots$, $y^{(n)}$ in (96-1) and remembering that, by hypothesis, y_1, y_2, $\cdots$, y_n satisfy (96-2) give the nth condition to be imposed upon the v_i, namely,

$$(96\text{-}6) \quad v_1' y_1^{(n-1)} + v_2' y_2^{(n-1)} + \cdots + v_n' y_n^{(n-1)} = f(x).$$

The $n - 1$ relations (96-5) together with (96-6) give n linear algebraic equations which can be solved for v_1', v_2', $\cdots$, v_n', provided that the determinant of the coefficients of the v_i', namely,

$$\begin{vmatrix} y_1 & y_2 & \cdots & y_n \\ y_1' & y_2' & \cdots & y_n' \\ \cdots\cdots\cdots\cdots\cdots\cdots \\ y_1^{(n-1)} & y_2^{(n-1)} & \cdots & y_n^{(n-1)} \end{vmatrix},$$

is not identically zero. But this determinant is the Wronskian and, since y_1, y_2, $\cdots$, y_n were assumed to be linearly independent, it is different from zero. Hence, the system of equations can always be solved for the v_i', and the expressions for the v_i are obtained by integration.

Example. As an illustration* of the application of this method of determining a particular integral, consider the equation

$$\frac{d^3y}{dx^3} - 3\frac{dy}{dx} + 2y = 2(\sin x - 2\cos x).$$

The general solution of the homogeneous equation is found to be

$$(c_1 + c_2 x)e^x + c_3 e^{-2x}.$$

Assume that a particular integral of the non-homogeneous equation is of the form

$$y = v_1 e^x + v_2 x e^x + v_3 e^{-2x},$$

where v_1, v_2, and v_3 are functions of x to be determined presently.

Computing y' gives

$$y' = v_1 e^x + v_2(x+1)e^x - 2v_3 e^{-2x} + v_1' e^x + v_2' x e^x + v_3' e^{-2x}.$$

The first condition to be imposed upon the v_i is

$$v_1' e^x + v_2' x e^x + v_3' e^{-2x} = 0, \tag{1}$$

so that

$$y'' = v_1 e^x + v_2(x+2)e^x + 4v_3 e^{-2x} + v_1' e^x + v_2'(x+1)e^x - 2v_3' e^{-2x}.$$

Imposing the second condition produces

$$v_1' e^x + v_2'(x+1)e^x - 2v_3' e^{-2x} = 0, \tag{2}$$

and computing y''' yields

$$y''' = v_1 e^x + v_2(x+3)e^x - 8v_3 e^{-2x} + v_1' e^x + v_2'(x+2)e^x + 4v_3' e^{-2x}.$$

Hence, the third condition to be satisfied by the v_i is

$$v_1' e^x + v_2'(x+2)e^x + 4v_3' e^{-2x} = 2(\sin x - 2\cos x). \tag{3}$$

Solving (1), (2), and (3) for v_1', v_2', and v_3' gives

$$v_1' = -\tfrac{2}{3}xe^{-x}(\sin x - 2\cos x) - \tfrac{2}{9}e^{-x}(\sin x - 2\cos x),$$
$$v_2' = \tfrac{2}{3}e^{-x}(\sin x - 2\cos x),$$
$$v_3' = \tfrac{2}{9}e^{2x}(\sin x - 2\cos x).$$

The integration† of these expressions yields

* For another illustration, see Example, Sec. 97.
† The integration in this case is quite tedious, and generally speaking it is easier to solve linear equations with constant coefficients by the methods

$$v_1 = \tfrac{1}{3}xe^{-x}(3 \sin x - \cos x) + e^{-x} \sin x + \tfrac{2}{9}e^{-x} \cos x,$$
$$v_2 = \tfrac{1}{3}e^{-x}(-3 \sin x + \cos x),$$
$$v_3 = -\tfrac{2}{9}e^{2x} \cos x,$$

in which the constants of integration are omitted because a particular integral is desired.

By hypothesis, a particular integral is given by

$$y = v_1e^x + v_2xe^x + v_3e^{-2x} = \sin x,$$

so that the general solution of the non-homogeneous equation is

$$y = (c_1 + c_2x)e^x + c_3e^{-2x} + \sin x.$$

PROBLEMS

1. Solve Probs. 1, 2, and 3, Sec. 89, by the method of variation of parameters.

2. Find the solution of

$$\frac{dy}{dx} + f_1(x)y = f_2(x)$$

by the method of variation of parameters, and compare your result with that of Sec. 85. The solution of the related homogeneous equation is obtained easily by separation of the variables.

3. By the method of variation of parameters, find a particular integral of

$$\frac{d^2y}{dx^2} - \frac{3}{x}\frac{dy}{dx} - \frac{5}{x^2}y = \log x,$$

where the general solution of the related homogeneous equation is

$$y = \frac{c_1}{x} + c_2x^5.$$

4. Find the general solution of

$$\frac{d^2y}{dx^2} + \frac{x}{1-x}\frac{dy}{dx} - \frac{1}{1-x}y = 1 - x,$$

where the general solution of the related homogeneous equation is $c_1e^x + c_2x$.

5. Find the general solution of

$$x^2y'' - 2xy' + 2y = x \log x,$$

discussed in Sec. 89. However, the method of the present section is of great value when the given equation has variable coefficients.

if the general solution of the related homogeneous equation is $y = c_1 x^2 + c_2 x$.

97. The Euler Equation. * Before proceeding to illustrate the method of solution in terms of infinite series, it will be well to discuss one type of differential equation with variable coefficients that can be reduced by a change of variable to a differential equation with constant coefficients.

Consider the linear equation

$$(97\text{-}1) \quad x^n \frac{d^n y}{dx^n} + a_1 x^{n-1} \frac{d^{n-1} y}{dx^{n-1}} + \cdots + a_{n-1} x \frac{dy}{dx} + a_n y = f(x),$$

where the a_i are constants. This equation can be transformed into one with constant coefficients by setting $x = e^z$. For if $x = e^z$, then

$$\frac{dx}{dz} = e^z \quad \text{and} \quad \frac{dz}{dx} = e^{-z}.$$

Moreover, if $D \equiv \dfrac{d}{dz}$, then

$$\frac{dy}{dx} = \frac{dy}{dz} \frac{dz}{dx} = e^{-z} \, Dy$$

and

$$\frac{d^2 y}{dx^2} = \frac{d^2 y}{dz^2} \left(\frac{dz}{dx} \right)^2 + \frac{dy}{dz} \frac{d^2 z}{dx^2} = e^{-2z} (D^2 - D) y.$$

Similarly,

$$\frac{d^3 y}{dx^3} = e^{-3z} (D^3 - 3D^2 + 2D) y.$$

Then, since $x = e^z$, it follows that

$$x \frac{dy}{dx} = Dy,$$

$$x^2 \frac{d^2 y}{dx^2} = (D^2 - D) y = D(D - 1) y,$$

$$\dotfill,$$

$$x^n \frac{d^n y}{dx^n} = D(D - 1)(D - 2) \cdots (D - n + 1) y,$$

* Also called Cauchy's equation.

so that (97-1) is replaced by an equation with constant coefficients,

$$[D(D-1) \, \cdots \, (D-n+1) + a_1 D(D-1) \, \cdots \, (D-n+2)$$
$$+ \cdots + a_{n-1}D + a_n]y = f(e^z).$$

Example.   Consider

$$x^3 \frac{d^3y}{dx^3} + x \frac{dy}{dx} - y = x \log x.$$

Upon making the substitution $x = e^z$, this equation becomes

$$[D(D-1)(D-2) + D - 1]y = ze^z$$

or

$$(D^3 - 3D^2 + 3D - 1)y = ze^z.$$

The roots of the auxiliary equation are $m_1 = m_2 = m_3 = 1$, so that the complementary function is

$$(c_1 + c_2z + c_3z^2)e^z.$$

The particular integral is

$$y = \frac{1}{(D-1)^3} ze^z = e^z \int \int \int e^{-z}ze^z \, (dz)^3 = \frac{e^z z^4}{24},$$

so that, in terms of z, the general solution is

$$y = (c_1 + c_2z + c_3z^2)e^z + \frac{z^4}{24} e^z$$

and, in terms of x,

$$y = [c_1 + c_2 \log x + c_3(\log x)^2]x + \frac{x(\log x)^4}{24}.$$

A particular integral for this example will be obtained by the method of variation of parameters in order to demonstrate the applicability of this method to equations with variable coefficients.   Care must be taken first to transform the equation so that it has unity for its leading coefficient, for the discussion of Sec. 96 was carried through for this type of equation.

Expressing the given equation in the form (96-1) gives

$$\frac{d^3y}{dx^3} + \frac{1}{x^2} \frac{dy}{dx} - \frac{1}{x^3} y = \frac{1}{x^2} \log x.$$

Since the general solution of the homogeneous equation was found to be

$$c_1x + c_2x \log x + c_3x(\log x)^2,$$

the equations of condition (96-5) and (96-6) are

$$v_1'x + v_2'x \log x + v_3'x(\log x)^2 = 0,$$
$$v_1' + v_2'(1 + \log x) + v_3'[(\log x)^2 + 2 \log x] = 0,$$
$$v_2'\frac{1}{x} + v_3'\left(\frac{2}{x} \log x + \frac{2}{x}\right) = \frac{1}{x^2} \log x.$$

Solving for v_1', v_2', and v_3' yields

$$v_1' = \frac{1}{2x} (\log x)^3, \qquad v_2' = -\frac{1}{x} (\log x)^2, \qquad v_3' = \frac{1}{2x} \log x,$$

which integrate into

$$v_1 = \tfrac{1}{8}(\log x)^4, \qquad v_2 = -\tfrac{1}{3}(\log x)^3, \qquad v_3 = \tfrac{1}{4}(\log x)^2.$$

Hence, a particular integral is

$$y = v_1x + v_2x \log x + v_3x(\log x)^2 = \frac{x(\log x)^4}{24}.$$

PROBLEMS

1. Find the general solution of the equation in Prob. 3, Sec. 96, by the method of Sec. 97.

2. Find the general solution of

$$x^2 \frac{d^2y}{dx^2} + 4x \frac{dy}{dx} + 2y = \log x.$$

Compute the particular integral by the method of variation of parameters.

3. Solve

$$x^2 \frac{d^2y}{dx^2} - 4x \frac{dy}{dx} + 6y = 0$$

by assuming a solution of the form $y = x^r$ and determining appropriate values of r.

4. Solve

$$x^2 \frac{d^2y}{dx^2} + 2x \frac{dy}{dx} - m(m + 1)y = 0$$

by assuming a solution to be of the form $y = x^r$.

5. Find the general solution of

$$x^3y''' - 4x^2y'' + 5xy' - 2y = 1.$$

6. Find the general solution of

$$x^2y'' + y = x^2.$$

7. Find the general solution of

$$x^2 y'' - 2xy' + 2y = x \log x.$$

98. Solution in Series.   Many differential equations occurring in applied mathematics cannot be solved with the aid of the methods described in the preceding sections, and it is natural to attempt to seek a solution in the form of an infinite power series. The method of solution of differential equations with the aid of infinite series is of great importance in both pure and applied mathematics, and there is a vast literature on the subject.   This section and the four following sections contain only a brief introduction to the formal procedure used in obtaining such solutions.

As an illustration of the method, consider the differential equation

(98-1) $y' - xy - x = 1,$

and assume that it is possible to obtain the solution of (98-1) in the form of a convergent power series

(98-2) $y = a_0 + a_1 x + a_2 x^2 + \cdots + a_n x^n + \cdots .$

Inasmuch as the series of derivatives of a convergent power series is convergent, one can write

(98-3) $y' = a_1 + 2a_2 x + \cdots + n a_n x^{n-1} + \cdots .$

Substituting (98-2) and (98-3) in (98-1) and collecting the coefficients of like powers of x give

(98-4) $a_1 + (2a_2 - a_0 - 1)x + (3a_3 - a_1)x^2 + \cdots$
$$+ (n a_n - a_{n-2})x^{n-1} + \cdots = 1.$$

By hypothesis, (98-2) is a solution of (98-1), and therefore* equating the coefficients of like powers of x in (98-4) leads to the following system of equations:

(98-5)
$$\begin{cases} a_1 = 1 & \text{(coefficient of } x^0\text{)}, \\ 2a_2 - a_0 - 1 = 0 & \text{(coefficient of } x\text{)}, \\ 3a_3 - a_1 = 0 & \text{(coefficient of } x^2\text{)}, \\ \dots\dots\dots\dots\dots\dots\dots\dots\dots\dots\dots\dots , \\ n a_n - a_{n-2} = 0 & \text{(coefficient of } x^{n-1}\text{)}, \\ \dots\dots\dots\dots\dots\dots\dots\dots\dots\dots\dots\dots \end{cases}$$

* See Theorem 5, Sec. 10.

The system of equations (98-5) is a system of linear equations in infinitely many unknowns a_0, a_1, $\cdots$, a_n, $\cdots$. Solving the second equation of (98-5) for a_2 in terms of a_0 gives

$$a_2 = \frac{a_0 + 1}{2}.$$

The third equation taken with the first demands that

$$a_3 = \frac{a_1}{3} = \frac{1}{3}.$$

Setting $n = 4$ in the coefficient of x^{n-1} gives

$$a_4 = \frac{a_2}{4} = \frac{a_0 + 1}{2 \cdot 4} = \frac{a_0 + 1}{2^2 \cdot 2!},$$

whereas $n = 5$ gives

$$a_5 = \frac{a_3}{5} = \frac{1}{3 \cdot 5}.$$

In general,

$$(98\text{-}6) \quad \begin{cases} a_{2n} = \dfrac{a_0 + 1}{2^n \cdot n!} \\ a_{2n+1} = \dfrac{1}{1 \cdot 3 \cdot 5 \, \cdots \, (2n + 1)}. \end{cases}$$

The substitution in (98-2) of the values of a_k given by (98-6) leads to a solution in the form

$$y = a_0 + x + \frac{a_0 + 1}{2} x^2 + \frac{1}{1 \cdot 3} x^3 + \frac{a_0 + 1}{2^2 \cdot 2!} x^4 + \frac{1}{1 \cdot 3 \cdot 5} x^5 + \cdots.$$

When the terms containing a_0 are collected, there results

$$(98\text{-}7) \quad y = \left[a_0 + \frac{a_0 + 1}{2} x^2 + \frac{a_0 + 1}{2^2 \cdot 2!} x^4 + \cdots \right.$$
$$\left. + \frac{a_0 + 1}{2^n \cdot n!} x^{2n} + \cdots \right] + \left[x + \frac{x^3}{1 \cdot 3} + \frac{x^5}{1 \cdot 3 \cdot 5} + \cdots \right.$$
$$\left. + \frac{x^{2n+1}}{1 \cdot 3 \cdot 5 \, \cdots \, (2n + 1)} + \cdots \right].$$

If $a_0 + 1$ is set equal to c, one can write (98-7) in the more compact form

$$(98\text{-}8) \quad y = c\left[1 + \frac{x^2}{2} + \frac{x^4}{2^2 \cdot 2!} + \cdots + \frac{x^{2n}}{2^n \cdot n!} + \cdots\right]$$
$$+ \left[-1 + x + \frac{x^3}{1 \cdot 3} + \cdots + \frac{x^{2n+1}}{1 \cdot 3 \cdots (2n+1)} + \cdots\right].$$

The two series appearing in (98-8) are easily shown to be convergent for all values of x, and hence they define functions of x. In fact, the first of the series is recognized as the Maclaurin expansion of $e^{\frac{x^2}{2}}$, so that (98-8) can be written as

$$(98\text{-}9) \quad y = ce^{\frac{x^2}{2}} + \left[-1 + x + \frac{x^3}{1 \cdot 3} + \cdots \right.$$
$$\left. + \frac{x^{2n+1}}{1 \cdot 3 \cdots (2n+1)} + \cdots\right].$$

This is the general solution of (98-1), for it contains one arbitrary constant.

Since (98-1) is a linear differential equation of the first order, its solution could have been obtained by using the formula (85-3), and it is readily verified that (85-3) gives

$$(98\text{-}10) \qquad y = ce^{\frac{x^2}{2}} - 1 + e^{\frac{x^2}{2}} \int e^{-\frac{x^2}{2}}\, dx.$$

The integral in (98-10) cannot be evaluated in closed form; but if the integrand is expanded in a power series in x, it is easy to show that (98-10) leads to (98-9).

Consider next the homogeneous linear differential equation of the second order

$$(98\text{-}11) \qquad\qquad y'' - xy' + y = 0,$$

and assume that the solution of (98-11) has the form

$$(98\text{-}12) \quad y = \sum_{n=0}^{\infty} a_n x^n \equiv a_0 + a_1 x + \cdots + a_n x^n + \cdots.$$

Then the series for y' and y'' are

$$y' = \sum_{n=1}^{\infty} na_n x^{n-1} \quad \text{and} \quad y'' = \sum_{n=2}^{\infty} n(n-1)a_n x^{n-2}.$$

If these expressions are substituted in (98-11), the result is

$$\sum_{n=2}^{\infty} n(n-1)a_n x^{n-2} - \sum_{n=1}^{\infty} na_n x^n + \sum_{n=0}^{\infty} a_n x^n = 0.$$

Combining the terms in like powers of x and setting the coefficient of each power of x equal to zero give the system of equations

$2 \cdot 1a_2 + a_0 = 0$ (coefficient of x^0),
$3 \cdot 2a_3 - a_1 + a_1 = 0$ (coefficient of x),
$4 \cdot 3a_4 - 2a_2 + a_2 = 0$ (coefficient of x^2),
....,
$(n+2)(n+1)a_{n+2} - na_n + a_n = 0$ (coefficient of x^n),
....

Hence,

(98-13) $$a_{n+2} = \frac{n-1}{(n+1)(n+2)} a_n.$$

This recursion formula can be used to determine the coefficients in (98-12) in terms of a_0 and a_1. Thus, substituting $n = 0$, 1, 2, $\cdots$ in (98-13) gives

$$a_2 = -\frac{1}{1 \cdot 2} a_0,$$

$$a_3 = \frac{0}{2 \cdot 3} a_1 = 0,$$

$$a_4 = \frac{1}{3 \cdot 4} a_2 = -\frac{1}{4!} a_0,$$

$$a_5 = \frac{2}{4 \cdot 5} a_3 = 0,$$

$$a_6 = \frac{3}{5 \cdot 6} a_4 = -\frac{3}{6!} a_0,$$

$$\cdots\cdots\cdots\cdots\cdots\cdots,$$

$$a_{2n+1} = 0,$$

$$a_{2n} = -\frac{1 \cdot 3 \cdot 5 \cdots (2n-3)}{(2n)!} a_0.$$

Therefore,

(98-14) $$y = a_0\left(1 - \frac{1}{2!}x^2 - \frac{1}{4!}x^4 - \frac{3}{6!}x^6 - \frac{15}{8!}x^8 - \cdots\right) + a_1 x,$$

where a_0 and a_1 are arbitrary. It is readily checked that the series is convergent, and, since it is a power series, it defines a continuous function of x.

The two linearly independent solutions of (98-11) are then

$$y = a_1 x$$

and

$$y = a_0 \left(1 - \frac{1}{2!} x^2 - \frac{1}{4!} x^4 - \frac{3}{6!} x^6 - \frac{15}{8!} x^8 - \cdots \right).$$

These solutions are obviously linearly independent, for one of them defines an odd function of x and the other defines an even function of x.

PROBLEMS

Integrate in series:

1. $\dfrac{d^2y}{dx^2} + y = 0.$

2. $\dfrac{dy}{dx} - y = 0.$

3. $(x^2 - 3x + 2) \dfrac{d^2y}{dx^2} + (x^2 - 2x - 1) \dfrac{dy}{dx} + (x - 3)y = 0.$

4. $\dfrac{d^2y}{dx^2} - y = 1.$

99. Existence of Power Series Solutions. It must be kept clearly in mind that the calculations performed in Sec. 98 are formal and depend on the assumption that the differential equations discussed there possess power series solutions. If, for example, an attempt had been made to apply the method of solution outlined in Sec. 98 to the equation

$$xy' - 1 = 0,$$

it would have been futile. The general solution of this equation is

$$y = \log x + c,$$

which cannot be expanded in a power series in x.

The task of determining beforehand whether a given differential equation possesses solutions in the form of power series represents one of the major problems of analysis. It will suffice in this introductory treatment to state, without proof, the conditions under which a homogeneous linear differential equation of the second order has a power series solution.

Theorem. *Let*

(99-1) $$y'' + f_1(x)y' + f_2(x)y = 0$$

have coefficients $f_1(x)$ and $f_2(x)$ that can be expanded in power series in x which converge for all values of x in the interval $-R < x < R$; then there will exist two linearly independent solutions of the form

$$y = \sum_{n=0}^{\infty} a_n x^n,$$

which will converge for all values of x in the interval $-R < x < R$.

It is clear from the statement of the theorem that the differential equation will possess power series solutions, which converge for all values of x, whenever $f_1(x)$ and $f_2(x)$ are polynomials in x.

It should be noted that the coefficient of the second derivative term in (99-1) is unity. Frequently, the differential equation has the form

$$p_0(x)y'' + p_1(x)y' + p_2(x)y = 0;$$

and if this differential equation is put in the form (99-1), then

$$f_1(x) = \frac{p_1(x)}{p_0(x)} \quad \text{and} \quad f_2(x) = \frac{p_2(x)}{p_0(x)}.$$

If $p_0(x)$ should vanish for some value of x in the interval within which the solution is desired, one must expect trouble. If $p_0(x)$, $p_1(x)$, and $p_2(x)$ are polynomials in x and if $p_0(0) \neq 0$, then one can surely expand $f_1(x)$ and $f_2(x)$ in power series in some interval, and the theorem enunciated above is applicable.

As an illustration, consider the differential equation

(99-2) $$(2 - x)y'' + (x - 1)y' - y = 0.$$

Inasmuch as

$$f_1(x) = \frac{x - 1}{2 - x} = (1 - x)(x - 2)^{-1}$$

and

$$f_2(x) = (x - 2)^{-1}$$

obviously possess power series expansions that are valid in the interval $-2 < x < 2$, it is reasonable to proceed to obtain the power series solution.

Substituting

$$y = \sum_{n=0}^{\infty} a_n x^n$$

in (99-2) gives

$$(2 - x) \sum_{n=0}^{\infty} n(n-1)a_n x^{n-2} + (x-1) \sum_{n=0}^{\infty} na_n x^{n-1} - \sum_{n=0}^{\infty} a_n x^n = 0.$$

Rearranging and combining terms give

$$\sum_{n=0}^{\infty} 2n(n-1)a_n x^{n-2} - \sum_{n=0}^{\infty} n^2 a_n x^{n-1} + \sum_{n=0}^{\infty} (n-1)a_n x^n = 0.$$

Equating the coefficients of the powers of x to zero gives

(99-3)
$$\begin{cases} 2 \cdot 2 \cdot 1 a_2 - a_1 - a_0 = 0, \\ 2 \cdot 3 \cdot 2 a_3 - 2^2 a_2 = 0, \\ 2 \cdot 4 \cdot 3 a_4 - 3^2 a_3 + a_2 = 0, \\ \dots\dots\dots\dots\dots\dots\dots\dots, \\ 2(n+2)(n+1)a_{n+2} - (n+1)^2 a_{n+1} + (n-1)a_n = 0, \\ \dots\dots\dots\dots\dots\dots\dots\dots\dots\dots\dots\dots \end{cases}$$

The coefficient of x^n provides the recursion formula

$$a_{n+2} = \frac{(n+1)^2 a_{n+1} - (n-1)a_n}{2(n+1)(n+2)};$$

and setting $n = 0, 1, 2, 3, \cdots$ gives

$$a_2 = \frac{a_0 + a_1}{2^2} \equiv \frac{c}{2 \cdot 2!}, \quad \text{where } c = a_0 + a_1,$$

$$a_3 = \frac{a_2}{3} = \frac{c}{2 \cdot 3!},$$

$$a_4 = \frac{3^2 a_3 - a_2}{4!} = \frac{c}{2 \cdot 4!},$$

$$a_5 = \frac{4^2 a_4 - 2a_3}{2 \cdot 4 \cdot 5} = \frac{c}{2 \cdot 5!}.$$

It is easily shown that in general

$$a_n = \frac{c}{2 \cdot n!},$$

so that

$$y = a_0 + a_1 x + a_2 x^2 + \cdots + a_n x^n + \cdots$$

$$= a_0 + a_1 x + \frac{a_0 + a_1}{2} \left(\frac{x^2}{2!} + \frac{x^3}{3!} + \cdots + \frac{x^n}{n!} + \cdots \right)$$

$$= a_0 + a_1 x + \frac{a_0 + a_1}{2} \left(1 + x + \frac{x^2}{2!} + \cdots + \frac{x^n}{n!} + \cdots \right)$$

$$- \frac{a_0 + a_1}{2} (1 + x)$$

$$= \frac{a_0 + a_1}{2} e^x + \frac{a_0 - a_1}{2} (1 - x)$$

$$= c_1 e^x + c_2 (1 - x),$$

where $c_1 = (a_0 + a_1)/2$ and $c_2 = (a_0 - a_1)/2$.

It happens in this illustration that the series appearing in the solution of the differential equation represent elementary functions, so that the general solution can be written in closed form. Ordinarily, the infinite series arising from the solution of linear differential equations with variable coefficients represent functions that cannot be expressed in terms of a finite number of elementary functions. This is the case discussed in the next section, where the series that provides the solution of the differential equation represents a class of functions of primary importance in a great many problems in applied mathematics.

It is quite obvious that the theorem of this section can be rephrased to include the case where the functions $f_1(x)$ and $f_2(x)$ possess series expansions in powers of $x - a$. In this case, there will exist two linearly independent solutions of the form

$$y = \sum_{n=0}^{\infty} a_n (x - a)^n.$$

PROBLEM

Solve

$$y'' - (x - 2)y = 0$$

by assuming the solution in the form $y = \sum_{n=0}^{\infty} a_n (x - 2)^n$. Also,

obtain the solution in the form $y = \sum_{n=0}^{\infty} a_n x^n$.

100. Bessel's Equation. An important differential equation was encountered by a distinguished German astronomer and mathematician, F. W. Bessel (1784–1846), in a study of planetary motion. The range of applications of the functions arising from the solution of this equation is partly indicated by the fact that these functions are indispensable in the study of vibration of chains, propagation of electric currents in cylindrical conductors, problems dealing with the flow of heat in cylinders, vibration of circular membranes, and in many other problem· arising in every branch of applied mathematics. Some of the uses of this equation are indicated in the chapter on Partial Differ·ntial Equations.

Bessel's equation has the form

$$(100\text{-}1) \qquad x^2 y'' + x y' + (x^2 - n^2) y = 0,$$

where n is a constant. It will be observed that this equation does not satisfy the conditions of the theorem of Sec. 99 because of the appearance of x^2 in the coefficient of y''. In the notation of Sec. 99,

$$f_1(x) = \frac{1}{x} \qquad \text{and} \qquad f_2(x) = 1 - \frac{n^2}{x^2},$$

and it is clear that $f_1(x)$ and $f_2(x)$ cannot be expanded in power series in x.

In order to solve (100-1), assume that the solution can be obtained in the form of a generalized power series, namely,

$$(100\text{-}2) \qquad y = x^m \sum_{r=0}^{\infty} a_r x^r,$$

where m is a constant to be determined later and where a_0 can be assumed to be distinct from zero because of the indeterminate nature of m.

Calculating the first and second derivatives with the aid of (100-2) and forming the terms entering into (100-1) give

$$x^2 \frac{d^2 y}{dx^2} = m(m-1)a_0 x^m + m(m+1)a_1 x^{m+1} + \cdots$$
$$+ a_k(m+k)(m+k-1)x^{m+k} + \cdots,$$

$$x \frac{dy}{dx} = m a_0 x^m + (m+1)a_1 x^{m+1} + \cdots + a_k(m+k)x^{m+k}$$
$$+ \cdots,$$

$$x^2 y = a_0 x^{m+2} + \cdots + a_{k-2} x^{m+k} + \cdots,$$
$$-n^2 y = -n^2 a_0 x^m - n^2 a_1 x^{m+1} - \cdots - n^2 a_k x^{m+k} - \cdots.$$

Adding the left-hand members of these expressions and equating the result to zero give (100-1). By hypothesis, (100-2) is a solution, and therefore the coefficient of each power of x in the sum must vanish. Hence,

$$(m^2 - n^2)a_0 = 0 \qquad \text{(coefficient of } x^m\text{)},$$
$$[(m + 1)^2 - n^2]a_1 = 0 \qquad \text{(coefficient of } x^{m+1}\text{)},$$
$$\dots\dots\dots\dots\dots\dots\dots\dots\dots\dots\dots\dots\dots\dots,$$
$$[(m + k)^2 - n^2]a_k + a_{k-2} = 0 \qquad \text{(coefficient of } x^{m+k}\text{)}.$$

The coefficient of the general term gives the recursion formula

$$(100\text{-}3) \qquad a_k = -\frac{a_{k-2}}{(m + k)^2 - n^2}.$$

The equation resulting from equating to zero the coefficient of the term of lowest degree in x (here, x^m) is known as the *indicial equation*. In order to satisfy the indicial equation, choose $m = \pm n$. If m is chosen as $+n$ or $-n$, a_0 is arbitrary and the second condition requires that $a_1 = 0$.

For $m = n$ the recursion formula becomes

$$a_k = -\frac{a_{k-2}}{(n + k)^2 - n^2} = -\frac{a_{k-2}}{k(2n + k)}.$$

Setting $k = 2, 3, 4, \cdots$ in turn gives

$$a_2 = -\frac{a_0}{2(2n + 2)},$$

$$a_3 = -\frac{a_1}{3(2n + 3)} = 0, \qquad \text{since } a_1 = 0,$$

$$a_4 = -\frac{a_2}{4(2n + 4)} = \frac{a_0}{2 \cdot 4(2n + 2)(2n + 4)},$$

$$a_5 = -\frac{a_3}{5(2n + 5)} = 0,$$

$$\dots\dots\dots\dots\dots\dots\dots\dots\dots\dots\dots\dots\dots\dots$$

In this manner as many coefficients as desired can be computed; and if their values in terms of a_0 are substituted in (100-2), there is obtained the following series, which converges for all values of x,

$$(100\text{-}4) \quad y = a_0 x^n \left[1 - \frac{x^2}{2(2n + 2)} + \frac{x^4}{2 \cdot 4(2n + 2)(2n + 4)} \right.$$
$$\left. - \frac{x^6}{2 \cdot 4 \cdot 6(2n + 2)(2n + 4)(2n + 6)} + \cdots \right].$$

If $m = -n$ is chosen, a_0 is again arbitrary and $a_1 = 0$, and the resulting series is

$$(100\text{-}5) \quad y = a_0 x^{-n} \left[1 + \frac{x^2}{2(2n-2)} + \frac{x^4}{2 \cdot 4(2n-2)(2n-4)} \right.$$
$$\left. + \frac{x^6}{2 \cdot 4 \cdot 6(2n-2)(2n-4)(2n-6)} + \cdots \right].$$

The series (100-4) and (100-5) become identical for $n = 0$. For positive integral values of n, (100-5) is meaningless, since some of the denominators of the coefficients become zero, and (100-4) is the only solution obtainable by this method. If n is a negative integer, (100-4) is meaningless and (100-5) is the only solution in power series in x. For $n \neq 0$ or an integer, both (100-4) and (100-5) are convergent and represent two distinct solutions. Then (100-4) multiplied by an arbitrary constant and added to (100-5) multiplied by an arbitrary constant gives the general solution of the Bessel equation.

The reason for the failure of this method to produce two distinct solutions when n is zero or an integer is not hard to find. The success of this method depends upon the assumption that the solutions are representable in power series. The analysis leading to the determination of the second particular solution of (100-1) when n is an integer is not given here.* It is sufficient to mention the fact that the second solution can be obtained by assuming that it has the form, when n is a positive integer,

$$(100\text{-}6) \qquad y_2 = C y_1(x) \log x + \sum_{k=0}^{\infty} a_k x^{-n+k},$$

where $y_1(x)$ is the solution (100-4) and C is a constant. Obviously, this solution becomes infinite when $x = 0$.

It will be of interest to consider the particular solution obtained from (100-4) by setting

$$a_0 = \frac{1}{2^n n!}.$$

* See Watson, G. N., Theory of Bessel Functions; Gray, A., G. B. Mathews, and J. M. MacRobert, A Treatise on Bessel Functions and Their Applications to Physics; Whittaker, E. T., and G. N. Watson, Modern Analysis; McLachlan, N. W., Bessel Functions for Engineers.

The series (100-4) then becomes

$$(100\text{-}7) \quad J_n(x) \equiv \frac{x^n}{2^n n!} - \frac{x^{n+2}}{2^{n+2}(n+1)!} + \frac{x^{n+4}}{2^{n+4}2!(n+2)!}$$
$$- \cdots + (-1)^k \frac{x^{n+2k}}{2^{n+2k}k!(n+k)!} + \cdots$$
$$\equiv \sum_{k=0}^{\infty} (-1)^k \frac{x^{n+2k}}{2^{n+2k}k!(n+k)!}.$$

The function defined by this series is called the Bessel function of the first kind of order n. This series holds for non-negative values of n. For $n = 0$,* (100-7) gives

$$J_0(x) = 1 - \frac{x^2}{2^2} + \frac{x^4}{2^4(2!)^2} - \cdots + (-1)^k \frac{x^{2k}}{2^{2k}(k!)^2} + \cdots,$$

and for $n = 1$,

$$J_1(x) = \frac{x}{2} - \frac{x^3}{2^3 \cdot 2!} + \frac{x^5}{2^5 2! 3!} - \cdots$$
$$+ (-1)^k \frac{x^{2k+1}}{2^{2k+1}k!(k+1)!} + \cdots,$$

which are called Bessel functions of the zero-th and first orders, respectively.

The formula (100-7) can be generalized for non-integral positive values of n with the aid of the Gamma function by writing $(n + k)! = \Gamma(n + k + 1)$, so that

$$(100\text{-}8) \quad J_n(x) = \sum_{k=0}^{\infty} (-1)^k \frac{x^{n+2k}}{2^{n+2k}k!\Gamma(n+k+1)}, \qquad n \geq 0.$$

For $n = \frac{1}{2}$, (100-8) becomes

$$J_{\frac{1}{2}}(x) = \sum_{k=0}^{\infty} (-1)^k \frac{x^{2k+\frac{1}{2}}}{2^{2k+\frac{1}{2}}k!\Gamma\left(\dfrac{2k+3}{2}\right)}.$$

* For $n = 0$, $n!$ is defined to be unity. This is consistent with the formula

$$(n - 1)! = \frac{n!}{n}$$

when $n = 1$, as well as with the general definition of $n!$ in Sec. 81.

It is not difficult to show that this reduces to*

$$J_{1/2}(x) = \sqrt{\frac{2}{\pi x}} \sin x.$$

This formula suggests that the behavior of Bessel functions may be somewhat similar to that of the trigonometric functions. This proves to be the case, and it will be shown in the next section that Bessel functions can be used to represent suitably restricted arbitrary functions in a way similar to that in which trigonometric functions are used in Fourier series.

It is clear that $J_0(x)$ is an even function and that $J_1(x)$ is an odd function of x. Their graphs are shown in Fig. 91. For large

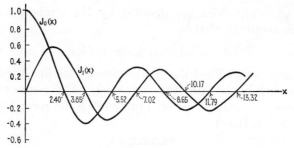

Fig. 91.

values of x the roots of $J_0(x) = 0$ and $J_1(x) = 0$ are spaced approximately π units apart. It can be shown that for large values of x the values of $J_n(x)$ are given approximately by the formula

$$J_n(x) \cong \sqrt{\frac{2}{\pi x}} \cos\left(x - \frac{\pi}{4} - \frac{n\pi}{2}\right).$$

It is not difficult to show with the aid of (100-6), by setting $y_1(x) = J_0(x)$, that the second solution of Bessel's equation of order zero has the form

$$K_0(x) = J_0(x) \log x + \frac{x^2}{2^2} - \frac{x^4}{2^2 \cdot 4^2}\left(1 + \frac{1}{2}\right) + \cdots$$

$$- (-1)^k \frac{x^{2k}}{2^2 \cdot 4^2 \cdots (2k)^2}\left(1 + \frac{1}{2} + \cdots + \frac{1}{k}\right) + \cdots.$$

This function is called the Bessel function of the zero-th order

* See Prob. 2 at the end of this section.

and the second kind. Thus, the general solution of the equation

$$y'' + \frac{1}{x} y' + y = 0$$

is

$$y = C_1 J_0(x) + C_2 K_0(x),$$

where C_1 and C_2 are arbitrary constants.

Bessel functions of the first kind and of negative integral order are defined* by the relation

$$J_{-n}(x) = (-1)^n J_n(x).$$

The values of Bessel functions are tabulated in many books.† Electrical engineers frequently use the real and imaginary parts of $J_n(\sqrt{-i}\, x)$, which are denoted by the symbols $ber_n x$ and $bei_n x$, respectively, that is,

$$J_n(\sqrt{-i}\, x) \equiv ber_n x + i\, bei_n x.$$

There are also modified Bessel functions of the first kind, which are denoted in the literature by $I_n(x)$. The commonly used notations for modified Bessel functions of the second kind are $Y_n(x)$, $N_n(x)$, $H_n(x)$.

PROBLEMS

1. Show that

$$\frac{d}{dx} J_0(x) = -J_1(x).$$

2. Show that

$$J_{\frac{1}{2}}(x) = \sqrt{\frac{2}{\pi x}} \sin x.$$

Note that $\Gamma(n + 1) = n\Gamma(n)$ and $\Gamma(\frac{1}{2}) = \sqrt{\pi}$.

3. Show that $y = J_0(kx)$ is a solution of the differential equation

$$xy'' + y' + k^2 xy = 0.$$

4. Show that

$$x^2 y'' + xy' + (k^2 x^2 - n^2)y = 0, \qquad k \neq 0,$$

can be reduced to the form

$$z^2 \frac{d^2 y}{dz^2} + z \frac{dy}{dz} + (z^2 - n^2)y = 0.$$

* See BYERLY, W. E., Fourier Series and Spherical Harmonics, Sec. 120, p. 219.

† JAHNKE-EMDE, Funktionentafeln; BYERLY, W. E., Fourier Series and Spherical Harmonics; WATSON, G. N., Theory of Bessel Functions.

Hint: Set $z = kx$, and hence $y' = \dfrac{dy}{dz}\dfrac{dz}{dx} = k\dfrac{dy}{dz}$

and $$y'' = \frac{d}{dx}\left(k\frac{dy}{dz}\right) = k^2\frac{d^2y}{dz^2}.$$

5. Show that $J_{-\frac{1}{2}}(x) = \sqrt{\dfrac{2}{\pi x}}\,\cos x$, so that the general solution of

Bessel's equation with $n = \frac{1}{2}$ is

$$y = c_1 J_{\frac{1}{2}}(x) + c_2 J_{-\frac{1}{2}}(x).$$

6. Show that $y = \sqrt{x}\,J_n(\lambda x)$ is a solution of the equation

$$4x^2 y'' + (4\lambda^2 x^2 - 4n^2 + 1)y = 0.$$

7. Show that $y = x^n J_n(x)$ is a solution of the equation

$$xy'' + (1 - 2n)y' + xy = 0.$$

8. Show that $y = x^{-n} J_n(x)$ is a solution of the equation

$$xy'' + (1 + 2n)y' + xy = 0.$$

101. Expansion in Series of Bessel Functions. It was pointed out in connection with the development of arbitrary functions in trigonometric series (Sec. 24) that the Fourier series development is only a special case of the expansion of a suitably restricted class of functions in series of orthogonal functions. It will be shown in this section that it is possible to build up sets of orthogonal functions with the aid of Bessel functions, so that one can represent an arbitrary function in a series of Bessel functions.

It is shown in the treatises* on Bessel functions that the equation $J_n(x) = 0$ has infinitely many positive roots $\lambda_1, \lambda_2, \cdots, \lambda_n, \cdots$, whose values can be calculated to any desired degree of accuracy. It will be established next that the functions

$$\sqrt{x}\,J_n(\lambda_1 x),\ \sqrt{x}\,J_n(\lambda_2 x),\ \cdots,\ \sqrt{x}\,J_n(\lambda_k x),\ \cdots$$

are orthogonal in the interval from $x = 0$ to $x = 1$, so that

$$(101\text{-}1) \qquad \int_0^1 \sqrt{x}\,J_n(\lambda_i x)\cdot\sqrt{x}\,J_n(\lambda_j x)\,dx = 0, \qquad \text{if } i \neq j,$$
$$= \tfrac{1}{2}[J_n'(\lambda_i)]^2, \quad \text{if } i = j.$$

The proof of this fact depends on the following identity, the validity of which, for the moment, will be taken for granted:

$$(101\text{-}2) \quad (\lambda^2 - \mu^2)\int_0^x x J_n(\lambda x)J_n(\mu x)\,dx$$
$$= x[\mu J_n(\lambda x)J_n'(\mu x) - \lambda J_n(\mu x)J_n'(\lambda x)].$$

* See the references given in the footnote, p. 335.

Let $\lambda = \lambda_j$ and $\mu = \lambda_i$, where $\lambda_i \neq \lambda_j$; then

$$\int_0^x \sqrt{x}\, J_n(\lambda_i x) \cdot \sqrt{x}\, J_n(\lambda_j x)\, dx$$

$$= \frac{x}{\lambda_j{}^2 - \lambda_i{}^2} [\lambda_i J_n(\lambda_j x) J_n{}'(\lambda_i x) - \lambda_j J_n(\lambda_i x) J_n{}'(\lambda_j x)].$$

Setting $x = 1$ and remembering that $J_n(\lambda_i) = J_n(\lambda_j) = 0$ give the first part of the formula (101-1).

In order to establish the second part, differentiate (101-2) partially with respect to λ, and thus obtain

$$(101\text{-}3) \quad 2\lambda \int_0^x x J_n(\lambda x) J_n(\mu x)\, dx + (\lambda^2 - \mu^2) \int_0^x x^2 J_n(\mu x) J_n{}'(\lambda x)\, dx$$

$$= x[\mu x J_n{}'(\lambda x) J_n{}'(\mu x) - J_n(\mu x) J_n{}'(\lambda x) - \lambda x J_n(\mu x) J_n{}''(\lambda x)].$$

Set $x = 1$, $\lambda = \mu$, and recall that if λ is a root of $J_n(x) = 0$ then $J_n(\lambda) = 0$. Upon simplification of (101-3), one obtains the second part of the formula (101-1).

In order to establish the identity (101-2), note that $y = \sqrt{x}\, J_n(\lambda x)$ is a solution of the equation*

$$4x^2 y'' + (4\lambda^2 x^2 - 4n^2 + 1) y = 0.$$

Setting $u = \sqrt{x}\, J_n(\lambda x)$ and $v = \sqrt{x}\, J_n(\mu x)$ gives the identities

$$4x^2 u'' + (4\lambda^2 x^2 - 4n^2 + 1) u = 0$$

and

$$4x^2 v'' + (4\mu^2 x^2 - 4n^2 + 1) v = 0.$$

Multiplying the first of these by v and the second by u and subtracting furnish the identity

$$-(\lambda^2 - \mu^2) uv = u''v - v''u.$$

The integration of both sides of this identity, between the limits 0 and x, yields

$$-(\lambda^2 - \mu^2) \int_0^x uv\, dx = \int_0^x (u''v - v''u)\, dx$$

$$= \left[u'v \Big|_0^x - \int_0^x u'v'\, dx \right] - \left[v'u \Big|_0^x - \int_0^x u'v'\, dx \right]$$

$$= \left[u'v - v'u \right]_0^x.$$

Recalling the definitions of u and v gives the desired identity (101-2).

Since the formula (101-1) is established, it is easy to see that if $f(x)$

* See Prob. 6, Sec. 100.

has an expansion of the form

$$f(x) = \sum_{i=1}^{\infty} a_i J_n(\lambda_i x),$$

which can be integrated term by term, then*

$$a_i = \frac{2 \int_0^1 x f(x) J_n(\lambda_i x) \, dx}{[J_n{}'(\lambda_i)]^2}.$$

The most common use of this formula is in connection with the expansion of functions in a series of Bessel functions of order zero.

PROBLEMS

1. Show that $\dfrac{d}{dx} [x J_1(x)] = x J_0(x)$.

2. Show that $f(x) = 1$, $0 < x < 1$, when expanded in a series of Bessel functions of order zero, gives

$$1 = \frac{2 J_0(\lambda_1 x)}{\lambda_1 J_1(\lambda_1)} + \frac{2 J_0(\lambda_2 x)}{\lambda_2 J_1(\lambda_2)} + \cdots + \frac{2 J_0(\lambda_n x)}{\lambda_n J_1(\lambda_n)} + \cdots.$$

Hint: Make use of the results of Prob. 1 above and Prob. 1, Sec. 100.

3. Show that

$$\frac{d}{dx} [x^n J_n(x)] = x^n J_{n-1}(x)$$

and

$$\frac{d}{dx} [x^{-n} J_n(x)] = -x^{-n} J_{n+1}(x).$$

4. Show that

$$J_{3/2}(x) = \sqrt{\frac{2}{\pi x}} \left(\frac{\sin x}{x} - \cos x \right)$$

and

$$J_{-3/2}(x) = \sqrt{\frac{2}{\pi x}} \left(-\sin x - \frac{\cos x}{x} \right).$$

5. Show, with the aid of the formulas of Prob. 3, that

$$J_{n-1}(x) - J_{n+1}(x) = 2 \frac{d}{dx} J_n(x)$$

and

$$J_{n-1}(x) + J_{n+1}(x) = \frac{2n}{x} J_n(x).$$

* See Sec. 24

6. Expand $e^{\frac{x}{2}\left(h-\frac{1}{h}\right)}$ in a power series in h to obtain

$$e^{\frac{x}{2}\left(h-\frac{1}{h}\right)} = \sum_{n=-\infty}^{n=\infty} A_n h^n,$$

and show that $A_n = J_n(x)$, so that

$$e^{\frac{x}{2}\left(h-\frac{1}{h}\right)} \equiv [J_0(x) + hJ_1(x) + h^2J_2(x) + \cdots + h^nJ_n(x) + \cdots]$$
$$+ [h^{-1}J_{-1}(x) + h^{-2}J_{-2}(x) + \cdots + h^{-n}J_{-n}(x) + \cdots].$$

102. Legendre's Equation.* The equation

$$(102\text{-}1) \qquad (1 - x^2)\frac{d^2y}{dx^2} - 2x\frac{dy}{dx} + n(n+1)y = 0,$$

where n is a constant, occurs frequently in practical investigations when spherical coordinates are used. One of the many uses of this equation in practical problems is indicated in the next chapter in connection with a study of the distribution of temperature in a conducting sphere.

Assume, as in Sec. 100, that

$$(102\text{-}2) \quad y = a_0x^m + a_1x^{m+1} + \cdots + a_kx^{m+k} + \cdots$$

is a solution of (102-1). Then,

$$\frac{d^2y}{dx^2} = m(m-1)a_0x^{m-2} + (m+1)ma_1x^{m-1}$$
$$+ (m+2)(m+1)a_2x^m + \cdots$$
$$+ (m+k)(m+k-1)a_kx^{m+k-2} + \cdots ,$$

$$-x^2\frac{d^2y}{dx^2} = -m(m-1)a_0x^m - \cdots$$
$$- (m+k-2)(m+k-3)a_{k-2}x^{m+k-2} - \cdots ,$$

$$-2x\frac{dy}{dx} = -2ma_0x^m - \cdots - 2(m+k-2)a_{k-2}x^{m+k-2}$$
$$- \cdots ,$$

$$n(n+1)y = n(n+1)a_0x^m + \cdots + n(n+1)a_{k-2}x^{m+k-2}$$
$$+ \cdots .$$

Adding these expressions and equating to zero the coefficients of x^{m-2}, x^{m-1}, $\cdots$, x^{m+k-2} give the system of equations

---

* A. M. Legendre (1752–1833), an outstanding French analyst who made many brilliant contributions to the theory of elliptic functions.

$$m(m-1)a_0 = 0,$$
$$m(m+1)a_1 = 0,$$
$$\cdots\cdots\cdots\cdots\cdots,$$
$$(m+k)(m+k-1)a_k$$
$$+ (n-m-k+2)(n+m+k-1)a_{k-2} = 0.$$

In order to satisfy the first of these equations, m can be chosen as either 0 or 1. If $m = 1$, the second equation requires that $a_1 \equiv 0$. For $m = 0$ the coefficient of x^{m+k-2} gives the recursion formula

$$a_k = -\frac{(n-k+2)(n+k-1)}{k(k-1)}a_{k-2},$$

from which, in a manner analogous to that employed in Sec. 100, the coefficients a_2, a_3, a_4, $\cdots$ can be determined. If $m = 0$, the second of the equations of the system allows a_1 to be arbitrary.

If the values of the coefficients in terms of a_0 and a_1 are substituted in (102-2), the following solution is obtained:

$$(102\text{-}3) \quad y = a_0\left[1 - \frac{n(n+1)}{2!}x^2 + \frac{n(n-2)(n+1)(n+3)}{4!}x^4\right.$$
$$\left. - \cdots\right] + a_1\left[x - \frac{(n-1)(n+2)}{3!}x^3\right.$$
$$\left. + \frac{(n-1)(n-3)(n+2)(n+4)}{5!}x^5 - \cdots\right].$$

It is readily shown by means of the ratio test that for non-integral values of n the interval of convergence of the series in (102-3) is $(-1, 1)$. Moreover, since the first series in (102-3) represents an even function and the second series represents an odd function, the two solutions are linearly independent. The sum of the two series, each multiplied by an arbitrary constant, gives the general solution of (102-1), which is certainly valid if $|x| < 1$. It can be verified directly that the choice of $m = 1$ does not lead to a new solution but merely reproduces the solution (102-3) with $a_0 = 0$.

An important and interesting case arises when n is a positive integer. It is clear that, when n is an even integer, the first series in (102-3) terminates and reduces to a polynomial, whereas, when n is an odd integer, the second series becomes a polynomial. If the arbitrary constants a_0 and a_1 are so adjusted as to give these polynomials the value unity when $x = 1$, then the following set of polynomials is obtained:

$$P_0(x) \equiv 1,$$
$$P_1(x) \equiv x,$$
$$P_2(x) \equiv \frac{3}{2} x^2 - \frac{1}{2},$$
$$P_3(x) \equiv \frac{5}{2} x^3 - \frac{3}{2} x,$$
$$P_4(x) \equiv \frac{7 \cdot 5}{4 \cdot 2} x^4 - 2 \frac{5 \cdot 3}{4 \cdot 2} x^2 + \frac{3 \cdot 1}{4 \cdot 2},$$
$$P_5(x) \equiv \frac{9 \cdot 7}{4 \cdot 2} x^5 - 2 \frac{7 \cdot 5}{4 \cdot 2} x^3 + \frac{5 \cdot 3}{4 \cdot 2} x,$$

$$\dotfill,$$

where the subscripts on P indicate the value of n.   Clearly, each of these polynomials is a particular solution of the Legendre equation in which n has the value of the subscript on P.   These polynomials are known as Legendre polynomials.   They are frequently used in applied mathematics.   Very often, they are denoted by $P_n(\cos \theta)$, where $\cos \theta = x$, so that, for example,

$$P_3(\cos \theta) \equiv \frac{5}{2} \cos^3 \theta - \frac{3}{2} \cos \theta.$$

The values of the Legendre polynomials (sometimes called surface zonal harmonics) are tabulated* for various values of x.

A solution that is valid for all values of x outside the interval $(-1, 1)$ can be obtained by assuming it to have the form of a series of descending powers of x.   A procedure analogous to that outlined above leads to the general solution of the form

$$y = a_0 \left[x^n - \frac{n(n-1)}{2(2n-1)} x^{n-2} + \frac{n(n-1)(n-2)(n-3)}{2 \cdot 4(2n-1)(2n-3)} x^{n-4} \right.$$
$$- \frac{n(n-1)(n-2)(n-3)(n-4)(n-5)}{2 \cdot 4 \cdot 6(2n-1)(2n-3)(2n-5)} x^{n-6} + \cdots \left. \right]$$
$$+ a_1 \left[x^{-n-1} + \frac{(n+1)(n+2)}{2 \cdot (2n+3)} x^{-n-3} \right.$$
$$+ \frac{(n+1)(n+2)(n+3)(n+4)}{2 \cdot 4(2n+3)(2n+5)} x^{-n-5}$$
$$+ \frac{(n+1)(n+2)(n+3)(n+4)(n+5)(n+6)}{2 \cdot 4 \cdot 6(2n+3)(2n+5)(2n+7)} x^{-n-7} + \cdots \left. \right]$$

which is valid for $|x| > 1$, and where n is a positive integer.

* See JAHNKE, E., und F. EMDE, Funktionentafeln; BYERLY, W. E., Fourier Series and Spherical Harmonics.

It will be shown next that the Legendre polynomials are orthogonal in the interval from -1 to 1, so that they can be used to represent a suitably restricted arbitrary function defined in the interval $(-1, 1)$.

Note that (102-1) can be written in an equivalent form as

$$\frac{d}{dx}[(1 - x^2)y'] + n(n + 1)y = 0,$$

and let $P_m(x)$ and $P_n(x)$ be two Legendre polynomials. Then,

$$\frac{d}{dx}[(1 - x^2)P_m'(x)] + m(m + 1)P_m(x) \equiv 0$$

and

$$\frac{d}{dx}[(1 - x^2)P_n'(x)] + n(n + 1)P_n(x) \equiv 0.$$

Multiplying the first of these identities by $P_n(x)$ and the second by $P_m(x)$ and subtracting give

$$P_m(x)\frac{d}{dx}[(1 - x^2)P_n'(x)] - P_n(x)\frac{d}{dx}[(1 - x^2)P_m'(x)]$$
$$+ (n - m)(n + m + 1)P_m(x)P_n(x) \equiv 0.$$

Integrating both members of this expression with respect to x between the limits -1 and $+1$ gives the formula

$$\int_{-1}^{1} P_m(x)\frac{d}{dx}[(1 - x^2)P_n'(x)]\,dx - \int_{-1}^{1} P_n(x)\frac{d}{dx}[(1 - x^2)P_m'(x)]\,dx$$
$$+ (n - m)(n + m + 1)\int_{-1}^{1} P_m(x)P_n(x)\,dx = 0.$$

The application of the formula for integration by parts to the first two integrals reduces this formula to

$$(n - m)(n + m + 1)\int_{-1}^{1} P_m(x)P_n(x)\,dx = 0.$$

Therefore,

$$\int_{-1}^{1} P_m(x)P_n(x)\,dx = 0, \qquad \text{if } m \neq n,$$

so that the Legendre polynomials are orthogonal.

It can be shown that

$$\int_{-1}^{1} [P_m(x)]^2\,dx = \frac{2}{2m + 1}.$$

The derivation of this formula is somewhat tedious and will not be given here.[*]

[*] See WHITTAKER, E. J., and G. N. WATSON, Modern Analysis, p. 305; MACROBERT, J. M., Spherical Harmonics; Byerly, W. E., Fourier Series and Spherical Harmonics, p. 170.

Consider next a function $f(x)$ that is defined in the interval $(-1, 1)$, and assume that it can be represented by a series of Legendre polynomials

$$(102\text{-}4) \qquad f(x) = \sum_{n=0}^{\infty} a_n P_n(x)$$

that can be integrated term by term. It follows immediately from Sec. 24 that the coefficients in the series (102-4) are given by the formula

$$a_n = \frac{2n + 1}{2} \int_{-1}^{1} f(x) P_n(x)\, dx, \qquad (n = 0, 1, 2, \cdots).$$

PROBLEMS

1. Show that the coefficients of h^n in the binomial expansion of $(1 - 2xh + h^2)^{-\frac{1}{2}}$ are the $P_n(x)$.

2. Verify that

$$P_n(x) = \frac{1}{2^n n!} \frac{d^n}{dx^n} (x^2 - 1)^n$$

by computing $P_n(x)$ for $n = 0, 1, 2, 3$.

3. Expand $f(x) = 1 + x - x^2$ in a series of Legendre polynomials.

4. Show that

$$P_{2n}(x) = P_{2n}(-x)$$

and

$$P_{2n+1}(x) = -P_{2n+1}(-x).$$

5. Show that

$$P_{2n}(0) = (-1)^n \frac{1 \cdot 3 \cdot 5 \, \cdots \, (2n - 1)}{2 \cdot 4 \cdot 6 \, \cdots \, 2n}$$

and

$$P_{2n+1}(0) = 0.$$

6. Show, with the aid of the formula

$$(1 - 2xh + h^2)^{-\frac{1}{2}} = \sum_{n=0}^{\infty} h^n P_n(x) \qquad (\text{see Prob. 1}),$$

that

$$P_n(1) = 1$$

and

$$P_n(-1) = (-1)^n.$$

103. Numerical Solution of Differential Equations. The method of infinite series solution of ordinary differential equations affords a powerful means of obtaining numerical approximations to the solutions of differential equations, but its usefulness is limited by the rapidity of convergence of the series.

Many differential equations occurring in physical problems cannot be solved with the aid of the methods discussed in this chapter, and one is obliged to resort to numerical methods. Only one of these methods, which was developed by the French mathematician E. Picard, is outlined in this section.*

Consider the problem of finding that particular solution of the equation of first order,

(103-1) $$\frac{dy}{dx} = f(x, y),$$

which assumes the value y_0 when $x = x_0$. If both members of (103-1) are multiplied by dx and the result is integrated between the limits x_0 and x, one obtains

$$\int_{y_0}^{y} dy = \int_{x_0}^{x} f(x, y)\, dx,$$

or

(103-2) $$y = y_0 + \int_{x_0}^{x} f(x, y)\, dx.$$

This is an *integral equation,* for it contains the unknown function y under the integral sign.

Since the desired integral curve passes through (x_0, y_0), assume as a first approximation to the solution of (103-2) that y, appearing in the right-hand member of (103-2), has the value y_0. Then, the first approximation to the solution of (103-2) is

$$y_1(x) = y_0 + \int_{x_0}^{x} f(x, y_0)\, dx.$$

Performing the indicated integration gives y_1 as an explicit function of x, and substituting $y_1(x)$ in the right-hand member of (103-2) gives the second approximation, namely

$$y_2(x) = y_0 + \int_{x_0}^{x} f[x, y_1(x)]\, dx.$$

The process can be repeated to obtain

$$y_3(x) = y_0 + \int_{x_0}^{x} f[x, y_2(x)]\, dx,$$

and so on. It is clear that the nth approximation has the form

$$y_n(x) = y_0 + \int_{x_0}^{x} f[x, y_{n-1}(x)]\, dx.$$

* For other methods see Bennett, Milne, and Bateman, Numerical Integration of Differential Equations, *Bulletin of National Research Council,* 1933.

The functions $y_1(x)$, $y_2(x)$, $\cdots$, $y_n(x)$ all take on the value y_0 when x is set equal to x_0, and it may happen that the successive approximations $y_1(x)$, $y_2(x)$, $\cdots$, $y_n(x)$ improve as n increases indefinitely; that is,

$$\lim_{n \to \infty} y_n(x) = y(x),$$

where $y(x)$ is the solution of Eq. (103-1). It may be remarked that, in order to establish the convergence of the sequence of approximating functions, it is sufficient to assume that $f(x, y)$ and $\partial f/\partial y$ are continuous in the neighborhood of the point (x_0, y_0). Despite the fact that these conditions are usually fulfilled in physical problems, the convergence may be so slow as to make the application of the method impracticable. The usefulness of the method is likewise limited by the complexity of the approximating functions. In many instances, it may be necessary to make use of numerical integration in order to evaluate the resulting integrals.*

The method just outlined can be extended to equations of higher order.

As an illustration of the application of the method to a specific problem, let it be required to find the integral curve of the equation

$$y' = 2x + y^2,$$

passing through $(0, 1)$.

Then (103-2) becomes

(103-3) $$y = 1 + \int_0^x (2x + y^2) \, dx,$$

and substituting $y = 1$ in the integrand of (103-3) gives

$$y_1 = 1 + \int_0^x (2x + 1) \, dx = 1 + x + x^2.$$

Then,

$$y_2 = 1 + \int_0^x [2x + (1 + x + x^2)^2] \, dx$$
$$= 1 + x + 2x^2 + x^3 + \tfrac{1}{2}x^4 + \tfrac{1}{5}x^5,$$

and

$$y_3 = 1 + \int_0^x [2x + (1 + x + 2x^2 + x^3 + \tfrac{1}{2}x^4 + \tfrac{1}{5}x^5)^2] \, dx$$
$$= 1 + x + 2x^2 + \tfrac{5}{3}x^3 + \tfrac{3}{2}x^4 + \tfrac{7}{5}x^5 + \tfrac{9}{10}x^6 + \tfrac{17}{35}x^7$$
$$+ \tfrac{9}{40}x^8 + \tfrac{13}{180}x^9 + \tfrac{1}{50}x^{10} + \tfrac{1}{275}x^{11}.$$

Even though the integrations in this case are elementary, the process of computing the next approximation is quite tedious. As a matter of

* See Sec. 167.

fact, in this case one can obtain the desired solution more easily by the method of infinite series.

Thus, assuming

$$y = \sum_{n=0}^{\infty} a_n x^n$$

and applying the method of Sec. 98 lead to the solution in the form

$$y = a_0 + a_0{}^2 x + (a_0{}^3 + 1)x^2 + \frac{3a_0{}^4 + 2a_0}{3} x^3 + \frac{6a_0{}^5 + 5a_0{}^2}{6} x^4$$
$$+ \frac{5a_0{}^6 + 5a_0{}^3 + 1}{5} x^5 + \cdots.$$

Since the integral curve must pass through $(0, 1)$, it follows that $a_0 = 1$, and the desired solution is

$$y = 1 + x + 2x^2 + \tfrac{5}{3}x^3 + 1\tfrac{1}{6}x^4 + 1\tfrac{1}{5}x^5 + \cdots.$$

This agrees with the solution obtained by Picard's method up to the terms in x^4.

PROBLEM

Find, by Picard's method, solutions of the following equations:

(a) $y' = xy$ through $(1, 1)$;

(b) $y' = x - y^2$ through $(0, \tfrac{1}{2})$;

(c) $y' = 1 + y^2$ through $\left(\dfrac{\pi}{4}, 1\right)$;

(d) $y' = x + y$ through $(1, 1)$.

CHAPTER VIII

PARTIAL DIFFERENTIAL EQUATIONS

104. Preliminary Remarks. An equation containing partial derivatives has been defined in Sec. 67 as a partial differential equation. This chapter contains a brief introduction to the solution of some of the simpler types of linear partial differential equations which occur frequently in practice. It will be seen that the problem of solving partial differential equations is inherently more difficult than that of solving the ordinary equations and that Fourier series, Bessel functions, and Legendre polynomials play an important part in the solution of some of the practical problems involving partial differential equations.

It was stated in Sec. 68 that the elimination of n arbitrary constants from a primitive $f(x, y, c_1, c_2, \cdots, c_n) = 0$ leads, in general, to an ordinary differential equation of order n. Conversely, the general solution of an ordinary differential equation has been defined to be that solution which contains n arbitrary constants. In the next section, it is indicated, by some examples, that one is led to partial differential equations by differentiating primitives involving arbitrary functions, and it follows that partial differential equations may have solutions which contain arbitrary functions. However, it is not always possible to eliminate n arbitrary functions from a given primitive by n successive differentiations, and the temptation to define the general solution of a partial differential equation as the one containing n arbitrary functions may lead to serious difficulties.

In some important cases of linear partial differential equations with constant coefficients, treated in Sec. 107, it is possible to obtain solutions that contain the number of arbitrary functions equal to the order of the differential equation, and the term *general solution* is used in this chapter only in connection with such equations. With the exception of the linear partial differential equations of the first order and of certain important types of linear equations of the second order, no extensive theory of the nature of solutions has been developed so far.

Just as in the case of the ordinary differential equations, the solution of a practical problem can be obtained by eliminating the element of arbitrariness with the aid of the initial or boundary conditions. In practical problems the boundary conditions frequently serve as a guide in choosing a particular solution, which satisfies the differential equation and the boundary conditions as well.

105. Elimination of Arbitrary Functions. Consider a family of surfaces defined by

$$z = f(x + y),$$

where f is an arbitrary function.

If the argument of f is denoted by s, then

$$z = f(x + y) \equiv f(s)$$

and

$$\frac{\partial z}{\partial x} = \frac{df}{ds}\frac{\partial s}{\partial x}.$$

Since $s = x + y$, it follows that

$$(105\text{-}1) \qquad \frac{\partial z}{\partial x} = f'(x + y),$$

where $f'(x + y)$ denotes the derivative of $f(x + y)$ with respect to its argument $x + y$. Similarly,

$$(105\text{-}2) \qquad \frac{\partial z}{\partial y} = f'(x + y).$$

Subtracting (105-2) from (105-1) leads to the partial differential equation of the first order

$$\frac{\partial z}{\partial x} - \frac{\partial z}{\partial y} = 0,$$

whose solution, clearly, is $z = f(x + y)$.

If

$$z = f\left(\frac{y}{x}\right),$$

then

$$\frac{\partial z}{\partial x} = \frac{df}{ds}\frac{\partial s}{\partial x} \qquad \text{and} \qquad \frac{\partial z}{\partial y} = \frac{df}{ds}\frac{\partial s}{\partial y},$$

where $s = y/x$.

Denoting df/ds by $f'(y/x)$ and substituting the values of $\partial s/\partial x$ and $\partial s/\partial y$ give

$$\frac{\partial z}{\partial x} = f'\left(\frac{y}{x}\right)\left(-\frac{y}{x^2}\right) \quad \text{and} \quad \frac{\partial z}{\partial y} = f'\left(\frac{y}{x}\right)\cdot\frac{1}{x},$$

from which $f'(y/x)$ can be eliminated to give

$$x\frac{\partial z}{\partial x} + y\frac{\partial z}{\partial y} = 0.$$

Again the result is a partial differential equation of the first order.

On the other hand, if

$$z = f_1(x) + f_2(y),$$

where $f_1(x)$ and $f_2(y)$ are arbitrary functions, differentiations with respect to x and y give

$$\frac{\partial z}{\partial x} = f_1'(x) \quad \text{and} \quad \frac{\partial z}{\partial y} = f_2'(y).$$

If the first of these relations is differentiated with respect to y, a partial differential equation of the second order results, namely,

$$\frac{\partial^2 z}{\partial x\,\partial y} = 0.$$

Differentiation of the second relation with respect to x will lead to the same equation, for the derivatives involved are assumed to be continuous.

Another example, which is of considerable importance in the theory of vibrations, will be given. Let

$$z = f_1(x + at) + f_2(x - at).$$

If $x + at \equiv r$ and $x - at \equiv s$, then

$$z = f_1(r) + f_2(s)$$

and

$$\frac{\partial z}{\partial x} = \frac{\partial(f_1 + f_2)}{\partial r}\frac{\partial r}{\partial x} + \frac{\partial(f_1 + f_2)}{\partial s}\frac{\partial s}{\partial x}$$
$$= f_1'(x + at) + f_2'(x - at).$$

Similarly,

$$(105\text{-}3) \qquad \frac{\partial^2 z}{\partial x^2} = f_1''(x + at) + f_2''(x - at).$$

Also,

$$\frac{\partial z}{\partial t} = \frac{\partial (f_1 + f_2)}{\partial r} \frac{\partial r}{\partial t} + \frac{\partial (f_1 + f_2)}{\partial s} \frac{\partial s}{\partial t}$$
$$= f_1'(x + at)a + f_2'(x - at)(-a)$$

and

$$(105\text{-}4) \qquad \frac{\partial^2 z}{\partial t^2} = f_1''(x + at)a^2 + f_2''(x - at)a^2.$$

Eliminating $f_1''(x + at)$ and $f_2''(x - at)$ from (105-3) and (105-4) gives

$$\frac{\partial^2 z}{\partial t^2} = a^2 \frac{\partial^2 z}{\partial x^2},$$

regardless of the character of f_1 and f_2. This partial differential equation is of primary importance in the study of vibration and will be considered in more detail in Secs. 106, 108, and 109.

106. Integration of Partial Differential Equations. This section contains two examples illustrating integration of partial differential equations.

Let the differential equation be

$$(106\text{-}1) \qquad \frac{\partial^2 z}{\partial x\,\partial y} = 0.$$

Integration with respect to y gives

$$(106\text{-}2) \qquad \frac{\partial z}{\partial x} = f(x),$$

where $f(x)$ is arbitrary. If (106-2) is integrated with respect to x, then

$$z = \int f(x)\,dx + \varphi(y)$$
$$\equiv \psi(x) + \varphi(y),$$

where ψ and φ are arbitrary functions.

Consider next

$$(106\text{-}3) \qquad \frac{\partial^2 z}{\partial t^2} = a^2 \frac{\partial^2 z}{\partial x^2}.$$

Change the variables in this equation by setting $r = x + at$ and $s = x - at$ so that z becomes a function of r and s. Then

$$\frac{\partial z}{\partial x} = \frac{\partial z}{\partial r} \frac{\partial r}{\partial x} + \frac{\partial z}{\partial s} \frac{\partial s}{\partial x};$$

and since $\partial r/\partial x = 1$ and $\partial s/\partial x = 1$, it follows that

$$\frac{\partial z}{\partial x} = \frac{\partial z}{\partial r} + \frac{\partial z}{\partial s}$$

and

(106-4)
$$\frac{\partial^2 z}{\partial x^2} = \left(\frac{\partial^2 z}{\partial r^2} \frac{\partial r}{\partial x} + \frac{\partial^2 z}{\partial r \, \partial s} \frac{\partial s}{\partial x} + \frac{\partial^2 z}{\partial s^2} \frac{\partial s}{\partial x} + \frac{\partial^2 z}{\partial s \, \partial r} \frac{\partial r}{\partial x} \right)$$
$$= \frac{\partial^2 z}{\partial r^2} + 2 \frac{\partial^2 z}{\partial r \, \partial s} + \frac{\partial^2 z}{\partial s^2}.$$

Similarly,

$$\frac{\partial z}{\partial t} = \frac{\partial z}{\partial r} \frac{\partial r}{\partial t} + \frac{\partial z}{\partial s} \frac{\partial s}{\partial t};$$

and since $\partial r/\partial t = a$ and $\partial s/\partial t = -a$, it follows that

$$\frac{\partial z}{\partial t} = a \frac{\partial z}{\partial r} - a \frac{\partial z}{\partial s}.$$

Differentiating this with respect to t gives

(106-5)
$$\frac{\partial^2 z}{\partial t^2} = a \frac{\partial^2 z}{\partial r^2} \frac{\partial r}{\partial t} + a \frac{\partial^2 z}{\partial r \, \partial s} \frac{\partial s}{\partial t} - a \frac{\partial^2 z}{\partial s^2} \frac{\partial s}{\partial t} - a \frac{\partial^2 z}{\partial s \, \partial r} \frac{\partial r}{\partial t}$$
$$= a^2 \frac{\partial^2 z}{\partial r^2} - 2a^2 \frac{\partial^2 z}{\partial r \, \partial s} + a^2 \frac{\partial^2 z}{\partial s^2}.$$

Substituting (106-4) and (106-5) in (106-3) gives the equation

$$\frac{\partial^2 z}{\partial r \, \partial s} = 0,$$

which is of the type (106-1), whose solution was found to be $z = \psi(r) + \varphi(s)$, where ψ and φ are arbitrary. Recalling that $r = x + at$ and $s = x - at$, it is seen that

(106-6)
$$z = \psi(x + at) + \varphi(x - at),$$

which is the solution in terms of the original variables. If in this solution ψ and φ are so chosen that

$$\psi(x + at) \equiv A \sin k(x + at),$$
$$\varphi(x - at) \equiv A \sin k(x - at),$$

where the variable t is thought to represent the time and x is the distance along the x-axis, then the first of these equations represents a sinusoidal wave of amplitude A and wave length $\lambda = 2\pi/k$ which is moving to the left with velocity a, whereas the second expression represents a similar wave moving with velocity a to the right (see Fig. 92). This can best be seen by recalling that the replacement of x by $x - at$ in $z = f(x)$ shifts the curve at units in the positive direction of x and that the substitution of $x + at$ for x translates the curve $z = f(x)$ at units in the opposite direc-

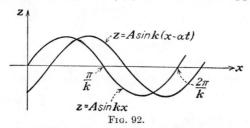

FIG. 92.

tion. Since t is a continuous variable representing the time, it is clear that the expression

$$A \sin k(x - at)$$

states that the sinusoid

$$z = A \sin kx$$

is advancing in the positive direction of the x-axis with the velocity a. The period of the wave

$$z = A \sin k(x - at)$$

is defined as the time required for the wave to progress a distance equal to one wave length, so that

$$\lambda = aT$$

or

$$T = \frac{\lambda}{a} = \frac{2\pi}{ka}.$$

Consider next the wave resulting from the superposition of the two moving sinusoids $A \sin k(x - at)$ and $A \sin k(x + at)$. Then,

$$z = A \sin k(x - at) + A \sin k(x + at)$$
$$= A(\sin kx \cos kat - \cos kx \sin kat)$$
$$+ A(\sin kx \cos kat + \cos kx \sin kat)$$

or

(106-7) $z = (2A \cos kat) \sin kx.$

The expression (106-7) is frequently referred to as a **standing wave**, because it may be thought of as representing a sinusoid

$\sin kx$ whose amplitude $2A \cos kat$ varies with the time t in a simply harmonic manner. Several curves

$$z = 2A \cos kat \sin kx$$

are drawn in Fig. 93 for various values of t. The points

$$x = \frac{n\pi}{k}, \qquad (n = 0, 1, 2, \cdots),$$

are stationary points of the curve and are called nodes.

Inasmuch as (106-7) is obtained from (106-6) by making a particular choice of ψ and φ, it satisfies the differential equation

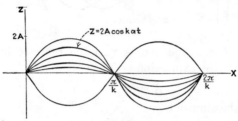

Fig. 93.

(106-3), whatever be the values of A and k. This fact is of great importance in the discussion of Sec. 108.

PROBLEMS

1. Form partial differential equations by eliminating arbitrary functions.

(a) $z = f(x - 2y) + 3x + 4y$.

(b) $z = f(x^2 + y^2 + z^2)$.

Note that $\dfrac{\partial z}{\partial x} = f'(x^2 + y^2 + z^2)\left(2x + 2z\dfrac{\partial z}{\partial x}\right)$.

(c) $z = e^x f(y - x)$.

(d) $z = f_1(x)f_2(y)$.

2. Prove that $z = f_1(x + iy) + f_2(x - iy)$ is a solution of

$$\frac{\partial^2 z}{\partial x^2} + \frac{\partial^2 z}{\partial y^2} = 0.$$

3. Form partial differential equations by eliminating the arbitrary functions, in which x and t are the independent variables.

(a) $z = f_1(x - 2t) + f_2(x + 2t)$;

(b) $z = f(x - t + z)$;

(c) $z = f_1(x + 2t) + f_2(x + 3t)$;

(d) $z = xf_1(x + t) + f_2(x + t)$;

(e) $x = f_1(z + x) + f_2(t)$;

(f) $z = f_1(x - t) + xf_2(x - t)$.

4. Show that $z = f(a_1y - a_2x)$ is a solution of the equation

$$a_1 \frac{\partial z}{\partial x} + a_2 \frac{\partial z}{\partial y} = 0,$$

where a_1 and a_2 are constants.

5. Verify that $z = f_1(y + 2x)$ and $z = f_2(y - 3x)$ satisfy the equation

$$\frac{\partial^2 z}{\partial x^2} + \frac{\partial^2 z}{\partial x \, \partial y} - 6 \frac{\partial^2 z}{\partial y^2} = 0,$$

and hence deduce that $z = f_1(y + 2x) + f_2(y - 3x)$ is also a solution of the equation.

6. Show that

$$z = f_1(y - ix) + xf_2(y - ix) + f_3(y + ix) + xf_4(y + ix)$$

is a solution of the equation

$$\frac{\partial^4 z}{\partial x^4} + 2 \frac{\partial^4 z}{\partial x^2 \, \partial y^2} + \frac{\partial^4 z}{\partial y^4} = 0,$$

provided that $i^2 = -1$.

107. Linear Partial Differential Equations with Constant Coefficients. A linear partial differential equation with constant coefficients that often occurs in applications has the form

$$(107\text{-}1) \quad a_0 \frac{\partial^n z}{\partial x^n} + a_1 \frac{\partial^n z}{\partial x^{n-1} \partial y} + a_2 \frac{\partial^n z}{\partial x^{n-2} \, \partial y^2}$$

$$+ \cdots + a_{n-1} \frac{\partial^n z}{\partial x \, \partial y^{n-1}} + a_n \frac{\partial^n z}{\partial y^n} = 0.$$

Frequently, such equations are called "homogeneous" because they involve only derivatives of the nth order.

This equation can be solved by a method similar to that employed in solving an ordinary linear equation with constant coefficients. Introduce the operators

$$D_1^n = \frac{\partial^n}{\partial x^n} \quad \text{and} \quad D_2^n = \frac{\partial^n}{\partial y^n},$$

with the aid of which (107-1) can be written as

$$(107\text{-}2) \quad (a_0 D_1^n + a_1 D_1^{n-1} D_2 + a_2 D_1^{n-2} D_2^2 + \cdots$$

$$+ a_{n-1} D_1 D_2^{n-1} + a_n D_2^n)z = 0.$$

It is readily established* that the operators D_1 and D_2 formally obey the ordinary laws of algebra, so that one can deal with differential operators of the form

$$L(D_1, D_2) \equiv a_0 D_1^n + a_1 D_1^{n-1} D_2 + \cdots + a_n D_2^n$$

just as one would with polynomials in the two variables D_1 and D_2. Accordingly, the left-hand member of (107-2) can be decomposed into a product of n linear factors, so that (107-2) reads

$$(107\text{-}3) \quad (\alpha_1 D_1 + \beta_1 D_2)(\alpha_2 D_1 + \beta_2 D_2) \cdots (\alpha_n D_1 + \beta_n D_2)z = 0,$$

where the quantities α_i and β_i, in general, are complex numbers. Now the system of equations

$$(\alpha_i D_1 + \beta_i D_2)z = 0, \quad (i = 1, 2, \cdots, n),$$

or

$$(107\text{-}4) \qquad \alpha_i \frac{\partial z}{\partial x} + \beta_i \frac{\partial z}{\partial y} = 0, \quad (i = 1, 2, \cdots, n),$$

can be readily solved. It is easy to verify that

$$z = F_i(\alpha_i y - \beta_i x),$$

where F_i is an arbitrary function, is a solution of (107-4). Consequently,† the solution of (107-3) can be written in the form

$$(107\text{-}5) \quad z = F_1(\alpha_1 y - \beta_1 x) + F_2(\alpha_2 y - \beta_2 x) + \cdots + F_n(\alpha_n y - \beta_n x).$$

If the linear factors appearing in (107-3) are all distinct, the solution (107-5) contains n arbitrary functions and will be called the *general solution* of (107-1).

If the α_i in (107-3) are all different from zero, one can write (107-3) as

$$(107\text{-}6) \quad (D_1 - m_1 D_2)(D_1 - m_2 D_2) \cdots (D_1 - m_n D_2)z = 0,$$

where $m_i = -\beta_i/\alpha_i$, $(i = 1, 2, \cdots, n)$. In this case, (107-5) assumes the form

$$(107\text{-}7) \quad z = F_1(y + m_1 x) + F_2(y + m_2 x) + \cdots + F_n(y + m_n x).$$

If some of the factors in (107-6) are alike, then the number of arbitrary functions in (107-7) will be less than n, but it is easy

---

* See the corresponding discussion in Sec. 87.

† See the corresponding case in Sec. 88.

to see that the equation

$$(D_1 - mD_2)^r z = 0$$

has the solution

$$z = F_1(y + mx) + xF_2(y + mx) + \cdots + x^{r-1}F_r(y + mx).$$

Consequently, one can obtain a solution of (107-6) that contains the number of arbitrary functions equal to the order of the differential equation even in the case when some of the factors in the left-hand member of (107-6) are not distinct.

As an illustration, consider the equation, which frequently occurs in the study of elastic plates,

$$\frac{\partial^4 z}{\partial x^4} + 2\frac{\partial^4 z}{\partial x^2 \, \partial y^2} + \frac{\partial^4 z}{\partial y^4} = 0,$$

or

$$(D_1^4 + 2D_1^2 D_2^2 + D_2^4)z = 0.$$

The decomposition into linear factors gives

$$(D_1 + iD_2)(D_1 - iD_2)(D_1 + iD_2)(D_1 - iD_2)z = 0,$$

where $i^2 = -1$. It follows that the general solution of this equation has the form

$$z = F_1(y - ix) + xF_2(y - ix) + F_3(y + ix) + xF_4(y + ix).$$

If the right-hand member of (107-1) is a function $f(x, y)$, then the general solution of the equation is

$$z = \Phi(x, y) + u(x, y),$$

where $u(x, y)$ is a particular integral and $\Phi(x, y)$ is the general solution of the related homogeneous equation. The determination of particular integrals of the equation

(107-8) $$L(D_1, D_2)z = f(x, y)$$

can be made to depend on the calculus of operators* as was done in Sec. 89. In many cases the particular integral can be obtained by inspection. If $f(x, y)$ is a homogeneous polynomial of degree k, then the particular integral has the form

(107-9) $$z = c_0 x^{k+n} + c_1 x^{k+n-1}y + \cdots + c_{k+n}y^{k+n},$$

in which the coefficients c_i can be determined by substituting (107-9) into (107-8) and comparing the coefficients of the corre-

---

* See, for example, M. Morris and O. Brown, Differential Equations, p. 248; A. Cohen, Differential Equations, p. 275.

sponding terms of the resulting equation.

As an example of this, consider

$$(107\text{-}10) \qquad \frac{\partial^2 z}{\partial x^2} + \frac{\partial^2 z}{\partial x\,\partial y} - 6\frac{\partial^2 z}{\partial y^2} = 6x^2 y,$$

which can be written as

$$(D_1{}^2 + D_1 D_2 - 6D_2{}^2)z = 6x^2 y,$$

or

$$(D_1 - 2D_2)(D_1 + 3D_2)z = 6x^2 y.$$

Assume the particular integral in the form

$$(107\text{-}11) \quad z = c_0 x^5 + c_1 x^4 y + c_2 x^3 y^2 + c_3 x^2 y^3 + c_4 x y^4 + c_5 y^5.$$

Substituting (107-11) in (107-10) gives

$$(20c_0 + 4c_1 - 12c_2)x^3 + (12c_1 + 6c_2 - 36c_3)x^2 y$$
$$+ (6c_2 + 6c_3 - 72c_4)xy^2 + (2c_3 + 4c_4 - 120c_5)y^3 = 6x^2 y.$$

Hence, equating the coefficients of like terms on both sides of this equation gives

$$5c_0 + c_1 - 3c_2 = 0,$$
$$12c_1 + 6c_2 - 36c_3 = 6,$$
$$c_2 + c_3 - 12c_4 = 0,$$
$$c_3 + 2c_4 - 60c_5 = 0.$$

This system of four equations in six unknowns can always be solved. Writing it as

$$c_1 - 3c_2 + 0c_3 + 0c_4 = -5c_0,$$
$$2c_1 + c_2 - 6c_3 + 0c_4 = 1,$$
$$0c_1 + c_2 + c_3 - 12c_4 = 0,$$
$$0c_1 + 0c_2 + c_3 + 2c_4 = 60c_5,$$

and solving for c_1, c_2, c_3, and c_4 in terms of c_0 and c_5 give a two-parameter family of solutions,

$$c_1 = \frac{-65c_0 + 6480c_5 + 21}{55},$$

$$c_2 = \frac{70c_0 + 2160c_5 + 7}{55},$$

$$c_3 = \frac{-10c_0 + 2520c_5 - 1}{55},$$

$$c_4 = \frac{780c_5 + 10c_0 + 1}{110}.$$

Setting $c_0 = c_5 = 0$ and substituting the values of the coefficients in (107-11) give a particular integral of (107-10) in the form

$$u(x, y) = 2\tfrac{1}{55}x^4y + \tfrac{7}{55}x^3y^2 - \tfrac{1}{55}x^2y^3 + \tfrac{1}{110}xy^4.$$

Therefore the general solution of (107-10) is

$$z = F_1(y + 2x) + F_2(y - 3x) + u(x, y),$$

where F_1 and F_2 are arbitrary functions.

PROBLEMS

1. Find the general solutions of

(a) $\dfrac{\partial^2 z}{\partial x^2} - a^2 \dfrac{\partial^2 z}{\partial y^2} = 0;$

(b) $\dfrac{\partial^2 z}{\partial x^2} + \dfrac{\partial^2 z}{\partial x\,\partial y} - 2\dfrac{\partial^2 z}{\partial y^2} = 0;$

(c) $2\dfrac{\partial^2 z}{\partial x^2} + \dfrac{\partial^2 z}{\partial x\,\partial y} - \dfrac{\partial^2 z}{\partial y^2} = 0;$

(d) $\dfrac{\partial^2 z}{\partial x^2} + \dfrac{\partial^2 z}{\partial y^2} = 0;$

(e) $\dfrac{\partial^2 z}{\partial x^2} + 2\dfrac{\partial^2 z}{\partial x\,\partial y} + \dfrac{\partial^2 z}{\partial y^2} = 0.$

2. Find particular integrals for the following equations:

(a) $2\dfrac{\partial^2 z}{\partial x^2} + \dfrac{\partial^2 z}{\partial x\,\partial y} - \dfrac{\partial^2 z}{\partial y^2} = 1;$

(b) $\dfrac{\partial^2 z}{\partial x^2} + 4\dfrac{\partial^2 z}{\partial x\,\partial y} - 5\dfrac{\partial^2 z}{\partial y^2} = y^2 + x;$

Hint: Obtain the particular integral for $f(x, y) = y^2$ and for $f(x, y) = x$ and add the solutions.

(c) $\dfrac{\partial^2 z}{\partial x^2} + 3\dfrac{\partial^2 z}{\partial x\,\partial y} + 2\dfrac{\partial^2 z}{\partial y^2} = x + y;$

(d) $\dfrac{\partial^2 z}{\partial x^2} - a^2\dfrac{\partial^2 z}{\partial y^2} = x^2.$

108. Transverse Vibration of Elastic String. Consider an elastic string or wire of length l stretched between two points on the x-axis that are l units apart, and let it be distorted into some curve whose equation is $y = f(x)$ (Fig. 94). At a certain instant, say $t = 0$, the string is released from rest and allowed to vibrate. The problem is to determine the position of any point P of the string at any later time t. It is assumed that the string is perfectly elastic and that it does not offer any resistance to bending.

The resulting vibration may be thought of as being composed of the two vibrations:

a. Transverse vibration, in which every particle of the string moves in the direction of the y-axis;

b. Longitudinal vibration, in which every particle oscillates in the direction of the x-axis.

It is tolerably clear that, if the stretching force T is large compared with the force of gravity, then the horizontal component of tension in the string will be sensibly constant. Therefore the displacement of the point P in the direction of the x-axis can be neglected compared with the displacement of P in the y-direction. In other words, the longitudinal oscillation of the string contributes so little to the resultant vibration that the entire vibration may be thought to be given by considering the transverse component-vibration.

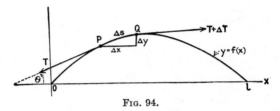

FIG. 94.

The relation connecting the coordinates of the point P with the time t can best be stated in the form of a differential equation. Thus, denote the length of the segment of the string between the points $P(x, y)$ and $Q(x + \Delta x, y + \Delta y)$ by Δs, and let the tension at P be T and at Q be $T + \Delta T$. In view of the assumption stated above, the horizontal components of tension at P and Q are nearly equal so that the difference ΔT of the tensions at the ends of the segment Δs is taken as equal to the difference between the vertical components of tension at Q and P. The vertical component of tension at P is

$$(T \sin \theta)_P = \left(T \lim_{\Delta s \to 0} \frac{\Delta y}{\Delta s} \right)_P = \left(T \frac{\partial y}{\partial s} \right)_x,$$

and the vertical component of tension at Q is

$$(T \sin \theta)_Q = \left(T \frac{\partial y}{\partial s} \right)_{x + \Delta x}.$$

If it is assumed that the transverse displacement of the string is so small that one can neglect the square of the slope of the string in comparison with the slope $\partial y / \partial x$, then the sine of the angle can be replaced by the tangent,* and the resultant of the forces at P and Q is

$$\left(T \frac{\partial y}{\partial x} \right)_{x+\Delta x} - \left(T \frac{\partial y}{\partial x} \right)_x .$$

By Newton's second law, this resultant must equal the mass of the element of the string of length Δx multiplied by the acceleration in the direction of the y-axis. Hence,

$$(108\text{-}1) \qquad \rho \, \Delta x \left(\frac{\partial^2 y}{\partial t^2} \right)_{x'} = T \left[\left(\frac{\partial y}{\partial x} \right)_{x+\Delta x} - \left(\frac{\partial y}{\partial x} \right)_x \right],$$

where ρ is the mass per unit length of the string and $(\partial^2 y / \partial t^2)_{x'}$ denotes the acceleration of the element PQ of the string.

Dividing both sides of (108-1) by $\rho \, \Delta x$ reduces it to

$$\left(\frac{\partial^2 y}{\partial t^2} \right)_{x'} = \frac{T}{\rho} \frac{\left(\dfrac{\partial y}{\partial x} \right)_{x+\Delta x} - \left(\dfrac{\partial y}{\partial x} \right)_x}{\Delta x},$$

and passing to the limit as $\Delta x \to 0$ gives

$$(108\text{-}2) \qquad \frac{\partial^2 y}{\partial t^2} = a^2 \frac{\partial^2 y}{\partial x^2},$$

where $a^2 = T/\rho$.

The solution of (108-2) was found in Sec. 106 to be

$$y = \psi(x + at) + \varphi(x - at),$$

where ψ and φ are arbitrary functions. These functions must be so chosen that, when $t = 0$,

$$y = \psi(x) + \varphi(x)$$

represents the equation of the curve into which the string was initially distorted. Furthermore, the string was supposed to have been released from rest, so that $\partial y/\partial t = 0$ when $t = 0$. It is beyond the scope of this book to prove that these boundary conditions suffice for the unique determination of the functions

---

* Note that

$$\frac{\partial y}{\partial s} = \sin \theta = \frac{\tan \theta}{\sqrt{1 + \tan^2 \theta}} = \frac{\dfrac{\partial y}{\partial x}}{\sqrt{1 + \left(\dfrac{\partial y}{\partial x} \right)^2}} \doteq \frac{\partial y}{\partial x}.$$

ψ and φ. It will be shown in the next section how the solution of this problem is obtained with the aid of Fourier series.

109. Fourier Series Solution. In the preceding section, it was established that the transverse vibrations of an elastic string are defined by the equation

$$(109\text{-}1) \qquad \frac{\partial^2 y}{\partial t^2} = a^2 \frac{\partial^2 y}{\partial x^2},$$

and in Sec. 106 it was shown that a particular solution of this equation is given by

$$(109\text{-}2) \qquad y = 2A \cos kat \sin kx$$

for arbitrary values of A and k. Moreover, it is clear that the sum of any number of solutions of the type (109-2) will satisfy (109-1).

Now, suppose that the string of length l is distorted into some curve $y = f(x)$, and then released without receiving any initial velocity. The subsequent behavior of the string is given by Eq. (109-1), the solution of which must be chosen so that it reduces to $y = f(x)$ when $t = 0$. In addition to this condition, $\partial y/\partial t = 0$ when $t = 0$, for, by hypothesis, the string is released without having any initial velocity imparted to it. Furthermore, since the string is fixed at the ends, $y = 0$ when $x = 0$ and when $x = l$.

Consider the infinite series

$$(109\text{-}3) \quad y = a_1 \cos \frac{\pi at}{l} \sin \frac{\pi x}{l} + a_2 \cos \frac{2\pi at}{l} \sin \frac{2\pi x}{l}$$
$$+ a_3 \cos \frac{3\pi at}{l} \sin \frac{3\pi x}{l} + \cdots,$$

each term of which is of the type (109-2), where k has been chosen so that each term reduces to zero when $x = 0$ and when $x = l$. When $t = 0$, the series becomes

$$(109\text{-}4) \quad a_1 \sin \frac{\pi x}{l} + a_2 \sin \frac{2\pi x}{l} + a_3 \sin \frac{3\pi x}{l} + \cdots.$$

If the coefficients a_n are chosen properly, (109-4) can be made to represent the equation $y = f(x)$ of the curve into which the string was initially distorted; for a function $f(x)$, subject to certain restrictions,* can be expanded in a series of sines (109-4)

* See Sec. 20.

and the coefficients are given by

$$(109\text{-}5) \qquad a_n = \frac{2}{l} \int_0^l f(x) \sin \frac{n\pi x}{l} \, dx.$$

It is readily verified that the derivative of (109-3) with respect to t satisfies the remaining boundary condition, $\partial y/\partial t = 0$ when $t = 0$. Hence the infinite series (109-3), where the values of a_n are given by (109-5), gives the formal solution of the problem.

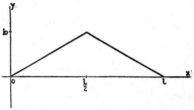

Illustration. If the initial distortion of the string (Fig. 95) is given by

Fig. 95.

$$y = \frac{2b}{l} x, \qquad\qquad 0 < x < \frac{l}{2},$$

$$y = -\frac{2b}{l} x + 2b, \qquad \frac{l}{2} < x < l,$$

then the solution of the problem is readily found to be

$$y = \frac{8b}{\pi^2} \left(\frac{1}{1^2} \sin \frac{\pi x}{l} \cos \frac{\pi a t}{l} - \frac{1}{3^2} \sin \frac{3\pi x}{l} \cos \frac{3\pi a t}{l} + \cdots \right).$$

PROBLEMS

1. Carry out solution of the problem given in the illustration, Sec. 109.

2. A taut string of length l, fastened at both ends, is disturbed from its position of equilibrium by imparting to each of its points an initial velocity of magnitude $f(x)$. Show that the solution of the problem is

$$y = \frac{2}{a\pi} \sum_{n=1}^{\infty} \left(\frac{1}{n} \sin \frac{n\pi x}{l} \sin \frac{n\pi a t}{l} \int_0^l f(\lambda) \sin \frac{n\pi \lambda}{l} \, d\lambda \right).$$

Hint: The schedule of conditions here is:

(a) $y = 0$, when $t = 0$;

(b) $\dfrac{\partial y}{\partial t} = f(x)$, when $t = 0$;

(c) $y = 0$, when $x = 0$;

(d) $y = 0$, when $x = l$.

Observe that

$$y = A \sin \frac{n\pi x}{l} \sin \frac{n\pi a t}{l}$$

satisfies conditions (a), (c), and (d), and build up a solution by forming

$$y = \sum_{n=1}^{\infty} A_n \sin \frac{n\pi x}{l} \sin \frac{n\pi at}{l}$$

and utilizing condition (b).

3. Show that the solution of the equation of a vibrating string of length l, satisfying the initial conditions

$$y = f(x), \quad \text{when } t = 0, \quad \text{and} \quad \frac{\partial y}{\partial t} = g(x), \quad \text{when } t = 0,$$

is

$$y = \sum_{n=1}^{\infty} a_n \sin \frac{n\pi x}{l} \cos \frac{n\pi at}{l} + \sum_{n=1}^{\infty} b_n \sin \frac{n\pi x}{l} \sin \frac{n\pi at}{l},$$

where

$$a_n = \frac{2}{l} \int_0^l f(x) \sin \frac{n\pi x}{l} \, dx$$

and

$$b_n = \frac{2}{n\pi a} \int_0^l g(x) \sin \frac{n\pi x}{l} \, dx.$$

4. The differential equation of a vibrating string that is viscously damped is

$$\frac{\partial^2 y}{\partial t^2} = a^2 \frac{\partial^2 y}{\partial x^2} - 2b \frac{\partial y}{\partial t}.$$

Show that the solution of this equation, when the initial velocity is zero, has the form

$$y = \sum_{n=0}^{\infty} a_n e^{-bt} \left[\sin \frac{n\pi x}{l} \left(\cos \alpha_n t + \frac{b}{\alpha_n} \sin \alpha_n t \right) \right],$$

where

$$\alpha_n{}^2 = \frac{n^2 \pi^2 a^2}{l^2} - b^2 \quad \text{and} \quad a_n = \frac{2}{l} \int_0^l f(x) \sin \frac{n\pi x}{l} \, dx.$$

5. Show that the differential equation of the transverse vibrations of an elastic rod carrying a load of $p(x)$ lb. per unit length is

$$EI \frac{\partial^4 y}{\partial x^4} = p(x) - m \frac{\partial^2 y}{\partial t^2},$$

where E is the modulus of elasticity, I is the moment of inertia of the cross-sectional area of the rod about a horizontal transverse axis through the center of gravity, and m is the mass per unit length.

Hint: For small deflections the bending moment M about a horizontal transverse axis at a distance x from the end of the rod is given by the Euler formula $M = EI \, d^2y/dx^2$, and the shearing load $p(x)$ is given by $d^2M/dx^2 = p(x)$.

6. Show that the small longitudinal vibrations of a long rod satisfy the differential equation

$$\frac{\partial^2 u}{\partial t^2} = \frac{E}{\rho}\frac{\partial^2 u}{\partial x^2},$$

where u is the displacement of a point originally at a distance x from the end of the rod, E is the modulus of elasticity, and ρ is the density.

Hint: From the definition of Young's modulus E, the force on a cross-sectional area q at a distance x units from the end of the rod is $Eq(\partial u/\partial x)_x$, for $\partial u/\partial x$ is the extension per unit length. On the other hand, the force on an element of the rod of length Δx is $\rho q\,\Delta x\,\partial^2 u/\partial t^2$.

7. If the rod of Prob. 6 is made of steel for which $E = 22 \cdot 10^8$ g. per square centimeter and whose specific gravity is 7.8, show that the velocity of propagation of sound in steel is nearly $5.3 \cdot 10^5$ cm. per second, which is about 16 times as great as the velocity of sound in air. Note that the c.g.s. system E must be expressed in dynes per square centimeter.

110. Heat Conduction.   Consider the slab cut from a body τ by two parallel planes Δs units apart, and suppose that the temperature of one of the planes is u and that of the second plane is $u + \Delta u$. It is known from the results of experiments that heat will flow from the plane at the higher temperature to that at the lower and that the amount of heat flowing across the slab, per unit area of the plane per second, is approximately given by

$$(110\text{-}1) \qquad\qquad k\frac{\Delta u}{\Delta s},$$

where k is a constant called the thermal conductivity* of the substance. If the distance Δs between the planes is decreased, then the limit of (110-1),

$$\lim_{\Delta s\to 0} k\frac{\Delta u}{\Delta s} = k\frac{\partial u}{\partial s},$$

gives the quantity of heat flowing per second per unit area of the surface whose normal is directed along s, and the quantity $\partial u/\partial s$ gives the rate of change of temperature in the direction of increasing s.

Now suppose that the initial temperature of such a body is given by

$$u = f(x,\,y,\,z),$$

and that it is required to find the temperature of the body at

* The dimensions of k in the c.g.s. system are cal./(cm.-sec. °C.).

some later instant t. It is known* that the function u, which gives the temperature at any later time t, must satisfy the partial differential equation

$$(110\text{-}2) \qquad \frac{\partial u}{\partial t} = \frac{k}{c\rho}\left(\frac{\partial^2 u}{\partial x^2} + \frac{\partial^2 u}{\partial y^2} + \frac{\partial^2 u}{\partial z^2}\right),$$

where c is the specific heat of the substance, ρ is the density of the body, and k is the conductivity.† Equation (110-2) is derived on the assumption that k, c, and ρ remain independent of the temperature u, whereas in reality they are not constant but vary slowly with the temperature. Moreover, this equation is not true if there is any heat generated within the body.‡ This equation must be solved subject to certain boundary conditions.

Thus, if the body is coated with some substance which makes it impervious to heat so that there is no heat flow across the surface of the body, then, if the direction of the exterior normal to the body is denoted by n, this boundary condition can be expressed mathematically as

$$k\frac{\partial u}{\partial n} = 0 \qquad \text{or} \qquad \frac{\partial u}{\partial n} = 0.$$

On the other hand, if the surface of the body radiates heat according to Newton's law of cooling,§ then

$$k\frac{\partial u}{\partial n} = e(u - u_0),$$

where u_0 is the temperature of the surrounding medium and e is a constant called the emissivity of the surface. It can be shown‖ that, if the initial and surface conditions are specified, then the problem of determining the temperature at any later time t has only one solution.

It should be observed that if the flow of heat is steady, so that the temperature u is independent of the time t, then $\partial u/\partial t = 0$

---

* See derivation of this equation in Sec. 130.

† The dimensions of c and ρ are, respectively, in calories per gram per degree centigrade and grams per cubic centimeter. The constant $k/c\rho = \alpha^2$ sq. cm. per second is frequently called the *diffusivity*.

‡ See Sec. 130.

§ See Problem 2, Sec. 73.

‖ For detailed treatment see Carslaw, "Introduction to the Mathematical Theory of the Conduction of Heat in Solids."

and (110-2) reduces to

(110-3) $$\frac{\partial^2 u}{\partial x^2} + \frac{\partial^2 u}{\partial y^2} + \frac{\partial^2 u}{\partial z^2} = 0.$$

This is known as Laplace's equation, and it occurs frequently in a large variety of physical problems.

It may be remarked that the problems of diffusion and the drying of porous solids are governed by an equation similar to (110-2), so that many problems on diffusion and heat conduction are mathematically indistinguishable.

111. Steady Heat Flow. Consider a large rectangular plate of width d, one face of which is kept at temperature $u = u_1$, whereas the other face is kept at temperature $u = u_2$. If one face of the plate is placed so as to coincide with the yz-plane (Fig. 96), the surface conditions can be expressed mathematically as

(111-1) $$\begin{cases} u = u_1 & \text{when } x = 0, \\ u = u_2 & \text{when } x = d, \end{cases}$$

and the temperature u must satisfy Eq. (110-3). In this formulation of the problem, it is assumed that the plate extends indefinitely in the y- and z-directions, a condition that is approximated by the large rectangular plate if the attention is restricted to the middle of the plate. With these assumptions, it is clear that the temperature u is independent of the y- and z-coordinates and that (110-3) reduces to

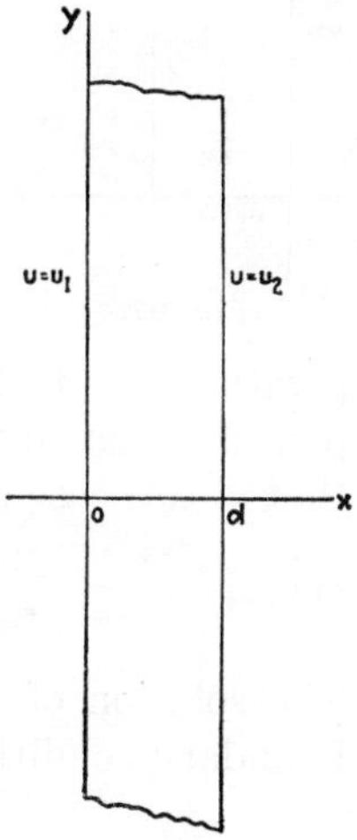

Fig. 96.

(111-2) $$\frac{\partial^2 u}{\partial x^2} = 0,$$

which is to be solved subject to the conditions (111-1).

The solution of (111-2) is easily found to be

(111-3) $$u = c_1 x + c_2,$$

where c_1 and c_2 are arbitrary constants which must be determined so that (111-3) satisfies (111-1). Substituting $x = 0$ and $x = d$ in (111-3) gives $u_1 = c_2$ and $u_2 = c_1 d + c_2$, so that

$$u = \frac{u_2 - u_1}{d} x + u_1$$

gives the solution of the problem. Recalling that the amount
of heat flowing per second per unit area of the plate is

$$k \frac{\partial u}{\partial x} = k \frac{u_2 - u_1}{d},$$

it is seen that the amount of heat flowing in t sec. over the area
A is given by

$$Q = \frac{k}{d} (u_2 - u_1)tA.$$

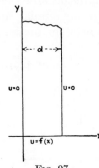

FIG. 97.

These results can be anticipated from physical
considerations.

A more difficult problem will be solved next.
Suppose that a "semi-infinite" rectangular plate
(that is, the plate extends indefinitely in the
positive direction of the y-axis), of thickness d,
has its faces kept at the constant temperature
$u = 0$, whereas its base $y = 0$ is kept at temperature $u = f(x)$ (Fig. 97). It is clear physically that the temperature u at any point of the plate will be independent of z, so
that in this case (110-3) becomes

(111-4)
$$\frac{\partial^2 u}{\partial x^2} + \frac{\partial^2 u}{\partial y^2} = 0.$$

The solution of (111-4) must be so chosen that it satisfies the
boundary conditions:

(111-5)
$$\begin{cases} u = 0 & \text{when } x = 0, \\ u = 0 & \text{when } x = d, \\ u = f(x) & \text{when } y = 0, \\ u = 0 & \text{when } y = \infty. \end{cases}$$

The last condition results from the observation that the temperature decreases as the point is chosen farther and farther from
the x-axis.

In order to solve (111-4), recourse is had to a scheme that
often succeeds in physical problems. Assume that it is possible
to express the solution of (111-4) as the product of two functions,
one of which is a function of x alone and the other a function of y
alone. Then,

(111-6)
$$u = X(x)Y(y).$$

Substitution of (111-6) in (111-4) and simplification **give**

$$(111\text{-}7) \qquad \frac{1}{X}\frac{d^2X}{dx^2} = -\frac{1}{Y}\frac{d^2Y}{dy^2}.$$

It will be observed that the left member of (111-7) is a function of x alone, whereas the right member is a function of y alone. Since x and y are independent variables, Eq. (111-7) can be true only if each member is equal to some constant, say $-a^2$. Hence, (111-7) can be written as

$$\frac{1}{X}\frac{d^2X}{dx^2} = -a^2 \qquad \text{and} \qquad \frac{1}{Y}\frac{d^2Y}{dy^2} = a^2$$

or

$$\frac{d^2X}{dx^2} + a^2X = 0 \qquad \text{and} \qquad \frac{d^2Y}{dy^2} - a^2Y = 0.$$

The linearly independent solutions* of these equations are

$$X = \sin ax,$$
$$X = \cos ax,$$
$$Y = e^{ay},$$
$$Y = e^{-ay},$$

and, since $u = XY$, the possible choices for u are

$$u = \begin{cases} e^{ay}\cos ax, \\ e^{ay}\sin ax, \\ e^{-ay}\cos ax, \\ e^{-ay}\sin ax. \end{cases}$$

The first two of these particular solutions for u obviously do not satisfy the last one of the boundary conditions (111-5). The third particular solution $e^{-ay}\cos ax$ does not satisfy the first of the conditions (111-5). But if u is chosen as $e^{-ay}\sin ax$, then $u = 0$ when $x = 0$ and $u = 0$ when $y = \infty$; and if a is chosen as $n\pi/d$, where n is an integer, then

$$(111\text{-}8) \qquad u = e^{-\frac{n\pi}{d}y}\sin\frac{n\pi x}{d}$$

satisfies all the conditions (111-5), except $u = f(x)$ when $y = 0$. It will satisfy this condition also if $f(x) = \sin\dfrac{n\pi x}{d}$.

Inasmuch as Eq. (111-4) is linear, any constant times a solution (111-8) will be a solution, and the sum of any number of such

* See Sec. 95.

solutions will be a solution. Hence,

$$(111\text{-}9) \qquad u = \sum_{n=1}^{\infty} a_n e^{-\frac{n\pi y}{d}} \sin \frac{n\pi x}{d}$$

is a formal solution. When $y = 0$, (111-9) becomes

$$u = \sum_{n=1}^{\infty} a_n \sin \frac{n\pi x}{d},$$

which must reduce to $f(x)$. But, in Sec. 20, it was shown that the constants a_n can be chosen so that the function is represented by a series of sines. Therefore, if

$$a_n = \frac{2}{d} \int_0^d f(x) \sin \frac{n\pi x}{d} \, dx,$$

then (111-9) will satisfy all the boundary conditions of the problem and hence it is the required solution.

Illustration. In the preceding problem suppose that $f(x) = 1$ and $d = \pi$. Then

$$a_n = \frac{2}{\pi} \int_0^\pi \sin nx \, dx,$$

and the solution (111-9) is easily found to be

$$u = \frac{4}{\pi} \left(e^{-y} \sin x + \frac{1}{3} e^{-3y} \sin 3x + \frac{1}{5} e^{-5y} \sin 5x + \cdots \right).$$

PROBLEMS

1. Using the result of the illustration just above, compute the temperatures at the following points: $(\pi/2, 1)$, $(\pi/3, 2)$, $(\pi/4, 10)$.

2. Obtain the solution of the problem treated in Sec. 109 by assuming that y can be expressed as the product of a function of x alone by a function of t alone and following the arguments of Sec. 111.

3. Compute the loss of heat per day per square meter of a large concrete wall whose thickness is 25 cm., if one face is kept at 0°C. and the other at 30°C. Use $k = 0.002$.

4. A refrigerator door is 10 cm. thick and has the outside dimensions 60 cm. × 100 cm. If the temperature inside the refrigerator is −10°C. and outside is 20°C. and if $k = 0.0002$, find the gain of heat per day across the door by assuming the flow of heat to be of the same nature as that across an infinite plate.

5. A semi-infinite plate 10 cm. in thickness has its faces kept at 0°C. and its base kept at 100°C. What is the steady-state temperature at any point of the plate?

112. Variable Heat Flow. Consider a rod of small uniform cross section and of length l. It will be assumed that the surface of the rod is impervious to heat and that the ends of the rod are kept at the constant temperature $u = 0°C$. At a certain time $t = 0$, the distribution of temperature along the rod is given by $u = f(x)$. The problem is to find the temperature at any point x of the rod at any later time t.

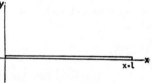

Fig. 98.

In this case the temperature u is a function of the distance along the rod and the time t, so that, if the rod (Fig. 98) is placed so as to coincide with the x-axis, (110-2) becomes

$$(112\text{-}1) \qquad \frac{\partial u}{\partial t} = \alpha^2 \frac{\partial^2 u}{\partial x^2},$$

where $\alpha^2 = k/c\rho$ is the diffusivity. In addition to satisfying (112-1) the solution u must satisfy the boundary conditions

$$(112\text{-}2) \qquad \begin{cases} u = 0 & \text{when } x = 0 \\ u = 0 & \text{when } x = l \\ u = f(x) & \text{when } t = 0. \end{cases} \text{ for all values of } t,$$

As in Sec. 111, assume that a solution of (112-1) is given by the product of two functions, one a function of x alone and the other a function of t alone. Then,

$$u = X(x)T(t),$$

and the substitution of this expression in (112-1) gives, after simplification,

$$\frac{1}{\alpha^2 T} \frac{dT}{dt} = \frac{1}{X} \frac{d^2 X}{dx^2}.$$

This equation can hold only if each member of it is equal to some constant, say $-\beta^2$. There result

$$\frac{dT}{dt} + \alpha^2 \beta^2 T = 0 \qquad \text{and} \qquad \frac{d^2 X}{dx^2} + \beta^2 X = 0.$$

The linearly independent solutions of these ordinary differential equations are readily found to be

$$T = e^{-\alpha^2 \beta^2 t},$$
$$X = \cos \beta x,$$
$$X = \sin \beta x.$$

Then, since by hypothesis $u = TX$, the possible choices for u are

$$u = e^{-\alpha^2 \beta^2 t} \cos \beta x,$$
$$u = e^{-\alpha^2 \beta^2 t} \sin \beta x.$$

The first particular solution does not satisfy the first one of the conditions (112-2). If β is chosen as $n\pi/l$, where n is an integer, then

(112-3)
$$u = e^{-\alpha^2 \left(\frac{n\pi}{l}\right)^2 t} \sin \frac{n\pi}{l} x$$

satisfies the first two conditions of (112-2) but not the last one.

The sum of solutions of the type (112-3), each multiplied by a constant, will be a solution of (112-1), since the equation is linear, so that

(112-4)
$$u = \sum_{n=1}^{\infty} a_n e^{-\alpha^2 \left(\frac{n\pi}{l}\right)^2 t} \sin \frac{n\pi}{l} x$$

is a solution. For $t = 0$, (112-4) reduces to

$$\sum_{n=1}^{\infty} a_n \sin \frac{n\pi}{l} x,$$

which can be made equal to $f(x)$, provided that

$$a_n = \frac{2}{l} \int_0^l f(x) \sin \frac{n\pi x}{l} dx.$$

Then,

(112-5)
$$u = \sum_{n=1}^{\infty} \left[\frac{2}{l} \int_0^l f(x) \sin \frac{n\pi x}{l} dx \right] e^{-\alpha^2 \left(\frac{n\pi}{l}\right)^2 t} \sin \frac{n\pi x}{l}$$

satisfies all the conditions of the problem and is therefore the required formal solution.

Next, consider an infinite slab of thickness l, whose faces are kept at temperature zero and whose temperature in the interior at the time $t = 0$ is given by $u = f(x)$. It is clear that the solution of this problem is independent of y and z, so that u satisfies the differential equation

$$\frac{\partial u}{\partial t} = \alpha^2 \frac{\partial^2 u}{\partial x^2}.$$

The boundary and initial conditions are

$$\begin{aligned} u &= 0 & \text{when } x = 0 \\ u &= 0 & \text{when } x = l \end{aligned} \Big\} \text{ for all } t,$$
$$u = f(x) \quad \text{when } t = 0$$

The mathematical formulation of this problem is identical with that of the preceding one, and therefore the solution of the problem is given by (112-5).

The solutions of other important problems on heat flow are outlined in detail in Probs. 5 and 6 at the end of this section.

PROBLEMS

1. Suppose that in the first problem of Sec. 112 the ends of the rod are impervious to heat, instead of being kept at zero temperature. The formulation of the problem in such a case is

$$\frac{\partial u}{\partial t} = \alpha^2 \frac{\partial^2 u}{\partial x^2},$$

$$\left. \begin{array}{ll} \dfrac{\partial u}{\partial x} = 0 & \text{when } x = 0 \\[2mm] \dfrac{\partial u}{\partial x} = 0 & \text{when } x = l \end{array} \right\} \text{ for all values of } t,$$

$$u = f(x) \quad \text{when } t = 0.$$

Show that the solution in this case is

$$u = \frac{a_0}{2} + \sum_{n=1}^{\infty} a_n e^{-\alpha^2 \left(\frac{\pi n}{l}\right)^2 t} \cos \frac{n\pi x}{l},$$

where

$$a_n = \frac{2}{l} \int_0^l f(x) \cos \frac{n\pi x}{l}\, dx.$$

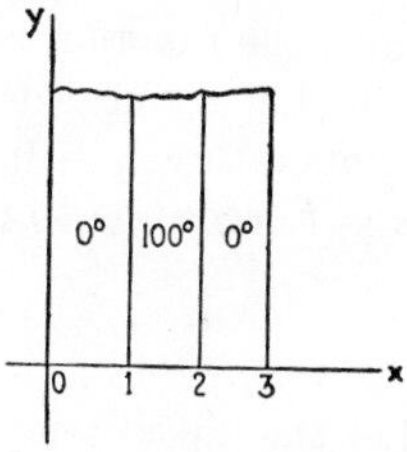

2. A large rectangular iron plate (Fig. 99) is heated throughout to 100°C. and is placed in contact with and between two like plates each at 0°C. The outer faces of these outside plates are maintained at 0°C. Find the temperature of the inner faces of the two plates and the temperature at the midpoint of the inner slab 10 sec. after the plates have been put together. Given: $\alpha = 0.2$ c.g.s. unit.

FIG. 99.

Hint: The boundary conditions are

$$\left. \begin{array}{ll} u = 0 & \text{when } x = 0 \\ u = 0 & \text{when } x = 3 \\ u = f(x) & \text{when } t = 0, \end{array} \right\} \text{for all } t,$$

where $f(x)$ is 0   when $0 < x < 1$,

$f(x)$ is 100 when $1 < x < 2$,

$f(x)$ is 0   when $2 < x < 3$.

Hence,

$$\int_0^3 f(x) \sin \frac{n\pi x}{3}\, dx = \int_1^2 100 \sin \frac{n\pi x}{3}\, dx.$$

3. An insulated metal rod 1 m. long has its ends kept at 0°C., and its initial temperature is 50°C. What is the temperature in the middle of the rod at any subsequent time? Use $k = 1.02$, $c = 0.06$, and $\rho = 9.6$.

4. The faces of an infinite slab 10 cm. thick are kept at temp. 0°C. If the initial temperature of the slab is 100°C., what is the state of temperature at any subsequent time?

5. Let the rod of Prob. 3 have one of its ends kept at 0°C. and the other at 10°C. If the initial temperature of the rod is 50°C., find the temperature of the rod at any later time.

Hint: Let the ends of the rod be at $x = 0$ and $x = 100$; then the conditions to be satisfied by the temperature function $u(x, t)$ are as follows: $u(0, t) = 0$, $u(100, t) = 10$, $u(x, 0) = 50$. Denote the solution of Prob. 3 by $v(x, t)$; then if the function $w(x, t)$ satisfies the conditions

$$\frac{\partial w}{\partial t} = \alpha^2 \frac{\partial^2 w}{\partial x^2}, \qquad w(0, t) = 0, \qquad w(100, t) = 10, \qquad w(x, 0) = 0,$$

$u(x, t) = v(x, t) + w(x, t)$ will be the solution of the problem. Assume the solution $w(x, t)$ in the form $w(x, t) = x/10 + \varphi(x, t)$, and determine the function $\varphi(x, t)$.

6. Let a rod of length l have one of its ends $x = 0$ maintained at a temperature $u = 0$, while the heat is dissipated from the other end $x = l$ according to the law

$$\left.\frac{\partial u}{\partial x}\right|_{x=l} = -hu(l, t).$$

Let the initial temperature be $u(x, 0) = f(x)$, where $f(x)$ is a prescribed function. Choose a particular solution of (112-1) in the form

$$e^{-\alpha^2\beta^2 t} \sin \beta x,$$

and show that the boundary conditions demand that

$$\beta \cos \beta l = -h \sin \beta l.$$

Write this transcendental equation in the form

$$\tan \beta l = -\frac{\beta}{h},$$

and show that it has infinitely many positive real roots $\beta_1, \beta_2, \cdots$. Hence, if

$$u(x, 0) = f(x) = \sum_{n=1}^{\infty} A_n \sin \beta_n x,$$

then the solution has the form

$$u(x, t) = \sum_{n=1}^{\infty} A_n e^{-\alpha^2\beta_n^2 t} \sin \beta_n x.$$

The functions $\sin \beta_n x$, $(n = 1, 2, \cdot \cdot \cdot)$, are easily shown to be orthogonal in the interval $(0, l)$, so that the coefficients A_n in the solution are given by the formula

$$A_n = \frac{\int_0^l f(x) \sin \beta_n x \, dx}{\int_0^l \sin^2 \beta_n x \, dx}.$$

113. Vibration of a Membrane. Consider an elastic membrane, of surface density ρ, which is under uniform tension T. By definition the tension is said to be uniform if the force exerted across a line of unit length in the plane of the membrane is independent of the orientation of the line. It will be assumed

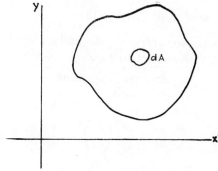

Fig. 100.

that the plane of the membrane coincides with the xy-plane of the rectangular coordinate system and that the displacement of any point of the membrane in the direction normal to the xy-plane is denoted by z. Then a consideration of the forces acting upon the element dA of the membrane (Fig. 100) leads to the equation

$$(113\text{-}1) \qquad \frac{\partial^2 z}{\partial t^2} = c^2 \left(\frac{\partial^2 z}{\partial x^2} + \frac{\partial^2 z}{\partial y^2} \right),$$

where $c^2 = T/\rho$. The analysis leading to (113-1) is quite similar to that used in deriving Eq. (108-2) for the vibrating string; and, just as in Sec. 108, the underlying assumption here is that the displacement z is not too great.

The solution of the problem of a vibrating membrane consists of determining the function $z = f(x, y, t)$, which satisfies the differential equation (113-1) as well as the boundary and initial conditions characteristic of the particular physical problem under consideration. These remarks will be illustrated by a brief treatment of the case in which the membrane is circular. In this case the shape of the membrane suggests the use of the cylindrical coordinate system in preference to the rectangular system. As will be seen presently, the choice of cylindrical coordinates is made because the boundary conditions assume particularly simple forms in these coordinates.

The transformation of (113-1) can be accomplished readily with the aid of the relations* connecting cylindrical coordinates with rectangular, namely,

$$x = r \cos \theta, \qquad y = r \sin \theta, \qquad z = z$$

or

$$r = \sqrt{x^2 + y^2}, \qquad \theta = \tan^{-1}\frac{y}{x}, \qquad z = z.$$

It will be necessary to express $\partial^2 z/\partial x^2$ and $\partial^2 z/\partial y^2$ in terms of the derivatives of z with respect to r and θ. Now†

$$\frac{\partial z}{\partial x} = \frac{\partial z}{\partial r}\frac{\partial r}{\partial x} + \frac{\partial z}{\partial \theta}\frac{\partial \theta}{\partial x}$$

and

$$\frac{\partial^2 z}{\partial x^2} = \frac{\partial^2 z}{\partial r^2}\left(\frac{\partial r}{\partial x}\right)^2 + \frac{\partial^2 r}{\partial x^2}\frac{\partial z}{\partial r} + \frac{\partial^2 z}{\partial \theta^2}\left(\frac{\partial \theta}{\partial x}\right)^2 + \frac{\partial^2 \theta}{\partial x^2}\frac{\partial z}{\partial \theta} + 2\frac{\partial^2 z}{\partial r\,\partial \theta}\frac{\partial r}{\partial x}\frac{\partial \theta}{\partial x}.$$

But

$$\frac{\partial r}{\partial x} = \frac{x}{\sqrt{x^2 + y^2}} = \cos \theta, \qquad \frac{\partial \theta}{\partial x} = -\frac{y}{x^2 + y^2} = -\frac{\sin \theta}{r},$$

$$\frac{\partial^2 r}{\partial x^2} = \frac{y^2}{(x^2 + y^2)^{3/2}} = \frac{\sin^2 \theta}{r}, \qquad \frac{\partial^2 \theta}{\partial x^2} = \frac{2xy}{(x^2 + y^2)^2} = \frac{2 \sin \theta \cos \theta}{r^2}.$$

Substituting these values in the expression for $\partial^2 z/\partial x^2$ gives

$$\frac{\partial^2 z}{\partial x^2} = \frac{\partial^2 z}{\partial r^2}\cos^2 \theta + \frac{\partial z}{\partial r}\frac{\sin^2 \theta}{r} + \frac{\partial^2 z}{\partial \theta^2}\frac{\sin^2 \theta}{r^2} + \frac{\partial z}{\partial \theta}\frac{2 \sin \theta \cos \theta}{r^2}$$
$$+ 2\frac{\partial^2 z}{\partial r\,\partial \theta}\frac{(-\cos \theta \sin \theta)}{r}.$$

Similarly,

$$\frac{\partial^2 z}{\partial y^2} = \frac{\partial^2 z}{\partial r^2}\sin^2 \theta + \frac{\partial z}{\partial r}\frac{\cos^2 \theta}{r} + \frac{\partial^2 z}{\partial \theta^2}\frac{\cos^2 \theta}{r^2} + \frac{\partial z}{\partial \theta}\frac{(-2 \sin \theta \cos \theta)}{r^2}$$
$$+ 2\frac{\partial^2 z}{\partial r\,\partial \theta}\left(\frac{\sin \theta \cos \theta}{r}\right),$$

* See Sec. 56.
† See Sec. 39.

so that

$$\frac{\partial^2 z}{\partial x^2} + \frac{\partial^2 z}{\partial y^2} = \frac{\partial^2 z}{\partial r^2} + \frac{1}{r}\frac{\partial z}{\partial r} + \frac{1}{r^2}\frac{\partial^2 z}{\partial \theta^2}$$

and (113-1) can be written as

$$(113\text{-}2) \qquad \frac{\partial^2 z}{\partial t^2} = c^2 \left(\frac{\partial^2 z}{\partial r^2} + \frac{1}{r}\frac{\partial z}{\partial r} + \frac{1}{r^2}\frac{\partial^2 z}{\partial \theta^2} \right).$$

It was remarked in Sec. 104 that the solution of such an equation contains two arbitrary functions, and in order to make the problem definite it is necessary to know the initial and boundary conditions. Thus, suppose that the membrane is of radius a and is fastened at the edges. Then it is evident that the solution of (113-2),

$$z = F(r, \theta, t),$$

must satisfy the condition $z = 0$ when $r = a$, for all values of t.

If, moreover, the membrane is distorted initially into some surface whose equation is a function of the radius only (that is, the initial distortion is independent of θ), say $z = f(r)$ when $t = 0$, then it is clear that the subsequent motion will preserve the circular symmetry and that the solution will be a function of r and t only. These conditions alone are not sufficient for the unique determination of the function

$$z = F(r, t),$$

and it is necessary to specify the initial velocity of the membrane in order to make the problem perfectly definite. If the membrane is distorted and thereafter released from rest, then

$$\frac{\partial z}{\partial t} = 0 \qquad \text{when } t = 0.$$

Since the solution is assumed to be independent of θ, (113-2) becomes

$$(113\text{-}3) \qquad \frac{\partial^2 z}{\partial t^2} = c^2 \left(\frac{\partial^2 z}{\partial r^2} + \frac{1}{r}\frac{\partial z}{\partial r} \right)$$

and its solution satisfying the boundary and initial conditions

$$(113\text{-}4) \qquad \begin{cases} z = 0 & \text{when } r = a, \\ z = f(r) & \text{when } t = 0, \\ \dfrac{\partial z}{\partial t} = 0 & \text{when } t = 0 \end{cases}$$

will be obtained by a method similar to that used in Sec. 111.

Assume that it is possible to express the solution of (113-3) as the product of two functions, one of which is a function of r alone whereas the other is a function of t alone. Then,

$$z = F(r, t) \equiv R(r)T(t).$$

Substitution of this relation in (113-3) leads to

$$R \frac{d^2T}{dt^2} = c^2 T \left(\frac{d^2R}{dr^2} + \frac{1}{r} \frac{dR}{dr} \right)$$

or

(113-5) $$\frac{1}{T} \frac{d^2T}{dt^2} = c^2 \left(\frac{1}{R} \frac{d^2R}{dr^2} + \frac{1}{rR} \frac{dR}{dr} \right).$$

Since the left-hand member of (113-5) is, by hypothesis, a function of t alone, whereas the right-hand member is a function of r alone, each member must be equal to some constant, say $-\omega^2$. Hence, (113-5) can be written as

(113-6) $$\frac{d^2T}{dt^2} + \omega^2 T = 0$$

and

(113-7) $$\frac{d^2R}{dr^2} + \frac{1}{r} \frac{dR}{dr} + k^2 R = 0,$$

where $k \equiv \omega/c$.

Equation (113-6) is the familiar equation of simple harmonic motion, and Eq. (113-7) is easily reducible to the Bessel equation by the substitution $x = kr$. Thus, if $x = kr$,

$$\frac{dR}{dx} = \frac{dR}{dr} \frac{dr}{dx} = \frac{1}{k} \frac{dR}{dr},$$

$$\frac{d^2R}{dx^2} = \frac{d}{dx} \left(\frac{1}{k} \frac{dR}{dr} \right) = \frac{1}{k} \frac{d^2R}{dr^2} \frac{dr}{dx} = \frac{1}{k^2} \frac{d^2R}{dr^2},$$

so that (113-7) assumes the form

$$\frac{d^2R}{dx^2} + \frac{1}{x} \frac{dR}{dx} + R = 0,$$

which possesses the solution (see Sec. 100)

$$R = J_0(x) = J_0(kr).$$

Therefore,

$$z = RT = J_0(kr) \sin \omega t$$

or

$$z = J_0(kr) \cos \omega t.$$

Since the last of the boundary conditions (113-4) requires

$$\frac{\partial z}{\partial t} = 0 \qquad \text{when } t = 0,$$

it is necessary to reject the solution involving sin ωt. Furthermore, the first of these conditions demands that

$$z = 0 \qquad \text{when } r = a,$$

so that

$$z = J_0(ka) \cos \omega t = 0$$

for all values of t. This condition will be satisfied if the arbitrary constant k is so chosen that $J_0(ka) = 0$. In other words, ka

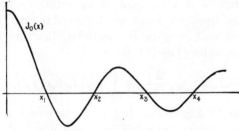

Fig. 101.

must be a root of the Bessel function of order zero (Fig. 101); and if the nth root of $J_0(kr)$ is denoted by

$$x_n = k_n a,$$

then

$$k_n = \frac{x_n}{a}.$$

Since $k = \omega/c$, it follows that

$$\omega = k_n c.$$

Hence, a solution of (113-3) that satisfies two of the boundary conditions (113-4) is given by

$$J_0(k_n r) \cos k_n c t.$$

The sum of any number of such solutions, each multiplied by an arbitrary constant, will be a solution, so that

$$(113\text{-}8) \qquad z = \sum_{n=1}^{\infty} A_n J_0(k_n r) \cos k_n c t$$

will be a formal solution of (113-3).

But when $t = 0$, the second of the boundary conditions demands that $z = f(r)$. Since (113-8) becomes, for $t = 0$,

$$(113\text{-}9) \qquad z = \sum_{n=1}^{\infty} A_n J_0(k_n r),$$

it follows that, if it is possible to choose the coefficients in the series (113-9) so as to make

$$(113\text{-}10) \qquad \sum_{n=1}^{\infty} A_n J_0(k_n r) \equiv f(r),$$

then (113-7) will be the required formal solution of (113-3) which satisfies all the conditions (113-4).

The problem of development of an arbitrary function in a series of Bessel functions has been discussed in Sec. 101, where it was indicated that a suitably restricted function $f(r)$ can be expanded in a series (113-10), where

$$A_n = \frac{2}{a^2 [J_1(k_n a)]^2} \int_0^a f(r) J_0(k_n r) \, r \, dr.$$

114. Laplace's Equation. Let it be required to determine the permanent temperatures within a solid sphere of radius unity when one half of the surface of the sphere is kept at the constant temperature 0°C. and the other half is kept at the constant temperature 1°C.

From the discussion of Sec. 110, it is evident that the temperature u within the sphere must satisfy Laplace's equation

$$\frac{\partial^2 u}{\partial x^2} + \frac{\partial^2 u}{\partial y^2} + \frac{\partial^2 u}{\partial z^2} = 0.$$

The symmetry of the region within which the temperature is sought suggests the use of spherical coordinates. If Laplace's equation is transformed with the aid of the relations* (Fig. 102)

$$x = r \sin \theta \cos \varphi,$$
$$y = r \sin \theta \sin \varphi,$$
$$z = r \cos \theta,$$

in a manner similar to that employed in Sec. 113, the equation becomes

$$(114\text{-}1) \quad r \frac{\partial^2 (ru)}{\partial r^2} + \frac{1}{\sin \theta} \frac{\partial}{\partial \theta} \left(\sin \theta \frac{\partial u}{\partial \theta} \right) + \frac{1}{\sin^2 \theta} \frac{\partial^2 u}{\partial \varphi^2} = 0.$$

* See Sec. 56.

It is necessary to seek a solution of this equation that will satisfy the initial conditions.

If the plane separating the unequally heated hemispheres is chosen so that it coincides with the xy-plane of the coordinate system and if the center of the sphere is taken as the origin, then it appears from symmetry that it is necessary to find the temperatures only for that portion of the sphere which lies to the right of the xz-plane (see Fig. 102). Moreover, it is clear that the temperatures will be independent of φ, so that (114-1) becomes

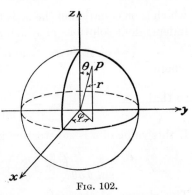

FIG. 102.

$$(114\text{-}2) \qquad r \frac{\partial^2(ru)}{\partial r^2} + \frac{1}{\sin \theta} \frac{\partial}{\partial \theta} \left(\sin \theta \frac{\partial u}{\partial \theta} \right) = 0.$$

The solution of (114-2) must be chosen so as to satisfy the boundary conditions

$$(114\text{-}3) \qquad \begin{cases} u = 1 & \text{for } 0 < \theta < \dfrac{\pi}{2} \text{ when } r = 1, \\[2mm] u = 0 & \text{for } \dfrac{\pi}{2} < \theta < \pi \text{ when } r = 1. \end{cases}$$

In order to solve (114-2), assume that the solution

$$u = F(r, \theta)$$

is expressible as the product of two functions, one of which is independent of θ and the other independent of r. Thus, let

$$u = R(r)\Theta(\theta).$$

The substitution of this expression in (114-2) leads to the two ordinary differential equations

$$r \frac{d^2(rR)}{dr^2} - \alpha^2 R = 0$$

and

$$(114\text{-}4) \qquad \frac{1}{\sin \theta} \frac{d}{d\theta} \left(\sin \theta \frac{d\Theta}{d\theta} \right) + \alpha^2 \Theta = 0,$$

where α^2 is an arbitrary constant.

The first of these equations can be expanded to read

$$r^2 \frac{d^2R}{dr^2} + 2r \frac{dR}{dr} - \alpha^2 R = 0,$$

which is an equation of the type treated in Sec. 97 and the linearly independent solutions of which are

$$R = r^m \qquad \text{and} \qquad R = 1/r^{m+1},$$

where

$$m = -\tfrac{1}{2} + \sqrt{\alpha^2 + \tfrac{1}{4}},$$

so that

$$\alpha^2 = m(m + 1).$$

If this value of α is substituted in (114-4), this equation becomes

$$\frac{1}{\sin \theta} \frac{d}{d\theta} \left(\sin \theta \frac{d\Theta}{d\theta} \right) + m(m + 1)\Theta = 0.$$

The change of the independent variable θ to x by means of $x = \cos \theta$ leads to Legendre's equation

$$(1 - x^2) \frac{d^2\Theta}{dx^2} - 2x \frac{d\Theta}{dx} + m(m + 1)\Theta = 0.$$

If m is an integer, particular solutions of this equation are the Legendre polynomials

$$P_m(x) = P_m(\cos \theta),$$

and hence the particular solutions of (114-2) are

$$u = r^m P_m(\cos \theta),$$
$$u = \frac{P_m(\cos \theta)}{r^{m+1}}.$$

The second of these solutions evidently cannot be used, for it becomes infinite when $r \to 0$. Therefore, it will be necessary to build up the expression for the temperature u within the sphere from terms of the type $r^m P_m(\cos \theta)$, where m is a positive integer.

Consider the infinite series

(114-5) $$u = \sum_{m=0}^{\infty} A_m r^m P_m(\cos \theta),$$

each term of which satisfies (114-2). When $r = 1$, (114-5) becomes

$$u = \sum_{m=0}^{\infty} A_m P_m(\cos \theta)$$

and, if it is possible to choose the undetermined constants A_m in such a way that (114-5) satisfies the boundary conditions (114-3), then (114-5) will be the desired solution of the problem. Now, it was indicated in Sec. 102 that a suitably restricted function

$$y = F(x)$$

can be expanded in the interval $(-1, 1)$ in a series of Legendre polynomials in the form

$$F(x) = \sum_{m=0}^{\infty} a_m P_m(x),$$

where the coefficients a_m are given by

$$(114\text{-}6) \qquad a_m = \frac{2m+1}{2} \int_{-1}^{1} F(x) P_m(x) \, dx.$$

In the problem under consideration,

$$u = f(\theta) = 1 \qquad \text{for } 0 < \theta < \frac{\pi}{2},$$

$$u = f(\theta) = 0 \qquad \text{for } \frac{\pi}{2} < \theta < \pi,$$

so that the problem is equivalent to expanding $F(x)$ as

$$F(x) = \sum_{m=0}^{\infty} A_m P_m(x),$$

where $F(x) = 0$ for $-1 < x < 0$, and $F(x) = 1$ for $0 < x < 1$.

If formula (114-6) is used, it is readily found that the solution of (114-2), which satisfies the initial conditions (114-3), is

$$u = \frac{1}{2} + \frac{3}{4} r P_1(\cos \theta) - \frac{1}{2} \cdot \frac{7}{8} r^3 P_3(\cos \theta)$$

$$+ \frac{1}{2} \cdot \frac{3}{4} \cdot \frac{11}{12} r^5 P_5(\cos \theta) - \cdots .$$

PROBLEMS

1. Find the steady-state temperature in a circular plate of radius a which has one half of its circumference at 0°C. and the other half at 100°C.

Hint: Use Laplace's equation for the plane in polar coordinates,

$$\frac{\partial^2 u}{\partial r^2} + \frac{1}{r} \frac{\partial u}{\partial r} + \frac{1}{r^2} \frac{\partial^2 u}{\partial \theta^2} = 0,$$

and assume that $u = R(r)\Theta(\theta)$ as in Sec. 114. Hence, show that the physically possible solution is of the form

$$u = a_0 + a_1 r \cos \theta + a_2 r^2 \cos 2\theta + a_3 r^3 \cos 3\theta + \cdots$$
$$+ b_1 r \sin \theta + b_2 r^2 \sin 2\theta + b_3 r^3 \sin 3\theta + \cdots.$$

Determine the coefficients a_i and b_i so as to satisfy the boundary conditions.

2. Show that Laplace's equation in cylindrical coordinates is

$$\frac{\partial^2 u}{\partial r^2} + \frac{1}{r} \frac{\partial u}{\partial r} + \frac{1}{r^2} \frac{\partial^2 u}{\partial \varphi^2} + \frac{\partial^2 u}{\partial z^2} = 0$$

and in spherical coordinates is

$$\frac{\partial}{\partial r}\left(r^2 \frac{\partial u}{\partial r}\right) + \frac{1}{\sin \theta} \frac{\partial}{\partial \theta}\left(\sin \theta \frac{\partial u}{\partial \theta}\right) + \frac{1}{\sin^2 \theta} \frac{\partial^2 u}{\partial \varphi^2} = 0.$$

3. Find the steady-state temperature at any point of a semicircular plate of radius a, if the bounding diameter of the plate is kept at the temperature 0°C. and the circumference is kept at the temperature 100°C.

Hint: Use Laplace's equation for the plane in polar coordinates, namely,

$$\frac{\partial^2 u}{\partial r^2} + \frac{1}{r} \frac{\partial u}{\partial r} + \frac{1}{r^2} \frac{\partial^2 u}{\partial \theta^2} = 0.$$

4. Outline the solution of the problem of the distribution of temperature in a long cylinder whose surface is kept at the constant temperature zero and whose initial temperature in the interior is unity.

115. Flow of Electricity in a Cable.   A simple problem of determining the distribution of current and voltage in an elec-

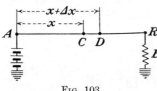

FIG. 103.

trical circuit, whose linear dimensions are so small that one can disregard the variation of the e.m.f. along the circuit, has been discussed in Secs. 90 and 91. This section is concerned with the more complicated problem of the flow of electricity in linear conductors (such as telephone wires or submarine cables) in which the current may leak to earth.

Let a long imperfectly insulated cable (Fig. 103) carry an electric current whose source is at A.   The current is assumed to flow to the receiving end at R through the load B and to return through the ground.   It is assumed that the leaks occur along the entire length of the cable because of imperfections in the insulating sheath.   Let the distance, measured along the length of the cable, be denoted by x; then both voltage and current will depend not only on the time t, but also on the distance x. Accordingly, the e.m.f. V (volts) and the current I (amperes) are functions of x and t. The resistance of the cable will be denoted by R (ohms per mile) and the conductance from sheath to ground by G (mhos per mile). It is known that the cable acts as an electrostatic condenser, and the capacitance of the cable to ground per unit length is assumed to be C (farads per mile); the inductance per mile will be denoted by L (henrys per mile).

Consider an element CD of the cable of length Δx. If the e.m.f. is V at C and $V + \Delta V$ at D, then the change in voltage across the element Δx is produced by the resistance and the inductance drops, so that one can write

$$\Delta V = - \left(IR\,\Delta x + \frac{\partial I}{\partial t} L\,\Delta x \right).$$

The negative sign signifies that the voltage is a decreasing function of x. Dividing through by Δx and passing to the limit as $\Delta x \to 0$ gives the equation for the voltage,

$$(115\text{-}1) \qquad \frac{\partial V}{\partial x} = -IR - L\frac{\partial I}{\partial t}.$$

The decrease in current, on the other hand, is due to the leakage and the action of the cable as a condenser. Hence, the drop in current, ΔI, across the element Δx of the cable is

$$\Delta I = -VG\,\Delta x - \frac{\partial V}{\partial t} C\,\Delta x.$$

so that

$$(115\text{-}2) \qquad \frac{\partial I}{\partial x} = -VG - C\frac{\partial V}{\partial t}.$$

Equations (115-1) and (115-2) are simultaneous partial differential equations for the voltage and current. The voltage V can be eliminated from these equations by differentiating (115-2) with respect to x to obtain

$$\frac{\partial^2 I}{\partial x^2} = -\frac{\partial V}{\partial x} G - C\frac{\partial^2 V}{\partial x\,\partial t}.$$

Substituting for $\partial V/\partial x$ from (115-1) gives

$$\frac{\partial^2 I}{\partial x^2} = IRG + LG\frac{\partial I}{\partial t} - C\frac{\partial^2 V}{\partial x\,\partial t},$$

from which $\partial^2 V/\partial x\,\partial t$ can be eliminated by using the expression for $\partial^2 V/\partial t\,\partial x$ obtained from the differentiation of (115-1). Thus, one is led to

$$(115\text{-}3)\quad \frac{\partial^2 I}{\partial x^2} - LC\frac{\partial^2 I}{\partial t^2} - (LG + RC)\frac{\partial I}{\partial t} - RGI = 0.$$

A similar calculation yields the equation for V, namely,

$$(115\text{-}4)\quad \frac{\partial^2 V}{\partial x^2} - LC\frac{\partial^2 V}{\partial t^2} - (LG + RC)\frac{\partial V}{\partial t} - RGV = 0,$$

which is identical in structure with (115-3).

In general, it is impossible to neglect the capacitance C of the cable in practical applications of these equations to problems in telephony and telegraphy, but the leakage G and the inductance L, normally, are quite small. Neglecting the leakage and inductance effects yields the following equations:

$$(115\text{-}5)\qquad \frac{\partial V}{\partial x} = -IR,$$

$$(115\text{-}6)\qquad \frac{\partial I}{\partial x} = -C\frac{\partial V}{\partial t},$$

$$(115\text{-}7)\qquad \frac{\partial^2 I}{\partial x^2} = RC\frac{\partial I}{\partial t},$$

$$(115\text{-}8)\qquad \frac{\partial^2 V}{\partial x^2} = RC\frac{\partial V}{\partial t}.$$

It is clear from (115-7) and (115-8) that the propagation of voltage and current, in this case, is identical with the flow of heat in rods.

In order to give an indication of the use of these equations, consider a line l miles in length, and let the voltage at the source A, under steady-state conditions, be 12 volts and at the receiving end R be 6 volts. At a certain instant $t = 0$, the receiving end is grounded, so that its potential is reduced to zero, but the potential at the source is maintained at its constant value of 12 volts. The problem is to determine the current and voltage in the line subsequent to the grounding of the receiving end.

It follows that one must solve Eq. (115-8) subject to the following boundary conditions:

$$V = 12, \quad \text{at } x = 0 \text{ for all } t \geq 0,$$
$$V = 0, \quad \text{at } x = l \text{ for all } t \geq 0.$$

In addition, it is necessary to specify the initial condition that describes the distribution of voltage in the line at the time $t = 0$. Now, prior to the grounding of the line, the voltage V is a function of x alone, so that (115-8) gives

$$\frac{d^2V}{dx^2} = 0,$$

the solution of which is

$$V = c_1 x + c_2.$$

Since, prior to grounding, $V = 12$ at $x = 0$ and $V = 6$ at $x = l$, it follows that $c_1 = -6/l$ and $c_2 = 12$, so that

$$V = -\frac{6x}{l} + 12 \qquad \text{at } t = 0.$$

Accordingly, it is necessary to find the solution of Eq. (115-8) subject to the following initial and boundary conditions:

$$(115\text{-}9) \qquad \begin{cases} V(0, t) = 12, \qquad V(l, t) = 0, \\ V(x, 0) = -\dfrac{6}{l} x + 12. \end{cases}$$

A reference to Sec. 112 shows that the mathematical formulation of this problem is similar to that of the problem of heat flow in a rod, except for the difference in the formulation of the end conditions.* Now, the voltage $V(x, t)$ in the line, subsequent to the grounding, can be thought of as being made up of a steady-state distribution $V_S(x)$ and the transient voltage $V_T(x, t)$, which decreases rapidly with the time. Thus,

$$V(x, t) \equiv V_S(x) + V_T(x, t).$$

After the line has been grounded, the voltage at the ends of the line must satisfy the following conditions:

$$V(0, t) = 12 \qquad \text{and} \qquad V(l, t) = 0.$$

It was noted above that the steady-state distribution of voltage is a linear function of x; and since after the lapse of some time t the transient effects will not be felt, it follows that

$$V_S(x) = -\frac{12}{l} x + 12.$$

* See, however, Prob. 5, Sec. 112.

Thus,

$$(115\text{-}10) \qquad V(x, t) = -\frac{12}{l} x + 12 + V_T(x, t).$$

The boundary conditions to be satisfied by the transient voltage $V_T(x, t)$ can now be determined from (115-9). Thus,

$$V(0, t) = 12 = 12 + V_T(0, t),$$
$$V(l, t) = 0 = V_T(l, t),$$
$$V(x, 0) = -\frac{6x}{l} + 12 = -\frac{12x}{l} + 12 + V_T(x, 0).$$

Hence, the function $V_T(x, t)$ satisfies the following initial and boundary conditions:

$$V_T(0, t) = V_T(l, t) = 0,$$
$$V_T(x, 0) = \frac{6x}{l}.$$

Since it is obvious from (115-10) that $V_T(x, t)$ satisfies (115-8), it becomes clear that the determination of the transient voltage $V_T(x, t)$ is identical with the problem of determining the distribution of the temperature in a rod when the initial distribution is the linear function $6x/l$. Referring to the solution (112-5) and setting $\alpha^2 = 1/(RC)$ give

$$V_T(x, t) = \sum_{n=1}^{\infty} \left(\frac{2}{l} \int_0^l \frac{6}{l} x \sin \frac{n\pi x}{l} \, dx \right) e^{-\frac{1}{RC}\left(\frac{n\pi}{l}\right)^2 t} \sin \frac{n\pi x}{l}.$$

Therefore, the problem of determining the distribution of voltage is solved.

The magnitude of the current in the line is obtained from (115-5). It is left as an exercise for the reader to calculate the expression for the current I. It is easy to see that the term-by-term differentiation of the series for $V_T(x, t)$ is valid for all values of $t > 0$.

From the discussion of this problem, it is clear that the determination of the temperature of a rod whose ends are kept at different fixed temperatures and whose initial temperature is a function of the distance along the rod can be effected in a similar way.

PROBLEMS

1. On the assumption that the length l of the line in Sec. 115 is 120 miles, $R = 0.1$ ohm per mile, and $C = 2 \cdot 10^{-8}$ farad per mile, find the

current in the line. Note particularly the behavior of the solution at $t = 0$. How do you account for this behavior?

2. Find the e.m.f. in the cable whose length is 100 miles and whose characteristics are as follows: $R = 0.3$ ohm per mile, $C = 0.08$ microfarad per mile, $L = 0$, $G = 0$. If the voltage at the source is 6 volts and at the terminal end 2 volts, what is the voltage after the terminal end has been suddenly grounded?

3. A rod 1 m. long has one of its ends kept at the constant temperature 0°C. and the other at 100°C. If the initial temperature of the rod is 50°C., what is the temperature at any later instant? The diffusivity α^2 is 0.04.

4. A glass rod 10 cm. long has one end kept at the temperature 0°C. and the other at 20°C. until temperatures indistinguishable from steady-state are reached. At a later time the temperature of the cooler end is raised suddenly to 10°C., and that of the warmer end is kept unchanged. What is the state of the temperature in the rod? Use $\alpha^2 = 0.057$.

5. Solve Prob. 4 if the rod is made of silver ($\alpha^2 = 1.74$).

6. A silver rod 1 m. long, having thermal conductivity $k = 1.04$ cal. per centimeter per degree per second, specific heat $c = 0.056$ cal. per gram per degree, and density $\rho = 10.6$ g. per centimeter, is kept at a temperature of 0°C. throughout. If the temperatures of its ends are suddenly raised to 100°C., what is the temperature of the rod at any later time t?

7. Find the current in a cable 1000 miles long, whose potential at the source, under steady-state conditions, is 1200 volts and at the terminal end is 1100 volts. What is the current in the cable after the terminal end has been suddenly grounded? Use $R = 2$ ohms per mile and $C = 3 \cdot 10^{-7}$ farad per mile.

CHAPTER IX

VECTOR ANALYSIS

The student who has had an elementary course in physics or mechanics undoubtedly has been impressed by the unnatural procedure of decomposing directed quantities such as force and velocity into their cartesian components along the coordinate axes, subjecting these components to some analytical transformations, and, then, in the final analysis, forming a picture of the effect of the magnitude by studying the effects produced by its components. It must have occurred to him that it ought to be possible to treat such a quantity as force, which is independent of coordinate systems, without the artificial process of referring it to an arbitrarily chosen set of coordinate axes. The present chapter answers some questions of this type and gives a brief development of the analytical shorthand known as the vector analysis.

116. Scalars and Vectors. Some measurable quantities appearing in the study of physical phenomena can be completely specified by their magnitude alone. Thus, the mass of a body can be described adequately by a single number, say the number of grams, the temperature by degrees on some scale, the volume by the number of cubic units, etc. A quantity that (after a suitable choice of the units of measure) can be completely characterized by a single number is called a *scalar*. There are also quantities, called *vectors*, that require for their complete characterization the specification of the direction as well as the magnitude. As a typical example of a vector quantity, one can take the displacement of translation of a particle. If a particle is displaced in a straight line from a position P to a new position P' (Fig. 104), then the change in position can be represented graphically by the directed line segment $\overrightarrow{PP'}$, whose length PP' equals the amount of the displacement and whose direction is from P to P'. Moreover, a force, of magnitude K dynes, that is

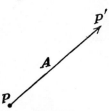

Fig. 104.

directed northeast can be represented by a line segment whose length is K units and whose direction coincides with that of the force.

The initial point P, of a directed line segment representing a vector, is called the origin. In a great many problems the location of the origin of a vector is immaterial, and this chapter, for the most part, will deal with such problems. Accordingly, a vector quantity will be represented by a directed line segment whose origin can be chosen at will. From this graphical mode of representing vectors, it is clear that two vectors are regarded as equal if the lengths of the line segments representing them are equal and if their directions are parallel.

In order to distinguish vectors from scalars, boldface type is used for vectors in this book. The magnitude of the vector **A** will be denoted either by $|\mathbf{A}|$ or simply by A. The equality of the vectors **A** and **B** will be denoted by the usual symbol, namely,

$$\mathbf{A} = \mathbf{B}.$$

If the magnitude A of the vector **A** is zero, then the vector is called a *zero* or a *null vector*. In this event the notion of the direction of the vector becomes meaningless.

117. Addition and Subtraction of Vectors. In formulating the laws of the fundamental operations of algebra for vector quantities, it is natural to be guided by the physical meaning of such operations. Thus, if the vector **A** represents a displacement of a particle, it is desirable to make the vector $-\mathbf{A}$ mean the displacement of the particle through a distance A in the direction opposite to that of **A**. Therefore, the vectors **A** and $-\mathbf{A}$ are equal in magnitude but opposite in direction. Again, if the particle is displaced from its initial posi-

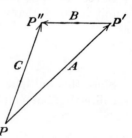

Fig. 105.

tion P to P', so that $\overrightarrow{PP'} = \mathbf{A}$, and subsequently it is displaced to a position P'' (Fig. 105), so that $\overrightarrow{P'P''} = \mathbf{B}$, then the displacement from the original position P to the final position P'' can be accomplished by the single displacement $\overrightarrow{PP''} = \mathbf{C}$. Thus, it is logical to write

$$\mathbf{A} + \mathbf{B} = \mathbf{C}.$$

This leads to the following definition of addition of two vectors: *If the initial point of the vector* **B** *is placed in coincidence with the terminal point of the vector* **A,** *then the vector* **C,** *which joins the initial point of* **A** *with the terminal point of* **B,** *is called the sum of* **A** *and* **B** *and is denoted by* $\mathbf{A} + \mathbf{B} = \mathbf{C}$. This is the familiar "parallelogram law of addition" used in physics, and its immediate extension to three or more vectors is obvious. Clearly, the commutative and associative laws hold for vector addition. Thus,

$$\mathbf{A} + \mathbf{B} = \mathbf{B} + \mathbf{A},$$
$$\mathbf{A} + (\mathbf{B} + \mathbf{C}) = (\mathbf{A} + \mathbf{B}) + \mathbf{C} = \mathbf{A} + \mathbf{B} + \mathbf{C}.$$

Subtraction of the vector **B** from the vector **A** is defined as the *addition of the negative vector* $-\mathbf{B}$ to **A.** Thus,

$$\mathbf{A} - \mathbf{B} \equiv \mathbf{A} + (-\mathbf{B});$$

and it follows that, if

$$\mathbf{A} + \mathbf{B} = 0,$$

then $\mathbf{A} = -\mathbf{B}$.

If n is a scalar, then $n\mathbf{A}$, or $\mathbf{A}n$, is defined as the vector **B** whose magnitude is $B = |n|A$ and whose direction is that of **A** if n is positive and is opposite to that of **A** if n is negative. If $n = 0$, then the product is also zero.

A vector whose magnitude is 1 is called a *unit vector*. Thus, a unit vector $\mathbf{a}_1$ that is directed along the vector **A** can be written as

$$\mathbf{a}_1 = \frac{\mathbf{A}}{A}.$$

Since the multiplication of a vector by a scalar does not alter the direction but simply multiplies the magnitude, it follows that

$$m(n\mathbf{A}) = (mn)\mathbf{A} = mn\mathbf{A}.$$

Also,

$$(n + m)\mathbf{A} = n\mathbf{A} + m\mathbf{A},$$

and

$$n(\mathbf{A} + \mathbf{B}) = n\mathbf{A} + n\mathbf{B}.$$

Thus, the rules governing the addition of vectors and the multiplication of vectors by scalars are identical with those of ordinary scalar algebra, and one is justified in using the algorithms of ordinary algebra in solving linear equations.

The equation of the line determined by the points A and B can be written down at once (Fig. 106).   Choose an arbitrary point O as the origin and let **a** represent the position vector locating A relative to O, and let **b** be the position vector locating B.   Then the vector $\overrightarrow{AB} = \mathbf{b} - \mathbf{a}$.   If P is any point of the line and is determined by the position vector **r**, then

$$\mathbf{r} = \overrightarrow{OA} + \overrightarrow{AP}$$
$$= \mathbf{a} + s(\mathbf{b} - \mathbf{a}),$$

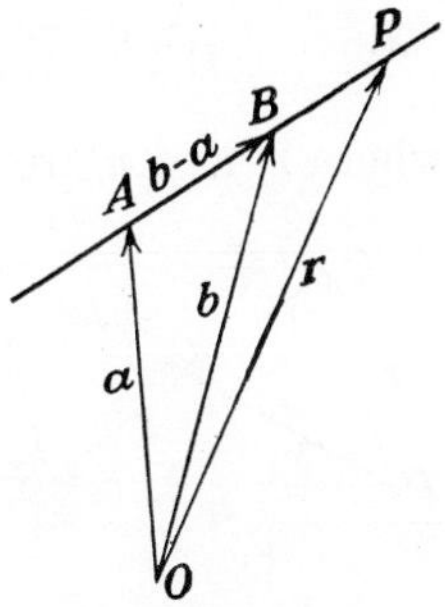

where s is a scalar number such that

$$s(\mathbf{b} - \mathbf{a}) = \overrightarrow{AP}.$$

Therefore,

$$\mathbf{r} = \mathbf{a} + s(\mathbf{b} - \mathbf{a})$$

is the equation of the straight line, where s is an arbitrary scalar parameter.   If $s = 0$,

Fig. 106.

$\mathbf{r} = \mathbf{a}$; if $s = 1$, $\mathbf{r} = \mathbf{b}$; for $s > 1$, the point P will lie on an extension of AB.

The proofs of many important geometrical theorems become surprisingly easy.   For example, let it be required to show that the diagonals of a parallelogram bisect each other.

Choose some point O as the origin, and locate the vertices of the parallelogram by position vectors, as shown in Fig. 107.

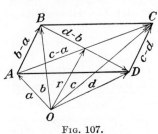

Let $\mathbf{r}_1$ be the position vector of the midpoint of AC; then, since $\overrightarrow{AC} = \mathbf{c} - \mathbf{a}$,

$$(117\text{-}1)\quad \mathbf{r}_1 = \mathbf{a} + \frac{1}{2}(\mathbf{c} - \mathbf{a}) = \frac{\mathbf{a} + \mathbf{c}}{2}.$$

Let $\mathbf{r}_2$ be the position vector of the midpoint of BD; then

Fig. 107.

$$(117\text{-}2)\quad \mathbf{r}_2 = \mathbf{b} + \frac{1}{2}(\mathbf{d} - \mathbf{b}) = \frac{\mathbf{b} + \mathbf{d}}{2}.$$

But since the figure is a parallelogram,

$$\mathbf{b} - \mathbf{a} = \mathbf{c} - \mathbf{d} \quad\text{or}\quad \mathbf{a} + \mathbf{c} = \mathbf{b} + \mathbf{d},$$

and it follows from (117-1) and (117-2) that $\mathbf{r}_1$ and $\mathbf{r}_2$ are equal and hence locate the same point.

Another proof of this theorem, although asymmetric in form, may be instructive.   Let D be the point of intersection of the diagonals of the parallelogram (Fig. 108), and choose the vertex P as the origin. Let

$$\overrightarrow{PS} = \mathbf{a} \qquad \text{and} \qquad \overrightarrow{PQ} = \mathbf{b};$$

then the diagonal $\overrightarrow{PR} = \mathbf{a} + \mathbf{b}$, and $\overrightarrow{QS} = \mathbf{a} - \mathbf{b}$. Now,

$$\overrightarrow{DS} = m(\mathbf{a} - \mathbf{b}) \qquad \text{and} \qquad \overrightarrow{PD} = n(\mathbf{a} + \mathbf{b}),$$

where m and n are certain scalars. But

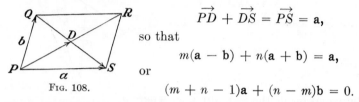

Fig. 108.

$$\overrightarrow{PD} + \overrightarrow{DS} = \overrightarrow{PS} = \mathbf{a},$$

so that

$$m(\mathbf{a} - \mathbf{b}) + n(\mathbf{a} + \mathbf{b}) = \mathbf{a},$$

or

$$(m + n - 1)\mathbf{a} + (n - m)\mathbf{b} = 0.$$

Since $\mathbf{a}$ and $\mathbf{b}$ are not collinear, this equation cannot be satisfied unless $m + n - 1 = 0$ and $n - m = 0$.   Therefore, $m = n = \frac{1}{2}$.

PROBLEMS

1. Show that the lines joining the midpoints of the opposite sides of a quadrilateral bisect each other.

2. Show that the medians of a triangle intersect in a point.

3. Show how to find the vectors **A** and **B** if their sum and their difference are known.

4. Discuss graphically the commutative and associative laws of addition of any three vectors.

5. Show that a line from a vertex of a parallelogram to the midpoint of a non-adjacent side trisects a diagonal.

6. Show that the equation of the plane determined by the three points A, B, and C, whose position vectors are $\mathbf{a}$, $\mathbf{b}$, and $\mathbf{c}$, respectively, is

$$\mathbf{r} = \mathbf{a} + s(\mathbf{b} - \mathbf{a}) + t(\mathbf{c} - \mathbf{a}).$$

7. Show that the bisectors of the angles of a triangle meet in a point.

Hint: Construct the unit vectors directed along the sides of the triangle; then, the resultant of the two unit vectors issuing from any vertex bisects the angle at that vertex.

118. Decomposition of Vectors. Base Vectors. It follows from the definition of the addition of vectors that any vector **A** lying in the plane of two non-collinear vectors **a** and **b** can be resolved into components directed along **a** and **b**. This resolution is accomplished by constructing the parallelogram whose sides are parallel to **a** and **b** (Fig. 109). Then one can write

$$\mathbf{A} = x\mathbf{a} + y\mathbf{b},$$

where x and y are the appropriate scalars.

If there are given three non-coplanar vectors **a**, **b**, and **c**, then any vector **v** can be expressed as

$$\mathbf{v} = x\mathbf{a} + y\mathbf{b} + z\mathbf{c},$$

where **v** is the diagonal of the parallelepiped whose edges are $x\mathbf{a}$, $y\mathbf{b}$, and $z\mathbf{c}$ (Fig. 110). The vectors **a**, **b**, and **c** are called the *base vectors*

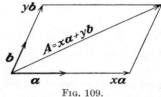

FIG. 109.

and the scalars x, y, and z the *measure numbers*. It is clear that, if the base vectors are known and the measure numbers are prescribed, then the vector **v** is uniquely determined, since there is only one way of constructing the diagonal of a parallelepiped whose edges are known. Thus, for the specification of a space vector one needs three scalar numbers.

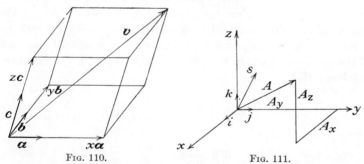

FIG. 110.   FIG. 111.

An important special case of the notion of base vectors is a system of three orthogonal unit vectors referred to a cartesian system of coordinate axes. Let **i**, **j**, **k** be the base vectors of unit length that are directed along the positive directions of the x-, y-, and z-axes, respectively (Fig. 111). It will be assumed henceforth that the system of axes is a right-handed system, that is, such that a right-hand screw directed along the positive z-axis will advance in the positive direction when it is rotated from the positive x-axis toward the positive y-axis through the smaller (90°) angle.

Any vector **A** can be represented uniquely in the form

$$A = A_x \mathbf{i} + A_y \mathbf{j} + A_z \mathbf{k},$$

where A_x, A_y, A_z are the coordinates of the terminal point of the vector **A**. Since the coordinates of the terminal point are A_x, A_y, A_z, the length A of the vector **A** is

$$A = \sqrt{A_x^2 + A_y^2 + A_z^2}.$$

The direction of the vector can be specified by the direction angles, that is, the angles which the vector makes with the coordinate axes. If the angles between **A** and the positive x-, y-, and z-axes are denoted by (A, x), (A, y), and (A, z), respectively, then

$$A_x = A \cos (A, x), \quad A_y = A \cos (A, y), \quad A_z = A \cos (A, z),$$

and, since $A = \sqrt{A_x^2 + A_y^2 + A_z^2}$,

(118-1) $\cos^2 (A, x) + \cos^2 (A, y) + \cos^2 (A, z) = 1.$

Thus, the direction angles are not independent and if any two of them are specified then the third must satisfy (118-1). The cosines of the direction angles are called the *direction cosines*.

Since the projection of **A** in any direction **s** is equal to the sum of the projections of the components of **A** in that same direction, it follows that

$$A_s = A \cos (A, s)$$
$$= A_x \cos (s, x) + A_y \cos (s, y) + A_z \cos (s, z).$$

Moreover,

$$\cos (A, x) = \frac{A_x}{A}, \quad \cos (A, y) = \frac{A_y}{A}, \quad \cos (A, z) = \frac{A_z}{A},$$

so that

$$\cos (A, s) = \cos (A, x) \cos (s, x) + \cos (A, y) \cos (s, y)$$
$$+ \cos (A, z) \cos (s, z),$$

which is the familiar formula for the cosine of the angle between the two directions specified by **A** and **s**. If **A** and **s** are orthogonal, then $\cos (A, s) = 0$.

PROBLEMS

1. Find the components of the vector $\mathbf{A} = 2\mathbf{i} - 3\mathbf{j} + 4\mathbf{k}$ in the direction of the two vectors whose direction angles are $70°$, $40°$, and $\gamma°$.

2. The vector whose magnitude is 10 units makes equal angles with the coordinate axes. Find A_x, A_y, A_z.

3. Find the direction and the magnitude of the vector whose components in the **i**, **j**, **k** system are 1, 3, 5, respectively.

4. If the vectors of lengths a, a, $\sqrt{a}$ are mutually orthogonal, what is the magnitude of their resultant and what are the angles between the direction of the resultant and the directions of the three vectors?

5. What is the cosine of the angle between the vectors

$$\mathbf{A} = 3\mathbf{i} + 4\mathbf{j} + \mathbf{k} \quad \text{and} \quad \mathbf{B} = \mathbf{i} - \mathbf{j} + \mathbf{k}?$$

119. Multiplication of Vectors. There are two kinds of multiplication used in vector analysis, *scalar* multiplication and *vector* multiplication. By the *scalar product* of two vectors **A** and **B** is meant the scalar quantity representing the product of the length of one of the vectors by the scalar projection of the other vector upon the first. The scalar product is sometimes called the *dot product* and is denoted by

$$(\mathbf{A}, \mathbf{B}) \quad \text{or} \quad \mathbf{A} \cdot \mathbf{B}.$$

It follows from the definition that

$$(\mathbf{A}, \mathbf{B}) = AB \cos (A, B).$$

Inasmuch as $\cos (A, B) = \cos (B, A)$, it is evident that

$$(\mathbf{A}, \mathbf{B}) = (\mathbf{B}, \mathbf{A}),$$

so that the commutative law holds for scalar products. If $(\mathbf{A}, \mathbf{B}) = 0$ and if **A** and **B** are both different from zero, then $\cos (A, B) = 0$, and the vectors **A** and **B** are orthogonal. Also $(\mathbf{A}, \mathbf{A}) = A^2$, since $\cos (A, A) = 1$. From the definition of the scalar product, it follows that the distributive law holds for scalar multiplication, that is

$$(\mathbf{A}, \mathbf{B} + \mathbf{C}) = (\mathbf{A}, \mathbf{B}) + (\mathbf{A}, \mathbf{C}).$$

Since the distributive law holds,

$$(119\text{-}1) \quad (\mathbf{A}, \mathbf{B}) \equiv (A_x\mathbf{i} + A_y\mathbf{j} + A_z\mathbf{k}, \ B_x\mathbf{i} + B_y\mathbf{j} + B_z\mathbf{k})$$
$$= A_xB_x + A_yB_y + A_zB_z.$$

This result is obtained by observing that

$$(\mathbf{i}, \mathbf{i}) = (\mathbf{j}, \mathbf{j}) = (\mathbf{k}, \mathbf{k}) = 1$$

and

$$(\mathbf{i}, \mathbf{j}) = (\mathbf{j}, \mathbf{i}) = (\mathbf{i}, \mathbf{k}) = (\mathbf{k}, \mathbf{i}) = (\mathbf{j}, \mathbf{k}) = (\mathbf{k}, \mathbf{j}) = 0.$$

Formula (119-1) is important in that it enables one to write down at once the scalar product of the two vectors whose cartesian components are

$$A_x, A_y, A_z \quad \text{and} \quad B_x, B_y, B_z.$$

The product obtained by the second kind of multiplication is called a *vector product* or a *cross product*. The vector product of **A** and **B** is a vector **C**, which is normal to the plane of the vectors **A** and **B** and so directed that the vectors **A**, **B**, **C** form a right-handed system. The absolute value or magnitude of **C** is equal to the product of the length of **A** by the length of **B** by the absolute value of the sine of the angle between them. The vector product of **A** and **B** is denoted by*

$$[\mathbf{A, B}] \quad \text{or} \quad \mathbf{A} \times \mathbf{B}.$$

Hence, if

$$[\mathbf{A, B}] = \mathbf{C},$$

then

$$C = AB \,|\sin (A, B)|.$$

Numerically, the value of C is equal to the area of the parallel-ogram constructed with **A** and **B** as sides (Fig. 112).

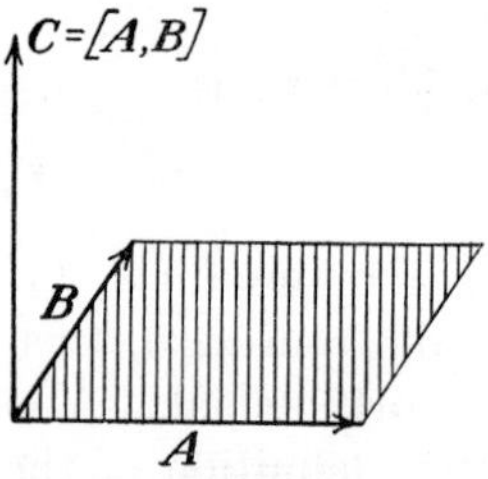

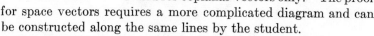

Since rotation from **B** to **A** is opposite to that from **A** to **B**, it is clear that

$$[\mathbf{A, B}] = -[\mathbf{B, A}],$$

so that the commutative law does not hold for vector products. The distributive law holds unrestrictedly, and this will be estab-

Fig. 112.

lished for coplanar vectors only. The proof for space vectors requires a more complicated diagram and can be constructed along the same lines by the student.

It is required to show that

$$[\mathbf{A + B, C}] \equiv [\mathbf{A, C}] + [\mathbf{B, C}].$$

This fact will be established by observing that $[\mathbf{A + B, C}]$ is a vector whose direction is normal to the plane of $\mathbf{A + B}$ and **C**, which is also the plane of **A**, **B**, and **C** inasmuch as **A**, **B**, and

---

* Since both notations are in common use, the reader is urged to rewrite all formulas of this and the succeeding sections with the aid of the dot and cross notation. It is important to acquire equal facility in reading both notations.

A + B are always coplanar. Each of the vectors **[A, C]** and **[B, C]** is perpendicular to the plane of **A, B,** and **C,** so that the direction of

$$[A, C] + [B, C]$$

is the same as that of

$$[A + B, C].$$

It remains to be shown that the magnitudes of the vectors are also equal, that is, to show that

$$\|[A + B, C]\| = \|[A, C]\| + \|[B, C]\|.$$

By definition the magnitude of a vector product is equal to the area of the parallelogram having the given vectors as sides. The parallelograms arising in this case have **C** as their common base, with the vectors **A + B, A,** and **B,** respectively, forming the second sides. Inasmuch as the parallelograms have a common base, they can be compared by comparing their altitudes $ps, rm,$ and $qn.$ From the geometry of Fig. 113 it is clear that

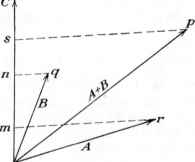

$$ps = rm + qn,$$

so that the magnitudes of the vectors in question are also equal.

Since the commutative law does not hold for vector prod-

Fɪɢ. 113.

ucts, care must be exercised not to permute the order of the vectors entering into vector products. The definitions of the vector product and the unit vectors **i, j, k** lead at once to the following formulas:

$$[i, i] = [j, j] = [k, k] = 0,$$
$$[i, j] = -[j, i] = k,$$
$$[j, k] = -[k, j] = i,$$
$$[k, i] = -[i, k] = j.$$

If the vectors **A** and **B** are given in terms of their cartesian components as

$$\mathbf{A} = A_x\mathbf{i} + A_y\mathbf{j} + A_z\mathbf{k} \quad \text{and} \quad \mathbf{B} = B_x\mathbf{i} + B_y\mathbf{j} + B_z\mathbf{k},$$

the application of the distributive law gives the following results:

$$[\mathbf{A}, \mathbf{B}] = [A_x\mathbf{i} + A_y\mathbf{j} + A_z\mathbf{k}, \ B_x\mathbf{i} + B_y\mathbf{j} + B_z\mathbf{k}]$$
$$= A_xB_x[\mathbf{i}, \mathbf{i}] + A_yB_x[\mathbf{j}, \mathbf{i}] + A_zB_x[\mathbf{k}, \mathbf{i}]$$
$$+ A_xB_y[\mathbf{i}, \mathbf{j}] + A_yB_y[\mathbf{j}, \mathbf{j}] + A_zB_y[\mathbf{k}, \mathbf{j}]$$
$$+ A_xB_z[\mathbf{i}, \mathbf{k}] + A_yB_z[\mathbf{j}, \mathbf{k}] + A_zB_z[\mathbf{k}, \mathbf{k}]$$
$$= (A_yB_z - A_zB_y)\mathbf{i} + (A_zB_x - A_xB_z)\mathbf{j}$$
$$+ (A_xB_y - A_yB_x)\mathbf{k}.$$

This result can be written conveniently in determinant form as

$$(119\text{-}2) \qquad [\mathbf{A}, \mathbf{B}] = \begin{vmatrix} \mathbf{i} & \mathbf{j} & \mathbf{k} \\ A_x & A_y & A_z \\ B_x & B_y & B_z \end{vmatrix}.$$

120. Relations between Scalar and Vector Products. There are two important vector relationships that occur frequently in vector analysis, and their proofs will be indicated in this section. These identities are

$$(120\text{-}1) \qquad (\mathbf{A}, [\mathbf{B}, \mathbf{C}]) \equiv (\mathbf{B}, [\mathbf{C}, \mathbf{A}]) \equiv (\mathbf{C}, [\mathbf{A}, \mathbf{B}])$$

and

$$(120\text{-}2) \qquad [\mathbf{A}, [\mathbf{B}, \mathbf{C}]] \equiv \mathbf{B}(\mathbf{A}, \mathbf{C}) - \mathbf{C}(\mathbf{A}, \mathbf{B}).$$

The proof of the first of these relations follows at once from geometric considerations. The vector product $[\mathbf{B}, \mathbf{C}]$ is numerically equal to the area of the parallelogram formed by the vectors $\mathbf{B}$ and $\mathbf{C}$, and the direction of this vector product is normal to the plane of $\mathbf{B}$ and $\mathbf{C}$. Thus, $(\mathbf{A}, [\mathbf{B}, \mathbf{C}])$ is numerically equal to the volume of the parallelepiped formed on the three vectors $\mathbf{A}, \mathbf{B}, \mathbf{C}$. The two other scalar products can be interpreted similarly as being equal numerically to the volume of the same parallelepiped. It is easy to verify that in cartesian coordinates

$$(\mathbf{A}, [\mathbf{B}, \mathbf{C}]) = \begin{vmatrix} A_x & A_y & A_z \\ B_x & B_y & B_z \\ C_x & C_y & C_z \end{vmatrix}.$$

The correctness of (120-2) can be established easily with the aid of (119-2). Observe that

$$[\mathbf{A}, [\mathbf{B}, \mathbf{C}]] = [\mathbf{A}, \mathbf{i}(B_yC_z - B_zC_y) + \mathbf{j}(B_zC_x - B_xC_z)$$
$$+ \mathbf{k}(B_xC_y - B_yC_x)]$$
$$= \mathbf{i}[A_y(B_xC_y - B_yC_x) - A_z(B_zC_x - B_xC_z)]$$
$$+ \mathbf{j}[A_z(B_yC_z - B_zC_y) - A_x(B_xC_y - B_yC_x)]$$
$$+ \mathbf{k}[A_x(B_zC_x - B_xC_z) - A_y(B_yC_z - B_zC_y)].$$

By adding and subtracting

$$iA_xB_xC_x + jA_yB_yC_y + kA_zB_zC_z,$$

the foregoing result can be written as

$$[A, [B, C]] = i[B_x(A_xC_x + A_yC_y + A_zC_z)$$
$$- C_x(A_xB_x + A_yB_y + A_zB_z)]$$
$$+ j[B_y(A_xC_x + A_yC_y + A_zC_z)$$
$$- C_y(A_xB_x + A_yB_y + A_zB_z)]$$
$$+ k[B_z(A_xC_x + A_yC_y + A_zC_z)$$
$$- C_z(A_xB_x + A_yB_y + A_zB_z)]$$
$$\equiv B(A, C) - C(A, B).$$

PROBLEMS

1. Prove that $(A, [A, B]) = (B, [A, B]) \equiv 0$.

2. Prove that $[[A, B], [C, D]] = C([A, B], D) - D([A, B], C)$.

3. Show that $([A, B], [C, D]) = (A, C)(B, D) - (A, D)(B, C)$.

4. With the aid of Prob. 2, show that

$$[[A, B], [A, C]] = A(A, [B, C]).$$

5. Given a vector whose initial point is at $(2, -4, 0)$ and whose terminal point is at $(5, 8, 4)$, write this vector in the form

$$iA_x + jA_y + kA_z.$$

6. Find the scalar and vector products of the vector of Prob. 5 with a unit vector that makes equal angles with the coordinate axes.

7. Rewrite the formulas of Sec. 119 in the dot and cross notation.

8. Show that the necessary and sufficient condition that the vectors **A, B,** and **C** be coplanar is that

$$(A, [B, C]) = 0.$$

9. Show that

$$[A, [B, C]] + [B, [C, A]] + [C, [A, B]] = 0.$$

10. Let the $X, Y. Z$ system of axes be rotated about the origin so as to occupy a new position X', Y', Z'. Let the unit vectors along the X-, Y-, Z-axes be **i, j, k,** respectively, and those along the X'-, Y'-, Z'-axes be **i', j', k',** respectively. If x, y, z are the components of the vector **A** referred to the X, Y, Z system and x', y', z' are the components of the same vector referred to the X', Y', Z' system, show that

$$x = x'(i, i') + y'(i, j') + z'(i, k'),$$
$$y = x'(j, i') + y'(j, j') + z'(j, k'),$$
$$z = x'(k, i') + y'(k, j') + z'(k, k')$$

and

$$x' = x(\mathbf{i}, \mathbf{i}') + y(\mathbf{j}, \mathbf{i}') + z(\mathbf{k}, \mathbf{i}'),$$
$$y' = x(\mathbf{i}, \mathbf{j}') + y(\mathbf{j}, \mathbf{j}') + z(\mathbf{k}, \mathbf{j}'),$$
$$z' = x(\mathbf{i}, \mathbf{k}') + y(\mathbf{j}, \mathbf{k}') + z(\mathbf{k}, \mathbf{k}').$$

These are the equations of transformation of rotation.

121. Applications of Scalar and Vector Products. The work done by a constant force $\mathbf{F}$ producing a displacement $\mathbf{s}$ in the direction of the force is defined as the product of the magnitude of $\mathbf{F}$ by the distance s. If the direction of the force makes an angle θ with the vector $\mathbf{s}$, denoting the displacement, then the work done by the force $\mathbf{F}$ is defined as

$$W \equiv F_s s = Fs \cos \theta,$$

where F_s is the component of $\mathbf{F}$ in the direction of $\mathbf{s}$. Thus, it is evident that W can be written in vector notation as

$$W = (\mathbf{F}, \mathbf{s}) \quad \text{or} \quad W = \mathbf{F} \cdot \mathbf{s}.$$

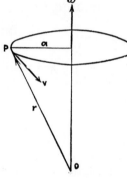

Fig. 114.

Two illustrations of the application of vector products will be chosen from dynamics. Let the vector $\boldsymbol{\omega}$ represent the angular velocity of a rotating body; that is, $\boldsymbol{\omega}$ is a vector whose magnitude is the angular speed in radians per second and whose direction is parallel to the axis of rotation. The positive sense of $\boldsymbol{\omega}$ is chosen as that in which a right-handed screw would advance if the screw were rotated in the same direction as the body. Let $\mathbf{r}$ be a vector locating any point P of the body relative to some point O. It is required to find the linear velocity $\mathbf{v}$ of the point P. If the distance of P from the axis of rotation is a, then (Fig. 114)

$$v = \omega a = \omega r \sin (r, \omega).$$

Moreover, $\mathbf{v}$ is normal to the plane of $\mathbf{r}$ and $\boldsymbol{\omega}$ and is so directed that $\boldsymbol{\omega}$, $\mathbf{r}$, and $\mathbf{v}$ form a right-handed system. Hence,

(121-1) $$\mathbf{v} = [\boldsymbol{\omega}, \mathbf{r}] \quad \text{or} \quad \mathbf{v} = \boldsymbol{\omega} \times \mathbf{r}.$$

If $\mathbf{v}$, $\boldsymbol{\omega}$, and $\mathbf{r}$ are expressed in terms of their cartesian components,

then

$$\mathbf{v} = \mathbf{i}v_x + \mathbf{j}v_y + \mathbf{k}v_z = \begin{vmatrix} \mathbf{i} & \mathbf{j} & \mathbf{k} \\ \omega_x & \omega_y & \omega_z \\ r_x & r_y & r_z \end{vmatrix},$$

so that

(121-2) $$\begin{cases} v_x = r_z\omega_y - r_y\omega_z, \\ v_y = r_x\omega_z - r_z\omega_x, \\ v_z = r_y\omega_x - r_x\omega_y. \end{cases}$$

These are the well-known expressions for the components of the linear velocity in terms of the components of the angular velocity. It must be observed that the single vector equation (121-1) is easier to remember and thus possesses a distinct advantage over the cumbersome set of cartesian equations (121-2).

Another example from dynamics will illustrate this compactness of the vector notation. Consider a rigid body τ, and let O be a fixed point in the body. Let the force $\mathbf{F}$ be applied at a point P, which is located by the vector $\mathbf{r}$, whose origin is at O. The force $\mathbf{F}$ establishes a torque, or moment of force, $\mathbf{T}$ which tends to rotate the body about an axis that passes through O and is normal to the plane of $\mathbf{r}$ and $\mathbf{F}$. The magnitude of $\mathbf{T}$ is given by

$$T = rF \left| \sin (r, F) \right|.$$

In addition, $\mathbf{r}$, $\mathbf{F}$, and $\mathbf{T}$ form a right-handed system, so that

$$\mathbf{T} = [\mathbf{r}, \mathbf{F}] \qquad \text{or} \qquad \mathbf{T} = \mathbf{r} \times \mathbf{F}.$$

It is clear from this formula that the torque does not change if the force is displaced along the line of action of the force.

If O is chosen as the origin of the cartesian coordinate system, then

$$\mathbf{r} = \mathbf{i}x + \mathbf{j}y + \mathbf{k}z$$

and

$$\mathbf{F} = \mathbf{i}X + \mathbf{j}Y + \mathbf{k}Z,$$

where X, Y, and Z are the rectangular components of $\mathbf{F}$. Hence

$$\mathbf{T} = \mathbf{i}T_x + \mathbf{j}T_y + \mathbf{k}T_z = \begin{vmatrix} \mathbf{i} & \mathbf{j} & \mathbf{k} \\ x & y & z \\ X & Y & Z \end{vmatrix},$$

and the cartesian components of the torque are given by

$$T_x = yZ - zY,$$
$$T_y = zX - xZ,$$
$$T_z = xY - yX.$$

122. Differential Operators. If in any region of space a function u is defined for every point of the region, then this region is called a *field*. It is assumed throughout the remainder of this chapter that the functions under consideration are single-valued, continuous functions, possessing continuous first space-derivatives in the regions under discussion. If the function u is a scalar point function, that is, if u is a function of the three variables x, y, z such that corresponding to every triplet of values x, y, z a scalar number u is defined, then the field is called a *scalar field*. Examples of such functions are the temperature and the electrostatic potential due to a charged body. If the function u is a vector point function, that is, a function that defines a vector at every point of the field, then the field is called a *vector field*. An example of a vector point function is the function representing the force at every point of the field under consideration.

It will be shown in this section that, with the aid of certain differential operators, it is possible to associate a vector field with each scalar field. This connection is of fundamental importance in many investigations in mathematical physics.

Let a scalar point function $u = f(x, y, z)$ be defined in a certain

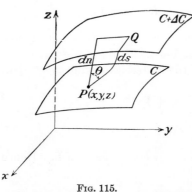

FIG. 115.

region of space, and consider those points of the field for which u has a fixed value C. The totality of points satisfying the equation $f(x, y, z) = C$ defines, in general, a surface. Such a surface is called a level surface, since at every point of the surface u has a constant value C. Let $f(x, y, z) = C$ and $f(x, y, z) = C + \Delta C$ define two neighboring level surfaces (Fig. 115). If one passes from the point $P(x, y, z)$ on the level surface C to some point Q on the surface $C + \Delta C$, the change in the value of u is ΔC. This change is entirely independent of the path PQ, but clearly the rate of increase of u per unit arc length PQ is not independent of the path. It is evident that the greatest rate of change of u will occur when the path PQ is chosen in the direction of the normal to the surface C. Hence, the maximum rate of change of u is

$$\lim_{\Delta n \to 0} \frac{\Delta u}{\Delta n} = \frac{du}{dn}.$$

It is seen from the figure that, if ds makes an angle θ with the direction of dn, then

$$ds = dn \sec \theta,$$

so that

$$\frac{du}{ds} = \frac{du}{dn} \cos \theta.$$

Let the unit vector directed along the arbitrarily chosen direction of the positive normal* to the surface be denoted by n_1, so that the vector

$$\frac{du}{dn} \, n_1$$

is a quantity which represents in magnitude and direction the greatest rate of increase of $u = f(x, y, z)$. This vector is called the *gradient* of u, and is denoted by grad u or by ∇u.† By definition

$$|\nabla u| \equiv |\text{grad } u| = \frac{du}{dn}.$$

On the other hand, the derivative of u in the direction s is

$$\frac{du}{ds} = \frac{\partial u}{\partial x}\frac{dx}{ds} + \frac{\partial u}{\partial y}\frac{dy}{ds} + \frac{\partial u}{\partial z}\frac{dz}{ds}$$

$$= \frac{\partial u}{\partial x} \cos (s, x) + \frac{\partial u}{\partial y} \cos (s, y) + \frac{\partial u}{\partial z} \cos (s, z).$$

Now, compare this equation with the component in the direction s of the vector $\mathbf{A} = \mathbf{i}A_x + \mathbf{j}A_y + \mathbf{k}A_z$ (see Sec. 118). This component is

$$A_s = A_x \cos (s, x) + A_y \cos (s, y) + A_z \cos (s, z),$$

which suggests that du/ds may be thought of as representing the

---

* If the surface is closed, then the direction of the exterior normal will be regarded as positive.

† The symbol ∇u is read "nabla u" or "del u."

component in the direction **s** of the vector

(122-1) $$\mathbf{i}\frac{\partial u}{\partial x} + \mathbf{j}\frac{\partial u}{\partial y} + \mathbf{k}\frac{\partial u}{\partial z}.$$

Inasmuch as the maximum component of any vector is in the direction of the vector itself, (122-1) represents the vector measuring the greatest rate of increase of u. Thus,

$$\nabla u = \mathbf{i}\frac{\partial u}{\partial x} + \mathbf{j}\frac{\partial u}{\partial y} + \mathbf{k}\frac{\partial u}{\partial z}$$

and

$$|\nabla u| = \sqrt{\left(\frac{\partial u}{\partial x}\right)^2 + \left(\frac{\partial u}{\partial y}\right)^2 + \left(\frac{\partial u}{\partial z}\right)^2}.$$

The symbol

$$\nabla \equiv \mathbf{i}\frac{\partial}{\partial x} + \mathbf{j}\frac{\partial}{\partial y} + \mathbf{k}\frac{\partial}{\partial z}$$

is of frequent occurrence in vector analysis and represents a vector differential operator somewhat similar to the differential operators studied in Chap. VII.

It should be borne in mind that the symbol ∇ does not itself represent a vector quantity. It is merely a symbol expressing the fact that certain operations of differentiation are to be performed on the scalar function which follows it. Thus, $\nabla(x^2yz)$ means

$$\mathbf{i}\frac{\partial(x^2yz)}{\partial x} + \mathbf{j}\frac{\partial(x^2yz)}{\partial y} + \mathbf{k}\frac{\partial(x^2yz)}{\partial z} = \mathbf{i}2xyz + \mathbf{j}x^2z + \mathbf{k}x^2y.$$

It will be observed that this result is a vector point function which was obtained from the scalar point function x^2yz. Hence, ∇u forms the vector field that is associated with the scalar field u.

As a physical example of an important scalar field, consider the gravitational potential Φ due to a concentrated mass m, namely,

$$\Phi = \frac{km}{r},$$

where r is the distance from the point (x, y, z) to the point of location of the mass. It was indicated in Sec. 66 that the components of force X, Y, and Z are given by $\partial\Phi/\partial x$, $\partial\Phi/\partial y$, and

$\partial\Phi/\partial z$, respectively, so that the resultant force is

$$\mathbf{F} = \mathbf{i}\,\frac{\partial\Phi}{\partial x} + \mathbf{j}\,\frac{\partial\Phi}{\partial y} + \mathbf{k}\,\frac{\partial\Phi}{\partial z}.$$

Therefore, the gravitational force is equal to the **gradient of the** gravitational potential.

PROBLEMS

1. Compute the component of a vector ∇u in the direction of a unit vector

$$\mathbf{s} = \mathbf{i}\,\frac{dx}{ds} + \mathbf{j}\,\frac{dy}{ds} + \mathbf{k}\,\frac{dz}{ds}.$$

Hint: $(\nabla u)_s = (\nabla u, \mathbf{s})$.

2. Find ∇u, if

(a) $u = xyz$;   (b) $u = x^2 + y^2 + z^2$;

(c) $u = (x^2 + y^2 + z^2)^{\frac{1}{2}}$;   (d) $u = \log(x^2 + y^2 + z^2)$;

(e) $u = (x^2 + y^2 + z^2)^{-\frac{1}{2}}$.

3. Show that

$$(\nabla u)^2 \equiv (\nabla u, \nabla u) = \left(\frac{\partial u}{\partial x}\right)^2 + \left(\frac{\partial u}{\partial y}\right)^2 + \left(\frac{\partial u}{\partial z}\right)^2.$$

4. If $\mathbf{ds} = \mathbf{i}\,dx + \mathbf{j}\,dy + \mathbf{k}\,dz$, show that

$$du = (\mathbf{ds}, \nabla u).$$

5. Compute the directional derivative at $(1, 2, 3)$ of $u = x^2 + y^2 + z^2$ in the direction of the line

$$\frac{x}{3} = \frac{y}{4} = \frac{z}{5}.$$

6. What is the greatest rate of increase of $u = xyz^2$ at $(1, 0, 3)$?

7. Show that

(a) $\nabla(u + v) = \nabla u + \nabla v$;

(b) $\operatorname{grad}(uv) = \nabla(uv) = u\nabla v + v\nabla u$.

123. Vector Fields. A definition of the line integral and a number of important theorems concerning such integrals were given in Chap. VI. This section will reestablish, with the aid of the vector differential operators, some of the results that were obtained in Chap. VI. A different interpretation of these results will be found in this and succeeding sections of this chapter.

Consider a region of space in which a vector **A** is defined. If P_0 and P are any two points of the region, which are joined by a continuous curve C (Fig. 116), then a vector $\mathbf{A}$ is defined at every point of C. Choose $n - 1$ points P_i, which divide the curve into n segments Δs_i, and form the sum

(123-1)
$$\sum_{i=0}^{n-1} (\mathbf{A}_i, \Delta\mathbf{C}_i),$$

where $\mathbf{A}_i$ is the value of $\mathbf{A}$ at $P_i(x, y, z)$, and $\Delta\mathbf{C}_i$ is the vector whose rectangular components are Δx_i, Δy_i, Δz_i and which joins P_{i-1} and P_i. Each term of the sum represents the product of the component of $\mathbf{A}$ in the direction ΔC_i by ΔC_i. If the sum (123-1) approaches a definite limit when the number of points of

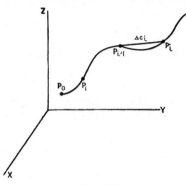

division is increased indefinitely so that $\Delta\mathbf{C}_i \to 0$, then this limit is defined as the line integral $\int_C A_s\, ds$ along the curve C. Thus

$$\lim_{n \to \infty} \sum_{i=0}^{n-1} (\mathbf{A}_i, \Delta\mathbf{C}_i) \equiv \int_C A_s\, ds.$$

A reference to Sec. 60 will suffice to establish the fact that this definition is equivalent to the one previously given.

Fig. 116.

In general, the value of this integral will depend upon the path C joining the end points P_0 and P. Now, suppose that the vector $\mathbf{A}$ is the gradient of some function u, that is,

$$\mathbf{A} = \nabla u \equiv \mathbf{i}\frac{\partial u}{\partial x} + \mathbf{j}\frac{\partial u}{\partial y} + \mathbf{k}\frac{\partial u}{\partial z}.$$

The restriction that the vector $\mathbf{A} = \mathbf{i}A_x + \mathbf{j}A_y + \mathbf{k}A_z$ is the gradient of u implies that

$$\frac{\partial A_x}{\partial y} = \frac{\partial^2 u}{\partial y\, \partial x} = \frac{\partial^2 u}{\partial x\, \partial y} = \frac{\partial A_y}{\partial x}.$$

Similarly,

$$\frac{\partial A_y}{\partial z} = \frac{\partial A_z}{\partial y} \quad \text{and} \quad \frac{\partial A_z}{\partial x} = \frac{\partial A_x}{\partial z}.$$

These conditions are precisely the same as those discovered in Sec. 63 and are the necessary and sufficient conditions that the expression

$$A_x\, dx + A_y\, dy + A_z\, dz$$

be an exact differential of some function u.

If the vector **ds** is defined by the equation

$$\mathbf{ds} = \mathbf{i}\, dx + \mathbf{j}\, dy + \mathbf{k}\, dz,$$

then the line integral $\int_C A_s\, ds$ can be written as $\int_C (\mathbf{A}, \mathbf{ds})$. Moreover, if $\mathbf{A} = \nabla u$, then

$$(\mathbf{A}, \mathbf{ds}) = \left(\mathbf{i}\, \frac{\partial u}{\partial x} + \mathbf{j}\, \frac{\partial u}{\partial y} + \mathbf{k}\, \frac{\partial u}{\partial z},\ \mathbf{i}\, dx + \mathbf{j}\, dy + \mathbf{k}\, dz\right)$$

$$= \frac{\partial u}{\partial x}\, dx + \frac{\partial u}{\partial y}\, dy + \frac{\partial u}{\partial z}\, dz \equiv du,$$

so that

$$(123\text{-}2) \quad \int_C A_s\, ds \equiv \int_C (\nabla u, \mathbf{ds}) = \int_C du = u(x, y, z)\Big|_{P_0}^{P} = u_P - u_{P_0},$$

a result that depends solely upon the values of u at the end points of C. If P_0 and P coincide, so that the curve C is closed, then the value of the integral is zero.* This is a familiar result, which was discussed in Sec. 63. The function u whose gradient is the vector **A** is called a *potential function*, and the integral (123-2) measures the difference of potential between P and P_0. The vector function **A** obtainable from a potential function u is usually called the force function, and it is clear that the integral (123-2) measures the work done in a force field in moving from P_0 to P. In this case ($\mathbf{A} = \nabla u$) the integral around the closed curve C is zero, and for that reason the field of force is called conservative. Examples of such fields are gravitational and electrostatic fields of force (see Sec. 66).

124. Divergence of a Vector. If some physical entity is generated within a certain region of the field, that region is termed a source. On the other hand, if the physical entity is absorbed, then the region is called a sink. Clearly, if there are no sources and sinks present in the field, then the net outflow of the incompressible physical entity over any part of the region is zero. If the total strength of the sources is greater than that of the sinks, the net outflow is said to be positive, and conversely.

---

* Note that the continuity of u and of its derivatives throughout the region enclosed by the curve C is assumed in the foregoing. In this connection, see Example 1, Sec. 63.

Consider a volume element $\Delta\tau$ (enclosing a point P) of a vector field. The net outflow per unit volume of a vector **A** over the surface of the element is

$$\frac{\int_{\Delta\sigma} A_n \, d\sigma}{\Delta\tau},$$

where A_n is the component of **A** along the exterior normal to the surface of the volume element under consideration and $\Delta\sigma$ is the surface enclosing $\Delta\tau$. The quantity

$$\lim \frac{\int_{\Delta\sigma} A_n \, d\sigma}{\Delta\tau},$$

where the limit is computed by shrinking $\Delta\tau$ to the point P, is called the *divergence* of **A** at P and is denoted by div **A**. This quantity does not take into account the direction of the outflow and is therefore a scalar quantity.

Inasmuch as it is inconvenient to compute div **A** directly from the defining equation

$$\text{div } \mathbf{A} \equiv \lim \frac{\int_{\Delta\sigma} A_n \, d\sigma}{\Delta\tau},$$

it is desirable to develop a simple formula for the computation of the divergence at any point of a vector field. Let the rectangular components of the vector **A**(x, y, z) be A_x, A_y, A_z, and consider a point (x, y, z) of the field. Surround the point with a parallelepiped whose edges have lengths Δx, Δy, Δz, in such a way that the point (x, y, z) is at the center of the parallelepiped (Fig. 117). The total outflow of the vector quantity over the surface will be computed next. Consider first the front face of the parallelepiped, whose area is $\Delta\sigma = \Delta y \, \Delta z$. The component of **A** normal to this face, A_x, is responsible for the outflow, and its value will be computed at the center of this front face. Now, if the volume element $\Delta\tau$ is small, the approximate outflow over

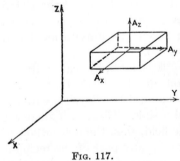

Fig. 117.

the front face is

$$A_n \, \Delta\sigma = (A_x)_{x+\frac{\Delta x}{2}} \, \Delta y \, \Delta z.$$

Moreover, the outflow over the back face which is parallel to the yz-plane is approximately

$$A_n \Delta\sigma = -(A_x)_{x-\frac{\Delta x}{2}} \, \Delta y \, \Delta z.$$

Then, the net outflow over the faces parallel to the yz-plane is

$$[(A_x)_{x+\frac{\Delta x}{2}} - (A_x)_{x-\frac{\Delta x}{2}}] \, \Delta y \, \Delta z.$$

Proceeding similarly for the other faces gives two analogous expressions, and the sum of these three results yields the total outflow over the surface, which is given by

$$(124\text{-}1) \quad [(A_x)_{x+\frac{\Delta x}{2}} - (A_x)_{x-\frac{\Delta x}{2}}] \, \Delta y \, \Delta z + [(A_y)_{y+\frac{\Delta y}{2}}$$
$$- (A_y)_{y-\frac{\Delta y}{2}}] \, \Delta x \, \Delta z + [(A_z)_{z+\frac{\Delta z}{2}} - (A_z)_{z-\frac{\Delta z}{2}}] \, \Delta x \, \Delta y.$$

If the value of $(A_x)_{x+\frac{\Delta x}{2}}$ is computed in terms of the values of A_x and its derivatives at the point (x, y, z), there results

$$(A_x)_{x+\frac{\Delta x}{2}} = (A_x)_x + \left(\frac{\partial A_x}{\partial x}\right)_x \frac{\Delta x}{2} + \frac{1}{2!}\left(\frac{\partial^2 A_x}{\partial x^2}\right)_x \left(\frac{\Delta x}{2}\right)^2 + \cdots.$$

Similar expressions can be obtained for $(A_x)_{x-\frac{\Delta x}{2}}$, $(A_y)_{y+\frac{\Delta y}{2}}$, etc.

When these series are substituted in (124-1), the expression for the net outflow becomes

$$\left[\left(\frac{\partial A_x}{\partial x}\right)_x \Delta x + \frac{2}{3!}\left(\frac{\partial^3 A_x}{\partial x^3}\right)_x \left(\frac{\Delta x}{2}\right)^3 + \cdots \right] \Delta y \, \Delta z$$
$$+ \left[\left(\frac{\partial A_y}{\partial y}\right)_y \Delta y + \frac{2}{3!}\left(\frac{\partial^3 A_y}{\partial y^3}\right)_y \left(\frac{\Delta y}{2}\right)^3 + \cdots \right] \Delta x \, \Delta z$$
$$+ \left[\left(\frac{\partial A_z}{\partial z}\right)_z \Delta z + \frac{2}{3!}\left(\frac{\partial^3 A_z}{\partial z^3}\right)_z \left(\frac{\Delta z}{2}\right)^3 + \cdots \right] \Delta x \, \Delta y.$$

Since $\Delta\tau = \Delta x \, \Delta y \, \Delta z$, the net outflow per unit volume is

$$(124\text{-}2) \quad \left[\left(\frac{\partial A_x}{\partial x}\right)_x + \left(\frac{\partial A_y}{\partial y}\right)_y + \left(\frac{\partial A_z}{\partial z}\right)_z + O(\overline{\Delta x}^2, \overline{\Delta y}^2, \overline{\Delta z}^2)\right],$$

where $O(\overline{\Delta x^2}, \overline{\Delta y^2}, \overline{\Delta z^2})$ represents the terms of the series containing the powers of Δx, Δy, and Δz which are higher than the first and which vanish as $\Delta x \to 0$, $\Delta y \to 0$, and $\Delta z \to 0$.

By definition, the limit of (124-2) as Δx, Δy, and Δz approach zero is the divergence of **A** at (x, y, z). Thus,

$$\text{div } \mathbf{A} = \frac{\partial A_x}{\partial x} + \frac{\partial A_y}{\partial y} + \frac{\partial A_z}{\partial z},$$

where it is understood that the values of the derivatives are computed at the point (x, y, z). This formula enables one to compute the divergence of **A** easily when **A** is given in the form $iA_x + jA_y + kA_z$. It is worth noting that, if ∇ is treated as a vector, then

$$(\nabla, \mathbf{A}) = \left(i\frac{\partial}{\partial x} + j\frac{\partial}{\partial y} + k\frac{\partial}{\partial z}, iA_x + jA_y + kA_z \right)$$

$$= \frac{\partial A_x}{\partial x} + \frac{\partial A_y}{\partial y} + \frac{\partial A_z}{\partial z} \equiv \text{div } \mathbf{A}.$$

Example. Consider the vector

$$\mathbf{A} = i3x^2 + j5xy^2 + kxyz^3.$$

Here,

$$A_x = 3x^2, \qquad A_y = 5xy^2, \qquad A_z = xyz^3,$$

and

$$\frac{\partial A_x}{\partial x} = 6x, \qquad \frac{\partial A_y}{\partial y} = 10xy, \qquad \frac{\partial A_z}{\partial z} = 3xyz^2,$$

so that

$$\text{div } \mathbf{A} = 6x + 10xy + 3xyz^2.$$

If the value of div **A** is desired at $(1, 2, 3)$, it is therefore

$$\text{div } \mathbf{A} = 6 + 20 + 54 = 80.$$

PROBLEMS

1. Find div **A** if

   (a) $\mathbf{A} = ix + jy + kz$;

   (b) $\mathbf{A} = i\dfrac{x}{r} + j\dfrac{y}{r} + k\dfrac{z}{r}$, where $r = \sqrt{x^2 + y^2 + z^2}$;

   (c) $\mathbf{A} = i(z - y) + j(x - z) + k(y - x)$.

2. Show that

$$\text{div } \nabla u = \frac{\partial^2 u}{\partial x^2} + \frac{\partial^2 u}{\partial y^2} + \frac{\partial^2 u}{\partial z^2} \equiv \nabla^2 u.$$

3. Compute ∇ div **A,** where $\mathbf{A} = iA_x + jA_y + kA_z$.

4. Show that

(a) div $(\mathbf{u} + \mathbf{v})$ = div $\mathbf{u}$ + div $\mathbf{v}$;

(b) div $(u\mathbf{v})$ = $\nabla \cdot (u\mathbf{v})$ = $(\nabla u, \mathbf{v})$ + $u(\nabla, \mathbf{v})$;

(c) div $[\mathbf{u}, \mathbf{v}]$ = $\nabla \cdot [\mathbf{u}, \mathbf{v}]$ = $(\mathbf{v}, [\nabla, \mathbf{u}])$ − $(\mathbf{u}, [\nabla, \mathbf{v}])$.

5. Show that div $[\mathbf{r}, \mathbf{c}]$ = 0 if $\mathbf{r}$ = $\mathbf{i}x + \mathbf{j}y + \mathbf{k}z$ and $\mathbf{c}$ is a constant vector.

6. Find div $(u\mathbf{v})$ if $u = x^2 + y^2 + z^2$ and $\mathbf{v}$ = $\mathbf{i}x + \mathbf{j}y + \mathbf{k}z$.

125. Divergence Theorem. An important theorem associated with the names of Green and Gauss permits one to express certain integrals calculated over the volume by means of surface integrals. It has many fruitful uses in applied mathematics and is commonly known as the *divergence theorem.*

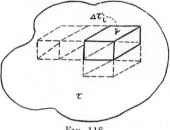

Consider a field in which a vector $\mathbf{A}$ is defined, and let a closed surface be taken in this field. Subdivide the volume enclosed by this surface into volume cells $\Delta\tau_i$, and

Fig. 118.

consider the divergence over one of these cells (Fig. 118). By definition,

$$\text{div } \mathbf{A} = \lim_{\Delta\tau_i \to 0} \frac{\int_{\Delta\sigma_i} A_n \, d\sigma}{\Delta\tau_i},$$

so that

$$\text{div } \mathbf{A} \, \Delta\tau_i = A_n \, \Delta\sigma_i + \epsilon_i \, \Delta\tau_i,$$

where $\Delta\sigma_i$ is the surface area of the cell $\Delta\tau_i$ and ϵ_i is an infinitesimal. If this equality is summed over the common surface area of two adjacent cells, $\Delta\sigma$ is identical in both, whereas A_n in one cell is the negative of A_n in the other (for A_n denotes the exterior normal). Hence, the terms $A_n \, \Delta\sigma$ will vanish over the common boundary. If the summation is extended over the entire volume τ, the only terms of the sum $\Sigma A_n \, \Delta\sigma_i$ which will contribute to the result are those which involve the exterior boundary, enclosing the volume τ. All the other terms will cancel each other in pairs.

Now, let the number of cells be increased indefinitely in such a manner that $\Delta\sigma$ and $\Delta\tau$, which represent the surface and the volume of the largest cell, approach zero. Then,

$$\lim_{\Delta\sigma \to 0} \sum A_n \, \Delta\sigma_i = \lim_{\Delta\tau \to 0} \sum \text{div } \mathbf{A} \, \Delta\tau_i - \lim_{\Delta\tau \to 0} \sum \epsilon_i \, \Delta\tau_i,$$

which can be written as

(125-1) $$\int_{\Sigma} A_n \, d\sigma = \int_{\tau} \operatorname{div} \mathbf{A} \, d\tau,$$

where the integral on the left is taken over the exterior surface Σ of the volume τ and the integral on the right is extended throughout the volume τ. The restrictions imposed on $\mathbf{A}$ in Sec. 122 permit one to show that

$$\lim_{\Delta\tau\to 0} \left| \sum \epsilon_i \, \Delta\tau_i \right| \leq \lim_{\Delta\tau\to 0} \left| \epsilon \sum \Delta\tau_i \right| = \tau \lim_{\Delta\tau\to 0} |\epsilon| = 0,$$

where $|\epsilon|$ is the value of the greatest $|\epsilon_i|$.

Recalling that

$$A_n = A_x \cos (x, n) + A_y \cos (y, n) + A_z \cos (z, n)$$

and

$$\operatorname{div} \mathbf{A} = \frac{\partial A_x}{\partial x} + \frac{\partial A_y}{\partial y} + \frac{\partial A_z}{\partial z},$$

enables one to write (125-1) in the form

$$\int_{\Sigma} [A_x \cos (x, n) + A_y \cos (y, n) + A_z \cos (z, n)] \, d\sigma$$

$$= \int_{\tau} \left(\frac{\partial A_x}{\partial x} + \frac{\partial A_y}{\partial y} + \frac{\partial A_z}{\partial z} \right) d\tau.$$

If the surface Σ encloses some sources and sinks, then it is clear that the total normal flow (flux) of the physical entity over the surface can be measured in two ways: (1) by summing the outward normal flux over the surface, or (2) by computing the algebraic sum of the sources and sinks throughout the volume. Stated in words the divergence theorem is: *In a vector field the surface integral of the normal component of flux is equal to the volume integral of the divergence taken throughout the volume.*

It is easy to establish, with the aid of the divergence theorem, the following useful formula:

(125-2) $$\int_{\tau} \nabla u \, d\tau = \int_{\Sigma} u\mathbf{n} \, d\sigma,$$

where $\mathbf{n}$ is the unit normal exterior to the surface Σ bounding the volume τ. Indeed,

$$\mathbf{n} = \mathbf{i} \cos (x, n) + \mathbf{j} \cos (y, n) + \mathbf{k} \cos (z, n).$$

Hence, (125-2) is equivalent to the three scalar equations

$$\int_\tau \frac{\partial u}{\partial x}\, d\tau = \int_\Sigma u \cos (x, n)\, d\sigma,$$

$$\int_\tau \frac{\partial u}{\partial y}\, d\tau = \int_\Sigma u \cos (y, n)\, d\sigma,$$

$$\int_\tau \frac{\partial u}{\partial z}\, d\tau = \int_\Sigma u \cos (z, n)\, d\sigma,$$

which are precisely the statements of the divergence theorem applied to the vectors iu, ju, and ku, respectively.

Example. Verify (125-1) for

$$\mathbf{A} = \mathbf{i}\frac{x}{r} + \mathbf{j}\frac{y}{r} + \mathbf{k}\frac{z}{r},$$

where $r^2 = x^2 + y^2 + z^2$ and τ is the sphere $x^2 + y^2 + z^2 = a^2$. The computation of div $\mathbf{A}$ gives

$$\frac{\partial A_x}{\partial x} = \frac{y^2 + z^2}{(x^2 + y^2 + z^2)^{3/2}}, \qquad \frac{\partial A_y}{\partial y} = \frac{x^2 + z^2}{(x^2 + y^2 + z^2)^{3/2}}$$

and

$$\frac{\partial A_z}{\partial z} = \frac{x^2 + y^2}{(x^2 + y^2 + z^2)^{3/2}},$$

so that

$$\text{div } \mathbf{A} = \frac{2}{r}.$$

Then

$$\int_\tau \text{div } \mathbf{A}\, d\tau = \int_\tau \frac{2}{r}\, d\tau = 8 \int_0^a \int_0^{\frac{\pi}{2}} \int_0^{\frac{\pi}{2}} \frac{2}{r}\, r^2 \sin\theta\, d\theta\, d\varphi\, dr$$
$$= 4\pi a^2,$$

since $d\tau = r^2 \sin\theta\, d\theta\, d\varphi\, dr$ in spherical coordinates. On the other hand, since the normal component of $\mathbf{A}$ is directed along the radius r and since the vector $\mathbf{A}$ is a unit vector, it is evident that

$$\int_\Sigma A_n\, d\sigma = \int_\Sigma 1 \cdot d\sigma = 4\pi a^2.$$

PROBLEMS

1. If u is a scalar and $\mathbf{A}$ is a vector, show that
$$\text{div } u\mathbf{A} = u \text{ div } \mathbf{A} + (\mathbf{A}, \nabla u).$$

2. If $\mathbf{n}$ is an exterior unit-normal to the closed surface Σ and $\mathbf{r}$ is the position vector of any point on Σ, show that

$$\int_\Sigma (\mathbf{n}, \mathbf{r})\, d\sigma = 3\tau,$$

where τ is the volume bounded by Σ.

3. If u and ρ are scalar point functions and $\mathbf{A} = \nabla u$ and $\nabla^2 u = \rho$ (see Prob. 2, Sec. 124), show that

$$\int_\Sigma \frac{du}{dn}\, d\sigma = \int_\tau \rho\, d\tau,$$

where τ is the volume bounded by Σ.

4. Substitute for $\mathbf{A}$ in (125-1) the vector $u\nabla v$, where u and v are scalar point functions. Then,

$$\int_\tau \operatorname{div}\, (u\nabla v)\, d\tau = \int_\Sigma (u\nabla v)_n\, d\sigma.$$

Show that this equation can be written as

$$\int_\tau u\nabla^2 v\, d\tau = \int_\Sigma u\frac{dv}{dn}\, d\sigma - \int_\tau \left(\frac{\partial u}{\partial x}\frac{\partial v}{\partial x} + \frac{\partial u}{\partial y}\frac{\partial v}{\partial y} + \frac{\partial u}{\partial z}\frac{\partial v}{\partial z}\right) d\tau.$$

In this last result set $v = u$ and obtain another important theorem bearing the name of Green,

$$\int_\tau u\nabla^2 u\, d\tau = \int_\Sigma u\frac{du}{dn}\, d\sigma - \int_\tau (\nabla u, \nabla u)\, d\tau.$$

5. Using Prob. 4, obtain the symmetrical form of Green's theorem,

$$\int_\tau (u\nabla^2 v - v\nabla^2 u)\, d\tau = \int_\Sigma \left(u\frac{dv}{dn} - v\frac{du}{dn}\right) d\sigma,$$

which is of frequent use in numerous investigations in mathematical physics.

126. Curl of a Vector. In Secs. 63 and 123 the necessary and sufficient conditions for independence of the path of the line integral were given. It will be shown in this section that these conditions are intimately connected with the notion of the curl of a vector, which will be developed next.

If a closed curve C is drawn in a vector field, then the line integral

(126-1) $$\int_C (\mathbf{A}, \mathbf{ds}) = \int_C A_s\, ds$$

depends in general upon the vector $\mathbf{A}$ and the contour C. The value of (126-1) is called the *circulation* of $\mathbf{A}$ around the path C. If the circulation of $\mathbf{A}$ is zero for every closed path C (that is, if $A_s\, ds$ is an exact differential), then the vector field is said to be *irrotational;* otherwise it is called *rotational.* The reason for this terminology will appear when the applications are discussed in Secs. 129, 130, and 131.

The average circulation of the vector **A** per unit area of an arbitrary surface Σ spanning C (that is, Σ passes through C and has C for its boundary) is

(126-2)
$$\frac{\int_C (\mathbf{A}, d\mathbf{s})}{\int_\Sigma d\sigma},$$

which clearly depends upon the path C and the area of Σ. Consider a point P on Σ, and let the contour C shrink to the point P. Then the limit of the quotient (126-2), if it exists, is called the circulation at the point P. It must be kept in mind that the circulation at a point depends, in general, upon the choice of the arbitrary surface Σ. However, if **A** fulfills the conditions imposed in Sec. 122, there will exist a unique limit that is independent of the type of surface Σ and of the mode of approach of Σ to zero. It will be assumed henceforth that such is the case.

It is possible to construct a vector whose component in the direction of the positive normal to Σ is the circulation at P; such a vector is called the *curl* of **A** at P and is denoted by the symbols curl **A** or rot **A**. Inasmuch as it is inconvenient to apply this definition for purposes of computation, it is desirable to develop a set of formulas for computing curl **A** when $\mathbf{A} = \mathbf{i}A_x + \mathbf{j}A_y + \mathbf{k}A_z$ is given.

It will be observed that the definition of curl **A** is somewhat similar to that of div **A** given in Sec. 124. A procedure similar to that employed in developing the formula for div **A** can be used in deriving the expression for curl **A**, considering one component of curl **A** at a time. That is, one can apply the defining equation

(126-3)
$$\operatorname{curl}_n \mathbf{A} = \lim_{\Delta\sigma\to 0} \frac{\int_C (\mathbf{A}, d\mathbf{s})}{\Delta\sigma}$$

to the elements of area $\Delta\sigma$ that are normal to the coordinate axes. As a result of such a development, it is found that curl **A** is a vector whose x, y, z components are

$$\operatorname{curl}_x \mathbf{A} = \frac{\partial A_z}{\partial y} - \frac{\partial A_y}{\partial z},$$

$$\operatorname{curl}_y \mathbf{A} = \frac{\partial A_x}{\partial z} - \frac{\partial A_z}{\partial x},$$

$$\operatorname{curl}_z \mathbf{A} = \frac{\partial A_y}{\partial x} - \frac{\partial A_x}{\partial y}.$$

Hence, in convenient determinant form,

(126-4)
$$\operatorname{curl} \mathbf{A} = \begin{vmatrix} \mathbf{i} & \mathbf{j} & \mathbf{k} \\ \dfrac{\partial}{\partial x} & \dfrac{\partial}{\partial y} & \dfrac{\partial}{\partial z} \\ A_x & A_y & A_z \end{vmatrix}.$$

Upon recalling that the operator ∇ represents

$$\mathbf{i}\frac{\partial}{\partial x} + \mathbf{j}\frac{\partial}{\partial y} + \mathbf{k}\frac{\partial}{\partial z},$$

(126-4) can be written compactly as

$$\operatorname{curl} \mathbf{A} = [\nabla, \mathbf{A}].$$

If $\operatorname{curl} \mathbf{A} \equiv 0$, it follows that

$$\operatorname{curl}_x \mathbf{A} = \operatorname{curl}_y \mathbf{A} = \operatorname{curl}_z \mathbf{A} = 0.$$

Hence,

$$\frac{\partial A_z}{\partial y} - \frac{\partial A_y}{\partial z} = 0, \qquad \frac{\partial A_x}{\partial z} - \frac{\partial A_z}{\partial x} = 0, \qquad \frac{\partial A_y}{\partial x} - \frac{\partial A_x}{\partial y} = 0,$$

which are precisely the necessary and sufficient conditions that

$$A_x\, dx + A_y\, dy + A_z\, dz$$

be an exact differential.*

Example. Compute curl $\mathbf{A}$ if

$$\mathbf{A} = \mathbf{i}xyz + \mathbf{j}xyz^2 + \mathbf{k}x^3yz.$$

Since

$$A_x = xyz, \qquad A_y = xyz^2, \qquad A_z = x^3yz,$$
$$\operatorname{curl} \mathbf{A} = \mathbf{i}(x^3z - 2xyz) + \mathbf{j}(xy - 3x^2yz) + \mathbf{k}(yz^2 - xz).$$

PROBLEMS

1. Find curl $\mathbf{A}$, if

(a) $\mathbf{A} = \mathbf{i}x + \mathbf{j}y + \mathbf{k}z$;

(b) $\mathbf{A} = \mathbf{i}\dfrac{x}{r} + \mathbf{j}\dfrac{y}{r} + \mathbf{k}\dfrac{z}{r}$, $r^2 = x^2 + y^2 + z^2$;

(c) Find curl ∇u where $u = x^2 + y^2 + z^2$.

2. Show that div curl $\mathbf{A} \equiv 0$.

3. Show that curl $\mathbf{A} \equiv 0$, if $\mathbf{A} = \nabla u$, where u is a scalar point function having continuous second partial derivatives.

4. Show that curl curl $\mathbf{A} = -\nabla^2\mathbf{A} + \nabla$ div $\mathbf{A}$.

* In this connection see Prob. 3, just below.

5. Show that curl **A** can be defined as

$$\lim_{\Delta\tau \to 0} \frac{1}{\Delta\tau} \int_{\Sigma} [\mathbf{n}, \mathbf{A}] \, d\sigma.$$

See Wills, A. P., Vector and Tensor Analysis, page 85.

6. Show that

(a) curl $(\mathbf{u} + \mathbf{v})$ = curl $\mathbf{u}$ + curl $\mathbf{v}$;

(b) curl $(u\mathbf{v})$ = $[\nabla u, \mathbf{v}]$ + $u[\nabla, \mathbf{v}]$.

7. Show that curl $r^n \mathbf{r} = 0$ if $\mathbf{r} = \mathbf{i}x + \mathbf{j}y + \mathbf{k}z$.

127. Stokes's Theorem. This important theorem permits one to transform certain integrals calculated over the surface into line integrals. It can be stated as follows:

THEOREM. *The line integral of the tangential component of a vector* **A** *around a closed path is equal to the surface integral of the normal component of curl* **A** *over the surface enclosed by the path.*

In symbols the statement of the theorem becomes

$$(127\text{-}1) \qquad \int_C A_s \, ds = \int_{\Sigma} \mathrm{curl}_n \, \mathbf{A} \, d\sigma,$$

or, when written out in full,

$$\int_C [A_x \cos (x, s) + A_y \cos (y, s) + A_z \cos (z, s)] \, ds$$

$$= \int_{\Sigma} \left[\left(\frac{\partial A_z}{\partial y} - \frac{\partial A_y}{\partial z} \right) \cos (x, n) + \left(\frac{\partial A_x}{\partial z} - \frac{\partial A_z}{\partial x} \right) \cos (y, n) \right.$$

$$\left. + \left(\frac{\partial A_y}{\partial x} - \frac{\partial A_x}{\partial y} \right) \cos (z, n) \right] d\sigma.$$

Since

$$\cos (x, s) = \frac{dx}{ds}, \qquad \cos (y, s) = \frac{dy}{ds}, \qquad \cos (z, s) = \frac{dz}{ds},$$

it is obvious that the line integral in the left-hand member can be written as

$$\int_C (A_x \, dx + A_y \, dy + A_z \, dz).$$

A proof of this theorem, which makes use of the definition of curl_n **A** [see (126-3)], can be constructed in a manner similar to that given for the divergence theorem in Sec. 125. If the surface Σ, bounded by the closed curve C, is divided into small triangular areas $\Delta\sigma_i$, of which ΔABC (Fig. 119) is typical, then from the definition (126-3) it follows that

$$\operatorname{curl}_n \mathbf{A}\, \Delta\sigma_i \doteq \int_{C_i} A_s\, ds + \epsilon_i\, \Delta\sigma_i,$$

where the integral is extended over the boundary of the triangular area $\Delta\sigma_i$ and ϵ_i is an infinitesimal. Form the sum

$$(127\text{-}2) \qquad \sum_i \operatorname{curl}_n \mathbf{A}\, \Delta\sigma_i = \sum_i \int_{C_i} A_s\, ds + \sum_i \epsilon_i\, \Delta\sigma_i,$$

where the summation extends over the entire area of Σ. The line integrals over the common parts of the boundaries of the

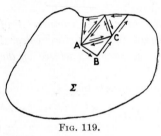

triangles $\Delta\sigma_i$ cancel, for these common parts of the boundaries will be traversed twice in opposite directions. Thus the integral in the right-hand member of (127-2) represents the line integral around the curve C. If the number of triangular areas is increased indefinitely, Eq. (127-2) reduces to (127-1). The passage

Fig. 119.

from (127-2) to (127-1) needs some justification, even though it may appear physically obvious.

128. Two Important Theorems. There are two theorems in vector analysis that are of cardinal importance in hydrodynamics, theory of elasticity, and electrodynamics.

THEOREM 1. *The necessary and sufficient condition that the curl of a vector vanish identically is that the vector be the nabla of some function.*

The proof of the sufficiency part of this theorem was given as an exercise in Prob. 3, Sec. 126; thus, assuming that $\mathbf{A} = \nabla u$ and computing curl $\mathbf{A}$ give curl $\mathbf{A} = $ curl $\nabla u \equiv 0$. In order to prove the necessity, assume that curl $\mathbf{A} \equiv 0$. Then, by Stokes's theorem,

$$\int_C A_s\, ds = \int_\Sigma \operatorname{curl}_n \mathbf{A}\, d\sigma \equiv 0,$$

and, since the integral around an arbitrary closed curve C is zero, the expression $A_s\, ds$ is an exact differential (see Sec. 123), so that

$$\mathbf{A} = \nabla u.$$

THEOREM 2. *The necessary and sufficient condition that the divergence of a vector vanish identically is that the vector be the curl of some other vector.*

To prove the sufficiency part, assume that $\mathbf{A} = \operatorname{curl} \mathbf{B}$. Then, by Prob. 2, Sec. 126,

$$\operatorname{div} \mathbf{A} = \operatorname{div} \operatorname{curl} \mathbf{B} \equiv 0.$$

The proof of the converse is not so simple as that given in the preceding theorem. It can be made to depend upon a demonstration of the existence of a solution of a certain partial differential equation and will not be given here.*

PROBLEMS

1. Show that $\int_C (\mathbf{r}, d\mathbf{r}) = 0$ if $\mathbf{r}$ is the position vector of a point on the closed contour C.

2. If u and v are scalar point functions, show that

$$\int_C u \frac{dv}{ds} ds = - \int_C v \frac{du}{ds} ds.$$

3. A vector field $\mathbf{A}$ whose divergence vanishes everywhere in the region (that is, div $\mathbf{A} \equiv 0$) is called *solenoidal*. Prove that the necessary and sufficient condition that the surface integral $\int_\Sigma (\mathbf{n}, \mathbf{A}) \, d\sigma$ shall be capable of transformation into a line integral around the contour bounding Σ is that the field be solenoidal at all points of the surface.

4. A vector field $\mathbf{A}$ is said to be *lamellar*, or *irrotational*, if curl $\mathbf{A} \equiv 0$ in the region. Show that the necessary and sufficient condition that the field is lamellar is that $\int_C (\mathbf{A}, d\mathbf{s}) = 0$ over all contours C bounding simply connected regions.

5. Show, with the aid of Green's theorem (Problem 4, Sec. 125), that a vector point function $\mathbf{A}$ is uniquely determined within a region τ, bounded by a surface Σ, when its divergence and curl are given throughout τ and the normal component of $\mathbf{A}$ is given over Σ.

129. Physical Interpretation of Divergence and Curl. From the definition of the divergence (Sec. 124), it is clear that the operator div applied to a vector function $\mathbf{A}$ gives at each point the rate per unit volume at which the physical entity is issuing from that point. If the vector $\mathbf{A}$ represents the flow of heat and

---

* The student who is interested in the proof and applications of this theorem will find it profitable to consult the mathematical appendix of an excellent treatise on electrodynamics by M. Mason and W. Weaver, The Electromagnetic Field.

if div **A** is positive at a point P, either there must be a source of heat located at P, or else heat must be leaving P so that the temperature at P is decreasing. If **A** represents the vector velocity of a fluid and if div **A** is positive at P, then there must be a source of the fluid at P or else the density at this point is decreasing. For an incompressible fluid a non-vanishing value of the divergence at P indicates the rate at which the fluid is being introduced or removed at P and thus gives the measure of the strength of the source or sink at P. If there are no sources or sinks in some portion of the incompressible fluid, then the divergence is zero at every point of such a region.

The physical interpretation of the curl of a vector is not so simple as that of the divergence. It will be shown that the curl of a vector function **A** gives a measure of the angular velocity at every point of the vector field. Let the vector **A** represent the velocity at every point of an incompressible fluid, and at a given instant consider a small sphere of fluid whose center is at the point P. At a later instant, this sphere may have been translated to a new position, or it may have been subjected to a strain that leaves it no longer a sphere, or it may have been rotated as a whole about some definite axis. The general motion of a small sphere of fluid is made up of the three types of motion just listed, and the curl of a vector gives the measure of the last one of the three enumerated.

For simplicity the only case considered will be that of rigid body motion. Let $\mathbf{v}_p$ be the instantaneous velocity of a point P of the body. It is known that $\mathbf{v}_p$ can be resolved into two components, one of which is the velocity of translation $\mathbf{v}_0$ of an arbitrarily chosen point O of the body, whereas the other is due to the angular velocity of rotation ω of the body about a line passing through O. Let **r** be the vector from O to P; then the velocity of any point P of the body [see (121-1)] is

$$\mathbf{v}_p = \mathbf{v}_0 + [\omega, \mathbf{r}],$$

and

$$\mathrm{curl}\ \mathbf{v}_p = \mathrm{curl}\ \mathbf{v}_0 + \mathrm{curl}\ [\omega, \mathbf{r}].$$

Now the velocity of translation $\mathbf{v}_0$, at a given instant of time, is the same for all points of the body, and hence it is independent of the coordinates x, y, z of the points of the body. Consequently, curl $\mathbf{v}_0 = 0$. If the point O is chosen as the origin of coordinates, then $\mathbf{r} = \mathbf{i}x + \mathbf{j}y + \mathbf{k}z$ and, from (121-2),

$$[\boldsymbol{\omega}, \mathbf{r}] = \mathbf{i}(\omega_y z - \omega_z y) + \mathbf{j}(\omega_z x - \omega_x z) + \mathbf{k}(\omega_x y - \omega_y x).$$

Calculating curl $[\boldsymbol{\omega}, \mathbf{r}]$ gives

$$\operatorname{curl} [\boldsymbol{\omega}, \mathbf{r}] = 2(\mathbf{i}\omega_x + \mathbf{j}\omega_y + \mathbf{k}\omega_z) = 2\boldsymbol{\omega}.$$

Thus the angular velocity of rotation $\boldsymbol{\omega}$, at any instant of time, is equal to one-half the curl of the velocity field $\mathbf{v}$.

The following two sections contain applications of the divergence and Stokes's theorems to the derivation of some important differential equations of mathematical physics.

PROBLEMS

1. Show that div $[\mathbf{A}, \mathbf{B}] = (\mathbf{B}, \operatorname{curl} \mathbf{A}) - (\mathbf{A}, \operatorname{curl} \mathbf{B})$.

2. Show that curl $[\mathbf{A}, \mathbf{B}] = \mathbf{A} \operatorname{div} \mathbf{B} - \mathbf{B} \operatorname{div} \mathbf{A} + (\mathbf{B}, \nabla)\mathbf{A} - (\mathbf{A}, \nabla)\mathbf{B}$. The symbol $\mathbf{C} \equiv (\mathbf{A}, \nabla)\mathbf{B}$ is a vector whose components are

$$C_x = A_x \frac{\partial B_x}{\partial x} + A_y \frac{\partial B_x}{\partial y} + A_z \frac{\partial B_x}{\partial z},$$

$$C_y = A_x \frac{\partial B_y}{\partial x} + A_y \frac{\partial B_y}{\partial y} + A_z \frac{\partial B_y}{\partial z},$$

$$C_z = A_x \frac{\partial B_z}{\partial x} + A_y \frac{\partial B_z}{\partial y} + A_z \frac{\partial B_z}{\partial z}.$$

3. Show that

$$\operatorname{curl} u\mathbf{A} = u \operatorname{curl} \mathbf{A} + [\nabla u, \mathbf{A}]$$

where u is a scalar point function.

130. Equation of Heat Flow.* The following derivation of the Fourier equation of heat flow illustrates admirably the use of the divergence theorem in mathematical physics.

It is known from empirical results that heat will flow from points at higher temperatures to those at lower temperatures. At any point the rate of decrease of temperature varies with the direction, and it is generally assumed that the amount of heat ΔH crossing an element of surface $\Delta\sigma$ in Δt sec. is proportional to the greatest rate of decrease of the temperature u, that is,

$$\Delta H = k \, \Delta\sigma \, \Delta t \left|\frac{\partial u}{\partial n}\right|.$$

Define the vector $\mathbf{q}$, representing the flow of heat, by the formula

$$\mathbf{q} = -k \, \nabla u,$$

* See also Sec. 110.

where k is a constant of proportionality known as the thermal conductivity of a substance. [(The units of k are cal./(cm. sec. °C.).] The negative sign is chosen in the definition because heat flows from points of higher temperature to those of lower, and the vector ∇u is directed normally to the level surface $u =$ const. in the direction of increasing u.

Then, the total amount of heat H flowing out in Δt sec. from an arbitrary volume τ bounded by a closed surface Σ is

$$(130\text{-}1) \qquad H = -\Delta t \int_\Sigma k \frac{\partial u}{\partial n}\, d\sigma = \Delta t \int_\Sigma q_n\, d\sigma,$$

since $q_n = -k\, \partial u/\partial n$.

On the other hand, the amount of heat lost by the body τ can be calculated as follows: In order to increase the temperature of a volume element by $\Delta u°$, one must supply an amount of heat that is proportional to the increase in temperature and to the mass of the volume element.   Hence

$$\Delta H = c\, \Delta u\, \rho\, \Delta \tau = c \frac{\partial u}{\partial t} \Delta t\, \rho\, \Delta \tau,$$

where c is the specific heat of the substance [cal./(gr. °C.)] and ρ is its density.   Therefore, the total loss of heat from the volume τ in Δt sec. is

$$(130\text{-}2) \qquad H = -\Delta t \int_\tau \frac{\partial u}{\partial t} c\rho\, d\tau.$$

Equating (130-1) and (130-2) gives

$$(130\text{-}3) \qquad \int_\Sigma q_n\, d\sigma = -\int_\tau \frac{\partial u}{\partial t} c\rho\, d\tau.$$

Applying the divergence theorem to the left-hand member of (130-3) yields

$$\int_\tau \operatorname{div} \mathbf{q}\, d\tau = -\int_\tau \frac{\partial u}{\partial t} c\rho\, d\tau;$$

and since $\mathbf{q} = -k\nabla u$, the foregoing equation assumes the form

$$(130\text{-}4) \qquad \int_\tau \left[\operatorname{div} (-k\nabla u) + c\rho \frac{\partial u}{\partial t} \right] d\tau \equiv 0.$$

Now,* if k is a constant,

$$\operatorname{div} (k\nabla u) = k\nabla^2 u$$

* See Prob. 2, Sec. 124.

and (130-4) becomes

$$(130\text{-}5) \qquad \int_\tau \left(-k\nabla^2 u + c\rho \frac{\partial u}{\partial t} \right) d\tau \equiv 0.$$

Since this integral must vanish for an arbitrary volume τ and the integrand is a continuous function, it follows that the integrand must be equal to zero. For if such were not the case, τ could be so chosen as to include a region throughout which the integrand has constant sign. But if the integrand had one sign throughout this region, then the integral would have the same sign and would not vanish as required by (130-5).

Therefore,

$$-k\nabla^2 u + c\rho \frac{\partial u}{\partial t} = 0$$

or

$$(130\text{-}6) \qquad \frac{\partial u}{\partial t} = h^2 \nabla^2 u,$$

where

$$h^2 \equiv \frac{k}{c\rho}.$$

Equation (130-6) was developed by Fourier in 1822 and is of basic importance in the study of heat conduction in solids. A similar equation occurs in the study of current flow in conductors and in problems dealing with diffusion in liquids and gases.

It follows from (130-6) that a steady distribution of temperatures is characterized by the solution of Laplace's equation,

$$\nabla^2 u = 0.$$

It was assumed in this derivation that the body is free from sources and sinks. If there are sources of heat continuously distributed within τ, then it is necessary to add to the right-hand member of (130-2) the integral

$$\int_\tau f(x, y, z, t)\, d\tau,$$

where $f(x, y, z, t)$ is a function representing the strengths of the sources. The reader will show that in this case one is led to the equation

$$\frac{\partial u}{\partial t} = h^2 \nabla^2 u + \frac{f}{c\rho},$$

provided that the thermal conductivity of the substance is constant.   Thus the presence of sources leads to a non-homogeneous partial differential equation.

131. Equations of Hydrodynamics.   Consider a region of space containing a fluid, and let **v** denote the velocity of a typical particle of the

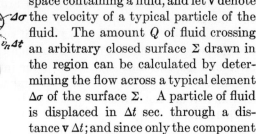

fluid.   The amount Q of fluid crossing an arbitrary closed surface Σ drawn in the region can be calculated by determining the flow across a typical element $\Delta\sigma$ of the surface Σ.   A particle of fluid is displaced in Δt sec. through a distance **v** Δt; and since only the component

FIG. 120.

of the vector **v** normal to the element $\Delta\sigma$ contributes to the flow across this element, the amount ΔQ of the fluid crossing $\Delta\sigma$ is

$$\Delta Q = \rho v_n \, \Delta\sigma \, \Delta t,$$

where ρ is the density (Fig. 120).

The entire amount Q of fluid flowing out of the volume τ, which is bounded by Σ, in Δt sec. is

$$Q = \Delta t \int_\Sigma \rho v_n \, d\sigma.$$

On the other hand, the quantity of the fluid originally contained in τ will have diminished by the amount

$$Q = -\Delta t \int_\tau \frac{\partial\rho}{\partial t} \, d\tau;$$

for the change in mass in Δt sec. is nearly equal to $(\partial\rho/\partial t) \, \Delta t \, \Delta\tau$, and the negative sign is taken because ρ is a decreasing function of t.

Equating these two expressions for Q gives

(131-1)
$$\int_\Sigma \rho v_n \, d\sigma = - \int_\tau \frac{\partial\rho}{\partial t} \, d\tau.$$

Applying the divergence theorem to the left-hand member of this equation gives

$$\int_\tau \text{div} \, (\rho\mathbf{v}) \, d\tau = - \int_\tau \frac{\partial\rho}{\partial t} \, d\tau,$$

or

$$\int_\tau \left[\text{div} \, (\rho\mathbf{v}) + \frac{\partial\rho}{\partial t} \right] d\tau = 0.$$

Since the integrand is continuous and the volume τ is arbitrary, one can conclude that

$$(131\text{-}2) \qquad \frac{\partial \rho}{\partial t} + \text{div } (\rho\mathbf{v}) = 0.$$

This is the basic equation of hydrodynamics, known as the equation of continuity. It merely expresses the law of conservation of matter.

It has been assumed that there are no sources or sinks within the region occupied by the fluid. If matter is created at the rate $k\rho(x, y, z, t)$, then the right-hand member of (131-1) should include a term that accounts for the increase of mass per second due to such sources, namely,

$$\int_\tau k\rho \, d\tau.$$

In this event the equation of continuity reads

$$\frac{\partial \rho}{\partial t} + \text{div } (\rho\mathbf{v}) = k\rho.$$

The constant of proportionality k is sometimes called the growth factor.

Since the density $\rho(x, y, z, t)$ of a particle of a fluid, located at the point (x, y, z) at the time t, changes as the particle is displaced, the total derivative of ρ with respect to t is

$$(131\text{-}3) \qquad \frac{d\rho}{dt} = \frac{\partial \rho}{\partial t} + \frac{\partial \rho}{\partial x}\frac{dx}{dt} + \frac{\partial \rho}{\partial y}\frac{dy}{dt} + \frac{\partial \rho}{\partial z}\frac{dz}{dt}.$$

In this equation, $d\rho/dt$ means the rate of change of density as one moves with the fluid, whereas $\partial \rho/\partial t$ is the rate of change of density at a fixed point.

Upon noting that

$$\mathbf{v} = \mathbf{i}\frac{dx}{dt} + \mathbf{j}\frac{dy}{dt} + \mathbf{k}\frac{dz}{dt},$$

and

$$\nabla\rho = \mathbf{i}\frac{\partial \rho}{\partial x} + \mathbf{j}\frac{\partial \rho}{\partial y} + \mathbf{k}\frac{\partial \rho}{\partial z},$$

the formula (131-3) can be written as

$$(131\text{-}4) \qquad \frac{d\rho}{dt} = \frac{\partial \rho}{\partial t} + (\nabla\rho, \mathbf{v}).$$

Substituting from (131-2) in (131-4) gives

(131-5) $$\frac{d\rho}{dt} = -\text{div}\,(\rho\mathbf{v}) + (\nabla\rho, \mathbf{v}).$$

But div $(\rho\mathbf{v}) = (\nabla\rho, \mathbf{v}) + \rho\,\text{div}\,\mathbf{v}$ [see Prob. 4(b), Sec. 124], so that (131-5) becomes

$$\frac{d\rho}{dt} = -\rho\,\text{div}\,\mathbf{v},$$

or

(131-6) $$\text{div}\,\mathbf{v} = -\frac{1}{\rho}\frac{d\rho}{dt}.$$

It is clear from (131-6) that div $\mathbf{v}$ is equal to the relative rate of change of the density ρ at any point of the fluid. Therefore, if the fluid is incompressible the velocity field is characterized by the equation

(131-7) $$\text{div}\,\mathbf{v} = 0.$$

If the flow of fluid is irrotational, then curl $\mathbf{v} = 0$, and one is assured that there exists a scalar function Φ such that*

$$\mathbf{v} = \nabla\Phi.$$

Substituting this in (131-7) gives the differential equation to be satisfied by Φ, namely,

(131-8) $$\nabla^2\Phi \equiv \frac{\partial^2\Phi}{\partial x^2} + \frac{\partial^2\Phi}{\partial y^2} + \frac{\partial^2\Phi}{\partial z^2} = 0.$$

The function Φ is called the *velocity potential*. A similar result was obtained in Sec. 66 for the two-dimensional flow.

If the fluid is ideal, that is, such that the force due to pressure on any surface element is always directed normally to that surface element, one can easily derive Euler's equations of hydrodynamics. Denote the pressure at any point of the fluid by p; then the force acting on a surface element $\Delta\sigma$ is $-p\mathbf{n}\,\Delta\sigma$, and the resultant force acting on an arbitrary closed surface Σ is

$$-\int_{\Sigma} p\mathbf{n}\,d\sigma.$$

The negative sign is chosen because the force due to pressure acts in the direction of the interior normal, whereas $\mathbf{n}$ denotes the unit exterior normal.

* See Theorem 1, Sec. 128.

Let the body force, per unit mass, acting on the masses contained within the region τ be $\mathbf{F}$; then the resultant of the body forces is

$$\int_\tau \mathbf{F}\rho \, d\tau.$$

Hence, the resultant $\mathbf{R}$ of the body and surface forces is

$$(131\text{-}9) \qquad \mathbf{R} = \int_\tau \mathbf{F}\rho \, d\tau - \int_\Sigma p\mathbf{n} \, d\sigma$$
$$= \int_\tau \mathbf{F}\rho \, d\tau - \int_\tau \nabla p \, d\tau,$$

where the last step is obtained by making use of (125-2).

From Newton's law of motion, the resultant force is equal to

$$(131\text{-}10) \qquad \mathbf{R} = \int_\tau \rho \frac{d^2\mathbf{r}}{dt^2} \, d\tau,$$

where $\mathbf{r} = \mathbf{i}x + \mathbf{j}y + \mathbf{k}z$ is the position vector of the masses relative to the origin of cartesian coordinates. It follows from (131-9) and (131-10) that

$$\int_\tau \left(\mathbf{F}\rho - \nabla p - \rho \frac{d^2\mathbf{r}}{dt^2} \right) d\tau = 0;$$

and since the volume element is arbitrary and the integrand is continuous,

$$(131\text{-}11) \qquad \rho \frac{d^2\mathbf{r}}{dt^2} = \mathbf{F}\rho - \nabla p.$$

This is the desired equation in vector form, and it is basic in hydro- and aerodynamical applications.

In books on hydrodynamics, the cartesian components of the velocity vector $d\mathbf{r}/dt$ are usually denoted by u, v, and w, so that

$$\frac{d\mathbf{r}}{dt} = \mathbf{i}u + \mathbf{j}v + \mathbf{k}w = \mathbf{i}\frac{dx}{dt} + \mathbf{j}\frac{dy}{dt} + \mathbf{k}\frac{dz}{dt}.$$

Since u, v, and w are functions of the coordinates of the point (x, y, z) and of the time t, it follows that

$$\frac{d^2\mathbf{r}}{dt^2} = \mathbf{i}\left(\frac{\partial u}{\partial t} + \frac{\partial u}{\partial x}\frac{dx}{dt} + \frac{\partial u}{\partial y}\frac{dy}{dt} + \frac{\partial u}{\partial z}\frac{dz}{dt} \right)$$
$$+ \mathbf{j}\left(\frac{\partial v}{\partial t} + \frac{\partial v}{\partial x}\frac{dx}{dt} + \frac{\partial v}{\partial y}\frac{dy}{dt} + \frac{\partial v}{\partial z}\frac{dz}{dt} \right)$$
$$+ \mathbf{k}\left(\frac{\partial w}{\partial t} + \frac{\partial w}{\partial x}\frac{dx}{dt} + \frac{\partial w}{\partial y}\frac{dy}{dt} + \frac{\partial w}{\partial z}\frac{dz}{dt} \right).$$

Substituting this expression in (131-11) and setting $\mathbf{F} = \mathbf{i}F_x$ $+ \mathbf{j}F_y + \mathbf{k}F_z$ lead to three scalar equations, which are associated with the name of Euler.*

$$(131\text{-}12) \quad \begin{cases} \dfrac{\partial u}{\partial t} + \dfrac{\partial u}{\partial x}\,u + \dfrac{\partial u}{\partial y}\,v + \dfrac{\partial u}{\partial z}\,w = F_x - \dfrac{1}{\rho}\dfrac{\partial p}{\partial x}, \\[2mm] \dfrac{\partial v}{\partial t} + \dfrac{\partial v}{\partial x}\,u + \dfrac{\partial v}{\partial y}\,v + \dfrac{\partial v}{\partial z}\,w = F_y - \dfrac{1}{\rho}\dfrac{\partial p}{\partial y}, \\[2mm] \dfrac{\partial w}{\partial t} + \dfrac{\partial w}{\partial x}\,u + \dfrac{\partial w}{\partial y}\,v + \dfrac{\partial w}{\partial z}\,w = F_z - \dfrac{1}{\rho}\dfrac{\partial p}{\partial z}. \end{cases}$$

It is possible to show with the aid of these equations (and by making some simplifying assumptions) that the propagation of sound is governed approximately by the wave equation

$$\frac{\partial^2 s}{\partial t^2} = a^2 \nabla^2 s.$$

In this equation, a is the velocity of sound and s is related to the density ρ of the medium by the formula

$$s = \frac{\rho}{\rho_0} - 1,$$

where ρ_0 is the density of the medium at rest.

PROBLEMS

1. Show that in the case of irrotational flow of a fluid the equations of the stream lines (that is, the curves having the direction of the velocity $\mathbf{v}$) are determined from

$$\frac{dx}{v_x} = \frac{dy}{v_y} = \frac{dz}{v_z}.$$

Note that the stream lines are normal to the equipotential surfaces.

2. Prove that for irrotational flow of a fluid the circulation around every closed path is zero.

3. In a certain two-dimensional flow of a fluid the velocity potential is $\Phi = \frac{1}{2} \log (x^2 + y^2)$. Find the components of velocity, and show that a suitable stream function is $\Psi = \tan^{-1} (y/x)$.

---

* For various applications of these equations to problems in hydro- and aerodynamics, see L. Prandtl and O. G. Tietjens, Fundamentals of Hydro- and Aeromechanics; L. Prandtl and O. G. Tietjens, Applied Hydro- and Aeromechanics; H. Lamb, Hydrodynamics.

An exposition of the fundamentals of hydrodynamics will also be found in L. Page, Introduction to Theoretical Physics, Chaps. V and VI; H. Lamb, Hydrodynamics.

4. Discuss the two-dimensional flow of a fluid for which the velocity potential is $\Phi = cx$. What is the stream function for this flow?

5. Find the velocity potential of a two-dimensional flow if the stream function is $\Psi = 2xy$.

132. Curvilinear Coordinates. One of the chief advantages of the vector representation is that the equations appear in a form that is independent of the particular choice of the coordinate system.

The choice of the coordinate system to be used in any particular problem is dictated by the simplicity of the equation of the boundary of the surface entering in the problem. Thus, in treating the problems of Sec. 111 it was found expedient to use the cartesian system, because the equations of the boundaries of the rectangular plate are simply expressed with the aid of the equation $x = $ const. The cylindrical coordinate system, on the other hand, was used in treating the problem of the vibrating membrane (Sec. 113), because the circular boundary of the membrane then has the simple equation $\rho = $ const. Likewise, the advisability of using spherical coordinates in Sec. 114 was dictated by the fact that the equation of a sphere is given by the simple relation $\rho = $ const. In ellipsoidal coordinates the boundary of an ellipsoid is represented by the equation $u = $ const.

Up to this point the vector equations have been "translated" into the language of orthogonal cartesian coordinates, and it remains to translate the expressions for various vector operators into the languages of other coordinate systems that are commonly used in applied mathematics. It will be seen that all the coordinate systems used in this book are merely special cases of the general curvilinear system which will be discussed next.

Consider the three independent functions u, v, w of the independent variables x, y, z,

$$u = f_1(x, y, z),$$
$$v = f_2(x, y, z),$$
$$w = f_3(x, y, z),$$

where, by independent functions, it is meant that these equations can be solved uniquely for x, y, and z to yield

$$x = \varphi_1(u, v, w),$$
$$y = \varphi_2(u, v, w),$$
$$z = \varphi_3(u, v, w).$$

For example, in the case of spherical coordinates the latter set of equations has the form

$$x = \rho \sin \theta \cos \varphi,$$
$$y = \rho \sin \theta \sin \varphi,$$
$$z = \rho \cos \theta,$$

where $u = \rho$, $v = \theta$, and $w = \varphi$; for the cylindrical coordinate system, they are

$$x = \rho \cos \theta,$$
$$y = \rho \sin \theta,$$
$$z = z,$$

where $u = \rho$, $v = \theta$, and $w = z$.

If u, v, and w are assigned the fixed values u_0, v_0, w_0, respectively, the equations

(132-1)
$$\begin{cases} f_1(x, y, z) = u_0, \\ f_2(x, y, z) = v_0, \\ f_3(x, y, z) = w_0 \end{cases}$$

determine three surfaces. Two of these surfaces intersect in general in a space curve, and the third intersects the space curve in a point. Thus, a triplet of values u_0, v_0, w_0 determines a point in space. The surfaces (132-1) are called the coordinate surfaces, and the space curves in which each pair of surfaces intersect are known as the coordinate lines.

The rectangular coordinate system is a very special case of the general curvilinear system which corresponds to the choice

$$f_1 = x, \qquad f_2 = y, \qquad f_3 = z,$$

so that the surfaces in question are the planes

$$x = u_0, \qquad y = v_0, \qquad z = w_0.$$

The intersection of any two planes is a straight line and the third plane cuts this line in the point (u_0, v_0, w_0).

If the three families of surfaces (132-1) intersect orthogonally, the coordinate system is said to be orthogonal. This section will be restricted to the discussion of orthogonal systems only, for most physical problems can be treated successfully with their aid.

Examples of orthogonal systems that are in frequent use are the cartesian, spherical, cylindrical, and ellipsoidal systems. In spherical coordinates the surfaces (132-1) are concentric spheres $\rho = $ **const.**, a family of cones $\theta = $ const. having a common axis and vertex, and a family of planes $\varphi = $ const. intersecting in one straight line. In cylindrical coordinates the surfaces (132-1) represent a family of coaxial cylinders $\rho = $ const., a family of planes $\varphi = $ const. intersecting in the axis of the cylinders, and a family of parallel planes $z = $ const. that cut the axis of the cylinders at right angles. The ellipsoidal coordinate system makes use of the three confocal families of ellipsoids, unparted hyperboloids, and biparted hyperboloids.

Although the expression for the element of distance ds in cartesian coordinates is

$$ds = \sqrt{(dx)^2 + (dy)^2 + (dz)^2},$$

it is not so simple in either spherical or cylindrical coordinates. In fact, if the polar coordinates (r, θ) locate a point in a plane, the element of distance ds is given not by $\sqrt{(dr)^2 + (d\theta)^2}$ but by $\sqrt{(dr)^2 + (r\,d\theta)^2}$, where dr represents the change in distance measured along the radius vector and $r\,d\theta$ is the distance along the circular arc in the direction of increasing θ (Fig. 121).

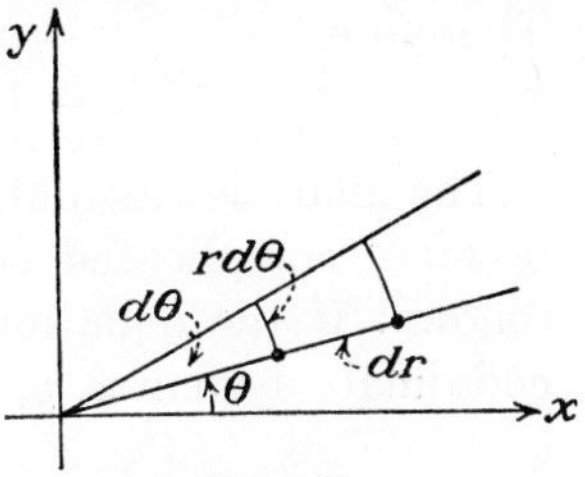

Similarly, in spherical coordinates the linear element of distance is given not by $\sqrt{(d\rho)^2 + (d\theta)^2 + (d\varphi)^2}$ but by

$$\sqrt{(d\rho)^2 + (\rho\,d\theta)^2 + (\rho \sin \theta \,d\varphi)^2},$$

FIG. 121.

where the distances in the direction of increasing ρ, θ, and φ, which are $d\rho$, $\rho\,d\theta$, and $\rho \sin \theta \,d\varphi$, are shown in Fig. 46.

By examining Fig. 47 the student can readily convince himself that the distances in cylindrical coordinates in the directions of increasing ρ, θ, and z are $d\rho$, $\rho\,d\theta$, and dz and that the element of distance is

$$ds = \sqrt{(d\rho)^2 + (\rho\,d\theta)^2 + (dz)^2}.$$

In general, the distance ds_u, measured in the direction of u between two surfaces for which u differs by an amount du, is

$$ds_u = e_1\,du,$$

where e_1 is some function of u, v, and w. Similarly,

$$ds_v = e_2\,dv$$

and

$$ds_w = e_3\,dw.$$

The quantities e_1, e_2, e_3 can be calculated analytically; but in most cases the functions e_1, e_2, e_3 can be obtained directly from a figure by inspection, for they are those quantities by which the increments du, dv, dw of the variables must be multiplied in order to give the distances measured in the directions of increasing u, v, and w. For example, in spherical coordinates the point is located with the aid of the numbers ρ, θ, φ. Setting $u = \rho$, $v = \theta$, $w = \varphi$, one obtains, from Fig. 46,

$$ds_\rho = d\rho, \qquad ds_\theta = \rho \, d\theta, \qquad ds_\varphi = \rho \sin \theta \, d\varphi,$$

so that

$$e_1 = 1, \qquad e_2 = \rho, \qquad e_3 = \rho \sin \theta.$$

In cylindrical coordinates,

$$u = \rho, \qquad v = \theta, \qquad w = z$$

and

$$ds_\rho = d\rho, \qquad ds_\theta = \rho \, d\theta, \qquad ds_z = dz.$$

Therefore,

$$e_1 = 1, \qquad e_2 = \rho, \qquad e_3 = 1.$$

The analytic calculation of the quantities e_1, e_2, e_3 in the case of more complicated coordinate systems can be performed as follows: If the equations of transformation from the cartesian coordinate system x, y, z to a curvilinear system u, v, w are

$$x = \varphi_1(u, v, w),$$
$$y = \varphi_2(u, v, w),$$
$$z = \varphi_3(u, v, w),$$

then

$$dx = \frac{\partial \varphi_1}{\partial u} du + \frac{\partial \varphi_1}{\partial v} dv + \frac{\partial \varphi_1}{\partial w} dw,$$

with similar expressions for dy and dz. Forming $(ds)^2 = (dx)^2 + (dy)^2 + (dz)^2$ with the aid of these expressions gives

$$
\begin{aligned}
(ds)^2 &= \left(\frac{\partial \varphi_1}{\partial u} du + \frac{\partial \varphi_1}{\partial v} dv + \frac{\partial \varphi_1}{\partial w} dw \right)^2 \\
&+ \left(\frac{\partial \varphi_2}{\partial u} du + \frac{\partial \varphi_2}{\partial v} dv + \frac{\partial \varphi_2}{\partial w} dw \right)^2 \\
&+ \left(\frac{\partial \varphi_3}{\partial u} du + \frac{\partial \varphi_3}{\partial v} dv + \frac{\partial \varphi_3}{\partial w} dw \right)^2 \\
&= g_{11} (du)^2 + 2g_{12} \, du \, dv + 2g_{13} \, du \, dw \\
&+ 2g_{23} \, dv \, dw + g_{22} (dv)^2 + g_{33} (dw)^2,
\end{aligned}
$$

where the coefficients g_{ij} are expressions in terms of the partial derivatives. For example,

$$g_{11} = \left(\frac{\partial \varphi_1}{\partial u}\right)^2 + \left(\frac{\partial \varphi_2}{\partial u}\right)^2 + \left(\frac{\partial \varphi_3}{\partial u}\right)^2,$$

$$g_{12} = \frac{\partial \varphi_1}{\partial u}\frac{\partial \varphi_1}{\partial v} + \frac{\partial \varphi_2}{\partial u}\frac{\partial \varphi_2}{\partial v} + \frac{\partial \varphi_3}{\partial u}\frac{\partial \varphi_3}{\partial v}, \text{ etc.}$$

If the system u, v, w is orthogonal, then it can be shown that $g_{ij} = 0$ if $i \neq j$, so that the quantities e_1, e_2, and e_3, defined above, are related to the "metric coefficients" g_{ij} as follows:

$$e_1 = \sqrt{g_{11}}, \qquad e_2 = \sqrt{g_{22}}, \qquad e_3 = \sqrt{g_{33}}.$$

Frequently, it is found more convenient to express a vector **A**, not in terms of its cartesian components as $A_x\mathbf{i} + A_y\mathbf{j} + A_z\mathbf{k}$, but in terms of its components in the direction of increasing u, v, and w. For example, in many problems requiring spherical symmetry it is found expedient to resolve a vector **A** in the directions specified by ρ, θ, and φ and express it in the form

$$\mathbf{A} = \boldsymbol{\rho}_1 A_\rho + \boldsymbol{\theta}_1 A_\theta + \hat{\boldsymbol{\phi}}_1 A_\varphi,$$

where $\boldsymbol{\rho}_1$, $\boldsymbol{\theta}_1$, and $\hat{\boldsymbol{\phi}}_1$ are the unit vectors in the directions of increasing ρ, θ, and φ, respectively.

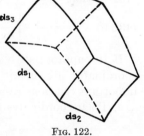

Consider a vector **A** that is expressed in terms of its components in the u-, v-, and w-directions as

(132-2) $\mathbf{A} = \mathbf{u}_1 A_u + \mathbf{v}_1 A_v + \mathbf{w}_1 A_w,$

where $\mathbf{u}_1$, $\mathbf{v}_1$, and $\mathbf{w}_1$ are unit vectors in the directions of increasing u, v, and w. The expression for the divergence of (132-2) can be obtained by the use of

Fig. 122.

a method employed in Sec. 124. All that is necessary is to replace $d\tau = dx\, dy\, dz$ by the corresponding volume element in curvilinear coordinates (see Fig. 122)

$$d\tau = ds_u\, ds_v\, ds_w = e_1 e_2 e_3\, du\, dv\, dw,$$

and the elements of area $dx\, dy$, $dy\, dz$, $dz\, dx$, by

$$d\sigma_{uv} = e_1 e_2\, du\, dv,$$
$$d\sigma_{vw} = e_2 e_3\, dv\, dw,$$
$$d\sigma_{uw} = e_1 e_3\, du\, dw.$$

The result of such substitutions leads to the general expression for div **A** in curvilinear coordinates, namely,

$$(132\text{-}3) \quad \operatorname{div} \mathbf{A} = \frac{1}{e_1 e_2 e_3} \left[\frac{\partial(A_u e_2 e_3)}{\partial u} + \frac{\partial(A_v e_1 e_3)}{\partial v} + \frac{\partial(A_w e_1 e_2)}{\partial w} \right].$$

Similarly, it is found that

$$(132\text{-}4) \quad \operatorname{curl} \mathbf{A} = \mathbf{u}_1 \frac{1}{e_2 e_3} \left[\frac{\partial(e_3 A_w)}{\partial v} - \frac{\partial(e_2 A_v)}{\partial w} \right]$$
$$+ \mathbf{v}_1 \frac{1}{e_3 e_1} \left[\frac{\partial(e_1 A_u)}{\partial w} - \frac{\partial(e_3 A_w)}{\partial u} \right] + \mathbf{w}_1 \frac{1}{e_1 e_2} \left[\frac{\partial(e_2 A_v)}{\partial u} - \frac{\partial(e_1 A_u)}{\partial v} \right].$$

The expression for the gradient of a scalar function is obtained readily, for

$$\nabla \Phi = \mathbf{u}_1 \frac{\partial \Phi}{\partial s_u} + \mathbf{v}_1 \frac{\partial \Phi}{\partial s_v} + \mathbf{w}_1 \frac{\partial \Phi}{\partial s_w},$$

so that

$$(132\text{-}5) \qquad \nabla \Phi = \frac{\mathbf{u}_1}{e_1} \frac{\partial \Phi}{\partial u} + \frac{\mathbf{v}_1}{e_2} \frac{\partial \Phi}{\partial v} + \frac{\mathbf{w}_1}{e_3} \frac{\partial \Phi}{\partial w}.$$

Inasmuch as div $\nabla \Phi = \nabla^2 \Phi$, it is checked readily with the aid of (132-3) that

$$(132\text{-}6) \quad \nabla^2 \Phi = \frac{1}{e_1 e_2 e_3} \left[\frac{\partial}{\partial u} \left(\frac{e_2 e_3}{e_1} \frac{\partial \Phi}{\partial u} \right) + \frac{\partial}{\partial v} \left(\frac{e_1 e_3}{e_2} \frac{\partial \Phi}{\partial v} \right) + \frac{\partial}{\partial w} \left(\frac{e_1 e_2}{e_3} \frac{\partial \Phi}{\partial w} \right) \right].$$

If the appropriate values of e_1, e_2, e_3, for various systems of coordinates, are substituted in (132-3) and (132-6), the following important relations result:

a. Polar coordinates in the plane:

$$\operatorname{div} \mathbf{A} = \frac{1}{r} \left[\frac{\partial(rA_r)}{\partial r} + \frac{\partial A_\theta}{\partial \theta} \right],$$

$$\nabla^2 \Phi = \frac{1}{r} \left[\frac{\partial}{\partial r} \left(r \frac{\partial \Phi}{\partial r} \right) + \frac{\partial}{\partial \theta} \left(\frac{1}{r} \frac{\partial \Phi}{\partial \theta} \right) \right].$$

b. Cylindrical coordinates:

$$\operatorname{div} \mathbf{A} = \frac{1}{\rho} \frac{\partial(\rho A_\rho)}{\partial \rho} + \frac{1}{\rho} \frac{\partial(A_\theta)}{\partial \theta} + \frac{\partial(A_z)}{\partial z},$$

$$\nabla^2 \Phi = \frac{1}{\rho} \frac{\partial \left(\rho \dfrac{\partial \Phi}{\partial \rho} \right)}{\partial \rho} + \frac{1}{\rho^2} \frac{\partial^2 \Phi}{\partial \theta^2} + \frac{\partial^2 \Phi}{\partial z^2}.$$

c. Spherical coordinates:

$$\text{div } \mathbf{A} = \frac{1}{\rho^2} \frac{\partial(\rho^2 A_\rho)}{\partial \rho} + \frac{1}{\rho \sin \theta} \frac{\partial(\sin \theta \, A_\theta)}{\partial \theta} + \frac{1}{\rho \sin \theta} \frac{\partial(A_\varphi)}{\partial \varphi},$$

$$\nabla^2 \Phi = \frac{1}{\rho^2} \frac{\partial \left(\rho^2 \dfrac{\partial \Phi}{\partial \rho} \right)}{\partial \rho} + \frac{1}{\rho^2 \sin \theta} \frac{\partial \left(\sin \theta \dfrac{\partial \Phi}{\partial \theta} \right)}{\partial \theta} + \frac{1}{\rho^2 \sin^2 \theta} \frac{\partial^2 \Phi}{\partial \varphi^2}.$$

PROBLEMS

1. Using (132-5), write the expressions for $\nabla \Phi$ in cylindrical and spherical coordinates.

2. Show that (132-4) can be written as

$$\text{curl } \mathbf{A} = \frac{1}{e_1 e_2 e_3} \begin{vmatrix} e_1 \mathbf{u}_1 & e_2 \mathbf{v}_1 & e_3 \mathbf{w}_1 \\ \dfrac{\partial}{\partial u} & \dfrac{\partial}{\partial v} & \dfrac{\partial}{\partial w} \\ e_1 A_u & e_2 A_v & e_3 A_w \end{vmatrix}.$$

3. Express curl $\mathbf{A}$ in cylindrical and spherical coordinates (see Prob. 2).

4. Show that $\Phi = 1/\rho$ satisfies Laplace's equation.

5. Find the metric coefficients g_{ij} and hence the quantities e_1, e_2, e_3 for polar and spherical coordinates. Verify that, in these cases, $g_{ij} = 0$ if $i \neq j$.

6. If the position vector of the point (u, v, w) is

$$\mathbf{r} = \mathbf{i}\varphi_1(u, v, w) + \mathbf{j}\varphi_2(u, v, w) + \mathbf{k}\varphi_3(u, v, w)$$
$$= \mathbf{i}x + \mathbf{j}y + \mathbf{k}z,$$

show that the metric coefficients g_{ij} are given by the formulas $g_{ij} = (\mathbf{a}_i, \mathbf{a}_j)$, where $\mathbf{a}_1 = \partial \mathbf{r}/\partial u$, $\mathbf{a}_2 = \partial \mathbf{r}/\partial v$, $\mathbf{a}_3 = \partial \mathbf{r}/\partial w$.
Hint: $(ds)^2 = (\mathbf{dr}, \mathbf{dr})$.

7. Referring to Prob. 6, show that the volume element is

$$d\tau = \pm (\mathbf{a}_1, [\mathbf{a}_2, \mathbf{a}_3]) \, du \, dv \, dw.$$

8. The expression for $(ds)^2$ in parabolic coordinates is

$$(ds)^2 = (u^2 + v^2)[(du)^2 + (dv)^2] + u^2 v^2 (d\varphi)^2.$$

What is the form assumed by Laplace's equation in these coordinates'

9. Show that

$$\Phi = \rho \cos \theta + \frac{\cos \theta}{\rho^2}$$

satisfies Laplace's equation in spherical coordinates.

10. The force per unit charge due to a dipole of constant strength p is given by

$$\mathbf{F} = \mathbf{r}_1 \frac{2p \cos \theta}{r^3} + \boldsymbol{\theta}_1 \frac{p \sin \theta}{r^3}.$$

Compute div $\mathbf{F}$ and curl $\mathbf{F}$.

CHAPTER X

COMPLEX VARIABLE

133. Complex Numbers. The analysis in the preceding chapters was concerned principally with functions of real variables, that is, such variables as can be represented graphically by points on a number axis, say the x-axis of the cartesian coordinate system. The reader is familiar with the fact that the calculation of the zeros of the function $f(x) = ax^2 + bx + c$, in the case where the discriminant $b^2 - 4ac$ is negative, necessitates the introduction of complex numbers of the form $u + iv$, where u and v are real numbers and i is a number such that $i^2 = -1$.

A number of the form $u + iv$ can be represented by a point in a plane referred to a pair of orthogonal x- and y-axes if it is agreed that the number u represents the abscissa and v the ordinate of

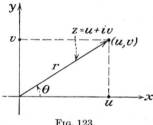

Fig. 123.

the point (Fig. 123). No confusion is likely to arise if the point (u, v), associated with the number $u + iv$, is labeled simply $u + iv$. It is clear that the point (u, v) can be located by the terminus of a vector z whose origin is at the origin O of the coordinate system. In this manner a one-to-one correspondence is established between the totality of vectors in the xy-plane and the complex numbers. The vector z may be thought to represent the resultant of two vectors, one of which is of magnitude u and directed along the x-axis, and the other of magnitude v and directed along the y-axis. Thus,

$$z = u + iv,$$

where u is spoken of as the real part of the complex number z and iv as the imaginary part. Therefore, if the points of the plane are referred to a pair of coordinate axes, one can establish a correspondence between the pair of real numbers (u, v) and a single complex number $u + iv$. In this case the xy-plane is called the plane of a complex variable, the x-axis is called the real axis, and the y-axis is called the imaginary axis.

If v vanishes, then

$$z = u + 0 \cdot i = u$$

is a number corresponding to some point on the real axis. Accordingly, this mode of representation of complex numbers (due to Gauss and Argand) includes as a special case the usual way of representing real numbers on the number axis.

The equality of two complex numbers,

$$a + ib = c + id,$$

is interpreted to be equivalent to the two equations

$$a = c \quad \text{and} \quad b = d.$$

In particular, $a + ib = 0$ is true if, and only if, $a = 0$ and $b = 0$.

If the polar coordinates of the point (u, v) (Fig. 123) are (r, θ), then

$$u = r \cos \theta \quad \text{and} \quad v = r \sin \theta$$

so that

$$r = \sqrt{u^2 + v^2} \quad \text{and} \quad \theta = \tan^{-1} \frac{v}{u}.$$

The number r is called the *modulus*, or *absolute value*, and θ is called the *argument*, or *amplitude*, of the complex number $z = u + iv$. It is clear that the argument of a complex number is not unique; and if one writes it as $\theta + 2k\pi$, where $-\pi < \theta \leq \pi$ and $k = 0, \pm 1, \pm 2, \cdots$, then θ is called the principal argument of z. The modulus of the complex number z is frequently denoted by using absolute value signs, so that

$$r = |z| = |u + iv| = \sqrt{u^2 + v^2},$$

and the argument θ is denoted by the symbol

$$\theta = \arg z.$$

The student is assumed to be familiar with the fundamental algebraic operations on complex numbers, and these will not be entered upon in detail here. It should be recalled that

$$z_1 + z_2 = (x_1 + iy_1) + (x_2 + iy_2) = (x_1 + x_2) + i(y_1 + y_2),$$
$$z_1 \cdot z_2 = (x_1 + iy_1) \cdot (x_2 + iy_2) = (x_1 x_2 - y_1 y_2) + i(x_1 y_2 + x_2 y_1),$$
$$\frac{z_1}{z_2} = \frac{x_1 + iy_1}{x_2 + iy_2} = \frac{x_1 x_2 + y_1 y_2}{x_2^2 + y_2^2} + i \frac{x_2 y_1 - x_1 y_2}{x_2^2 + y_2^2},$$

provided that $|z_2| = \sqrt{x_2^2 + y_2^2} \neq 0$.

It follows from the polar mode of representation that

$$z_1 \cdot z_2 = r_1(\cos \theta_1 + i \sin \theta_1) \cdot r_2(\cos \theta_2 + i \sin \theta_2)$$
$$= r_1 r_2[\cos (\theta_1 + \theta_2) + i \sin (\theta_1 + \theta_2)];$$

that is, *the modulus of the product is equal to the product of the moduli and the argument of the product is equal to the sum of the arguments.* Moreover,

$$\frac{z_1}{z_2} = \frac{r_1 \ (\cos \theta_1 + i \sin \theta_1)}{r_2 \ (\cos \theta_2 + i \sin \theta_2)} = \frac{r_1}{r_2} [\cos (\theta_1 - \theta_2) + i \sin (\theta_1 - \theta_2)],$$

so that *the modulus of the quotient is the quotient of the moduli and the argument of the quotient is obtained by subtracting the argument*

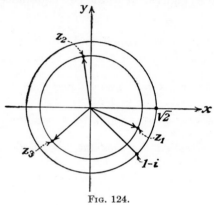

Fig. 124.

of the denominator from that of the numerator. If n is a positive integer, one obtains the formulas of De Moivre, namely,

$$z^n = [r(\cos \theta + i \sin \theta)]^n = r^n(\cos n\theta + i \sin n\theta),$$

$$\sqrt[n]{z} = \{r[\cos (\theta + 2k\pi) + i \sin (\theta + 2k\pi)]\}^{\frac{1}{n}}$$
$$= r^{\frac{1}{n}} \left(\cos \frac{\theta + 2k\pi}{n} + i \sin \frac{\theta + 2k\pi}{n} \right)$$
$$= R(\cos \varphi + i \sin \varphi),$$

so that

$$\varphi = \frac{\theta + 2k\pi}{n}, \qquad (k = 0, 1, 2, \cdots, n - 1).$$

This last formula can be illustrated by finding the expressions for the cube roots of $z = 1 - i$. Since $u = 1$ and $v = -1$, it follows that $r = \sqrt{2}$ and $\theta = \tan^{-1} \left(\frac{-1}{1} \right)$. Hence

$$\sqrt[3]{z} = \sqrt[6]{2}\left(\cos\frac{-\dfrac{\pi}{4} + 2k\pi}{3} + i\sin\frac{-\dfrac{\pi}{4} + 2k\pi}{3}\right).$$

Assigning k the values 0, 1, and 2 gives the values of the three roots as (Fig. 124)

$$z_1 = \sqrt[6]{2}\left[\cos\left(-\frac{\pi}{12}\right) + i\sin\left(-\frac{\pi}{12}\right)\right],$$

$$z_2 = \sqrt[6]{2}\left(\cos\frac{7\pi}{12} + i\sin\frac{7\pi}{12}\right),$$

and

$$z_3 = \sqrt[6]{2}\left(\cos\frac{5\pi}{4} + i\sin\frac{5\pi}{4}\right).$$

The following important inequalities will be recalled, for they are used frequently in this chapter.

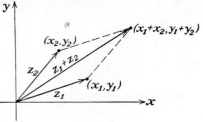

(133-1) $|z_1 + z_2|$
      $\leq |z_1| + |z_2|,$

that is, *the modulus of the sum is less than or equal to the sum of the moduli.* This follows at once upon observing (Fig. 125) that the sum of two

Fig. 125.

sides of the triangle is not less than the third side.

(133-2) $|z_1 + z_2| \geq |z_1| - |z_2|,$

that is, *the modulus of the sum is greater than or equal to the differ-ence of the moduli.* This follows from the fact that the length of one side of a triangle is not less than the difference of the other two sides.

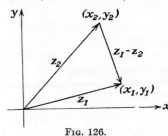

Fig. 126.

(133-3) $|z_1| - |z_2|$
      $\leq |z_1 - z_2| \leq |z_1| + |z_2|.$

This follows from Fig. 126.

PROBLEMS

1. Find the modulus and argument of

(a) $1 + i\sqrt{3}$,   (b) $2 + 2i$,   (c) $(1 + i)/(1 - i)$

2. If $z_1 = 3e^{\frac{\pi}{4}i}$ and $z_2 = e^{-\frac{\pi}{6}i}$, find $z_1 \cdot z_2$ and z_1/z_2. Illustrate the results graphically.

3. Under what conditions does one have the following relations?

(a) $|z_1 + z_2| = |z_1| + |z_2|$;

(b) $|z_1 + z_2| = |z_1| - |z_2|$.

4. Setting $z = r(\cos \theta + i \sin \theta)$, show, with the aid of the formula of De Moivre $z^n = r^n(\cos n\theta + i \sin n\theta)$, that

$$\cos 2\theta = \cos^2 \theta - \sin^2 \theta \quad \text{and} \quad \sin 2\theta = 2 \sin \theta \cos \theta.$$

5. Find all the fifth roots of unity, and represent them graphically.

6. Find all the values of $\sqrt[5]{1 + i}$ and $\sqrt[3]{i}$, and represent them graphically.

7. Find all the roots of the equation $z^n - 1 = 0$.

8. Write the following complex numbers in the form $a + bi$:

(a) $\sqrt{i}$;

(b) $\sqrt{1 - i}$;

(c) $(1 - \sqrt{3}\, i)^3$;

(d) $\dfrac{(1 + i)^2}{1 - i}$;

(e) $\dfrac{2 - \sqrt{3}\, i}{1 + i}$.

9. Express the following functions in the form $u + iv$:

(a) $\dfrac{1}{z - i}$;

(b) $\dfrac{z - i}{z + i}$;

(c) $z^2 - z + 1$;

(d) $\dfrac{1}{z^2 + i}$;

(e) $\dfrac{1}{z}$.

10. The conjugate of a complex number $a + ib$ is defined as $a - ib$. Prove that

(a) The conjugate of the product of two complex numbers is equal to the product of the conjugates of the complex numbers.

(b) The conjugate of the quotient of two complex numbers is equal to the quotient of the conjugates of the complex numbers.

134. Elementary Functions of a Complex Variable. A complex quantity $z = x + iy$, where x and y are real variables, is called a complex variable. If the assignment of values to z determines corresponding values of some expression $f(z)$, then $f(z)$ is said to be a *function of the complex variable z*. For example, if

$$f(z) = z^2,$$

the values of $f(z)$ can be determined by recalling that, if $z = x + iy$, then

$$z^2 = x^2 - y^2 + 2ixy.$$

So long as the functions under consideration involve only the operations of addition, subtraction, multiplication, division, and root extraction, the discussion of Sec. 133 provides methods of determining the values of these functions when arbitrary values are assigned to z. Thus, if $f(z)$ is any rational function of z, that is, the quotient of two polynomials so that

$$f(z) = \frac{a_0 z^n + a_1 z^{n-1} + \cdots + a_n}{b_0 z^m + b_1 z^{m-1} + \cdots + b_m},$$

there is no difficulty in ascertaining its values. The discussion permits one to ascribe a meaning even to such an expression as

$$f(z) = \frac{1}{\sqrt{z^2 - 1}}.$$

For, if $z = x + iy$, then

$$\sqrt{z^2 - 1} = \sqrt{x^2 - y^2 - 1 + 2ixy}$$
$$= [r(\cos \theta + i \sin \theta)]^{\frac{1}{2}},$$

where

$$r = \sqrt{(x^2 - y^2 - 1)^2 + 4x^2 y^2} \quad \text{and} \quad \theta = \tan^{-1} \frac{2xy}{x^2 - y^2 - 1}.$$

Applying De Moivre's formula gives

$$\sqrt{z^2 - 1} = r^{\frac{1}{2}}[\cos \tfrac{1}{2}(\theta + 2k\pi) + i \sin \tfrac{1}{2}(\theta + 2k\pi)], \quad (k = 0, 1),$$

and therefore,

$$\frac{1}{\sqrt{z^2 - 1}} = r^{-\frac{1}{2}} \left(\cos \frac{\theta + 2k\pi}{2} - i \sin \frac{\theta + 2k\pi}{2} \right), \quad (k = 0, 1).$$

Matters become somewhat more involved when it is necessary to define transcendental functions of z such as

$$e^z, \sin z, \log z, \text{ etc.}$$

It is evident that it is desirable to define these functions so that they will include as special cases the corresponding functions of the real variable x. It was indicated in Sec. 73 that the series

$$e^x = 1 + x + \frac{x^2}{2!} + \frac{x^3}{3!} + \cdots,$$

which converges for all real values of x, can be used to define the function e^z, where $z = x + iy$, so that

$$e^z = e^{x+iy} = e^x e^{iy} = e^x \left[\left(1 - \frac{y^2}{2!} + \frac{y^4}{4!} - \cdots \right) \right.$$
$$\left. + i \left(y - \frac{y^3}{3!} + \frac{y^5}{5!} - \cdots \right) \right] = e^x(\cos y + i \sin y).$$

Also, from Sec. 73,

$$\cos y = \frac{e^{yi} + e^{-yi}}{2},$$
$$\sin y = \frac{e^{yi} - e^{-yi}}{2i}.$$

These formulas lead one to define the trigonometric functions for a complex variable z as

$$\cos z = \frac{e^{zi} + e^{-zi}}{2}, \qquad \sin z = \frac{e^{zi} - e^{-zi}}{2i},$$

$$\tan z = \frac{\sin z}{\cos z}, \qquad \cot z = \frac{\cos z}{\sin z},$$

$$\sec z = \frac{1}{\cos z}, \qquad \csc z = \frac{1}{\sin z}.$$

It can be easily verified by the reader that these definitions permit one to use the usual relations between these functions, so that, for example,

$$e^{z_1} \cdot e^{z_2} = e^{z_1 + z_2},$$
$$\sin^2 z + \cos^2 z = 1,$$
$$\sin (z_1 + z_2) = \sin z_1 \cos z_2 + \cos z_1 \sin z_2.$$

The logarithm of a complex number z is defined in the same way as in the real variable analysis. Thus, if

$$w = \log z,$$

then

$$z = e^w.$$

Setting $w = u + iv$ gives

$$z = e^{u+iv} = e^u(\cos v + i \sin v).$$

On the other hand, z can be written as

$$z = x + iy = r(\cos \theta + i \sin \theta).$$

Therefore,

$$r(\cos\,\theta + i\,\sin\,\theta) = e^u(\cos\,v + i\,\sin\,v),$$

which gives

$$e^u = r, \qquad v = \theta + 2k\pi, \qquad (k = 0, \pm 1, \pm 2, \pm \cdots).$$

Then, since u and r are real, $u = \log r$, so that

$$(134\text{-}1) \qquad w = u + iv = \log z = \log r + (\theta + 2k\pi)i.$$

Hence, the logarithm of a complex number has infinitely many values, corresponding to the different choices of the argument of the complex number. Setting $k = 0$, one obtains the principal argument of $\log z$, if it is assumed that $-\pi < \theta \le \pi$.

It is obvious that (134-1) provides a suitable definition of $\log z$ for all values of z with the exception of $z = 0$, for which $\log z$ is undefined.

The definition (134-1) permits one to interpret the complex power w of a complex variable z by means of the formula

$$z^w = e^{w\,\log z};$$

and since $\log z$ is an infinitely many-valued function, it follows that, in general, z^w likewise has infinitely many values.

PROBLEMS

1. Verify the formulas

(a) $e^{z_1} \cdot e^{z_2} = e^{z_1 + z_2}$;

(b) $\sin^2 z + \cos^2 z = 1$;

(c) $\cos\,(z_1 + z_2) = \cos z_1 \cos z_2 - \sin z_1 \sin z_2$;

(d) $\cos iz = \cosh z$;

(e) $\sin iz = i \sinh z$.

2. Represent graphically the complex numbers defined by the following:

(a) $\log i$;

(b) $\log\,(-1)$;

(c) $\log\,(1 - \sqrt{3}\,i)$;

(d) i^i;

(e) $e^{\pi i}$.

3. Show that

(a) $\tan z = \dfrac{1}{i}\,\dfrac{e^{i2z} - 1}{e^{i2z} + 1}$;

(b) $\cot z = i\,\dfrac{e^{i2z} + 1}{e^{i2z} - 1}$.

4. Express tan z in the form $u + iv$.

5. Express sin z in the form $u + iv$.

6. If a and b are real integers, show that

$$(re^{\theta i})^{a+bi} = r^a e^{-b\theta}[\cos(a\theta + b\log r) + i\sin(a\theta + b\log r)].$$

7. Write in the form $r(\cos\theta + i\sin\theta)$

(a) $(1 + i)^i$; (d) 1^i;

(b) $(1 - i)^{1-i}$; (e) 2^{1+i}.

(c) $i^{(1-i)}$;

135. Properties of Functions of a Complex Variable. Let $w = f(z)$ denote some functional relationship connecting w with z. If z is replaced by $x + iy$, w can be written as

$$w = f(x + iy) = u(x, y) + iv(x, y),$$

where $u(x, y)$ and $v(x, y)$ are real functions of the variables x and y. As an example, one may consider the simple function

$$w = z^2 = (x + iy)^2 = x^2 - y^2 + 2ixy.$$

If x and y are allowed to approach the values x_0 and y_0, respectively, then it is said that the complex variable $z = x + iy$ approaches $z_0 = x_0 + iy_0$. Thus the statement

$$z \to z_0, \qquad \text{or} \qquad x + iy \to x_0 + iy_0,$$

is equivalent to the two statements

$$x \to x_0 \qquad \text{and} \qquad y \to y_0.$$

Since $f(z_0)$ is, in general, a complex number, one extends the definition of continuity in the following way: *The function $f(z)$ is said to be continuous at the point $z = z_0$ provided that*

(135-1) $$f(z) \to f(z_0) \qquad \text{when } z \to z_0.$$

Since $f(z) = u(x, y) + iv(x, y)$ and $f(z_0) = u(x_0, y_0) + iv(x_0, y_0)$, the statement (135-1) implies the continuity of the functions $u(x, y)$ and $v(x, y)$. If the function $f(z)$ is continuous at every point of some region R in the z-plane, then $f(z)$ is said to be *continuous in the region R.*

The complex quantities z and w can be represented on separate complex planes, which will be called the z-plane and the w-plane, respectively. Thus the functional relationship $w = f(z)$ sets up a correspondence between the points (x, y) of the z-plane and the points (u, v) of the w-plane (Figs. 127 and 128).

If the variable $z = x + iy$ acquires an increment Δz, then (Fig. 127)

$$z + \Delta z = (x + \Delta x) + i(y + \Delta y)$$

and

$$\Delta z = \Delta x + i\Delta y.$$

The change in $w = f(z)$, which corresponds to the change Δz in z, can be denoted by Δw (Fig. 128), and one defines the derivative of w with respect to z to be the function $f'(z)$ such that

$$(135\text{-}2) \qquad f'(z) = \lim_{\Delta z \to 0} \frac{f(z + \Delta z) - f(z)}{\Delta z},$$

where the limit must exist and be independent of the mode of approach of Δz to zero.

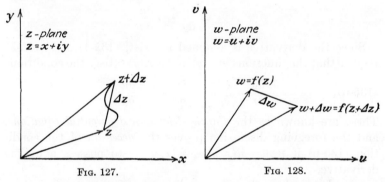

FIG. 127.   FIG. 128.

It should be noted that this requirement, that the limit of the difference quotient have the same value no matter how Δz is allowed to approach zero, narrows down greatly the class of functions of a complex variable that possess derivatives. Thus, consider the point P in the z-plane that corresponds to $z = x + iy$, and let Q be determined by $z + \Delta z = (x + \Delta x) + i(y + \Delta y)$. In allowing the point Q to approach P, one can choose any one of infinitely many paths joining Q with P, and the definition (135-2) demands that the limit $f'(z)$ be the same regardless of which one of the paths is chosen.

Let it be assumed for the moment that $w = f(z)$ has a unique* derivative at the point P; then

---

* It is assumed throughout that we are concerned with single-valued functions; hence, the discussion of the derivatives of such functions as $\sqrt{1 - z}$, for example, is restricted to a study of one of the branches of the function.

$$(135\text{-}3) \qquad f'(z) = \lim_{\Delta z \to 0} \frac{f(z + \Delta z) - f(z)}{\Delta z},$$

where

$$f(z) = u(x, y) + iv(x, y).$$

If Q is to approach P along a straight line parallel to the x-axis, then $\Delta y = 0$, $\Delta z = \Delta x$, and

$$(135\text{-}4) \qquad \frac{df}{dz} = \frac{\partial f}{\partial x} = \frac{\partial u}{\partial x} + i \frac{\partial v}{\partial x}.$$

On the other hand, if Q approaches P along a line parallel to the y-axis, then $\Delta x = 0$, $\Delta z = i \, \Delta y$, and

$$(135\text{-}5) \qquad \frac{df}{dz} = \frac{1}{i} \frac{\partial f}{\partial y} = \frac{1}{i} \left(\frac{\partial u}{\partial y} + i \frac{\partial v}{\partial y} \right)$$
$$= \frac{\partial v}{\partial y} - i \frac{\partial u}{\partial y}.$$

Since the derivative is assumed to exist, (135-4) and (135-5) require that the functions $u(x, y)$ and $v(x, y)$ satisfy the conditions

$$(135\text{-}6) \qquad \frac{\partial u}{\partial x} = \frac{\partial v}{\partial y}, \qquad \frac{\partial v}{\partial x} = - \frac{\partial u}{\partial y}.$$

These are known as the *Cauchy-Riemann differential equations*, and the foregoing discussion proves the *necessity* of the condition (135-6) if $f(z) = u(x, y) + iv(x, y)$ is to possess a unique derivative.

In order to show that the conditions (135-6) are *sufficient* for the existence of the unique derivative $f'(z)$, one must suppose that the functions $u(x, y)$ and $v(x, y)$ possess continuous partial derivatives.*

It is not difficult to show that the usual formulas for the differentiation of the elementary functions of a real variable remain valid, so that, for example,

$$\frac{dz^n}{dz} = nz^{n-1}, \qquad \frac{de^z}{dz} = e^z, \qquad \frac{d \sin z}{dz} = \cos z, \text{ etc.}$$

As an illustration of the application of the formulas (135-4) and (135-5), consider the calculation of the derivative of

$$w = e^z = e^{x+iy}$$

or

$$w = u + iv = e^x(\cos y + i \sin y).$$

---

* Only the existence of these derivatives was required in the proof of the necessity. See references at the end of Sec. 141.

Here, $u = e^x \cos y$, $v = e^x \sin y$, and it follows that

$$\frac{\partial u}{\partial x} = e^x \cos y, \qquad \frac{\partial u}{\partial y} = -e^x \sin y,$$

$$\frac{\partial v}{\partial x} = e^x \sin y, \qquad \frac{\partial v}{\partial y} = e^x \cos y.$$

Since Eqs. (135-6) are satisfied and the partial derivatives are continuous, dw/dz can be calculated with the aid of either (135-4) or (135-5). Then,

$$\frac{dw}{dz} = e^x \cos y + i e^x \sin y = e^z.$$

The functions of a complex variable z that possess derivatives are called *analytic* or *holomorphic.**   A point at which an analytic function ceases to have a derivative is called a *singular point*. It is possible to prove† that, if $f(z)$ is analytic in some region R of the z-plane, then not only the first partial derivatives of u and v exist throughout the region R, but also those of all higher orders.

This last statement leads to an important consequence of Eqs. (135-6).   Differentiating (135-6) gives

$$\frac{\partial}{\partial x}\left(\frac{\partial u}{\partial x}\right) = \frac{\partial}{\partial x}\left(\frac{\partial v}{\partial y}\right) \qquad \text{and} \qquad \frac{\partial}{\partial y}\left(\frac{\partial v}{\partial x}\right) = -\frac{\partial}{\partial y}\left(\frac{\partial u}{\partial y}\right),$$

and adding gives

$$\frac{\partial^2 u}{\partial x^2} + \frac{\partial^2 u}{\partial y^2} = 0.$$

Similarly, one obtains

$$\frac{\partial^2 v}{\partial x^2} + \frac{\partial^2 v}{\partial y^2} = 0.$$

Hence, the real and imaginary parts of an analytic function satisfy Laplace's equation.

On the other hand, if a function $u(x, y)$ satisfying Laplace's equation is given, one can construct an analytic function $f(z)$ whose real part is u.   Multiplying the first of Eqs. (135-6) by dy and the second by dx and adding give

$$dv = \frac{\partial v}{\partial x}\,dx + \frac{\partial v}{\partial y}\,dy = -\frac{\partial u}{\partial y}\,dx + \frac{\partial u}{\partial x}\,dy.$$

Then, since $\partial u/\partial y$ and $\partial u/\partial x$ are known,

$$(135\text{-}7) \qquad v(x, y) = \int_{(x_0, y_0)}^{(x, y)} \left(-\frac{\partial u}{\partial y}\,dx + \frac{\partial u}{\partial x}\,dy \right),$$

* The term *regular* is also used.
† See Sec. 140.

where the line integral (135-7) will not be ambiguous if it is independent of the path joining some fixed point (x_0, y_0) to the point (x, y). Applying the conditions for the independence of the path,* namely,

$$\frac{\partial}{\partial y}\left(-\frac{\partial u}{\partial y}\right) = \frac{\partial}{\partial x}\left(\frac{\partial u}{\partial x}\right),$$

gives

$$\frac{\partial^2 u}{\partial x^2} + \frac{\partial^2 u}{\partial y^2} = 0,$$

which is precisely the condition assumed to be satisfied by $u(x, y)$. Since the line integral (135-7) depends on the choice of the point (x_0, y_0), it is clear that the function $v(x, y)$ is determined to within an arbitrary real constant, and hence the function $f(z) = u + iv$ is determined save for a pure imaginary additive constant.

It may be further remarked that the function $v(x, y)$ may turn out to be multiple-valued (if the region of integration is not simply connected) even though $u(x, y)$ is single-valued. The connection of analytic functions with Laplace's equation is one of the principal reasons for the great importance of the theory of functions of a complex variable in applied mathematics.†

PROBLEMS

1. Determine which of the following functions are analytic functions of the variable $z = x + iy$:

(a) $x - iy$;

(b) $x^2 - y^2 + 2ixy$;

(c) $\frac{1}{2} \log (x^2 + y^2) + i \tan^{-1} (y/x)$;

(d) $x/(x^2 + y^2) + iy/(x^2 + y^2)$;

(e) $x/(x^2 + y^2) - iy/(x^2 + y^2)$.

2. Verify the following formulas:

(a) $\dfrac{d(\cos z)}{dz} = -\sin z$;

(b) $\dfrac{d(\log z)}{dz} = \dfrac{1}{z}$;

(c) $\dfrac{d(\tan z)}{dz} = \sec^2 z \cdot$

* See Sec. 63.

† See, in this connection, Secs. 66, 111, and 130.

(d) $\dfrac{d\sqrt{1+z}}{dz} = \dfrac{1}{2\sqrt{1+z}}$;

(e) $\dfrac{d}{dz}\left(\dfrac{1}{1-z}\right) = \dfrac{1}{(1-z)^2}$.

3. Find a function w such that $w = u + iv$ is analytic if

(a) $u = x^2 - y^2$;

(b) $u = \dfrac{x}{(x^2 + y^2)}$;

(c) $u = x$;

(d) $u = \log\sqrt{x^2 + y^2}$;

(e) $u = \cosh y \cos x$.

4. Prove that

(a) $\sinh z \equiv \frac{1}{2}(e^z - e^{-z})$ is analytic;

(b) $\cos(z + 2k\pi) = \cos z$, $(k = 0, \pm 1, \pm 2, \cdots)$;

(c) $\sinh(z + 2ik\pi) = \sinh z$, $(k = 0, \pm 1, \pm 2, \cdots)$;

(d) $\log z_1 z_2 = \log z_1 + \log z_2$;

(e) $\log z^a = a \log z$, where a is a complex number.

5. Show how to construct an analytic function $f(z) = u(x, y) + iv(x, y)$ if $v(x, y)$ is given, and construct $f(z)$ if $v = 3x^2y - y^3$.

6. An incompressible fluid flowing over the xy-plane has the velocity potential $\Phi = x^2 - y^2$. Find a stream function Ψ.

7. Referring to Prob. 6, what is the velocity potential if the stream function is $\Psi = 3x^2y - y^3$?

136. Integration of Complex Functions. Let C be a curve defined by the parametric equations

$$x = \varphi(t),$$
$$y = \psi(t),$$

where φ and ψ are real differentiable functions of the real variable t. Consider a continuous (but not necessarily analytic) function $f(z)$, of the complex variable $z = x + iy$, defined at all points

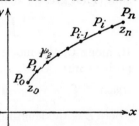

FIG. 129.

of C. Divide the curve C into n parts by inserting the points $P_0, P_1, \cdots, P_{n-1}, P_n$, where P_0 coincides with the initial point z_0 of the curve and P_n with the end point z_n (Fig. 129). Let ζ_i be any point on the arc of the curve joining P_{i-1} with P_i, and form the sum

$$S_n = \sum_{i=1}^{n} f(\zeta_i)(z_i - z_{i-1}).$$

The limit* of this sum as $n \to \infty$ in such a way that each element of arc $P_{i-1}P_i$ approaches zero is called the line integral of $f(z)$ along the contour C, that is,

$$(136\text{-}1) \qquad \int_C f(z)\,dz \equiv \lim_{n \to \infty} \sum_{i=1}^{n} f(\zeta_i)(z_i - z_{i-1}).$$

The fact that this integral exists follows at once from the existence of the real line integrals into which (136-1) can be transformed.   Indeed, separating $f(z)$ into real and imaginary parts as

$$f(z) = u(x, y) + iv(x, y)$$

and noting that $dz = dx + i\,dy$ give

$$(136\text{-}2) \qquad \int_C f(z)\,dz = \int_C (u\,dx - v\,dy) + i \int_C (v\,dx + u\,dy).$$

Thus, the evaluation of the line integral of a complex function can be reduced to the evaluation of two line integrals of real functions.   It follows directly from the properties of real line integrals that the integral of the sum of two continuous complex functions is equal to the sum of the integrals, that a constant can be taken outside the integral sign, and that the reversal of the direction of integration merely changes the sign of the integral.

It follows from (136-1), upon noting that the modulus of the sum is not greater than the sum of the moduli, that

$$\left| \int_C f(z)\,dz \right| \le \int_C |f(z)| \cdot |dz|.$$

If, along C, the modulus of $f(z)$ does not exceed in value some positive number M, then

$$(136\text{-}3) \qquad \left| \int_C f(z)\,dz \right| \le M \int_C |dz| = M \int_C |dx + i\,dy| = M \int_C ds = ML,$$

where L is the length of C.

* The precise meaning of the symbol *lim* in (136-1) is the following: Consider any particular mode of subdivision of the arc into n_1 parts and denote the maximum value of $|z_i - z_{i-1}|$ in this subdivision by δ_1, and let S_{n_1} stand for $\sum_{i=1}^{n_1} f(\zeta_i)(z_i - z_{i-1})$.   A new sum, corresponding to the subdivision of the arc into n_2 parts, is denoted by S_{n_2}; and the maximum value of $|z_i - z_{i-1}|$ in this new subdivision is δ_2, etc.   In this way, one forms a sequence of numbers $S_{n_1}, S_{n_2}, \cdots, S_{n_m}, \cdots$ in which the numbers n_m are assumed to increase indefinitely in such a way that the $\delta_i \to 0$

137. Cauchy's Integral Theorem. The discussion of the preceding section involved no assumption of the analyticity of the function $f(z)$ and is applicable to any continuous complex function, such as for example $f(z) = \bar{z} = x - iy$, in which event

$$\int_C \bar{z}\, dz \equiv \int_C (x - iy)(dx + i\, dy).$$

If the integral (136-1) is to be independent of the path, then it immediately follows from (136-2) that

$$\frac{\partial u}{\partial y} = -\frac{\partial v}{\partial x}, \qquad \frac{\partial v}{\partial y} = \frac{\partial u}{\partial x}.$$

Thus, the conditions that the integral of a complex function $f(z)$ be independent of the path are precisely the Cauchy-Riemann conditions; in other words, the function $f(z)$ must be analytic.

Now, let R be any region of the z-plane in which $f(z)$ is analytic, and let C be a simple closed curve lying entirely within R; then it follows from the properties of line integrals that* the following important theorem holds:

Cauchy's Integral Theorem. *If $f(z)$ is analytic within and on a simple closed contour C, then $\int_C f(z)\, dz = 0$.*

It should be noted carefully that the theorem has been established essentially with the aid of Green's theorem, which requires not only the continuity of the functions u and v but also the continuity of the derivatives. Thus, the proof given above implies not merely the existence of $f'(z)$ but its continuity as well.† It is possible to establish the validity of Cauchy's theorem under the sole hypothesis that $f'(z)$ exists and then prove that the existence of the first derivative implies the existence of derivatives of all orders. Accordingly, the proof given above imposes no practical limitation on the applicability of the theorem.

138. Extension of Cauchy's Theorem. In establishing Cauchy's theorem in Sec. 137, it was assumed that the curve C is a simple closed curve, so that the region bounded by C is simply connected. It is easy to extend the theorem of Cauchy to multiply connected regions in a manner indicated in Sec. 64. Thus, consider a doubly connected region (Fig. 130) bounded

* See Sec. 63.
† See (135-4) and (135-5).

by the closed contours C_1 and C_2, where C_2 lies entirely within C_1. It will be assumed that the function $f(z)$ is analytic in the region exterior to C_2 and interior to C_1 and analytic on C_2 and C_1. The requirement of analyticity on C_1 and C_2 implies that the function $f(z)$ is analytic in an extended region (indicated by the dotted curves K_1 and K_2) that contains the curves C_1 and C_2.

If some point A of the curve C_1 is joined with a point B of C_2 by a crosscut AB, then the region becomes simply connected and the theorem of Cauchy is applicable. Integrating in the positive direction gives

$$(138\text{-}1) \quad \int_{APAQ} f(z)\, dz + \int_{AB} f(z)\, dz + \int_{BQBQ} f(z)\, dz + \int_{BA} f(z)\, dz = 0,$$

where the subscripts on the integrals indicate the directions of integration along C_1, the crosscut AB, and C_2. Since the second and the fourth integrals in (138-1) are calculated over the same path in opposite directions, their sum is zero and one has

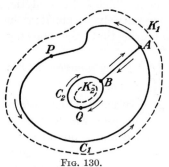

Fig. 130.

$$(138\text{-}2) \quad \int_{C_1Q} f(z)\, dz$$
$$+ \int_{C_2Q} f(z)\, dz = 0,$$

where the integral along C_1 is trav-- ersed in the counterclockwise direction and that along C_2 in the clockwise direction. Changing the order of integration in the second integral in (138-2) gives*

$$(138\text{-}3) \quad \int_{C_1Q} f(z)\, dz = \int_{C_2Q} f(z)\, dz.$$

This important result can be extended in an obvious way to multiply connected regions bounded by several contours, to yield the following valuable theorem.

THEOREM. *If the function $f(z)$ is analytic in a multiply connected region bounded by the exterior contour C and the interior contours $C_1, C_2, \cdots, C_n$, then the integral over the exterior contour C is equal to the sum of the integrals over the interior contours $C_1, C_2, \cdots, C_n$. It is assumed, of course, that the integration over*

* See Sec. 64.

all the contours is performed in the same direction and that f(z) is analytic on all the contours.

139. The Fundamental Theorem of Integral Calculus. Let $f(z)$ be analytic in some simply connected region R, and let the curve C join two points P_0 and P of R (Fig. 131). The coordinates of P_0 and P will be determined by the complex numbers z_0 and z. Now consider the function $F(z)$ defined by the formula $F(z) = \int_{z_0}^{z} f(z)\, dz$. The function $F(z)$ will not depend upon the path joining z_0 with z so long as these points lie entirely within R.

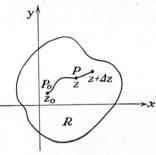

Fig. 131.

Forming the difference quotient gives

$$\frac{F(z + \Delta z) - F(z)}{\Delta z} = \frac{1}{\Delta z}\left[\int_{z_0}^{z+\Delta z} f(z)\, dz - \int_{z_0}^{z} f(z)\, dz \right]$$

$$= \frac{1}{\Delta z}\left[\int_{z_0}^{z} f(z)\, dz + \int_{z}^{z+\Delta z} f(z)\, dz - \int_{z_0}^{z} f(z)\, dz \right]$$

$$= \frac{1}{\Delta z} \int_{z}^{z+\Delta z} f(z)\, dz.$$

In order to avoid the confusion that may occur if the variable z appears in the limits and also as the variable of integration, denote the latter by ζ, so that

$$(139\text{-}1) \quad \frac{F(z + \Delta z) - F(z)}{\Delta z} = \frac{1}{\Delta z} \int_{z}^{z+\Delta z} f(\zeta)\, d\zeta$$

$$= \frac{1}{\Delta z} \int_{z}^{z+\Delta z} [f(\zeta) - f(z) + f(z)]\, d\zeta$$

$$= \frac{1}{\Delta z} \left\{ f(z) \int_{z}^{z+\Delta z} d\zeta + \int_{z}^{z+\Delta z} [f(\zeta) - f(z)]\, d\zeta \right\}$$

$$= f(z) + \frac{1}{\Delta z} \int_{z}^{z+\Delta z} [f(\zeta) - f(z)]\, d\zeta,$$

since $\int_{z}^{z+\Delta z} d\zeta = \Delta z$.

Now if

$$(139\text{-}2) \quad \lim_{\Delta z \to 0} \frac{1}{\Delta z} \int_{z}^{z+\Delta z} [f(\zeta) - f(z)]\, d\zeta = 0,$$

then it follows from (139-1) that

$$\frac{dF(z)}{dz} = f(z).$$

In order to prove that (139-2) holds, one merely has to make use of (136-3) and note that max $|f(\zeta) - f(z)| \to 0$ as $\Delta z \to 0$. Any function $F_1(z)$ such that

$$\frac{dF_1(z)}{dz} = f(z)$$

is called a *primitive* or an *indefinite integral* of $f(z)$, and it is easy to show that if $F_1(z)$ and $F_2(z)$ are any two indefinite integrals of $f(z)$ then they can differ only by a constant.* Hence, if $F_1(z)$ is an indefinite integral of $f(z)$, it follows that

$$F(z) = \int_{z_0}^{z} f(z) \, dz = F_1(z) + C.$$

In order to evaluate the constant C, set $z = z_0$; then, since $\int_{z_0}^{z_0} f(z) \, dz = 0$, $C = F_1(z_0)$. Thus

(139-3) $$F(z) = \int_{z_0}^{z} f(z) \, dz = F_1(z) - F_1(z_0).$$

The statement embodied in (139-3) establishes the connection between line and indefinite integrals and is called the *fundamental theorem of integral calculus* because of its importance in the evaluation of line integrals. It states that *the value of the line integral of an analytic function is equal to the difference in the values of the primitive at the end points of the path of integration.*

As an example consider

$$\int_{0}^{\pi i} e^z \, dz = e^z \Big|_{0}^{\pi i} = e^{\pi i} - 1 = -2.$$

This integral can also be evaluated by recalling that

$$e^z = e^{x+iy} = e^x \cos y + ie^x \sin y.$$

* **Proof:** Since $F_1'(z) = F_2'(z) = f(z)$, it is evident that

$$F_1'(z) - F_2'(z) = d(F_1 - F_2)/dz \equiv dG/dz = 0.$$

But if $dG/dz = 0$, this means that $G'(z) = \dfrac{\partial u}{\partial x} + i\dfrac{\partial v}{\partial x} = \dfrac{\partial v}{\partial y} - i\dfrac{\partial u}{\partial y} = 0$, so

that $\dfrac{\partial u}{\partial x} = \dfrac{\partial v}{\partial x} = \dfrac{\partial u}{\partial y} = \dfrac{\partial v}{\partial y} = 0$, and u and v do not depend on x and y.

Then,

$$\int_0^{\pi i} e^z \, dz = \int_{(0,0)}^{(0,\pi)} (e^x \cos y + ie^x \sin y)(dx + i \, dy)$$

$$= \int_{(0,0)}^{(0,\pi)} (e^x \cos y \, dx - e^x \sin y \, dy)$$

$$+ i \int_{(0,0)}^{(0,\pi)} (e^x \sin y \, dx + e^x \cos y \, dy).$$

As a more interesting example, consider

$$\int_{z_0}^{z} (z - a)^n \, dz,$$

where n is an integer and the integral is evaluated over some curve joining z_0 and z. If $n \neq -1$, an indefinite integral is

$$F(z) = \frac{1}{n+1} (z - a)^{n+1}.$$

For $n \geq 0$, the integrand $f(z) = (z - a)^n$ is analytic throughout the finite z-plane and hence

$$(139\text{-}4) \qquad \int_{z_0}^{z} (z - a)^n \, dz = \frac{1}{n+1} [(z - a)^{n+1} - (z_0 - a)^{n+1}].$$

If the variable point z is allowed to start from z_0 and move along some closed contour C back to z_0, then

$$\oint_C (z - a)^n \, dz = 0.$$

Of course, the latter result could have been obtained directly from Cauchy's integral theorem.

Suppose next that $n < -1$ and that the path of integration does not pass through the point a. If the point a is outside the closed contour C, then the integrand is analytic and it follows at once from Cauchy's integral theorem that

$$\oint_C (z - a)^n \, dz = 0.$$

Suppose now that the point a is within the contour C. Delete the point a by enclosing it in a small circle of radius ρ, and consider the simply connected region R shown in Fig. 132. Then, so long as $n \neq -1$, the single-valued function $f(z) = (z - a)^n$ is analytic in R and (139-4) is applicable to any curve C joining z_0 and z in R. Now if z is allowed to approach z_0, then it follows from the right-hand member of (139-4) that

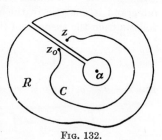

FIG. 132.

$$\oint_C (z - a)^n \, dz = 0 \qquad \text{for } n \neq -1.$$

There remains to be investigated the case when $n = -1$. For any path C not containing $z = a$, one obtains

$$(139\text{-}5) \quad \int_{z_0}^{z} \frac{dz}{z - a} = \log (z - a)\Big|_{z_0}^{z} = \log \frac{z - a}{z_0 - a}$$

$$= \log \left|\frac{z - a}{z_0 - a}\right| + i \arg \frac{z - a}{z_0 - a}$$

$$= \log \left|\frac{z - a}{z_0 - a}\right| + i \arg (z - a) - i \arg (z_0 - a).$$

Now if the point z starts from z_0 and describes a closed path C in such a way that a is within the contour, then the argument of $z - a$ changes by 2π, and therefore

$$\int_C \frac{dz}{z - a} = 2\pi i.$$

If a is outside the contour, then $(z - a)^{-1}$ is analytic within and on C and hence the line integral is zero by Cauchy's theorem.

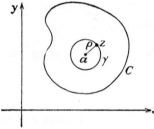

FIG. 133.

A different mode of evaluating the integral

$$\int_C (z - a)^{-n} dz,$$

where n is an integer greater than unity and C is a closed contour, will be given next. If the point a is outside C, then the value of the integral is zero by Cauchy's theorem. Accordingly, consider the case when a is inside C. Draw a circle γ of radius ρ about the point a (Fig. 133) and, since the integrand is analytic in the region exterior to γ and interior to C, it follows from the theorem of Sec. 138 that

$$\int_C (z - a)^{-n} dz = \int_{\gamma} (z - a)^{-n} dz.$$

But $z - a = \rho e^{\theta i}$ and $dz = i\rho e^{\theta i} d\theta$ on γ, so that

$$\int_C \frac{dz}{(z - a)^n} = \int_0^{2\pi} \frac{i\rho e^{i\theta} d\theta}{\rho^n e^{in\theta}} = \frac{i}{\rho^{n-1}} \int_0^{2\pi} e^{(1-n)\theta i} d\theta$$

$$= \frac{i}{\rho^{n-1}} \frac{e^{(1-n)\theta i}}{(1 - n)i}\Big|_0^{2\pi} = 0, \qquad \text{if } n \neq 1.$$

This is the same result as that obtained above by a different method. The reader should apply the latter method to show that, if a is inside C, then $\int_C (z - a)^{-1} dz = 2\pi i$.

PROBLEMS

1. Show that $\int_{z_0}^{z} z\, dz = \frac{1}{2}(z^2 - z_0^2)$ for all paths joining z_0 with z.

2. Evaluate the integral $\int_C (z - a)^{-1}\, dz$, where C is a simple closed curve and a is interior to C, by expressing it as a sum of two real line integrals over C.
Hint: Set $z - a = \rho e^{\theta i}$; then $dz = e^{\theta i}(d\rho + i\, \rho d\theta)$.

3. Evaluate $\int_C z^{-2}\, dz$ where the path C is the upper half of the unit circle whose center is at the origin. What is the value of this integral if the path is the lower half of the circle?

4. Evaluate $\int_C z^{-1}\, dz$, where C is the path of Prob. 3.

5. Evaluate $\int_C (z^2 - 2z + 1)\, dz$, where C is the circle $x^2 + y^2 = 2$.

6. Discuss the integral $\int_C (z + 1)/z^2\, dz$, where C is a path enclosing the origin.

7. What is the value of the integral $\int_C (1 + z^2)^{-1}\, dz$, where C is the circle $x^2 + y^2 = 9$?

8. Discuss Prob. 7 by noting that $\dfrac{1}{1 + z^2} = \dfrac{1}{2i}\left(\dfrac{1}{z - i} - \dfrac{1}{z + i}\right)$ and evaluating the integrals over the unit circles whose centers are at $z = i$ and $z = -i$. Note the theorem of Sec. 138.

140. Cauchy's Integral Formula. The remarkable formula that is derived in this section permits one to calculate the value of an analytic function $f(z)$, at any interior point of the region bounded by a simple closed curve C, from the prescribed boundary values of $f(z)$ on C.

Let $f(z)$ be analytic throughout the region R enclosed by a simple closed curve C and also on the curve C. If a is some point interior to the region R (see Fig. 133), then the function

$$(140\text{-}1) \qquad \frac{f(z)}{z - a}$$

is analytic throughout the region R, with the possible exception of the point $z = a$, where the denominator of (140-1) vanishes. If the point a is excluded from the region R by a circle γ of radius ρ and with center at a, then (140-1) is analytic throughout the region exterior to γ and interior to C, and it follows from Cauchy's integral theorem that

$$\int_{C_0} \frac{f(z)}{z - a}\, dz + \int_{\gamma_0} \frac{f(z)}{z - a}\, dz = 0,$$

or

(140-2)
$$\int_{C_O} \frac{f(z)}{z-a}\, dz = \int_{\gamma_O} \frac{f(z)}{z-a}\, dz.$$

The integral in the right-hand member of (140-2) can be written as

(140-3)
$$\int_{\gamma} \frac{f(z)}{z-a}\, dz = \int_{\gamma} \frac{f(z)-f(a)}{z-a}\, dz + f(a) \int_{\gamma} \frac{dz}{z-a}.$$

It was demonstrated in Sec. 139 that

$$\int_{\gamma} \frac{dz}{z-a} = 2\pi i,$$

and it will be shown next that the first integral in the right-hand member of (140-3) has the value zero. Set $z - a = \rho e^{\theta i}$; then, so long as z is on γ, $dz = i\rho e^{i\theta}\, d\theta$, and hence

(140-4)
$$\int_{\gamma} \frac{f(z)-f(a)}{z-a}\, dz = i \int_{\gamma} [f(z)-f(a)]\, d\theta.$$

If the maximum of $|f(z)-f(a)|$ is denoted by M, then it follows from Sec. 136 that

(140-5)
$$\left| \int_{\gamma} \frac{f(z)-f(a)}{z-a}\, dz \right| \le M \int_{0}^{2\pi} d\theta = 2\pi M.$$

Now if the circle γ is made sufficiently small, it follows from the continuity of $f(z)$ that $|f(z)-f(a)|$ can be made as small as desired. On the other hand, it follows from (138-3) that the value of the integral (140-4) is independent of the radius ρ of the circle γ, so long as γ is interior to R. Thus the left-hand member of (140-5) is independent of ρ; and since $M \to 0$ when $\rho \to 0$, it follows that the value of the integral is zero.

Accordingly, (140-2) becomes

(140-6)
$$\int_{C} \frac{f(z)\, dz}{z-a} = 2\pi i f(a),$$

where a, which plays the role of a parameter, is any point interior to C. Denote the variable of integration in (140-6) by ζ, and let z be any point interior to C; then (140-6) can be written as

(140-7)
$$f(z) = \frac{1}{2\pi i} \int_{C} \frac{f(\zeta)\, d\zeta}{\zeta - z}.$$

The relationship stated by (140-7) is known as *Cauchy's integral formula.*

It is not difficult to show that an integral of the form (140-7) can be differentiated with respect to the parameter z as many times as desired,* so that

$$
(140\text{-}8) \quad
\begin{cases}
f'(z) = \dfrac{1}{2\pi i} \displaystyle\int_C \dfrac{f(\zeta)}{(\zeta - z)^2} \, d\zeta, \\[3mm]
f''(z) = \dfrac{2!}{2\pi i} \displaystyle\int_C \dfrac{f(\zeta)}{(\zeta - z)^3} \, d\zeta, \\[3mm]
\cdots\cdots\cdots\cdots\cdots\cdots\cdots\cdots, \\[3mm]
f^{(n)}(z) = \dfrac{n!}{2\pi i} \displaystyle\int_C \dfrac{f(\zeta)}{(\zeta - z)^{n+1}} \, d\zeta.
\end{cases}
$$

In fact, if $f(z)$ is any continuous (not necessarily analytic) function of the complex variable z, then the integral

$$
\int_C \frac{f(\zeta)}{\zeta - z} \, d\zeta \equiv F(z)
$$

defines an analytic function $F(z)$. To show this, all that is necessary is to form the difference quotient $[F(z + \Delta z) - F(z)]/\Delta z$ and to evaluate its limit as $\Delta z \to 0$. It follows from such a calculation that

$$
F'(z) = \int_C \frac{f(\zeta)}{(\zeta - z)^2} \, d\zeta.
$$

The assertion made in Sec. 137, concerning the fact that the continuity of the derivative of an analytic function follows from the assumption that the derivative exists, is now made clear.

PROBLEMS

1. If

$$
f(z) = \int_C \frac{3\zeta^2 + 7\zeta + 1}{\zeta - z} \, d\zeta,
$$

where C is the circle of radius 2 about the origin, find the values of $f(1 - i)$ and $f''(1 - i)$.

2. Apply Cauchy's integral formula to Prob. 7, Sec. 139. Use the integrand in the form given in Prob. 8.

---

* Form the difference quotient $[f(z + \Delta z) - f(z)]/\Delta z$, and investigate the behavior of the quotient as $\Delta z \to 0$.

3. Evaluate with the aid of Cauchy's integral formula

$$\int_C \frac{3\zeta^2 + \zeta}{\zeta^2 - 1} \, d\zeta,$$

where C is the circle $|\zeta| = 2$.

4. What is the value of the integral of Prob. 3 when evaluated over the circle $|\zeta - 1| = 1$?

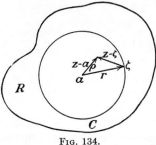

5. Evaluate

$$\int_C \frac{3z^2 + 2z - 1}{z} \, dz,$$

where C is the circle $|z| = 1$.

141. Taylor's Expansion. Let $f(z)$ be analytic in some region R, and let C be a circle lying wholly in R and having its center at a. If z is

Fig. 134.

any point interior to C (Fig. 134), then it follows from Cauchy's integral formula that

$$(141\text{-}1) \qquad f(z) = \frac{1}{2\pi i} \int_C \frac{f(\zeta)}{\zeta - z} \, d\zeta$$

$$= \frac{1}{2\pi i} \int_C \frac{f(\zeta)}{\zeta - a} \left(\frac{1}{1 - \dfrac{z - a}{\zeta - a}} \right) d\zeta.$$

But $\dfrac{1}{1 - t} = 1 + t + t^2 + \cdots + t^{n-1} + \dfrac{t^n}{1 - t}$, and substituting this expression, with $t = (z - a)/(\zeta - a)$, in (141-1) leads to

$$f(z) = \frac{1}{2\pi i} \left[\int_C \frac{f(\zeta)}{\zeta - a} \, d\zeta + (z - a) \int_C \frac{f(\zeta)}{(\zeta - a)^2} \, d\zeta + \cdots \right.$$

$$\left. + (z - a)^{n-1} \int_C \frac{f(\zeta)}{(\zeta - a)^n} \, d\zeta \right] + R_n,$$

where

$$R_n = \frac{(z - a)^n}{2\pi i} \int_C \frac{f(\zeta)}{(\zeta - a)^n (\zeta - z)} \, d\zeta.$$

Making use of (140-8) gives

$$(141\text{-}2) \quad f(z) = f(a) + f'(a)(z - a) + \frac{f''(a)}{2!} (z - a)^2$$

$$+ \cdots + \frac{f^{(n-1)}(a)}{(n - 1)!} (z - a)^{n-1} + R_n.$$

By taking n sufficiently large, the modulus of R_n may be made as small as desired. In order to show this fact, let the maximum value attained by the modulus of $f(\zeta)$ on C be M, the radius of the circle C be r, and the modulus of $z - a$ be ρ. Then $|\zeta - z| \geq r - \rho$, and

$$|R_n| = \frac{|z - a|^n}{2\pi} \left| \int_C \frac{f(\zeta)}{(\zeta - a)^n(\zeta - z)} \, d\zeta \right|$$
$$\leq \frac{\rho^n}{2\pi} \frac{M 2\pi r}{r^n(r - \rho)} = \frac{Mr}{r - \rho} \left(\frac{\rho}{r} \right)^n.$$

Since $\rho/r < 1$, it follows that $\lim\limits_{n \to \infty} |R_n| = 0$ for every z interior to C.

Thus, one can write the infinite series

$$f(z) = f(a) + f'(a)(z - a) + \frac{f''(a)}{2!}(z - a)^2 + \cdots$$
$$+ \frac{f^{(n)}(a)}{n!}(z - a)^n + \cdots,$$

which converges to $f(z)$ at every point z interior to any circle C that lies entirely within the region R in which $f(z)$ is analytic. This series is known as the Taylor's series.*

PROBLEMS

1. Obtain the Taylor's series expansions, about $z = 0$, for the following functions:

    (a) e^z, (b) $\sin z$, (c) $\cos z$, (d) $\log (1 + z)$.

2. Verify the following expansions:

    (a) $\tan z = z + \dfrac{z^3}{3} + \dfrac{2z^5}{15} + \cdots$;

    (b) $\sinh z = z + \dfrac{z^3}{3!} + \dfrac{z^5}{5!} + \cdots$;

    (c) $\cosh z = 1 + \dfrac{z^2}{2!} + \dfrac{z^4}{4!} + \cdots$;

    (d) $(1 + z)^m = 1 + mz + \dfrac{m(m - 1)}{2!} z^2 + \cdots$.

142. Conformal Mapping. It was mentioned in Sec. 135 that the functional relationship $w = f(z)$ sets up a correspondence

---

* For a more extensive treatment, see D. R. Curtiss, Analytic Functions of a Complex Variable; E. J. Townsend, Functions of a Complex Variable; H. Burkhardt and S. E. Rasor, Theory of Functions of a Complex Variable.

between the points $z = x + iy$, of the complex z-plane, and $w = u + iv$, of the complex w-plane. If $w = f(z)$ is analytic in some region R of the z-plane, then the totality of values w belongs to some region R' of the w-plane, and it is said that the region R maps into the region R'. If C is some curve drawn in the region R and the point z is allowed to move along C, then the corresponding point w will trace a curve C' in the w-plane (Fig. 135), and C' is called the map of the curve C.

The relationship of the curves C and C' is interesting. Consider a pair of points z and $z + \Delta z$ on C, and let the arc length between them be $\Delta s = PQ$. The corresponding points in the

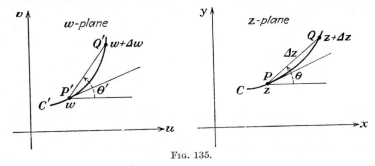

Fig. 135.

region R' are denoted by w and $w + \Delta w$, and the arc length between them by $\Delta s' = P'Q'$. Since the ratio of the arc lengths has the same limit as the ratio of the lengths of the corresponding chords,

$$\lim_{\Delta z \to 0} \frac{\Delta s'}{\Delta s} = \lim_{\Delta z \to 0} \frac{|\Delta w|}{|\Delta z|} = \lim_{\Delta z \to 0} \left|\frac{\Delta w}{\Delta z}\right| = \left|\frac{dw}{dz}\right|.$$

The function $w = f(z)$ is assumed to be analytic, so that dw/dz has a unique value regardless of the manner in which $\Delta z \to 0$. Hence, the transformation causes elements of arc, passing through P in any direction, to experience a change in length whose magnitude is given by the value of the modulus of dw/dz at P. For example, if $w = z^3$, then the linear dimensions at the point $z = 1$ are stretched threefold, but at the point $z = 1 + i$ they are multiplied by 6.

It will be shown next that the argument of dw/dz determines the orientation of the element of arc $\Delta s'$ relative to Δs. The argument of the complex number Δz is measured by the angle θ made by the chord PQ with the x-axis, while $\arg \Delta w$ measures the corresponding angle θ' between the u-axis and the chord $P'Q'$. Hence, the difference between the angles θ' and θ is equal to

$$\arg \Delta w - \arg \Delta z = \arg \frac{\Delta w}{\Delta z},$$

for the difference of the arguments of two complex numbers is equal to the argument of their quotient. As $\Delta z \to 0$, the vectors Δz and Δw tend to coincidence with the tangents to C at P and C' at P', respectively, and hence* $\arg dw/dz$ is the angle of rotation of the element of arc $\Delta s'$ relative to Δs. It follows immediately from this statement that if C_1 and C_2 are two curves which intersect at P at an angle τ (Fig. 136), then the corre-

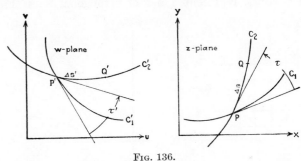

Fig. 136.

sponding curves C_1' and C_2' in the w-plane also intersect at an angle τ, for the tangents to these curves are rotated through the same angle.

A transformation that preserves angles is called *conformal*, and thus one can state the following theorem:

THEOREM. *The mapping performed by an analytic function $f(z)$ is conformal at all points of the z-plane where $f'(z) \neq 0$.*

143. Method of Conjugate Functions. The angle-preserving property of the transformations by analytic functions has many immediate and important physical applications.

For example, if an incompressible fluid flows over a plane with a velocity potential $\Phi(x, y)$ (so that $v_x = \partial\Phi/\partial x$, $v_y = \partial\Phi/\partial y$), then it is known that the stream lines will be directed at right angles to the equipotential curves $\Phi(x, y) = $ const. Moreover, it was shown† that the functions Φ and Ψ satisfy the Cauchy-

* Note that this statement assumes that $dw/dz \neq 0$ at the point P.

† See Sec. 66.

Riemann equations, and hence one can assert that the functions Φ and Ψ are the real and imaginary parts, respectively, of some analytic function $f(z)$, that is,

$$f(z) = \Phi(x, y) + i\Psi(x, y).$$

Now, let $w = f(z) = \Phi + i\Psi$, and consider the two families of curves in the w-plane defined by

(143-1) $\Phi(x, y) = $ const.   and $\Psi(x, y) = $ const.

The orthogonality of the curves $\Phi = $ const. and $\Psi = $ const. in the z-plane follows at once from the conformal properties of the transformation by the analytic function $f(z)$. For $\Phi = $ const. and $\Psi = $ const. represent a net of orthogonal lines (Fig. 137)

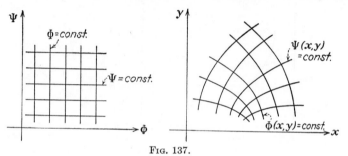

FIG. 137.

parallel to the coordinate axes in the w-plane, and they are transformed by the analytic function $w = \Phi + i\Psi$ into a net of orthogonal curves in the z-plane.

It is obvious then that every analytic function $f(z) = u(x, y) + iv(x, y)$ furnishes a pair of real functions of the variables x and y, namely, $u(x, y)$ and $v(x, y)$, each of which is a solution of Laplace's equation. The functions $u(x, y)$ and $v(x, y)$ are called *conjugate functions*, and the method of obtaining solutions of Laplace's equation with the aid of analytic functions of a complex variable is called the method of conjugate functions.

Example. The process of obtaining pairs of conjugate functions from analytic functions is indicated in the following example. Let

$$w = u + iv = \sin z = \sin (x + iy);$$

then,

$$u + iv = \sin x \cos iy + \cos x \sin iy,$$
$$= \sin x \cosh y + i \cos x \sinh y,$$

so that

$$u(x, y) = \sin x \cosh y,$$
$$v(x, y) = \cos x \sinh y.$$

It is not difficult to show that the inverse of an analytic function is, in general, analytic. Thus, the solution of the equations

$$u = \Phi(x, y) \quad \text{and} \quad v = \Psi(x, y)$$

for x and y in terms of u and v furnishes one with a pair of functions

$$x = \varphi(u, v) \quad \text{and} \quad y = \psi(u, v)$$

that satisfy Laplace's equation in which u and v are the independent variables.

The following three sections are devoted to an exposition of the method of conjugate functions as it is employed in solving important engineering problems.*

PROBLEMS

1. Discuss the mapping properties of the transformations defined by the following functions. Draw the families of curves $u =$ const. and $v =$ const.

(a) $w = u + iv = z + a$, where a is a constant;

(b) $w = bz$, where b is a constant;

(c) $w = bz + a$, where a and b are constants;

(d) $w = z^2$;

(e) $w = 1/z$.

2. Obtain pairs of conjugate functions from

(a) $w = \cos z$;

(b) $w = e^z$;

(c) $w = z^3$;

(d) $w = \log z$;

(e) $w = 1/z$.

* The material contained in Secs. 144 to 146 is extracted from a lecture on conformal representation, which was delivered by invitation at the S. P. E. E. Summer Session for Teachers of Mathematics to Engineering Students at Minneapolis, in September, 1931, by Dr. Warren Weaver, director of the Division of Natural Sciences of the Rockefeller Foundation, and formerly professor of mathematics at the University of Wisconsin.

The authors did not feel that they could improve upon the lucidity and clarity of Dr. Weaver's exposition of the subject and are grateful for his kind permission to make use of the lecture, which was printed in the October, 1932, issue of the *American Mathematical Monthly*.

144. Problems Solvable by Conjugate Functions. Specific examples of the method of conjugate functions will be given later, but it may be well to indicate here two general sorts of problems. Suppose that an analytic function $w = u + iv = f(z) = f(x + iy)$ maps a curve C of the z-plane (see Fig. 138), whose equation

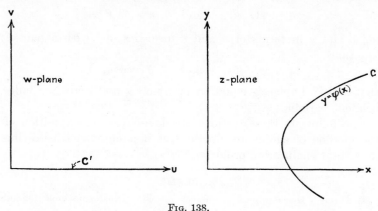

FIG. 138.

is $y = \varphi(x)$, onto the entire real axis $v = 0$ of the w-plane. This will obviously occur if, and only if,

$$v[x, \varphi(x)] \equiv 0.$$

Then the function

$$\Phi(x, y) \equiv v(x, y)$$

clearly is a solution of Laplace's equation that reduces to zero on the curve C. In an important class of problems of applied mathematics, one requires a solution of Laplace's equation that reduces to zero, or some other constant, on some given curve. Thus, one may, so to speak, go at such problems backward; and, by plotting in the z-plane the curves $u(x, y) = $ const. and $v(x, y) = $ const., he finds for what curves C a given analytic function solves the above problem. Similarly, one may interchange the roles of u, v and x, y and may plot in the w-plane the curves $x(u, v) = $ const. and $y(u, v) = $ const. Thus a properly drawn picture of the plane transformation indicates to the eye what problems, of this sort, are solved by a given analytic function. It must be emphasized that the picture must be "properly drawn"; that is, one requires, in one plane, the two families of curves obtained by setting equal to various constants the coordinate variables of the other plane.

In a second and more general sort of problem, it is necessary to obtain a solution $\Phi(x, y)$ of Laplace's equation which, on a given curve C whose equation is $y = \varphi(x)$, reduces to some given function $\Phi^*(x, y)$. The previous problem is clearly a very special case of this second problem. Suppose, now, that an analytic function $w = f(z)$ map the curve C of the z-plane onto the axis of reals $v = 0$, of the w-plane. Since the curve C maps onto $v = 0$ in the w-plane, $v[x, \varphi(x)] \equiv 0$, and the values of Φ^* at points on C are equal to the values of

$$\Phi^*[x(u, 0), y(u, 0)] \equiv \Phi_*(u)$$

at the corresponding points on the transformed curve $v = 0$. Suppose now that the function $\Psi(u, v)$ be a solution of Laplace's equation (u and v being viewed as independent variables), such that

$$\Psi(u, 0) \equiv \Phi_*(u).$$

It is easily checked that

$$\Phi(x, y) = \Psi[u(x, y), v(x, y)]$$

is a solution of Laplace's equation, x and y being viewed as independent variables. Moreover, on the curve C one has

$$\Phi[x, \varphi(x)] = \Psi(u, 0) = \Phi_*(u) = \Phi^*(x, y),$$

so that Φ is the solution sought.

The chief service, in this case, of the method of conjugate functions, is that the form of the boundary condition is much simplified. Rather than seeking a function that takes on prescribed values on some *curve C*, one has rather to find a function that takes on prescribed values on a *straight line*, namely, the axis of abscissas. This latter problem is so much simpler than the former that it can, indeed, be solved in general form for a very general function Φ_*. This solution will be referred to later, in Sec. 146c.

145. Examples of Conformal Maps. As a preparation for the consideration of applications, this section will present six specific instances of the conformal mapping of one plane on another. The examples chosen are not precisely those which one would select if, building up from the simplest cases, one were to study the mathematical theory in detail. The examples are chosen for their characteristic features and because of their important and direct applications. The first case is:

a. The Transformation $w = z^m$, m a Positive Integer. If one write both z and w in polar form, so that

$$z = re^{i\varphi},$$
$$w = Re^{i\Phi},$$

then

$$w \equiv Re^{i\Phi} = z^m = r^m e^{im\varphi},$$

and

$$R = r^m,$$
$$\Phi = m\varphi.$$

Thus the curve $r =$ const. in the z-plane (that is, a circle about the origin) transforms into a curve $R =$ const. in the w-plane

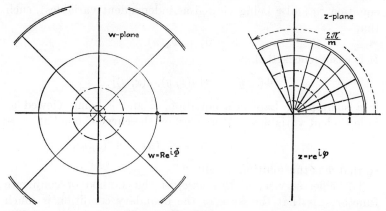

Fig. 139.

(also a circle about the origin), the radius of the circle in the w-plane being equal to the mth power of the radius of the circle in the z-plane. Also, a radial line $\varphi =$ const. in the z-plane transforms into a new radial line $\Phi =$ const., the amplitude angle for the transformed radial line being m times the amplitude angle of the original radial line. Thus, a sector of the z-plane of central angle $2\pi/m$ is "fanned out" to cover the entire w-plane, this sector also being stretched radially (see Fig. 139, drawn for $m = 3$). One notes the characteristic feature that a set of orthogonal curves in one plane transform into a set of orthogonal curves in the other plane.

This example suggests several interesting questions which cannot be discussed here. The "angle-true" property clearly does not hold at the origin, which indicates that this point deserves special study. Further, it is clear that only a portion of the z-plane maps onto the entire w-plane. In the case for which the figure is drawn, it would require *three* w-planes, so to speak, if the entire z-plane were to be unambiguously mapped. This consideration leads to the use of many-sheeted surfaces, called Riemann surfaces. Such questions and apparent difficulties correctly indicate that a thorough knowledge of the mathematical theory of analytical functions is essential to a proper and complete understanding of even simple instances of conformal representation.[1]

To get a clear idea of the way in which the z-plane maps onto the w-plane, one may choose various convenient families of curves in one plane and determine the corresponding curves in the other plane. The resulting picture, as was mentioned earlier, does not give any indication of the immediate physical applications of the transformation in question unless one of the sets of curves, in one plane or the other, consists of the straight lines parallel to the coordinate axes. It should thus be clear that Fig. 139 does not give a direct indication of the type of problem immediately solvable by the transformation $w = z^3$. The curves in the w-plane obtained by setting $x =$ const. and $y =$ const. are, in fact, cubic curves; and no simple physical problem is directly solved by this transformation. This transformation may, however, be used to solve various physical problems for a wedge-shaped region, since the bounding curve C of such a wedge (say the line $\varphi = 0$ and the line $\varphi = \pi/3$) is transformed into a curve C' of the w-plane that consists of the entire real axis. Thus the transformation can be used, in the way indicated in Sec. 144, to solve problems in which one desires a solution of Laplace's equation that reduces to a given function (or a constant) on the boundary of a wedge.

b. The Transformation $w = \dfrac{\left(z + \dfrac{1}{z}\right)}{2}$. This again is a trans-

---

[1] BIEBERBACH, L., Einführung in die konforme Abbildung, Berlin, 1927; LEWENT, L., Conformal Representation, London, 1925; OSGOOD, W. F., Lehrbuch der Funktionentheorie, vol. 1, Chap. XIV.

formation that does not have immediate applicability. It has, however, interesting features, and subsequent discussion will indicate how it may be made to serve a practical purpose.

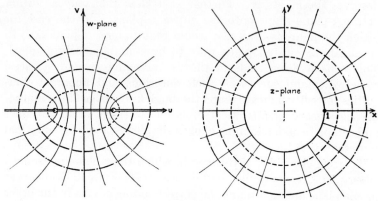

Fɪɢ. 140.

If, as before, one write z in the polar form $re^{i\varphi}$, then

$$w = u + iv = \frac{\left(z + \dfrac{1}{z}\right)}{2} = \frac{re^{i\varphi}}{2} + \frac{e^{-i\varphi}}{2r},$$

$$= \frac{1}{2}\left(r + \frac{1}{r}\right)\cos\varphi + i\,\frac{1}{2}\left(r - \frac{1}{r}\right)\sin\varphi,$$

so that

$$u = \frac{1}{2}\left(r + \frac{1}{r}\right)\cos\varphi,$$

$$v = \frac{1}{2}\left(r - \frac{1}{r}\right)\sin\varphi.$$

Thus, φ and r being eliminated in turn,

$$\frac{u^2}{\left(r + \dfrac{1}{r}\right)^2} + \frac{v^2}{\left(r - \dfrac{1}{r}\right)^2} = \frac{1}{4},$$

$$\frac{u^2}{\cos^2\varphi} - \frac{v^2}{\sin^2\varphi} = 1.$$

From these equations, it follows by inspection that the circles $r = $ const. of the z-plane transform into a family of ellipses of the w-plane (see Fig. 140), the ellipses being confocal, since

$$\left(r + \frac{1}{r}\right)^2 - \left(r - \frac{1}{r}\right)^2 = 4 = \text{const.}$$

It is also clear that two circles of reciprocal radii transform into the same ellipse. Similarly, the radial lines $\varphi = \text{const.}$ of the z-plane transform into a family of hyperbolas which, again, are confocal, since

$$\cos^2 \varphi + \sin^2 \varphi = 1 = \text{const.}$$

Thus the exterior of the unit circle of the z-plane transforms into the entire w-plane. The unit circle itself "flattens out" to form the segment from -1 to $+1$ of the real axis of the w-plane. All larger circles are less strenuously "flattened out" and form ellipses, while the radial lines of the z-plane form the associated confocal hyperbolas of the w-plane. A similar statement can be made for the inside of the unit circle.

c. The Transformation $w = e^z$. If one set $w \equiv Re^{i\Phi}$ and $z = x + iy$, then

$$Re^{i\Phi} = e^{x+iy} = e^x \cdot e^{iy},$$

so that

$$R = e^x,$$
$$\Phi = y.$$

It is thus clear that vertical lines of the z-plane map into circles of the w-plane, the radius being greater or less than 1, according as x is positive or negative. Horizontal lines of the z-plane, on the other hand, map into the radial lines of the w-plane, and it is clear that any horizontal strip of the z-plane of height 2π will cover the entire w-plane once (see Fig. 141).

The curves in the w-plane of Fig. 141 are drawn by setting equal to a constant one or the other of the coordinates of the z-plane. Thus these curves give direct indication of physical problems to which this analytic function may be applied. For example, one could obtain the electrostatic field due to a charged right circular cylinder, the lines of flow from a single line source of current or liquid, the circulation of a liquid around a cylindrical obstacle, etc.

By considering this example in conjunction with the preceding example, one gives new significance to Fig. 140. In fact, if one starts with the z-plane of Fig. 141 and then uses the w-plane of Fig. 141 as the z-plane of Fig. 140, it is clear that the curves drawn in the w-plane of Fig. 140 then are obtainable by setting equal to various constants the coordinates of the z-plane of Fig. 141. That is to say, the w-plane curves of Fig. 140 give direct evidence of physical problems that can be solved by the pair of transformations

$$z_1 = e^z,$$

$$w = \frac{\left(z_1 + \dfrac{1}{z_1}\right)}{2}.$$

d. The Transformation $w = \cosh z$. If, in the two preceding equations, one eliminates the intermediate variable z_1 (so he may

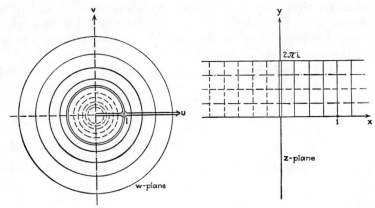

Fig. 141.

pass directly from the z-plane of Fig. 141 to the w-plane of Fig. 140), the result is

$$w = \frac{e^z + e^{-z}}{2} = \cosh z.$$

Thus

$$u + iv = \cosh (x + iy) = \cosh x \cosh iy + \sinh x \sinh iy,$$
$$= \cosh x \cos y + i \sinh x \sin y,$$

so that

$$u = \cosh x \cos y$$
$$v = \sinh x \sin y,$$

or

$$\frac{u^2}{\cosh^2 x} + \frac{v^2}{\sinh^2 x} = 1,$$

$$\frac{u^2}{\cos^2 y} - \frac{v^2}{\sin^2 y} = 1.$$

This transformation is shown in Fig. 142, and it may be used to obtain the electrostatic field due to an elliptic cylinder, the electrostatic field due to a charged plane from which a strip has been removed, the circulation of liquid around an elliptical cylinder, the flow of liquid through a slit in a plane, etc.

The transformation from the z-plane to the w-plane may be described geometrically as follows: Consider the horizontal strip of the z-plane between the lines $y = 0$ and $y = \pi$; and think of these lines as being broken and pivoted at the points where $x = 0$. Rotate the strip 90° counterclockwise, and at the same

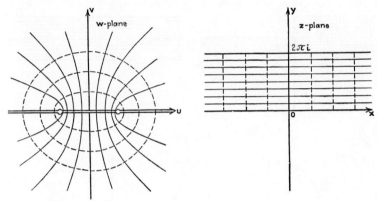

Fig. 142.

time fold each of the broken lines $y = 0$ and $y = \pi$ back on itself, the strip thus being doubly "fanned out" so as to cover the entire w-plane.

e. The Transformation $w = z + e^z$. One has

$$u + iv = x + iy + e^{x+iy},$$
$$= x + iy + e^x(\cos y + i \sin y),$$

so that

$$u = x + e^x \cos y,$$
$$v = y + e^x \sin y.$$

This transformation is shown in Fig. 143. If one considers the portion of the z-plane between the lines $y = \pm\pi$, then the portion of the strip to the right of $x = -1$ is to be "fanned out" by rotating the portion of $y = +1$ (to the right of $x = -1$) counterclockwise and the portion of $y = -1$ (to the right of $x = -1$) clockwise until each line is folded back on itself. This trans-

formation gives the electrostatic field at the edge of a parallel
plate condenser, the flow of liquid out of a channel into an open
sea, etc.

f. The Schwartz Transformation. The transformations just
considered are simple examples and are necessarily very special
in character. This list of illustrations will be concluded by a

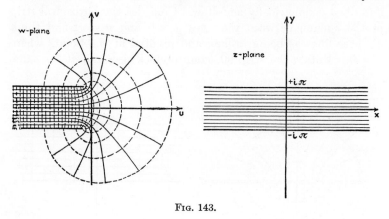

FIG. 143.

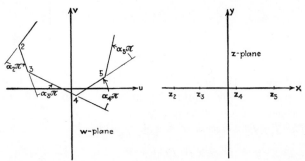

FIG. 144.

more general transformation. Suppose one has (see Fig. 144) a
rectilinear polygon, in the w-plane, whose sides change direction
by an angle $\alpha_i\pi$ when one passes the ith vertex, going around the
boundary of the polygon so that the interior lies to the left.
The interior of this polygon can be mapped onto the upper
half z-plane by the transformation

$$w = A \int \frac{dz}{(z - z_1)^{\alpha_1}(z - z_2)^{\alpha_2} \cdots (z - z_n)^{\alpha_n}} + B,$$

where z_1, z_2, $\cdot$ $\cdot$ $\cdot$, z_n are the (real) points, on the x-axis of the z-plane, onto which map the first, second, $\cdot$ $\cdot$ $\cdot$, nth vertex of the polygon, and where A and B are constants which are to be determined to fit the scale and location of the polygon. Three of the points z_i may be chosen at will, and the values of the remaining ones may be calculated.

This theorem may be used to find, for example, the analytic transformation that solves the problem of determining the electrostatic field around a charged cylindrical conductor of any polygonal cross section. It should be noted, however, that one requires for this purpose the function $y(u, v)$, whereas the theorem gives one w as a function of z. It is often exceedingly difficult and laborious to solve this relation for z as a function of w, so that one may obtain the function y. It should further be remarked that this theorem may be applied to polygons some of whose vertices are not located in the finite plane and that the theorem is of wide applicability and importance in connections less direct and simple than the one just mentioned.

146. Applications of Conformal Representation. *a. Applications to Cartography.* It is natural that a mathematical theory which discusses the "mapping" of one plane on another should have application to the problems connected with the drawing of geographic maps. Since the surface of a sphere cannot be made plane without distortion of some sort, one has to decide, when mapping a portion of the sphere on a plane, what type of distortion to choose and what to avoid. For some purposes, it is essential that areas be represented properly; for other purposes, it is most important that the angles on the map faithfully represent the actual angles on the sphere.

The first problem, in conveniently mapping a sphere on a plane, is to map the sphere on the plane in some fashion or other and then, if this fashion be unsatisfactory, to remap this plane onto a second plane. The first problem can be done in a wide variety of ways[1] which include, as important examples, stereographic projection and Mercator's projection. Both these examples are *conformal* projections, in that they preserve the true values of all angles. Having once mapped the sphere on the plane (or on a portion of the plane), one may now remap onto a second

[1] The Encyclopaedia Britannica article on maps lists and discusses nearly thirty such projections actually used in map making.

plane, and it is here that the theory of conformal representation finds its application; for one can determine the analytic function that will conformally remap the original map onto a new region of any desired shape and size. Not only are all angles preserved in this process of conformal remapping, but the distortion in the neighborhood of a point is always a pure magnification. Thus the shapes of all small objects or regions are preserved. Such maps do not give a true representation of areas, and for this reason many maps are based on compromises between conformal transformations and area-preserving transformations.

b. Applications to Hydrodynamics. When the velocities of all particles of a moving liquid lie in planes parallel to one plane that we may conveniently choose as the xy-plane and when all particles having the same x and y have equal velocities, then the motion is said to be two-dimensional. Such cases clearly arise if a very thin sheet of liquid is flowing in some manner over a plane or if a thick layer of liquid circulates over a plane, there being no motion and no variation of motion normal to the plane. Let the x- and y-components of velocity at any point (x, y) be u and v, respectively. The motion is said to be irrotational if the curl of the velocity vector vanishes. Analytically, this demands that

$$\frac{\partial u}{\partial y} = \frac{\partial v}{\partial x},$$

whereas physically it states that the angular velocity of an infinitesimal portion of the liquid is zero. The equation just written assures that

$$-(u\,dx + v\,dy)$$

is the perfect differential of some function, say Φ. This function is known as the velocity potential, since by a comparison of the two equations

$$d\Phi = -u\,dx - v\,dy,$$

$$d\Phi = \frac{\partial \Phi}{\partial x}\,dx + \frac{\partial \Phi}{\partial y}\,dy,$$

it follows that

(146-1) $$u = -\frac{\partial \Phi}{\partial x}, \qquad v = -\frac{\partial \Phi}{\partial y}.$$

Now, if the liquid be incompressible, the amount of it that flows into any volume in a given time must equal the amount that flows out. This demand imposes on the components of velocity the restriction that

$$\frac{\partial u}{\partial x} + \frac{\partial v}{\partial y} = 0,$$

this being known as the equation of continuity. From the last two equations, it follows that

$$\frac{\partial^2 \Phi}{\partial x^2} + \frac{\partial^2 \Phi}{\partial y^2} \equiv \nabla^2 \Phi = 0.$$

That is, the velocity potential satisfies Laplace's equation.

Just as the vanishing of the curl of the velocity demands that $u\,dx + v\,dy$ be an exact differential, so the equation of continuity demands that $v\,dx - u\,dy$ be an exact differential of some function, say Ψ. That is,

$$d\Psi = v\,dx - u\,dy,$$
$$d\Psi = \frac{\partial \Psi}{\partial x}\,dx + \frac{\partial \Psi}{\partial y}\,dy,$$

so that

(146-2) $$v = \frac{\partial \Psi}{\partial x}, \qquad u = -\frac{\partial \Psi}{\partial y}.$$

From (146-1) and (146-2), it follows at once that

$$\frac{\partial \Phi}{\partial x}\frac{\partial \Psi}{\partial x} + \frac{\partial \Phi}{\partial y}\frac{\partial \Psi}{\partial y} = 0,$$

which expresses the geometric fact that the curves $\Phi = $ const. and $\Psi = $ const. intersect everywhere orthogonally. It is clear from (146-1) that there is no component of velocity in the direction of the curves on which Φ is a constant, so that the velocity of the liquid is everywhere orthogonal to the equipotential curves $\Phi = $ const. That is, the curves $\Psi = $ const. depict everywhere the direction of flow. For this reason, Ψ is called the stream function and the curves $\Psi = $ const. are called the stream lines. From (146-2) and the vanishing of the curl of the velocity, it follows that the stream function Ψ is also a solution of Laplace's equation.

Thus, the velocity potential Φ and the stream function Ψ in the case of the irrotational flow of a perfect incompressible liquid both satisfy Laplace's equation, and the curves $\Phi = $ const.

and Ψ = const. form two orthogonal families. Every analytic function therefore furnishes the solution to four such problems, the four solutions resulting from the fact that one may choose the pair x, y or the pair u, v as independent variables, and that one may interchange the roles of the potential function and the stream function. Figure 142, for example, indicates two of the four problems solved by the analytic transformation $w =$ cosh z. If one treats u and v as the independent variables and identifies the (solid) curves $y(u, v)$ = const. in the w-plane with the curves Φ = const., then the dotted curves $x(u, v) =$ Ψ = const. give the stream lines, and one has solved the problem of the circulation of liquid around an elliptic cylinder. If, however, one sets $y(u, v) = \Psi$ and $x(u, v) = \Phi$, then the solid curves of the w-plane are the stream lines, and one has solved the problem of the flow of liquid through a slit. The other two problems solved by this same function are to be obtained by drawing, in the z-plane, the curves $u(x, y)$ = const. and $v(x, y)$ = const. and identifying Ψ and Φ with u and v, and *vice versa*. The z-plane curves u = const. and v = const. are very complicated and do not correspond to any simple or important physical problem, and hence they are not drawn on the figure. In fact, it is usually the case that only two of the possible four problems are sufficiently simple to be of any practical use.

It should be emphasized that it is never sufficient, in obtaining the analytical solution of a definite physical problem, merely to know that certain functions satisfy Laplace's equation. One must also have certain boundary conditions. The graphs shown above disclose to the eye what physical problem has been solved precisely because they show what sort of boundary conditions are satisfied. For example, if the dotted curves of Fig. 142 are stream lines, then the problem solved is the circulation around an elliptical obstacle just because these dotted stream lines satisfy the boundary condition for such a problem; namely, because the flow at any point on the boundary of the obstacle is parallel to the boundary of the obstacle.

It is interesting to note that this same transformation $w =$ cosh z (or, slightly more generally, $w = a$ cosh z) can be used to solve a hydrodynamic problem of a different sort. When liquid seeps through a porous soil, it is found that the component in any direction of the velocity of the liquid is proportional to the negative pressure gradient in that same direction. Thus, in a problem of two-dimensional flow,

$$u = -k\frac{\partial p}{\partial x}, \qquad v = -k\frac{\partial p}{\partial y}.$$

If these values be inserted in the equation of continuity, namely, in the equation

$$\frac{\partial u}{\partial x} + \frac{\partial v}{\partial y} = 0,$$

the result is

$$\nabla^2 p \equiv \frac{\partial^2 p}{\partial x^2} + \frac{\partial^2 p}{\partial y^2} = 0.$$

Suppose, then, one considers the problem of the seepage flow under a gravity dam which rests on material that permits such seepage. One seeks (see Fig. 145) a function p that satisfies

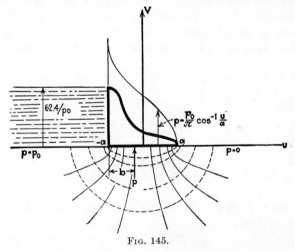

Fɪɢ. 145.

Laplace's equation and that satisfies certain boundary conditions on the surface of the ground. That is, the pressure must be uniform on the surface of the ground upstream from the heel of the dam and zero on the surface of the ground downstream from the toe of the dam. If we choose a system of cartesian coordinates u, v with origin at the midpoint of the base of the dam (Fig. 145) and u-axis on the surface of the ground, then it is easily checked that $p(u, v) = p_0 y(u, v)/\pi$, where

$$w = u + iv = a \cosh{(x + iy)},$$

satisfies the demands of the problem. In fact, it was seen in Sec. 145*d*, where the transformation $w = \cosh z$ was studied, that the line $y = \pi$ of the z-plane folds up to produce the portion to the left of $u = -1$ of the u-axis in the w-plane, and the line $y = 0$ of the z-plane folds up to produce the portion to the right of $u = +1$ of the u-axis. The introduction of the factor a in the transformation merely makes the width of the base of the dam $2a$ rather than 2. These remarks show that $p(u, v)$ reduces to the constant π on the surface of the ground upstream from the heel of the dam. If the head above the dam is such as to produce a hydrostatic pressure p_0, one merely has to set

$$p(u, v) = \frac{p_0 y(u, v)}{\pi}.$$

One may now easily find the distribution of uplift pressure across the base of the dam. In fact, the base of the dam is the representation, in the uv-plane, of the line $x = 0$, $0 \leqq y \leqq \pi$, of the xy-plane. Hence, on the base of the dam the equations

$$u = a \cosh x \cos y,$$
$$v = a \sinh x \sin y$$

reduce to

$$u = a \cos y,$$
$$v = 0,$$

so that

$$p(u, 0) = \frac{p_0}{\pi} \cos^{-1} \frac{u}{a}$$

This curve is drawn in the figure. The total uplift pressure (per foot of dam)

$$P = \frac{p_0}{\pi} \int_{-a}^{+a} \cos^{-1} \frac{u}{a}\, du = p_0 a,$$

which is what the uplift pressure would be if the entire base of the dam were subjected to a head just one-half the head above the dam or if the pressure decreased uniformly (linearly) from the static head p_0 at the heel to the value zero at the toe. The point of application of the resultant uplift is easily calculated to be at a distance $b = 3a/4$ from the heel of the dam.

c. Applications to Elasticity. If opposing couples be applied to the ends of a right cylinder or prism of homogeneous material, the cylinder twists and shearing stresses are developed. Choose the axis of the prism for the z-axis of a rectangular system of coordinates. The angle of twist per unit length, say τ, and the shearing stresses, due to an applied couple T, can both be calculated if one can determine a function $\Phi(x, y)$ satisfying Laplace's equation and reducing, on the boundary of a section of the prism, to the function $\Phi^* = (x^2 + y^2)/2$. In fact,[1]

$$\tau = \frac{T}{C},$$

where

$$C = 2G \iint (\Phi - \Phi^*) \, dx \, dy,$$

in which G is the modulus of rigidity of the material, whereas the shearing stresses are given by

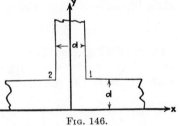

$$X_z = G\tau \left(\frac{\partial \Phi}{\partial y} - y \right),$$

$$Y_z = -G\tau \left(\frac{\partial \Phi}{\partial x} - x \right).$$

Exact analytical solutions of this important technical problem have been obtained for several

Fig. 146.

simple sections, notably circular, elliptical, rectangular, and triangular.[2] Only recently[3] the problem was solved for an infinite T section (see Fig. 146). From the general discussion given in Sec. 144, it is clear that, to solve this latter problem, one requires first an analytic function that will map the boundary of this T section onto the entire real axis of the new w-plane. This section, moreover, is a rectilinear polygon, so that one can use the Schwartz transformation theory to produce the desired analytic relation. One finds that the desired mapping is carried out by the function

[1] Love, A. E. H., Theory of Elasticity, 3d ed., pp. 315–333, 1920.

[2] Trayer, W., and H. W. March, The Torsion of Members Having Sections Common in Aircraft Construction, *Bur. Aeronautics Navy Dept.*, *Separate Rept.* 334; also contained in *Nat. Adv. Comm. Aeronautics*, *15th Ann. Rept.*, 1929, pp. 675–719.

[3] Sokolnikoff, I. S., On a Solution of Laplace's Equation with an Application to the Torsion Problem for a Polygon with Reentrant Angles, *Trans. Amer. Math. Soc.*, vol. 33, pp. 719–732.

$$z = A \int \frac{(w^2 - 1)^{\frac{1}{2}}}{(w^2 - a^2)} \, dw + B,$$

$$= \frac{di}{\pi} \log (w + \sqrt{w^2 - 1}) + \frac{2 \, di}{\pi} \tan^{-1} \frac{\sqrt{w^2 - 1}}{2w} + \frac{d}{2} + id,$$

where the first line is furnished directly by the Schwartz theorem and where, in the second line, the constants a, A, B have been evaluated so as to fit the dimensions and location of the T section.

It is next necessary to break z up into its real and imaginary parts so as to obtain x and y as functions of u and v. These values, when substituted into

$$\Phi^* = \frac{x^2 + y^2}{2},$$

give, because $v = 0$ on the boundary of the section, the function

$$\Phi^*[x(u, 0), y(u, 0)] \equiv \Phi_*(u).$$

The remaining essential step is to obtain a function $\Psi(u, v)$ satisfying Laplace's equation and reducing, on the axis of reals $v = 0$, to the function $\Phi_*(u)$. Such a function is[1]

$$\Psi = \frac{1}{\pi} \int_{-\infty}^{+\infty} \frac{\Phi_*(\xi)\rho \sin \theta}{\rho^2 - 2\xi\rho \cos \theta + \xi^2} \, d\xi,$$

where

$$w = u + iv = \rho e^{i\theta}.$$

The solution to the original problem is then given, as was earlier indicated in Sec. 144, by $\Phi = \Psi$. It is obviously a difficult and laborious job to carry out these calculations, but formulas have been obtained, in the paper referred to, from which practical calculations can be made.

d. Applications to Electrostatics. The methods of complex variable theory are peculiarly applicable to two-dimensional electrical problems. In order that the problems be two-dimensional, we shall understand that the conductors under consideration are exceedingly long cylinders whose axes are normal to the $z = x + iy$ plane. Under these circumstances the various

---

[1] SOKOLNIKOFF, I. S., On a Solution of Laplace's Equation with an Application to the Torsion Problem for a Polygon with Reentrant Angles, *Trans. Amer. Math. Soc.*, vol. 33, pp. 719–732. This formula is the general solution, spoken of in Sec. 144, of Laplace's equation subject to specified boundary values on the entire axis of abscissas.

electrical quantities do not change appreciably in the direction normal to the z-plane, and one has to determine these quantities as functions of x and y only. In certain problems, one or more of the conductors present will have very small cross sections and will be given a charge of, say e' per unit length. Such a conductor will be called a line charge of strength e'.

The electrostatic problem for such conductors is solved when one has obtained a function $\Phi(x, y)$, known as the electrostatic potential, satisfying the following conditions:[1]

(146-3)

(a)
$$\nabla^2\Phi = \frac{\partial^2\Phi}{\partial x^2} + \frac{\partial^2\Phi}{\partial y^2} = 0$$

at all points in free space.

(b) Φ reduces, on the surface of the kth conductor, to a constant Φ_k.

(c) In the neighborhood of a line charge of strength e', Φ becomes infinite as

$$\frac{-e' \log r}{2\pi},$$

where r measures distance to the line.

(d) Φ behaves at infinity as

$$-\frac{\log R\Sigma e'}{2\pi},$$

where $\Sigma e'$ is the total charge per unit length of all conductors present and where R measures distance from some reference point in the finite plane. In case $\Sigma e' = 0$, Φ approaches zero as $1/R$.

It is readily shown, by standard methods, that the solution of such a problem is unique. This remark is of great practical importance, since it assures one that a function Φ satisfying these conditions is, however it may have been obtained, the correct solution of the physical problem.

Physically one wishes to know the distribution of charge and the electrostatic force at any point. These data may be obtained

---

[1] See MASON, M., and W. WEAVER, The Electromagnetic Field, pp. 134, 146, 1929; and REIMANN-WEBER, Die Differentialgleichungen der Physik, vol. 2, p. 290, 1927. The units used in the above discussion are the rational units used in Mason and Weaver, *loc. cit.*

from the function Φ in the following manner: The component E_s in any direction s of the electrostatic force per unit charge is given in terms of Φ by the relation

$$E_s = -\frac{\partial \Phi}{\partial s};$$

and the surface density of charge η on any conductor is given by

$$\eta = -\frac{\partial \Phi}{\partial n},$$

where n measures distance along the external normal to the conductor in question.

Now if

$$w = u + iv = f(z) = f(x + iy)$$

and if the function

$$\Phi(x, y) = u(x, y)$$

satisfies condition (146-3), then

$$E_x = -\frac{\partial \Phi}{\partial x} = -\frac{\partial u}{\partial x} = -\frac{\partial v}{\partial y},$$

the last step following from the Cauchy-Riemann equations (135-6). Similarly

$$E_y = -\frac{\partial \Phi}{\partial y} = -\frac{\partial u}{\partial y} = +\frac{\partial v}{\partial x}.$$

Thus,

$$E_x - iE_y = -\frac{\partial v}{\partial y} + i\frac{\partial u}{\partial y} = i\left(\frac{\partial u}{\partial y} + i\frac{\partial v}{\partial y}\right),$$

$$= i\frac{\partial w}{\partial y} = +\frac{dw}{dz},$$

the last step resulting from the fundamental fact that the value of the derivative of an analytic function w is independent of the mode in which z approaches zero. Now the complex number $a - ib$ is called the "conjugate" of the complex number $a + ib$ and one often denotes a conjugate by a bar, thus:

$$a - ib = \overline{a + bi}.$$

With this standard notation, the "complex electric force" $E \equiv E_x + iE_y$ is given by

(146-4) $$E \equiv E_x + iE_y = -\overline{\frac{dw}{dz}},$$

and the magnitude $\sqrt{E_x^2 + E_y^2}$ of the electrostatic force at any point is given by

(146-5) $$\sqrt{E_x^2 + E_y^2} = \left|\frac{dw}{dz}\right|.$$

If one chooses $\Phi \equiv v(x, y)$, then (146-4) and (146-5) are replaced by

(146-6) $$E = E_x + iE_y = -i\frac{\overline{dw}}{dz},$$

(146-7) $$\sqrt{E_x^2 + E_y^2} = \left|\frac{dw}{dz}\right|.$$

Three types of electrostatic problems will now be briefly considered. The first and simplest two-dimensional electrostatic problem is that of a single long cylindrical conductor with a given charge. One then seeks a function that satisfies Laplace's equation and, in accordance with (146-3)b, reduces to a constant on the curve that bounds a section of the conductor. This is the analytical problem whose solution was indicated in Sec. 144. One requires a function $w = u + iv = f(z) = f(x + iy)$ such that either a vertical straight line $u = $ const. or a horizontal straight line $v = $ const. of the w-plane maps into the bounding curve C of the conductor's section in the z-plane. Then $\Phi(x, y)$ $\equiv u(x, y)$ or $\Phi(x, y) \equiv v(x, y)$ solves the problem, and the physically important quantities are given by (146-4), (146-5) or by (146-6), (146-7), respectively.

Secondly, suppose that a single long cylindrical conductor is in the presence of a parallel line charge of strength e'. We suppose the line charge to be outside the conductor. Let C be the bounding curve in the z-plane of a section of the conductor, and let the line charge be located at $z = z_0$. We may conveniently suppose the cylindrical conductor to be grounded, so that we seek a solution of Laplace's equation that reduces to zero on C and becomes infinite as indicated in (146-3)c at $z = z_0$. Let $\zeta = f(z)$ transform C onto the entire axis of reals and the exterior of C conformally upon the upper half ζ-plane. Then if

$$w = u + iv = \frac{e'}{2\pi} \log \frac{f(z) - \overline{f(z_0)}}{f(z) - f(z_0)},$$

the function $\Phi \equiv u(x, y)$ is the solution sought. In fact, for values of z sufficiently close to z_0, $f(z) - f(z_0)$ behaves, except for a constant factor, as $(z - z_0)$. Thus, if one writes

$$z - z_0 = re^{i\theta},$$

then, for values of z very near to z_0,

$$w = u + iv = \frac{e'}{2\pi} \log \frac{1}{re^{i\theta}} + A = \frac{e'}{2\pi} \log \frac{1}{r} - i \frac{e'\theta}{2\pi} + A,$$

where A remains finite as $z \doteq z_0$. Therefore,

$$u = \frac{e'}{2\pi} \log \frac{1}{r} + B,$$

where B remains finite as $z \doteq z_0$. Thus $u(x, y)$ has the proper type of infinity at $z = z_0$. Furthermore, for points z on C, $f(z)$ is on the axis of reals in the ζ-plane, so that the modulus of $f(z) - f(z_0)$ equals the modulus of $f(z) - \overline{f(z_0)}$. Hence the modulus of

$$\frac{f(z) - \overline{f(z_0)}}{f(z) - f(z_0)}$$

is unity. However, since

$$\log \rho e^{i\varphi} = \log \rho + i\varphi,$$

it is clear that the real part of the logarithm of a complex quantity is the logarithm of the modulus of the complex quantity. Since the logarithm of unity is zero, it is clear that u vanishes on C. As regards the behavior of $u(x, y)$ at infinity, one notes that u is the logarithm of the ratio of the (real) distances of $\zeta = f(z)$ to $\zeta_0 = \overline{f(z_0)}$ and to $\zeta_0 = f(z_0)$. As z becomes infinite, this ratio differs from unity by an amount whose leading term is equal to or less than a constant times the reciprocal distance from $f(z)$ to one of the points $f(z_0)$ or $\overline{f(z_0)}$. Thus the leading term in the logarithm of this ratio is a constant times this reciprocal distance; and $\Phi = u$ behaves at ∞ in the required manner.

In the third type of problem there are two conductors present, one raised to the potential Φ_0 while the other is at a potential zero. Thus, suppose that the cross section of two long cylindrical conductors consists of two curves C_0 and C_1, such as those shown in Fig. 147, which do not intersect at a finite point but which, if one takes account of the intersection of B_1 and B_0 and of A_0 and A_1 at $z = \infty$, divide the extended plane into two simply connected regions, one of which may be called the "interior" and the other the "exterior" of the closed curve $C_0 + C_1$. Now suppose that $\zeta = f(z)$ maps C_0 onto the entire negative axis of reals in the ζ-plane, with the infinitely distant point along B_0 mapped onto $\zeta = 0$, that $\zeta = f(z)$ also maps C_1 onto the entire positive axis of reals with the infinitely distant point along B_1 mapped onto $\zeta = 0$, and that $\zeta = f(z)$ maps the interior of $C_0 + C_1$ conformally on the upper half ζ-plane. Then, if

$$w = u + iv = \frac{\Phi_0}{\pi} \log f(z),$$

the function $\Phi = v(x, y)$ satisfies $\nabla^2 \Phi = 0$ at every point in the interior of $C_0 + C_1$, reduces to zero on C_1, and reduces to Φ_0 on C_0.

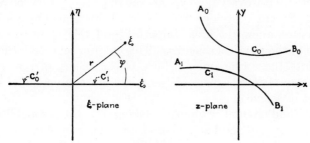

FIG. 147.

In fact, the imaginary part of the logarithm of a complex number is merely the amplitude of the complex number; and for points on C_0, $f(z)$ has an amplitude of π, while for points on C_1, $f(z)$ has an amplitude of zero. Then,

$$\frac{dw}{dz} = \frac{\Phi_0}{\pi} \frac{\dfrac{ds}{dz}}{f(z)},$$

and the electrostatic force is given by (146-5) and (146-7).

This third type of problem is of frequent and important practical occurrence. Many electrical engineering problems that have been solved by this method of conformal representation are referred to in an expository article, devoted largely to the Schwarz transformation, by E. Weber.[1] In an earlier article in the same journal,[2] for instance, the theory of conformal representation is applied to the problem of studying the leakage voltage and the breakdown potential between the high- and low-potential portions of oil-immersed transformers. The cases studied come under the third type of problem discussed above.

[1] WEBER, E., Archiv für Elektrotechnik, vol. 18, p. 174, 1926.

[2] DREYFUS, L., Archiv für Elektrotechnik, vol. 13, p. 123, 1924.

CHAPTER XI

PROBABILITY

There is no branch of mathematics that is more intimately connected with everyday experiences than the theory of probability. Recent developments in mathematical physics have emphasized anew the great importance of this theory in every branch of the physical sciences. This chapter sets forth the bare outline of those fundamental facts of the theory of probability which should form a part of the minimum equipment of every student of science.

147. Fundamental Notions. Asking for the probability or for a measure of the happening of any event implies the possibility of the non-occurrence of this event. Unless there exists some ignorance concerning the happening of an event, the problem does not belong to the theory of probability. Thus, the question "What is the probability that New Year's day in 1984 will fall on Monday?" is trivial, inasmuch as this question can be settled by referring to a calendar. On the other hand, the query "What is the probability of drawing the ace of hearts from a deck of 52 cards?" constitutes a problem to which the theory of probability gives a definite answer. In fact, one can reason as follows: Granting that the deck is perfect, one card is *just as likely* to appear as any other and, since there are 52 cards, the chance that the ace of hearts will be drawn is 1 out of 52. The words "just as likely," used in the preceding sentence, imply the existence of the ignorance that is essential to remove any problem of probability from triviality. The term "equally likely," or "just as likely," applied to a future event that can happen or fail to happen in a certain number of ways, indicates that the possible ways are so related that there is no reason for expecting the occurrence of any one of them rather than that of any other.

If an event can happen in N ways, which are equally likely, and if, among these N ways, m are favorable, then the probability of the occurrence of the event in a single trial is

$$p = \frac{m}{N}.$$

Thus, the probability that the six will appear when a die is thrown is $\frac{1}{6}$, since the total number of ways in which a die can fall is 6, and of these six ways only one is favorable. The probability of drawing a heart from a deck of 52 cards is $\frac{1}{4}$, since there are 13 hearts and the total number of equally likely ways in which a card can be drawn is 52.

It is clear that, if an event is certain to happen, then the probability of its occurrence is 1, for all the possible ways are favorable. On the other hand, if an event is certain not to occur, the probability of its occurrence is zero. It is clear also that, if the probability of the happening of an event is p, then the probability of its failure to happen is

$$q = 1 - p.$$

The concept of "equally likely" plays a fundamental role in the theory of probability. The need for caution and a careful analysis of the problem will be illustrated by several examples.

Let two coins be tossed simultaneously. What will be the probability that they both show heads? The following reasoning is at fault. The total number of ways in which the coins can fall is three, since the possible combinations are two heads, two tails, and a head and a tail. Of these three ways, only one is favorable, and therefore the probability is $\frac{1}{3}$. The fault in this reasoning lies in the failure to account for all the equally likely cases. The number of ways in which one head and one tail can fall is two, since the head can appear on the first coin and the tail on the second, or the head can appear on the second coin and the tail on the first. Thus, the total number of equally likely ways is 4, and the probability of both coins showing heads is $\frac{1}{4}$. The probability of one head and one tail showing is $\frac{2}{4}$, so that a head and a tail are twice as likely to appear as either two heads or two tails.

Another example may prove useful. Suppose that a pair of dice is thrown. What is the probability that a total of eight shows? The total number of ways in which two dice can fall is 36. (This follows from the fundamental principle of combinatory analysis: *if one thing can be done in m different ways and another thing can be done in n different ways, then both things can be done together, or in succession, in mn different ways.*) The sum of 8 can be obtained as follows: 2 and 6, 3 and 5, 4 and 4. Now, there are two ways in which 2 and 6 can fall: 2 on the first die and 6 on the second, and *vice versa*. Similarly, there are two ways in which 3 and 5 can fall, but there is only one way in which 4 and 4 can fall. Hence, the total number of equally likely and favorable cases is 5, so that the desired probability is $\frac{5}{36}$.

The two foregoing examples were solved simply by enumerating all the possible and all the favorable cases. Frequently, such enumeration is laborious and it is convenient to resort to formulas. Thus, let it be required to find the probability of drawing 4 white balls from an urn containing 10 white, 4 black, and 3 red balls. The number of ways in which 4 white balls can be chosen from 10 white balls is equal to the number of combinations of 10 things taken 4 at a time, namely,

$$_{10}C_4 = \frac{10!}{4!\,6!}.$$

The total number of ways in which 4 balls can be chosen from the 17 available is

$$_{17}C_4 = \frac{17!}{4!\,13!}.$$

Hence, the probability of success is

$$p = \frac{_{10}C_4}{_{17}C_4} = \frac{10!\,4!\,13!}{4!\,6!\,17!} = \frac{3}{34}.$$

Another example will illustrate further the use of formulas. Suppose that it is desired to find the probability of drawing 4 white, 3 black, and 2 red balls from the urn in the preceding illustration. In this case the number of ways in which 4 white balls can be drawn is $_{10}C_4$; the 3 black balls can be chosen in $_4C_3$ ways; and the 2 red ones in $_3C_2$ ways. An application of the fundamental principle of combinatory analysis gives the required probability as

$$p = \frac{_{10}C_4 \cdot {}_4C_3 \cdot {}_3C_2}{_{17}C_9} = \frac{252}{2431}.$$

PROBLEMS

1. What is the probability that the sum of 7 appears in a single throw with two dice? What is the probability of the sum of 11? Show that 7 is the more probable throw.

2. An urn contains 20 balls: 10 white, 7 black, and 3 red. What is the probability that a ball drawn at random is red? White? Black? If 2 balls are drawn, what is the probability that both are white? If 10 balls are drawn, what is the probability that 5 are white, 2 black, and 3 red?

148. Independent Events. A set of events is said to be *independent* if the occurrence of any one of them is not influenced by the occurrence of the others. On the other hand, if the occurrence of any one of the events affects the occurrence of the others, the events are said to be *dependent*.

THEOREM 1. *If the probabilities of occurrence of a set of n independent events are p_1, p_2, $\cdots$, p_n, then the probability that all of the set of events will occur is $p = p_1 p_2 \cdots p_n$.*

The proof of this theorem follows directly from the fundamental principle. Thus, let there be only two events, whose probabilities of success are

$$p_1 = \frac{m_1}{N_1} \quad \text{and} \quad p_2 = \frac{m_2}{N_2}.$$

The total number of ways in which both the events may succeed is $m_1 m_2$, and the total number of ways in which these events can succeed and fail to succeed is $N_1 N_2$. Hence, the probability of the occurrence of both of the events is

$$p = \frac{m_1 m_2}{N_1 N_2} = \frac{m_1}{N_1} \cdot \frac{m_2}{N_2} = p_1 p_2.$$

Obviously, this proof can be extended to any number of events.

Illustration. A coin and a die are tossed. What is the probability that the ace and the head will appear? The probability that the ace will appear is $\frac{1}{6}$, and the probability that the head will appear is $\frac{1}{2}$. Therefore, the probability that both head and ace will appear is

$$\frac{1}{6} \cdot \frac{1}{2} = \frac{1}{12}.$$

THEOREM 2. *If the probability of occurrence of an event is p_1 and if, after that event has occurred, the probability of occurrence* *of* a second event is p_2, then the probability of occurrence of both events in succession is $p_1 p_2$.

The proof of this theorem is similar to that of Theorem 1 and will be left to the student. Obviously, the theorem can be extended to more than two events.

Illustration 1. What is the probability that 2 aces be drawn in succession from a deck of 52 cards? The probability that an ace will be drawn on the first trial is $\frac{4}{52}$. After the first ace has been drawn, the probability of drawing another ace from the remaining 51 cards is $\frac{3}{51}$, so that the probability of drawing 2 aces is

$$\frac{4}{52} \cdot \frac{3}{51} = \frac{1}{221}.$$

Illustration 2. What is the probability that the ace appears at least once in n throws of a die? The probability of the ace appearing in a single throw of the die is $\frac{1}{6}$, and the probability that it will not appear is $\frac{5}{6}$. The probability that the ace will not appear in n successive throws is

$$\left(\frac{5}{6}\right)^n.$$

Hence, the probability that the ace will appear at least once is

$$1 - \left(\frac{5}{6}\right)^n.$$

Illustration 3. An urn contains 30 black balls and 20 white balls. What is the probability that (*a*) A white ball and a black ball are drawn in succession? (*b*) A black ball and a white ball are drawn in succession? (*c*) Three black balls are drawn in succession?

a. The probability of drawing a white ball is $\frac{20}{50}$. After a white ball is drawn, the probability of drawing a black ball is $\frac{30}{49}$. Hence, the probability of drawing a white ball and a black ball in the order stated is

$$p = \frac{20}{50} \cdot \frac{30}{49} = \frac{12}{49}.$$

b. The probability of drawing a black ball is $\frac{30}{50}$, and the probability that the second drawing yields a white ball is $\frac{20}{49}$, so that

$$p = \frac{30}{50} \cdot \frac{20}{49} = \frac{12}{49}.$$

c. The probability of drawing 3 black balls in succession is

$$p = \frac{30}{50} \cdot \frac{29}{49} \cdot \frac{28}{48} = \frac{29}{140}.$$

Illustration 4. The probability that Paul will solve a problem is $\frac{1}{4}$, and the probability that John will solve it is $\frac{2}{3}$. What is the probability that the problem will be solved if Paul and John work independently?

The problem will be solved unless both Paul and John fail. The probability of John's failure to solve it is $\frac{1}{3}$ and of Paul's failure to solve it is $\frac{3}{4}$. Therefore, the probability that Paul and John both fail is

$$\frac{1}{3} \cdot \frac{3}{4} = \frac{1}{4},$$

and the probability that the problem will be solved is

$$1 - \frac{1}{4} = \frac{3}{4}.$$

PROBLEMS

1. What is the probability that 5 cards dealt from a pack of 52 cards are all of the same suit?

2. Five coins are tossed simultaneously. What is the probability that at least one of them shows a head? All show heads?

3. What is the probability that a monkey seated before a typewriter having 42 keys with 26 letters will type the word *sir?*

4. If Paul hits a target 80 times out of 100 on the average and John hits it 90 times out of 100, what is the probability that at least one of them hits the target if they shoot simultaneously?

5. The probability that Paul will be alive 10 years hence is $\frac{5}{8}$, and that John will be alive is $\frac{3}{4}$. What is the probability that both Paul and John will be dead 10 years hence? Paul alive and John dead? John alive and Paul dead?

149. Mutually Exclusive Events. Events are said to be *mutually exclusive* if the occurrence of one of them prevents the occurrence of the others. An important theorem concerning such events is the following:

THEOREM. *The probability of the occurrence of either one or the other of two mutually exclusive events is equal to the sum of the probabilities of the single events.*

The proof of this theorem follows from the definition of probability. Consider two mutually exclusive events A and B. Inasmuch as the events are mutually exclusive, A and B cannot occur simultaneously and the possible cases are the following: (*a*) A occurs and B fails to occur, (*b*) B occurs and A fails to occur, (*c*) both A and B fail. Let the number of equally likely cases in which (*a*) A can occur and B fail be α, (*b*) B can occur and A fail be β, (*c*) both A and B fail be γ.

Then the total number of equally likely cases is $\alpha + \beta + \gamma$. The probability that either A or B occurs is

$$\frac{\alpha + \beta}{\alpha + \beta + \gamma},$$

the probability of occurrence of A is

$$\frac{\alpha}{\alpha + \beta + \gamma},$$

and the probability of occurrence of B is

$$\frac{\beta}{\alpha + \beta + \gamma}.$$

Therefore, the probability of occurrence of either A or B is equal to the sum of the probabilities of occurrence of A alone and of B alone. Obviously, this theorem can be extended to any number of mutually exclusive events.

The task of determining when a given set of events is mutually exclusive is frequently difficult, and care must be exercised that this theorem is applied only to mutually exclusive events. Thus, in Illustration 4, Sec. 148, the probability that either Paul or John will solve the problem cannot be obtained by adding $\frac{1}{4}$ and $\frac{2}{3}$, for solution of the problem by Paul does not eliminate the possibility of its solution by John. The events in this case are not mutually exclusive and the theorem of this section does not apply.

Illustration 1. A bag contains 10 white balls and 15 black balls. Two balls are drawn in succession. What is the probability that one of them is black and the other is white?

The mutually exclusive events in this problem are: (*a*) drawing a white ball on the first trial and a black on the second; (*b*) drawing a black ball on the first trial and a white on the second. The probability of (*a*) is $\frac{10}{25} \cdot \frac{15}{24}$ and that of (*b*) is $\frac{15}{25} \cdot \frac{10}{24}$, so that the probability of either (*a*) or (*b*) is

$$\frac{10}{25} \cdot \frac{15}{24} + \frac{15}{25} \cdot \frac{10}{24} = \frac{1}{2}.$$

Illustration 2. Paul and John are to engage in a game in which each is to draw in turn one coin at a time from a purse containing 3 silver and 2 gold coins. The coins are not replaced after being drawn. If Paul is to draw first, find the probability for each player that he is the first to draw a gold coin.

The probability that Paul succeeds in drawing a gold coin on the first trial is $\frac{2}{5}$. The probability that Paul fails and John succeeds in his first trial is

$$\tfrac{3}{5} \cdot \tfrac{2}{4} = \tfrac{3}{10}.$$

The probability that Paul fails, John fails, and then Paul succeeds is

$$\tfrac{3}{5} \cdot \tfrac{2}{4} \cdot \tfrac{2}{3} = \tfrac{1}{5}.$$

The probability that Paul fails, John fails, Paul fails again, and John succeeds is

$$\tfrac{3}{5} \cdot \tfrac{2}{4} \cdot \tfrac{1}{3} \cdot \tfrac{2}{2} = \tfrac{1}{10},$$

for after three successive failures to draw a gold coin there remain only the two gold coins in the purse and John is certain to draw one of them. Therefore, Paul's total probability is

$$\tfrac{2}{5} + \tfrac{1}{5} = \tfrac{3}{5}$$

and John's probability is

$$\tfrac{3}{10} + \tfrac{1}{10} = \tfrac{2}{5}.$$

PROBLEMS

1. One purse contains 3 silver and 7 gold coins; another purse contains 4 silver and 8 gold coins. A purse is chosen at random, and a coin is drawn from it. What is the probability that it is a gold coin?

2. Paul and John are throwing alternately a pair of dice. The first man to throw a doublet is to win. If Paul throws first, what is his chance of winning on his first throw? What is the probability that Paul fails and John wins on his first throw?

3. On the average a certain student is able to solve 60 per cent of the problems assigned to him. If an examination contains 8 problems and a minimum of 5 problems is required for passing, what is the student's chance of passing?

4. Two dice are thrown; what is the probability that the sum is either 7 or 11?

5. How many times must a die be thrown in order that the probability that the ace appear at least once shall be greater than $\frac{1}{2}$?

6. Twenty tickets are numbered from 1 to 20, and one of them is drawn at random. What is the probability that the number is a multiple of 5 or 7? A multiple of 3 or 5?

Note that in solving the second part of this problem, it is incorrect to reason as follows: The number of tickets bearing numerals that are multiples of 3 is 6, and the number of multiples of 5 is 4. Hence, the probability that the number drawn is either a multiple of 3 or of 5 is $\frac{6}{20} + \frac{4}{20} = \frac{1}{2}$. Why?

7. A publishing concern submits a copy of a proposed book to three independent critics. The odds that a book will be reviewed favorably by these critics are 5 to 4, 4 to 3, and 2 to 3. What is the probability that a majority of the three reviews will be favorable?

8. If on the average in a shipment of 10 cases of certain goods 1 case is damaged, what is the probability that out of 5 cases expected at least 4 will not be damaged?

150. Expectation. The expectation of winning any prize is defined as the value of the prize multiplied by the probability of winning it. Let it be required to determine the price one should pay for the privilege of participating in the following game. A purse contains 5 silver dollars and 7 fifty-cent pieces, and a player is to retain the two coins that he draws from the purse. It can be argued fallaciously as follows: The mutually exclusive cases are (a) 2 dollar coins, (b) 2 half-dollar coins, (c) 1 dollar coin and 1 half-dollar coin. Therefore, the values of the prizes are $2, $1, and $1.50, and the fair price to pay for the privilege of participating is $1.50. But, the probability of obtaining (a) is

$$p_a = \frac{{}_5C_2}{{}_{12}C_2} = \frac{5}{33},$$

that of obtaining (b) is

$$p_b = \frac{{}_7C_2}{{}_{12}C_2} = \frac{7}{22},$$

and that of obtaining (c) is

$$p_c = \frac{5.7}{{}_{12}C_2} = \frac{35}{66}.$$

Hence, the expectation of obtaining (a) is

$$\epsilon_a = 2 \cdot \frac{5}{33} = 0.30,$$

that of obtaining (b) is

$$\epsilon_b = 1 \cdot \frac{7}{22} = 0.32,$$

and that of obtaining (c) is

$$\epsilon_c = 1.50 \cdot \frac{35}{66} = 0.80.$$

It follows that the total expectation is

$$\$0.30 + \$0.32 + \$0.80 = \$1.42,$$

instead of $1.50.

PROBLEMS

1. A batch of 1000 electric lamps is 5 per cent bad. If 5 lamps are tested, what is the probability that no defective lamps appear? What is the chance that a test batch of 5 lamps is 80 per cent defective? What is a fair price to pay for a batch of 500 such lamps if the perfect ones can be bought for 10 cts. each?

2. What is a fair price to pay for a lottery ticket if there are 100 tickets and 5 prizes of $100 each, 10 prizes of $50 each, and 20 prizes of $5 each?

3. What is the expected number of throws of a coin necessary to produce 3 heads?

151. Repeated and Independent Trials. Frequently it is required to compute the probability of the occurrence of an event in n trials when the probability of the occurrence of that event in a single trial is known. For example, it may be required to find the probability of throwing exactly one ace in 6 throws of a single die. The possible mutually exclusive cases are as follows:

(1) An ace on the first throw, and none on the remaining 5 throws.

(2) No ace on the first throw, an ace on the second, and no aces on the remaining 4 throws.

(3) No ace on the first 2 throws, an ace on the third, and no aces on the last 3 throws.

(4) No aces on the first 3 throws, an ace on the fourth, and no aces on the last 2 throws.

(5) No aces on the first 4 throws, an ace on the fifth, and no ace on the last throw.

(6) No aces on the first 5 throws, and an ace on the last throw.

The probability of the occurrence of (1) is

$$\tfrac{1}{6} \cdot (\tfrac{5}{6})^5,$$

since the probability of throwing an ace on the first trial is $\tfrac{1}{6}$ and the probability that the ace will not appear on the succeeding 5 throws is $(\tfrac{5}{6})^5$. The probability of (2) is

$$\tfrac{5}{6} \cdot \tfrac{1}{6} \cdot (\tfrac{5}{6})^4,$$

the probability of (3) is

$$\tfrac{5}{6} \cdot \tfrac{5}{6} \cdot \tfrac{1}{6} \cdot (\tfrac{5}{6})^3,$$

and it is clear that the probability of any one of the 6 specified combinations is

$$(\tfrac{1}{6})(\tfrac{5}{6})^5.$$

Since the cases are mutually exclusive, the probability that some one of the 6 combinations will occur is

$$p = 6 \cdot \tfrac{1}{6} \cdot (\tfrac{5}{6})^5 = (\tfrac{5}{6})^5.$$

It should be observed that the probability of obtaining any combination of 1 ace and 5 not-aces is always the same, so that in order to obtain the probability of occurrence of one of the set of mutually exclusive cases all that is necessary is to multiply the probability of the occurrence of any specified combination by the number of distinct ways in which the events may occur. This leads to the formulation of an important theorem which is frequently termed the binomial law.

THEOREM 1 (Binomial Law). *If the probability of occurrence of an event in a single trial is p, then the probability that it will occur exactly r times in n independent trials is*

$$p_r = {}_nC_r p^r (1 - p)^{n-r},$$

where

$$_nC_r = \frac{n!}{r!(n - r)!}.$$

The method of proof of this theorem is obvious from the discussion of the specific case that precedes the theorem. The probability that an event will occur in a particular set of r trials and fail in the remaining $n - r$ trials is $p^r(1 - p)^{n-r}$. But since the number of trials is n, the number of ways in which the event can succeed r times and fail $n - r$ times is equal to the number of the combinations of n things taken r at a time, or

$$_nC_r = \frac{n!}{r!(n - r)!}.$$

Hence the probability of exactly r successes and $n - r$ failures is

$$(151\text{-}1) \qquad p_r = \frac{n!}{r!(n - r)!} p^r (1 - p)^{n-r}.$$

Illustration 1. What is the chance that the ace will appear exactly 4 times in the course of 10 throws of a die?

Formula (151-1) gives

$$p_4 = \frac{10!}{4!\,6!}\left(\frac{1}{6}\right)^4\left(\frac{5}{6}\right)^6 = \frac{656,250}{60,466,176} = 0.0108.$$

Illustration 2. Ten coins are tossed simultaneously. What is the chance that exactly 2 of them show heads?

Here

$$p_2 = \frac{10!}{2!\,8!}\left(\frac{1}{2}\right)^2\left(\frac{1}{2}\right)^8 = \frac{45}{1024} = 0.0439.$$

If in the example at the beginning of this section it had been required to determine the probability that the ace would appear *at least once* in the course of the 6 trials, the problem would be solved with the aid of the following argument: The ace will appear at least once if it appears exactly once, or exactly twice, or exactly three times, and so on. But the probability that it appears exactly once is

$$p_1 = {}_6C_1\,(\tfrac{1}{6})(\tfrac{5}{6})^5;$$

exactly twice,

$$p_2 = {}_6C_2\,(\tfrac{1}{6})^2(\tfrac{5}{6})^4;$$

exactly three times,

$$p_3 = {}_6C_3(\tfrac{1}{6})^3(\tfrac{5}{6})^3;$$

etc. These compound events are mutually exclusive, so that the probability of the ace appearing at least once is the sum of the probabilities

$$p_1,\ p_2,\ p_3,\ \cdots,\ p_6.$$

The general theorem, which includes this problem as a special case, is the following.

THEOREM 2. *If the probability of the occurrence of an event on a single trial is p, then the probability that the event will occur at least r times in the course of n independent trials is*

$$p_{\geq r} = p^n + {}_nC_1 p^{n-1}q + {}_nC_2 p^{n-2}\,q^2 + \cdots + {}_nC_{n-r}p^r q^{n-r},$$

where $q = 1 - p$.

It should be noted that ${}_nC_r = {}_nC_{n-r}$ is the coefficient of p^r in the binomial expansion for $(p + q)^n$ and that $p_{\geq r}$ is equal to the sum of the first $n - r + 1$ terms in the expansion for $(p + q)^n$.

Illustration 3. The probability that at least 2 of the coins show heads when 5 coins are tossed simultaneously is

$$p_{\geq 2} = (\tfrac{1}{2})^5 + {}_5C_1(\tfrac{1}{2})^4(\tfrac{1}{2}) + {}_5C_2(\tfrac{1}{2})^3(\tfrac{1}{2})^2 + {}_5C_3(\tfrac{1}{2})^2(\tfrac{1}{2})^3 = \tfrac{13}{16}.$$

The first term of this sum represents the probability of exactly 5 heads, the second represents that of exactly 4 heads, the third that of exactly 3 heads, and the last represents that of exactly 2 heads.

PROBLEMS

1. If 5 dice are tossed simultaneously, what is the probability that (*a*) exactly 3 of them turn the ace up? (*b*) At least 3 turn the ace up?

2. If the probability that a man aged 60 will live to be 70 is 0.65, what is the probability that out of 10 men now 60, at least 7 will live to be 70?

3. A man is promised $1 for each ace in excess of 1 that appears in 6 consecutive throws of a die. What is the value of his expectation?

4. A bag contains 20 black balls and 15 white balls. What is the chance that at least 4 in a sample of 5 balls are black?

5. Solve Prob. 3, Sec. 149.

152. Distribution Curve. Some interesting and useful conclusions can be deduced regarding the formula for repeated independent events from the consideration of an example that presents some features of the general case. Consider a purse in which are placed 2 silver and 3 gold coins, and let it be required to determine the probability of drawing exactly r silver coins in n repeated trials, the coin being replaced after each drawing. The probability of exactly r successes in n trials is given by the binomial law [see (151-1)]

$$p_r = {}_nC_r p^r (1 - p)^{n-r},$$

where p, the probability of drawing a silver coin on a single trial, is $\frac{2}{5}$.

If the number of drawings is taken as $n = 5$, the probability that none of the drawings yields a silver coin is

$$p_0 = {}_5C_0 (\tfrac{2}{5})^0 (\tfrac{3}{5})^5 = 0.07776,$$

the probability that 5 trials yield exactly 1 silver coin is

$$p_1 = {}_5C_1 (\tfrac{2}{5}) (\tfrac{3}{5})^4 = 0.2592,$$

and the probability that exactly 2 silver coins will appear is

$$p_2 = {}_5C_2 (\tfrac{2}{5})^2 (\tfrac{3}{5})^3 = 0.3456.$$

In this manner, it is possible to construct a table of the values that represent the probabilities of drawing exactly 0, 1, 2, 3, 4, 5 silver coins in 5 trials. Such a table, where the values of p_r are computed to four decimal places, is given next.

PROBABILITY OF EXACTLY r SUCCESSES IN 5 TRIALS

r	p_r	r	p_r
0	0.0778	3	0.2304
1	0.2592	4	0.0768
2	0.3456	5	0.0102

It will be observed that $r = 2$ gives the greatest, or "most probable," value for p_r, which seems reasonable in view of the fact that the probability of drawing a silver coin on a single trial is $\frac{2}{5}$ and one would "expect" that 2 silver coins should result from 5 repeated drawings.

If the number of trials is $n = 10$, the formula

$$p_r = {}_{10}C_r(\tfrac{2}{5})^r(\tfrac{3}{5})^{10-r}$$

gives the following set of probabilities for 0, 1, 2, 3, $\cdots$, 10 successes.

PROBABILITY OF EXACTLY r SUCCESSES IN 10 TRIALS

r	p_r	r	p_r	r	p_r
0	0.0060	4	0.2508	8	0.0106
1	0.0403	5	0.2007	9	0.0016
2	0.1209	6	0.1115	10	0.0001
3	0.2150	7	0.0425		

Again it appears that the most probable number of successes in n trials is equal to the probability of success in a single trial multiplied by the number of trials.

If a similar table is constructed for $n = 30$, the resulting probabilities are as shown below.

PROBABILITY OF EXACTLY r SUCCESSES IN 30 TRIALS

r	p_r	r	p_r	r	p_r
≤ 2	0.0000	9	0.0823	16	0.0489
3	0.0003	10	0.1152	17	0.0269
4	0.0012	11	0.1396	18	0.0129
5	0.0041	12	0.1474	19	0.0054
6	0.0115	13	0.1360	20	0.0020
7	0.0263	14	0.1100	21	0.0006
8	0.0505	15	0.0783	22	0.0002
				≥ 23	0.0000

In this table the entry 0.0000 is made for $0 \leq r \leq 2$ and for $r \geq 23$ because the values of p_r were computed to four decimal places, and in these cases p_r was found to be less than 0.00005. For example, the probability of drawing exactly 1 silver coin in 30 trials is

$$p_1 = 30(\tfrac{2}{5})(\tfrac{3}{5})^{29} = 0.00000442149,$$

and the probability of drawing exactly 23 silver coins in 30 trials is

$$p_{23} = {}_{30}C_{23}(\tfrac{2}{5})^{23}(\tfrac{3}{5})^7 = 0.000040128.$$

Therefore, for all values $23 \leq r \leq 30$, the values of p_r are less than 0.00005 and must be recorded as 0.0000.

Just as in the foregoing tables, the most probable number is equal to $\tfrac{2}{5}n$, although the probability of drawing exactly 12

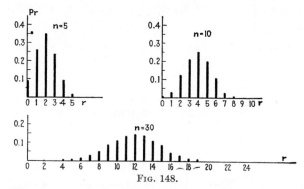

Fig. 148.

silver coins, 0.1474, is less than the probability of drawing the most probable number of silver coins in the case of 10 trials.

These tabulated results can be more conveniently represented in a graphical form, where the values of r are plotted as abscissas and the values of p_r as ordinates. Such graphs are known as distribution charts (Fig. 148).

An alternative method of graphical representation is obtained by erecting rectangles of unit width on the ordinates which represent the probabilities p_r of occurrence of r successes. Since the width of each rectangle is unity, its area is equal, numerically, to the probability of the value of r over which it is erected. In such graphs the vertical lines are not essential to the interpretation of the graph and hence are omitted. The resulting broken curve constitutes what is known as a distribution curve. The

area under each step of the curve represents the value of p_r;
and the entire area under the distribution curve is unity, for it
represents the sum of the probabilities of 0, 1, 2, $\cdots$, n successes. Such curves, corresponding to the distribution charts
(Fig. 148), are drawn in Fig. 149.

It appears that, as the number of drawings, n, is increased, the
probability of obtaining the most probable number of silver coins
decreases. Moreover, there is a greater spread of the chart as
the number of trials is increased, so that the probability of missing
the most probable number by more than a specified amount
increases with the increase in the number of drawings.

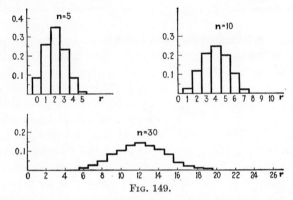

Fig. 149.

The following observations will serve to clarify the last statement. In the case of 5 trials the probability of missing the
most probable number of successes by 5 is zero, for the deviation
from the most probable number 2 cannot be greater than 3.
But in the case of 10 trials the probability of missing the most
probable number by this same amount has a definite non-zero
value. Thus, in order to miss the most probable number 4
by 5, r must be either 9 or 10. Hence, the probability of missing
4 is $0.0016 + 0.0001 = 0.0017$. In the case of 30 trials the
most probable number of successes is 12; and, in order to miss
12 by 5, r must be less than 8 or greater than 16. Therefore the
probability of missing 12 by 5 is the sum

$$\sum_{r=0}^{7} p_r + \sum_{r=17}^{30} p_r = 0.0914.$$

If the number of drawings n is made 1,000,000, the most probable number of successes is 400,000, and the probability of missing it by 5 is very nearly unity. On the other hand, the probability of obtaining the most probable number 400,000 is a very small quantity.

The important facts obtained from the foregoing considerations are the following:

1. The most probable number of successes appears to be equal to pn.

2. The probability of obtaining the most probable number of successes decreases with the increase in the number of trials n.

3. The probability of missing the most probable number by a specified amount increases with the increase in the number of trials.

It can be established that the last two facts, inferred from the special example, are true in general. The first fact, concerning the size of the most probable number, clearly is meaningless if pn is not an integer. Thus, if the number of drawings is $n = 24$ and $p = \frac{2}{5}$, then $pn = \frac{48}{5}$. It can be shown in general that the most probable number is pn, provided pn is an integer; otherwise, the most probable number is one of the two integers between which pn lies. In fact, the following is the complete statement of the theorem:* *The most probable number of successes is the greatest integer less than $np + p$. If $np + p$ is an integer, there are two most probable numbers, namely, $np + p$ and $np + p - 1$. Since $p < 1$, it is clear that the most probable number of successes is approximately equal to np. This number np is called the "expected" number of successes.*

PROBLEM

A penny is tossed 100 times. What is the most probable number of heads? What is the probability of this most probable number of heads? If the penny is tossed 1000 times, what is the probability of the most probable number of heads?

153. Stirling's Formula. The binomial law (151-1), on which the major portion of the theory of probability is based, is exact, but it possesses the distinct disadvantage of being too complicated for purposes of computation. The labor of computing the values of the factorials that enter in the term $_nC_r$ becomes

---

* For proof and further discussion see T. C. Fry, Probability and Its Engineering Uses, Chap. IV.

prohibitive when n is a large number.   Accordingly, it is desirable to develop an approximation formula for $n!$, when n is large.

An asymptotic formula, which furnishes a good approximation to $n!$, was developed by J. Stirling.   By an *asymptotic formula* is meant an ex p re s s io n such that the *percentage of error* made by using the formula as an approximation to $n!$ *is small when n is sufficiently large,* whereas the *error itself increases with the increase in n.*   It will be indicated that for values of n greater than 10 the error made in using Stirling's formula*

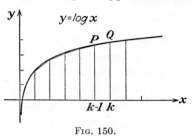

Fig. 150.

(153-1) $$n! \simeq n^n e^{-n} \sqrt{2\pi n}$$

is less than 1 per cent.

Consider the function $y = \log x$, and observe that, for $k \geq 2$,

$$\int_{k-1}^{k} \log x \, dx > \tfrac{1}{2}[\log (k - 1) + \log k],$$

since the right-hand member represents the trapezoidal area formed by the chord (Fig. 150) joining the points P and Q on the curve $y = \log x$.   Denote the area between the chord and the curve by a_k, so that

(153-2) $$\int_{k-1}^{k} \log x \, dx = \tfrac{1}{2}[\log (k - 1) + \log k] + a_k.$$

Setting $k = 2, 3, \cdots, n$ in (153-2) and adding give

$$\int_{1}^{n} \log x \, dx = \tfrac{1}{2}(\log 1 + \log 2) + \tfrac{1}{2}(\log 2 + \log 3) + \cdots$$
$$+ \tfrac{1}{2}[\log (n - 1) + \log n] + (a_2 + a_3 + \cdots + a_n).$$

Integrating the left-hand member and combining the terms of the right-hand member give

$$n \log n - n + 1 = \log n! - \tfrac{1}{2} \log n + \sum_{i=2}^{n} a_i.$$

Hence,

(153-3) $$\log n! = (n + \tfrac{1}{2}) \log n - n + 1 - \sum_{i=2}^{n} a_i.$$

* The symbol $\simeq$, which is read "asymptotically equal to," is used instead of $=$ to call attention to the fact that the formula is asymptotic.

Since each a_i is positive, it follows that

$$\log n! < (n + \tfrac{1}{2}) \log n - n + 1,$$

and hence

(153-4) $$n! < e \sqrt{n}\, n^n e^{-n}.$$

The expression on the right of the inequality (153-4) is, therefore, an upper bound for $n!$.

To get a lower bound, solve (153-2) for a_k, perform the integration, and obtain

(153-5) $$a_k = \left(k - \frac{1}{2}\right) \log \frac{k}{k-1} - 1.$$

Now, since the integrand is non-negative,

(153-6) $$\int_{k-1}^{k} \left(\frac{1}{x} - \frac{1}{k}\right)^2 dx > 0,$$

and the evaluation of (153-6) leads to the formula

$$\log \frac{k}{k-1} < \frac{2k-1}{2k(k-1)}.$$

By the use of this inequality, (153-5) gives

$$a_k < \frac{1}{4k(k-1)} = \frac{1}{4}\left(\frac{1}{k-1} - \frac{1}{k}\right).$$

Hence,

$$\sum_{i=2}^{n} a_i < \frac{1}{4}\left[\left(1 - \frac{1}{2}\right) + \left(\frac{1}{2} - \frac{1}{3}\right) + \cdots + \left(\frac{1}{n-1} - \frac{1}{n}\right)\right] < \frac{1}{4}.$$

By means of this result and (153-3), one obtains

$$\log n! > (n + \tfrac{1}{2}) \log n - n + 1 - \tfrac{1}{4},$$

whence

(153-7) $$n! > e^{3/4} \sqrt{n}\, n^n e^{-n}.$$

Combining (153-4) and (153-7) furnishes the inequality*

$$e^{3/4} \sqrt{n}\, n^n e^{-n} < n! < e \sqrt{n}\, n^n e^{-n},$$

for all values of $n > 1$. Since $e = 2.718$, $e^{3/4} = 2.117$, and $\sqrt{2\pi} = 2.507$, it follows that

$$n! \simeq n^n e^{-n} \sqrt{2\pi n}.$$

---

* The derivation of this result is given by P. M. Hummel, in *Amer. Math. Monthly*, vol. 47, p. 97, 1940.

It is possible to obtain a sharper lower bound for $n!$ by using the integral*

$$(153\text{-}8) \qquad \int_{k-1}^{k} \left[\frac{1}{x} - \frac{2k - 1 - x}{k(k-1)} \right]^2 dx > 0$$

instead of (153-6).

To gain some insight into the accuracy of this formula, note that (153-1) gives for $n = 10$ the value 3,598,696, whereas the true value of 10! is 3,628,800. The percentage of error in this case is 0.8 per cent. For $n = 100$, (153-1) gives 9.324847×10^{157}, whereas the true value of 100! is $9.3326215 \times 10^{157}$, so that the percentage of error is 0.08. It is worth noting that, even for $n = 1$, the error is under 10 per cent and that for $n = 5$ it is in the neighborhood of 2 per cent.

PROBLEM

Make use of (153-8) in order to show that

$$e^{1\frac{1}{12}} \sqrt{n}\, n^n e^{-n} < n!, \qquad \text{if } n > 1,$$

and compare the value of $e^{1\frac{1}{12}}$ with that of $\sqrt{2\pi}$.

154. Probability of the Most Probable Number. It was mentioned in Sec. 152 that the most probable number of successes is either equal, or very nearly equal, to the expected number $\epsilon = np$. Very often it is desirable to compute the probability of the expected or the most probable number of successes. Of course, p_ϵ can be computed from the exact law by substituting in it $r = np$, but formula (151-1) is cumbersome to use when factorials of large numbers appear in $_nC_r$. An approximate formula can be obtained by replacing $n!$ and $(np)!$ by their approximate values with the aid of Stirling's formula. It is readily verified that, when these replacements are made, the probability of the most probable number of successes is approximately

$$(154\text{-}1) \qquad p_\epsilon = \frac{1}{\sqrt{2\pi npq}},$$

where $q = 1 - p$. It must be kept in mind that (154-1) is subject to the same restrictions as (153-1) and gives good results for $np \geq 10$.

* See problem at the end of this section.

Thus, if a die is tossed 100 times, the most probable number of aces is 16. The exact formula gives

$$p_{16} = \frac{100!}{16!\,84!} \left(\frac{1}{6}\right)^{16} \left(\frac{5}{6}\right)^{84} = 0.296,$$

whereas the approximation (154-1) gives

$$p_{16} = \frac{1}{\sqrt{2\pi 100(\frac{1}{6})(\frac{5}{6})}} = 0.309.$$

The percentage of error is quite small.

PROBLEMS

1. Two hundred and fifty votes were cast for two equally likely candidates for an office. What is the probability of a tie?

2. What is the most probable number of aces in 1200 throws of a die? What is the probability of the most probable number?

3. Solve, with the aid of the approximate formula, the problem at the end of Sec. 152.

155. Approximations to Binomial Law. With the aid of formula (153-1), it is possible to devise various formulas approximating the binomial law (151-1). One of these approximations is known as the Poisson formula or the law of small numbers. The wide range of applicability of this law can be inferred from the fact that it has been used successfully in dealing with such problems as those of beta-ray emission, telephone traffic, transmission-line surges, and the expected sales of commodities. *The law of small numbers gives a good approximation to* (151-1) *in those problems in which r is small compared with the large number n, and p represents the probability of occurrence of a rare event in a single trial.*

Replacing $n!$ and $(n - r)!$ in (151-1) with the aid of Stirling's formula (153-1) leads to

$$(155\text{-}1) \quad p_r \simeq \frac{n^n e^{-n} \sqrt{2\pi n}}{r!(n - r)^{n-r} e^{-(n-r)} \sqrt{2\pi(n - r)}} \, p^r(1 - p)^{n-r}$$

$$= \frac{n^r e^{-r}}{r! \left(1 - \dfrac{r}{n}\right)^{n-r+\frac{1}{2}}} \, p^r(1 - p)^{n-r}.$$

By hypothesis, r is small compared with n, so that

$$\left(1 - \frac{r}{n}\right)^{n-r+\frac{1}{2}}$$

is very nearly equal to

$$\left(1 - \frac{r}{n}\right)^n$$

which,* for large values of n, differs little from e^{-r}. Similarly,

$$(1 - p)^{n-r} \doteq (1 - p)^n,$$

which in turn is nearly equal to e^{-np}, since

$$(1 - p)^n = 1 - np + \frac{n(n - 1)}{2!} p^2 - \cdots .$$

and

$$e^{-np} = 1 - np + \frac{n^2 p^2}{2!} - \cdots .$$

The substitution of e^{-r} for

$$\left(1 - \frac{r}{n}\right)^{n-r+\frac{1}{2}}$$

and e^{-np} for

$$(1 - p)^{n-r}$$

in (155-1) leads to the desired law of small numbers,

(155-2) $$p_r = \frac{(np)^r}{r!} e^{-np}.$$

Formula (155-2) is frequently written in a slightly different form. It will be recalled that the expected number of successes is $\epsilon = np$, so that (155-2) can be written

$$p_r = \frac{\epsilon^r}{r!} e^{-\epsilon}.$$

An application of this law to some specific cases may prove interesting. Suppose that it is known that, on the average, in a large city two persons die daily of tuberculosis. What is the probability that r persons will die on any day? In this case the expected number of deaths is $\epsilon = 2$, so that

$$p_r = \frac{2^r}{r!} e^{-2}.$$

---

* Note that $\lim\limits_{n \to \infty} (1 + 1/n)^n = e$. For a rigorous discussion, see I. S. Sokolnikoff, Advanced Calculus, pp. 28–31.

Therefore,

r	p_r	r	p_r	r	p_r
0	0.136	2	0.272	4	0.091
1	0.272	3	0.181	5	0.036

A glimpse into the accuracy of this law can be gained by considering the following example.

Example. What is the probability that the ace of spades will be drawn from a deck of cards at least once in 104 consecutive trials? This problem can be solved with the aid of the exact law (151-1) as follows: The probability that the ace will not be drawn in the 104 trials is

$$p_0 = {}_{104}C_0(\tfrac{1}{52})^0(^5\tfrac{1}{52})^{104} = 0.133,$$

and the probability that the ace will be drawn at least once is $1 - 0.133 = 0.867$. On the other hand, Poisson's law (155-2) gives for the probability of failure to draw the ace

$$p_0 = \frac{(104 \cdot \tfrac{1}{52})^0}{0!} e^{-104\tfrac{1}{52}} = e^{-2}.$$

Hence, the probability of drawing at least one ace of spades is $1 - e^{-2} = 0.865$.

Another important approximation to the binomial law (151-1), namely,

$$(155\text{-}3) \qquad p_r = \frac{n!}{r!(n-r)!}\, p^r q^{n-r},$$

where $q = 1 - p$, is obtained by assuming that r, n, and $n - r$ are all large enough to permit the use of the Stirling formula. Replacing $n!$, $r!$, and $(n - r)!$ by Stirling's approximations gives, upon simplification,

$$(155\text{-}4) \qquad p_r \sim \left(\frac{np}{r}\right)^r \left(\frac{nq}{n-r}\right)^{n-r} \sqrt{\frac{n}{2\pi r(n-r)}}.$$

Let δ denote the deviation of r from the expected value np; that is,

$$\delta = r - np.$$

Then,

$$n - r = nq - \delta,$$

and (155-4) becomes

$$p_r = \frac{1}{\sqrt{2\pi npq\left(1 + \dfrac{\delta}{np}\right)\left(1 - \dfrac{\delta}{nq}\right)}}\left(1 + \frac{\delta}{np}\right)^{-(np+\delta)}\left(1 - \frac{\delta}{nq}\right)^{-(nq-\delta)},$$

or

$$p_r A = \left(1 + \frac{\delta}{np}\right)^{-(np+\delta)}\left(1 - \frac{\delta}{nq}\right)^{-(nq-\delta)},$$

where

$$A = \sqrt{2\pi npq\left(1 + \frac{\delta}{np}\right)\left(1 - \frac{\delta}{nq}\right)}.$$

Then,

$$\log p_r A = -(np + \delta)\log\left(1 + \frac{\delta}{np}\right) - (nq - \delta)\log\left(1 - \frac{\delta}{nq}\right).$$

Assuming that $|\delta| < npq$, so that

$$\left|\frac{\delta}{np}\right| < 1 \quad \text{and} \quad \left|\frac{\delta}{nq}\right| < 1,$$

permits one to write the two convergent series

$$\log\left(1 + \frac{\delta}{np}\right) = \frac{\delta}{np} - \frac{\delta^2}{2n^2 p^2} + \frac{\delta^3}{3n^3 p^3} - \cdots,$$

and

$$\log\left(1 - \frac{\delta}{nq}\right) = -\frac{\delta}{nq} - \frac{\delta^2}{2n^2 q^2} - \frac{\delta^3}{3n^3 q^3} - \cdots.$$

Hence,

$$\log p_r A = -\frac{\delta^2}{2npq} - \frac{\delta^3(p^2 - q^2)}{2 \cdot 3n^2 p^2 q^2} - \frac{\delta^4(p^3 + q^3)}{3 \cdot 4n^3 p^3 q^3} - \cdots.$$

Now, if $|\delta|$ is so small in comparison with npq that one can neglect all terms in this expansion beyond the first and can replace A by $\sqrt{2\pi npq}$, then there results the approximate formula

$$(155\text{-}5) \qquad p_r = \frac{1}{\sqrt{2\pi npq}}\, e^{-\frac{\delta^2}{2npq}},$$

which bears the name of Laplace's, or the normal, approximation. Since the maximum value of the exponential e^{-x}, for $x \geq 0$, is unity, it follows that the normal approximation gives for the probability that r will assume its most probable value the same value as was obtained in Sec. 154. It is obvious that the normal approximation gives best results when p and q are nearly equal. If the mean error σ is defined by the formula

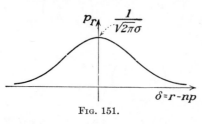

$$\sigma = \sqrt{npq},$$

then (155-5) assumes the form

$$p_r = \frac{1}{\sigma \sqrt{2\pi}} e^{-\frac{\delta^2}{2\sigma^2}},$$

Fig. 151.

and the graph of p_r as a function of δ is a bell-shaped curve (Fig. 151), known as the normal distribution curve.*

PROBLEMS

1. What is the probability of throwing an ace with a die exactly 10 times in 1200 trials?

2. A wholesale electrical dealer noticed that a shipment of 10,000 electric lamps contained, on the average, 20 defective lamps. What is the probability that a shipment of 10,000 lamps is 1 per cent defective?

3. In a certain large city, on the average, two persons die daily of cancer. What is the probability of no persons dying on any day? One person dying? Two? Three? Four? Five?

4. Two dice are tossed 1000 times. What is, approximately, the probability of getting a sum of 4 the most probable number of times?

5. What is the approximate probability that a sum of 4 will appear 500 times in a set of 1000 tosses?

156. The Error Function. Let $m_1, m_2, \cdots, m_n$ be a set of n measurements, of some physical quantity, that are made independently and that are equally trustworthy. If the best estimate of the value of the measurements is m, then the "errors" in individual measurements are

$$x_1 = m_1 - m, \qquad x_2 = m_2 - m, \cdots, \qquad x_n = m_n - m,$$

and the sum of the errors is

$$(156\text{-}1) \quad x_1 + x_2 + \cdots + x_n = (m_1 + m_2 + \cdots + m_n) - mn.$$

If it is assumed that on the average the positive and negative errors are equally balanced, then their sum is zero, and (156-1) becomes

$$mn = m_1 + m_2 + \cdots + m_n$$

* For a detailed discussion see T. C. Fry, Probability and Its Engineering Uses.

or

(156-2)
$$m = \frac{\sum\limits_{i=1}^{n} m_i}{n}.$$

It is important to note that the best value m is the arithmetic average of the individual measurements when it is assumed that the positive and negative errors are equally likely. In performing a set of measurements, not all the errors x_i are equally likely to occur. In general, large errors are less likely to occur than small ones. For instance, the probability of making an error of 1 ft. in measuring the length of a table is less than that of making an error of 1 in.

Let the probability of making an error x_i be denoted by $\varphi(x_i)$. The assumption that positive and negative errors are equally likely to occur demands that

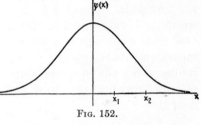

FIG. 152.

$$\varphi(x_i) = \varphi(-x_i),$$

which states that $\varphi(x)$ is an even function. Furthermore, the hypothesis that small errors are more likely to occur than large ones requires $\varphi(x)$ to be a decreasing function for $x \geq 0$; and since infinitely large errors cannot occur,

$$\varphi(\infty) = 0.$$

These observations lead to the conclusion that the function $\varphi(x)$, which gives the probability of occurrence of the error x, must have the appearance shown in Fig. 152, where the errors x_i are arranged in order of increasing magnitude. Upon recalling the fact that the ordinates represent the probability of occurrence of an error of any size x, it is clear that the area under this curve from $-\infty$ to $+\infty$ must be unity, for all the errors are certain to lie in the interval $(-\infty, \infty)$. Hence,

$$\int_{-\infty}^{\infty} \varphi(x) \, dx = 1.$$

Moreover, the probability that the error lies between the limits x_i and $x_i + \Delta x$ is equal to the area bounded by curve $y = \varphi(x)$.

the ordinates $y = x_i$ and $y = x_i + \Delta x$, and the x-axis, which is equal to the value of the integral

$$\int_{x_i}^{x_i + \Delta x} \varphi(x) \, dx.$$

By hypothesis the measurements m_i were made independently, so that the probability of simultaneous occurrence of the errors $x_1, x_2, \cdots, x_n$ is equal to the product of the probabilities of occurrence of the individual errors, or

$$(156\text{-}3) \quad P = \varphi(x_1)\varphi(x_2) \cdots \varphi(x_n)$$
$$= \varphi(m_1 - m)\varphi(m_2 - m) \cdots \varphi(m_n - m).$$

The expression (156-3) is a function of the best value m, in which the functional form of φ is not known. Now, if it be assumed that the best value m is also the most probable value, that is, the value which makes P a maximum, then it is possible to determine the functional form of φ by a method due to Gauss. In other words, it is taken as a fundamental axiom that the probability (156-3) is a maximum when m is the arithmetic average of the measurements $m_1, m_2, \cdots, m_n$. But if (156-3) is a maximum, its logarithm is also a maximum. Differentiating the logarithm of (156-3) with respect to m and setting the derivative equal to zero give

$$(156\text{-}4) \quad \frac{\varphi'(m_1 - m)}{\varphi(m_1 - m)} + \frac{\varphi'(m_2 - m)}{\varphi(m_2 - m)} + \cdots + \frac{\varphi'(m_n - m)}{\varphi(m_n - m)} = 0.$$

This equation is subject to the condition $\sum\limits_{i=1}^{n} x_i = 0$.

If

$$\frac{\varphi'(m_i - m)}{\varphi(m_i - m)}$$

is set equal to $F(x_i)$, $(i = 1, 2, \cdots, n)$, Eq. (156-4) can be written as

$$(156\text{-}5) \quad F(x_1) + F(x_2) + \cdots + F(x_n) = 0$$

with $\sum\limits_{i=1}^{n} x_i = 0$. If there are only two measurements, (156-5) reduces to

$$F(x_1) + F(x_2) = 0,$$

with $x_1 + x_2 = 6$, or $x_2 = -x_1$. Therefore,

$$F(x_1) + F(-x_1) = 0,$$

or

(156-6) $$F(x) = -F(-x).$$

Similarly, if there are only three measurements, then

$$F(x_1) + F(x_2) + F(x_3) = 0,$$

with $x_1 + x_2 + x_3 = 0$. Therefore,

$$F(x_1) + F(x_2) = -F(x_3).$$

But, from (156-6),

$$F(x_3) = -F(-x_3);$$

and since $-x_3 = x_1 + x_2$,

$$F(x_1) + F(x_2) = F(x_1 + x_2).$$

Differentiating this expression partially with respect to x_1 and x_2 leads to

$$F'(x_1) = F'(x_1 + x_2) \qquad \text{and} \qquad F'(x_2) = F'(x_1 + x_2),$$

or

(156-7) $$F'(x_1) = F'(x_2).$$

Since x_1 and x_2 are independent, (156-7) can be true only if

$$F'(x_1) = F'(x_2) = c,$$

so that

$$F(x_1) = cx_1 \qquad \text{and} \qquad F(x_2) = cx_2.$$

Recall that, by definition,

$$F(x) = \frac{\varphi'(x)}{\varphi(x)},$$

so that the differential equation for φ is

$$\frac{\varphi'(x)}{\varphi(x)} = cx,$$

which, upon integration, gives

(156-8) $$\varphi(x) = Ke^{\frac{1}{2}cx^2},$$

where K and c are arbitrary constants.

One of these constants can be determined at once, for it is known that

$$\int_{-\infty}^{\infty} \varphi(x)\, dx = 1.$$

The substitution of $\varphi(x)$ in this integral gives

$$K \int_{-\infty}^{\infty} e^{-h^2 x^2}\, dx = 1,$$

where $-h^2 \equiv c/2$.

This integral can be evaluated by means of a procedure similar to that used in Sec. 81.   Set

$$I = \int_0^{\infty} e^{-x^2}\, dx,$$

and then

$$I^2 = \int_0^{\infty} e^{-x^2}\, dx \int_0^{\infty} e^{-y^2}\, dy$$

$$= \int_0^{\infty} \int_0^{\infty} e^{-(x^2 + y^2)}\, dx\, dy$$

$$= \int_0^{\frac{\pi}{2}} \int_0^{\infty} e^{-r^2} r\, dr\, d\varphi = \frac{\pi}{4},$$

where the last step results from the transformation of the double integral into polar coordinates and has been described in Sec. 81.   Hence,

$$I = \int_0^{\infty} e^{-x^2}\, dx = \frac{\sqrt{\pi}}{2}.$$

But

$$K \int_{-\infty}^{\infty} e^{-h^2 x^2}\, dx = 2K \int_0^{\infty} e^{-h^2 x^2}\, dx = 1,$$

so that

$$K = \frac{1}{2 \int_0^{\infty} e^{-h^2 x^2}\, dx} = \frac{h}{2 \int_0^{\infty} e^{-h^2 x^2}\, d(hx)} = \frac{h}{\sqrt{\pi}}.$$

Thus, (156-8) can be written as

$$(156\text{-}9) \qquad\qquad \varphi(x) = \frac{h}{\sqrt{\pi}} e^{-h^2 x^2},$$

which is called the Gaussian law of error.   The undetermined constant h, as will be seen in the next section, measures the accuracy of the observer and is known as the precision constant.

It is easy to verify the fact that the choice of φ, specified by (156-9), gives a maximum for the product (156-3) when the sum of the squares of the errors is a minimum. In fact, since $x_i = m_i - m$, (156-3) becomes

$$P = \left(\frac{h}{\sqrt{\pi}}\right)^n e^{-h^2 \sum\limits_{i=1}^{n} x_i^2}$$

and the maximum value of P is clearly that which makes the sum of the squares of the errors a minimum.

In order to verify the assumption that the choice of the arithmetic average for the best value leads to the least value for the sum of the squares of the errors, all that is necessary is to minimize

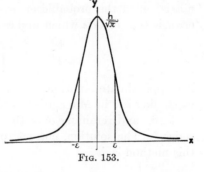

$$\sum_{i=1}^{n} x_i^2 \equiv \sum_{i=1}^{n} (m_i - m)^2.$$

The theory of errors based upon the Gaussian law (156-9) is often called the theory of least squares.

157. Precision Constant. Probable Error. In the pre-

Fig. 153.

ceding section, it was established that the probability of committing an error of magnitude x is given by the ordinate of the curve

$$y = \frac{h}{\sqrt{\pi}} e^{-h^2 x^2}.$$

This curve is called the probability curve. Clearly, the probability of an error lying in the interval between $x = -\epsilon$ and $x = +\epsilon$ is equal, numerically, to the area bounded by the probability curve (Fig. 153), the ordinates $x = -\epsilon$ and $x = +\epsilon$, and the x-axis. If only the absolute value of the error is of interest, then the probability that the absolute value of the error does not exceed ϵ is

$$P = \frac{2h}{\sqrt{\pi}} \int_0^\epsilon e^{-h^2 x^2}\, dx.$$

If hx is set equal to t, this integral assumes the form

$$P = \frac{2}{\sqrt{\pi}} \int_0^{h\epsilon} e^{-t^2} \, dt,$$

which shows that P is a function of $h\epsilon$, and, for a fixed value of ϵ, P increases with h. For large values of h, the probability curve decreases very rapidly from its maximum value, $h/\sqrt{\pi}$ at $x = 0$, to very small values, so that the probability of making large errors is very small. On the other hand, if h is small, the probability curve falls off very slowly so that the observer is almost as likely to make fairly large errors as he is to make small ones. For this reason the constant h is known as the precision constant.

That particular error which is just as likely to be exceeded as not is called the probable error. More precisely, the probable error is that error ϵ which makes $P = \frac{1}{2}$, or

$$\frac{1}{2} = \frac{2}{\sqrt{\pi}} \int_0^{h\epsilon} e^{-t^2} \, dt.$$

An approximate solution of this equation can be obtained by expanding e^{-t^2} in Maclaurin's series, integrating the result term by term, and retaining only the first few terms of the resulting series.* The solution, correct to four decimal places, found by this method is

$$h\epsilon = 0.4769,$$

so that the probable error is $0.4769/h$. It is commonly denoted by the letter r.

In addition to the probable error, the mean absolute error and the mean square error are of importance in statistics. The mean absolute error is defined as

$$|\bar{x}| = \frac{2h}{\sqrt{\pi}} \int_0^{\infty} x e^{-h^2 x^2} \, dx = \frac{1}{h\sqrt{\pi}} = \frac{0.5643}{h},$$

and the mean square error is defined as

$$\overline{x^2} = \frac{2h}{\sqrt{\pi}} \int_0^{\infty} x^2 e^{-h^2 x^2} \, dx = \frac{1}{2h^2}.$$

It will be observed that the mean absolute error is the x-coordinate of the center of gravity of the area bounded by the proba-

* See Prob. 3, at the end of this section.

bility curve and the positive coordinate axes, and that the square root of the mean square error is the radius of gyration of that area about the y-axis.

The values of these mean errors can actually be computed for any set of observations. Thus,

$$|\bar{x}| = \frac{\sum\limits_{i=1}^{n} |m_i - m|}{n} = \frac{\sum\limits_{i=1}^{n} |x_i|}{n} = \frac{1}{h\sqrt{\pi}},$$

so that

$$(157\text{-}1) \qquad\qquad h = \frac{1}{|\bar{x}|\sqrt{\pi}}.$$

Also,

$$\overline{x^2} = \frac{\sum\limits_{i=1}^{n} (m_i - m)^2}{n} = \frac{\sum\limits_{i=1}^{n} x_i^2}{n} = \frac{1}{2h^2},$$

so that h computed from this equation is

$$(157\text{-}2) \qquad\qquad h = \frac{1}{\sqrt{\overline{x^2}}\,\sqrt{2}}.$$

These two expressions for the precision constant give a means of computing h for any set of observation data. The two values of h cannot be expected to be identical; but unless there is a fair agreement between them, experience indicates that the data are not reliable. The value of $\sqrt{\overline{x^2}} \equiv \sigma$ is commonly called the *standard deviation,* and it follows from the foregoing that the probable error is equal to 0.6745σ.

PROBLEMS

1. Evaluate the integral $\int_0^x e^{-t^2}\, dt$ by expanding the integrand in series, and show that

$$\int_0^x e^{-t^2}\, dt = x - \frac{x^3}{3\cdot 1!} + \frac{x^5}{5\cdot 2!} - \frac{x^7}{7\cdot 3!} + \frac{x^9}{9\cdot 4!} - R,$$

where $R < x^{11}/1320$.

2. The expression for the probability integral given in the preceding problem is not suitable for computation purposes when x is large. But

$$\int_0^x e^{-t^2} \, dt = \int_0^\infty e^{-t^2} \, dt - \int_x^\infty e^{-t^2} \, dt$$

$$= \frac{\sqrt{\pi}}{2} - \int_x^\infty e^{-t^2} \, dt.$$

Show, by integrating by parts, that

$$\int_x^\infty e^{-t^2} \, dt = \int_x^\infty \frac{1}{t} e^{-t^2} t \, dt = \frac{e^{-x^2}}{2x} \left(1 - \frac{1}{2x^2} + \frac{1 \cdot 3}{2^2 x^4} \right) - \frac{1 \cdot 3 \cdot 5}{2^3} \int_x^\infty \frac{e^{-t^2} \, dt}{t^6},$$

and thus obtain an asymptotic expansion for the probability integral that can be used to compute its value when x is large. Also, show that the asymptotic series

$$\int_0^x e^{-t^2} \, dt \simeq \frac{\sqrt{\pi}}{2} - \frac{e^{-x^2}}{2x} \left[1 - \frac{1}{2x^2} + \frac{1 \cdot 3}{(2x^2)^2} - \frac{1 \cdot 3 \cdot 5}{(2x^2)^3} + \cdots \right]$$

gives a value for the integral which differs from its true value by less than the last term which is used in the series.

3. Show, with the aid of Horner's method, that the value of the probable error is

$$r = \frac{0.4769}{h}.$$

4. Compute the probable errors for the following set of observation data:

$$m_1 = 1.305, \quad m_2 = 1.301, \quad m_3 = 1.295, \quad m_4 = 1.286,$$
$$m_5 = 1.318, \quad m_6 = 1.321, \quad m_7 = 1.283, \quad m_8 = 1.289,$$
$$m_9 = 1.300, \quad m_{10} = 1.286,$$

by using (157-1) and (157-2).

5. With reference to Prob. 4, what is the probability of committing an error whose absolute value is less than 0.03?

6. Two observers bring the following two sets of data, which represent measurements of the same quantity:

(a) $m_1 = 105.1, \quad m_2 = 103.4, \quad m_3 = 104.2, \quad m_4 = 104.7,$
$\quad m_5 = 104.8, \quad m_6 = 105.0, \quad m_7 = 104.9.$

(b) $m_1 = 105.3, \quad m_2 = 105.1, \quad m_3 = 104.8, \quad m_4 = 105.2,$
$\quad m_5 = 106.7, \quad m_6 = 102.9, \quad m_7 = 103.1.$

Which set of data is the more reliable?

7. Discuss the problem of a rational way of proportioning the salaries of two observers whose precision constants are h_1 and h_2.

CHAPTER XII

EMPIRICAL FORMULAS AND CURVE FITTING

An empirical formula is a formula that is inferred by some scheme in an attempt to express the relation existing between quantities whose corresponding values are obtained by experiment. For example, it may be desired to obtain the relation connecting the load applied to a bar and the resulting elongation of the bar. Various loads are applied, and the consequent elongations are measured. Then, by one of the methods to be given in this chapter, a formula is obtained that represents the relationship existing between these two quantities for the observed values. With certain restrictions, this formula can then be used to predict the elongation that will result when an arbitrary load is applied.

It is possible to obtain several equations of different types that will express the given data approximately or exactly. The question arises as to which of these equations will give the best "fit" and be most successful for use in predicting the results of the experiment for additional values of the quantities involved. If there are n sets of observed values then, theoretically at least, it is possible to fit the given data with an equation that involves n arbitrary constants. What would be the procedure if it were desired to obtain an equation representing these data but involving less than n arbitrary constants? Questions of this type will be considered in the succeeding sections.

158. Graphical Method. The graphical method of obtaining an empirical formula and curve to represent given data is probably already somewhat familiar to the student from elementary courses. It is particularly applicable when the given data can be represented by equations of the three types

$$(1) \ y = mx + b; \qquad (2) \ y = a + bx^n; \qquad (3) \ y = ka^{mx}.$$

If the corresponding values (x_i, y_i) of the given data are plotted on rectangular coordinate paper and the points thus plotted lie approximately on a straight line, it is assumed that the equation

$$y = mx + b$$

will represent the relationship. In order to determine the values of the constants m and b, the slope and y-intercept may be read from the curve, or they can be determined by solving the two simultaneous equations

$$y_1 = mx_1 + b, \qquad y_2 = mx_2 + b$$

obtained by assuming that any two suitably chosen points (x_1, y_1) and (x_2, y_2) lie on the line. Obviously the values of m and b will depend upon the judgment of the investigator regardless of which method is used for their determination.

Consider the equation

$$y = a + bx^n.$$

If the substitution $x^n = t$ is made, then the graph of $y = a + bt$ is a straight line and the determination of a and b is precisely the same as in the preceding case. In the special case $y = bx^n$, taking logarithms on both sides gives

$$\log y = \log b + n \log x,$$

which is linear in $\log y$ and $\log x$ and gives a straight line on logarithmic paper. The slope of this line and the intercept on the log y-axis can be read from the graph. Hence, if the corresponding values (x_i, y_i), when plotted on logarithmic paper, give points that lie approximately on a straight line, the data can be represented by the equation

$$y = bx^n,$$

whose constants can be read from the graph.

Similarly, if the data can be represented by a relation

$$y = ka^{mx},$$

the corresponding values, when plotted on semilogarithmic* paper, will give points that lie approximately on a straight line. For taking logarithms on both sides of this equation gives

$$\log y = \log k + (m \log a)x,$$

---

* For a discussion of logarithmic and semilogarithmic paper, see C. S. Slichter, Elementary Mathematical Analysis.

which is linear in log y and x and therefore plots as a straight line on semilogarithmic paper.

The three types of equations cited here are, of course, not the only ones to which the graphic method is applicable. However, they are the simplest because of the fact that their graphs, on appropriate paper, give straight lines. When the points representing the observed values do not approximate a straight line, some other method is usually preferable.

PROBLEMS

1. Find the equation that represents the relation connecting x and y if the given data are

x	3	4	5	6	7	8	9	10	11	12
y	5	5.6	6	6.4	7	7.5	8.2	8.6	9	9.5

2. Find the equation of the type $y = bx^n$ that represents the relation between x and y.

x	1	2	3	4	5	6	7	8	9
y	2.5	3.5	4.3	5	5.6	6.2	6.6	7.1	7.5

3. From the following data, find the relation of the type $y = k10^{mx}$ between x and y:

x	1	2	3	4	5	6	7	8
y	0.5	0.8	1.2	1.9	3	4.8	7.5	11.9

159. Differences. Before proceeding to investigate rules for the choice of the particular type of equation that will represent the observed values, it is advisable to define and discuss differences.

Let the observed values be (x_i, y_i), $(i = 0, 1, 2, \cdots, n)$. The first differences are defined by

$$(159\text{-}1) \qquad \Delta y_i \equiv y_{i+1} - y_i.$$

The second differences are given by

$$\Delta^2 y_i \equiv \Delta y_{i+1} - \Delta y_i.$$

In general, for $k > 1$, the differences of order k, or the kth differences, are defined as

$$(159\text{-}2) \qquad \Delta^k y_i \equiv \Delta^{k-1} y_{i+1} - \Delta^{k-1} y_i.$$

It should be noted that, if the jth differences are constant, then all of the differences of order higher than j will be zero.

From (159-1) and (159-2) it follows that

$$y_1 = y_0 + \Delta y_0,$$
$$y_2 = y_1 + \Delta y_1 = (y_0 + \Delta y_0) + (\Delta^2 y_0 + \Delta y_0)$$
$$= y_0 + 2\Delta y_0 + \Delta^2 y_0,$$
$$y_3 = y_2 + \Delta y_2 = (y_0 + 2\Delta y_0 + \Delta^2 y_0) + (\Delta^2 y_1 + \Delta y_1)$$
$$= (y_0 + 2\Delta y_0 + \Delta^2 y_0)$$
$$\qquad\qquad + (\Delta^3 y_0 + \Delta^2 y_0 + \Delta^2 y_0 + \Delta y_0)$$
$$= y_0 + 3\Delta y_0 + 3\Delta^2 y_0 + \Delta^3 y_0.$$

These results can be written symbolically as

$$y_1 = (1 + \Delta)y_0, \qquad y_2 = (1 + \Delta)^2 y_0, \qquad y_3 = (1 + \Delta)^3 y_0,$$

in which $(1 + \Delta)^i$ acts as an operator on y_0, with the exponent on the Δ indicating the order of the difference. This operator is analogous to the differential operators discussed in Chap. VII. By mathematical induction, it is established easily that

$$(159\text{-}3) \qquad y_k = (1 + \Delta)^k y_0.$$

160. Equations That Represent Special Types of Data. There are certain types of data which suggest the equation that will represent the relation connecting the observed values of x and y. Some of the more common types will be discussed in this section.

a. Suppose that a number of pairs of observed values (x_i, y_i) have been obtained by experiment. If the x_i form an arithmetical progression and the rth differences of the y_i are constant, then the relation connecting the variables is

$$y = a_0 + a_1 x + a_2 x^2 + \cdots + a_r x^r.$$

For if the rth differences are constant, all differences of order higher than r are zero, and hence, from (159-3),

$$(160\text{-}1) \quad y_k = y_0 + \binom{k}{1} \Delta y_0 + \binom{k}{2} \Delta^2 y_0 + \cdots + \binom{k}{r} \Delta^r y_0,$$

where

$$(160\text{-}2) \quad \binom{k}{r} = {}_kC_r = \frac{k(k-1)(k-2)\cdots(k-r+1)}{r!}$$

is simply the coefficient of a^r in the binomial expansion for $(1 + a)^k$. Moreover, it was assumed that the x_i are in arithmetical progression so that, if $x_1 - x_0 = \Delta x$, then $x_k - x_0 = k\,\Delta x$ and

$$k = \frac{x_k - x_0}{\Delta x}.$$

Now, the expression (160-2) is a polynomial of degree r in k, and therefore of degree r in x_k. It follows that, upon substitution of

$$k = \frac{x_k - x_0}{\Delta x}$$

and the collection of like powers of x_k in (160-1), this equation assumes the form

$$y_k = a_0 + a_1 x_k + a_2 x_k^2 + \cdots + a_r x_k^r.$$

The relation is true for all integral values of k, and therefore

(160-3) $\qquad y = a_0 + a_1 x + a_2 x^2 + \cdots + a_r x^r$

gives the relation existing between the variables for the given set of observed values.

In general, a given set of observed values will not possess constant differences of any order, but it may be that the rth differences are sensibly constant. Then an equation of the type (160-3) will be a good approximation for the relation between the variables.

Various modifications of (160-3) can be made. If the values of x_i^n form an arithmetical progression, whereas the values of the rth differences of the y_i^m are constant, then the relation connecting the variables is

(160-4) $\qquad y^m = a_0 + a_1 x^n + a_2(x^n)^2 + \cdots + a_r(x^n)^r.$

Here m and n can take either positive or negative values. The derivation of the formula is exactly like that given above if x_i^n is replaced by X_i and y_i^m by Y_i.

If, in (160-4), $m = n = -1$ and $r = 1$, the equation assumes the form

$$y^{-1} = a_0 + a_1 x^{-1} \quad \text{or} \quad \frac{1}{y} = a_0 + \frac{a_1}{x} \quad \text{or} \quad y = \frac{x}{a_1 + a_0 x}.$$

Curves having this equation are frequently of use in fitting data to observations measuring flux density against field intensity. The curve is the hyperbola having the lines

$$x = -\frac{a_1}{a_0} \quad \text{and} \quad y = \frac{1}{a_0}$$

for asymptotes. If the values of $1/y$ are plotted against those for $1/x$, the result is a straight line. A few of these curves are plotted in Fig. 154.

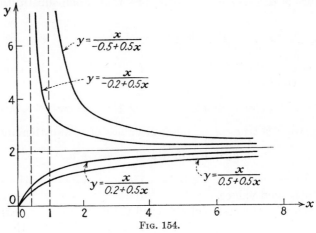

Fig. 154.

Example 1.   Consider the following set of observed data:

x	y	Δy	$\Delta^2 y$	$\Delta^3 y$	$\Delta^4 y$
1	2.105				
		0.703			
2	2.808		0.103		
		0.806		0.081	
3	3.614		0.184		−0.002
		0.990		0.079	
4	4.604		0.263		−0.001
		1.253		0.078	
5	5.857		0.341		+0.003
		1.594		0.081	
6	7.451		0.422		−0.001
		2.016		0.080	
7	9.467		0.502		
		2.518			
8	11.985				

In this case the third differences are sensibly constant and the relation between x and y is approximately of the form

$$y = a_0 + a_1 x + a_2 x^2 + a_3 x^3.$$

The question of determining the values of the constants will be considered in a later section.

b. If the set of pairs of observed values (x_i, y_i) is such that the values of x_i form an arithmetical progression and the corresponding values of y_i form a geometrical progression, then the equation representing the relation between the variables is

(160-5) $y = ka^x.$

For, taking logarithms of both sides, the equation becomes

$$\log y = \log k + x \log a,$$

which is linear in x and $\log y$. Hence, if the values x_i form an arithmetical progression, the values $\log y_i$ will do likewise. But

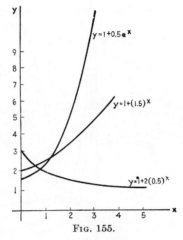

$y = 1 + 0.5 e^x$

$y = 1 + (1.5)^x$

$y = 1 + 2(0.5)^x$

FIG. 155.

then $\log y_i - \log y_{i-1} = c$ (for each value of i), so that

$$\frac{y_i}{y_{i-1}} = e^c = C \qquad \text{and} \qquad y_i = C y_{i-1}.$$

Therefore, the numbers y_i form a geometrical progression.

It can be proved that, if the values of the rth differences of the y_i form a geometrical progression when the values of the x_i form an arithmetical progression, then the relation between x and y is

(160-6) $y = a_0 + a_1 x + \cdots + a_{r-1} x^{r-1} + ka^x.$

If $r = 1$ in (160-6), the equation becomes

$$y = a_0 + ka^x.$$

If $a > 1$, the values of y increase indefinitely as x is increased. If $a < 1$, the curve falls off from its value at $x = 0$ and approaches the line $y = a_0$ as an asymptote. Three of these curves are plotted in Fig. 155.

Example 2.   Consider the data given in the following table:

x	1	2	3	4	5	6	7
y	2.157	3.519	4.198	4.539	4.708	4.792	4.835
Δy		1.362	0.679	0.341	0.169	0.084	0.043

Since the first differences have values very nearly equal to the numbers that form the geometrical progression whose first term is 1.362

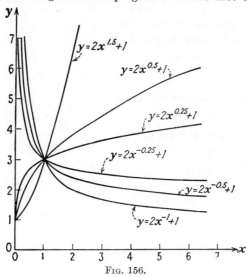

Fig. 156.

and whose ratio is $\frac{1}{2}$, the relation between x and y is very nearly of the form

$$y = a_0 + ka^x.$$

c. The equation

(160-7) $y = ax^n$

represents the relation existing between the variables if, when the x_i form a geometrical progression, the y_i also form a geometrical progression.   For if

$$x_i = rx_{i-1},$$

then (160-7) states that

$$y_i = ax_i^n = a(rx_{i-1})^n = r^n(ax_{i-1}^n) = r^n y_{i-1}.$$

Hence, the y_i form a geometrical progression whose ratio is $R \equiv r^n$.

If the first differences of the y_i form a geometrical progression when the x_i form a geometrical progression, then the equation giving the relation between x and y is

$$(160\text{-}8) \qquad\qquad y = k + ax^n.$$

For if $x_i = rx_{i-1}$, then (160-8) requires that

$$\Delta y_i = y_i - y_{i-1} = k + ax_i^n - (k + ax_{i-1}^n)$$
$$= a(x_i^n - x_{i-1}^n) = a(r^n x_{i-1}^n - x_{i-1}^n)$$
$$= ax_{i-1}^n(r^n - 1) = ar^n x_{i-2}^n(r^n - 1)$$

and, similarly,

$$\Delta y_{i-1} = ax_{i-2}^n(r^n - 1).$$

Then

$$\Delta y_i = r^n \, \Delta y_{i-1},$$

and therefore the Δy_i form a geometrical progression whose ratio is $R \equiv r^n$.

The curves (160-8) are parabolic if $n > 0$ and hyperbolic if $n < 0$. Three of each type are plotted in Fig. 156.

Example 3.   Let the pairs of observed values be

x	0.16	0.4	1.0	2.5	6.25	15.625
y	2	2.210	2.421	2.661	2.929	3.222

The values of x_i form a geometrical progression with ratio $r = 2.5$, and the values of y_i are approximately equal to the terms of the geometrical progression whose first term is 2 and whose ratio is $R = 1.1$. Hence, the relation between x and y is very nearly of the type $y = ax^n$; and since $R = r^n$, it follows that $1.1 = (2.5)^n$ or $\log 1.1 = n \log 2.5$ and

$$n = \frac{\log 1.1}{\log 2.5}.$$

PROBLEMS

1. A flat surface is exposed to a wind velocity of v miles per hour, and it is desired to find the relation between v and p, which is the pressure per square foot on the surface. By experiment the following set of observed values is obtained. Find the type of formula to fit them.

v	10	15	22.5	33.75	50.625	75.937
p	0.3	0.675	1.519	3.417	7.689	17.300

2. The temperature θ of a heated body, surrounded by a medium kept at the constant temperature 0°C., decreases with the time. Find the kind of formula which expresses the relation between θ and t that is indicated by the following pairs of observed values:

t	0	1	2	3	4	5	6	7	8
θ	60.00	51.66	44.46	38.28	32.94	28.32	24.42	21.06	18.06

3. If C represents the number of pounds of coal burned per hour per square foot of grate and H represents the height of the chimney in feet, find the type of formula connecting H and C, using the following data:

C	19	20	21	22	23	24	25
H	81	90.25	100.00	110.25	121.00	132.25	144.00

161. Constants Determined by Method of Averages. Several different methods are employed in determining the constants which appear in the equation that expresses the relation existing between the variables whose observed values are given. The method to be described in this section is known as the method of averages. It is based on certain assumptions concerning the so-called "residuals" of the observations. Let the pairs of observed values be (x_i, y_i), and let $y = f(x)$ be the equation that represents the relation between x and y for these values. Then, the expressions

$$v_i = f(x_i) - y_i$$

are defined as the residuals of the observations. The method of averages is based on the assumption that the sum Σv_i is zero.

This assumption gives only one condition on the constants that appear in $y = f(x)$. If there are r of these constants and if $f(x)$ is linear in them, the further assumption is made that, if the residuals are divided into r groups, then $\Sigma v_i = 0$ for each group. This second assumption leads to r equations in the r unknown constants. It is obvious that different methods of choosing the groups will lead to different values for the constants. Ordinarily, the groups are chosen so as to contain approximately the same number of residuals; and if there are to be k residuals in each group, the first group contains the first k residuals, the second group contains the succeeding k residuals, and so on.

A modification of this method is sometimes used when $f(x)$ is not linear in its constants, but it will not be discussed here.*

Example. Determine the constants in the equation that represents the data given in Example 1, Sec. 160.

It was shown in this example that the equation is of the type

$$f(x) = a_0 + a_1x + a_2x^2 + a_3x^3.$$

Therefore,

$$
\begin{aligned}
v_1 &= a_0 + a_1 + a_2 + a_3 - 2.105, \\
v_2 &= a_0 + 2a_1 + 4a_2 + 8a_3 - 2.808, \\
v_3 &= a_0 + 3a_1 + 9a_2 + 27a_3 - 3.614, \\
v_4 &= a_0 + 4a_1 + 16a_2 + 64a_3 - 4.604, \\
v_5 &= a_0 + 5a_1 + 25a_2 + 125a_3 - 5.857, \\
v_6 &= a_0 + 6a_1 + 36a_2 + 216a_3 - 7.451, \\
v_7 &= a_0 + 7a_1 + 49a_2 + 343a_3 - 9.467, \\
v_8 &= a_0 + 8a_1 + 64a_2 + 512a_3 - 11.985.
\end{aligned}
$$

Let the assumptions be that

$$v_1 + v_2 = 0, \qquad v_3 + v_4 = 0, \qquad v_5 + v_6 = 0, \qquad v_7 + v_8 = 0.$$

Then the conditions on the constants are

$$
\begin{aligned}
2a_0 + 3a_1 + 5a_2 + 9a_3 &= 4.913, \\
2a_0 + 7a_1 + 25a_2 + 91a_3 &= 8.218, \\
2a_0 + 11a_1 + 61a_2 + 341a_3 &= 13.308, \\
2a_0 + 15a_1 + 113a_2 + 855a_3 &= 21.452.
\end{aligned}
$$

The solution of these equations is

$$a_0 = 1.433, \qquad a_1 = 0.685, \qquad a_2 = -0.025, \qquad a_3 = 0.013.$$

Hence, the equation, as determined by the method of averages, is

$$y = 1.433 + 0.685x - 0.025x^2 + 0.013x^3.$$

PROBLEMS

1. Use the method of averages to find the constants in the equation

$$y = a_0 + a_1x + a_2x^2,$$

which is to represent the given data

x	1	2	3	4	5	6
y	3.13	3.76	6.94	12.62	20.86	31.53

2. Find, by the method of averages, an equation to fit the data given in Prob. 3 at the end of Sec. 160.

* See SCARBOROUGH, Numerical Analysis.

3. Find the constants in the equation of the type

$$y = a_0 + a_1x + a_2x^2 + a_3x^3,$$

which fits the data given in the table

x	1	2	3	4	5	6	7	8
y	3.161	3.073	3.104	3.692	5.513	9.089	15.123	24.091

4. Find, by the method of averages, the constants in the equation $y = a + be^x$ if it is to fit the following data:

x	0.5	1	1.5	2	2.5	3
y	1.630	1.844	2.196	2.778	3.736	5.318

5. Use the method of averages to determine the constants in $y = ae^x + b \sin x + cx^2$ so that the equation will represent the data in the table.

x	0.4	0.6	0.8	1	1.2	1.4	1.6	1.8	2
y	0.258	0.470	0.837	1.392	2.133	3.069	4.225	5.608	7.216

162. Method of Least Squares. This section introduces another method of determining the constants that appear in the equation chosen to represent the given data. It is probably the most useful method and the one most frequently applied. The two methods already described give different values of the constants depending upon the judgment of the investigator, either in reading from a graph or in combining the residuals into groups. This method has the advantage of giving a unique set of values to these constants. Moreover, the constants determined by this method give the "most probable" equation in the sense that the values of y computed from it are the most probable values of the observations, it being assumed that the residuals follow the Gaussian law of error. In short, the principle of least squares asserts that the best representative curve is that for which the sum of the squares of the residuals is a minimum.

Suppose that the given set of observed values (x_i, y_i), $(i = 1, 2, \cdots, n)$, can be represented by the equation

$$y = f(x)$$

containing the r undetermined constants $a_1, a_2, \cdots, a_r$.   Then, the n observation equations

$$y_i = f(x_i)$$

are to be solved for these r unknowns.   If $n = r$, there are just enough conditions to determine the constants; if $n < r$, there are not enough conditions and the problem is indeterminate; but, in general, $n > r$, and there are more conditions than there are unknowns.   In the general case, the values of the a_k which satisfy any r of these equations will not satisfy the remaining $n - r$ equations, and the problem is to determine a set of values of the a_k that will give the most probable values of y.   Let

$$v_i = \bar{y}_i - y_i$$

be the residuals, or deviations of the computed values from the observed values, where $\bar{y}_i$ is the value of y obtained by substituting $x = x_i$ in $y = f(x)$.   On the basis of the Gaussian law of error, the probability of obtaining the observed values y_i is

$$P = \left(\frac{h}{\sqrt{\pi}}\right)^n e^{-h^2 \sum_{i=1}^{n} v_i^2}.$$

Obviously, P is a maximum when $\sum_{i=1}^{n} v_i^2$ is a minimum.

Since $S \equiv \sum_{i=1}^{n} v_i^2$ is a function of the r unknowns $a_1, a_2, \cdots,$ a_r, it follows that necessary conditions for a minimum are

$$(162\text{-}1) \qquad \frac{\partial S}{\partial a_1} = 0, \qquad \frac{\partial S}{\partial a_2} = 0, \cdots, \qquad \frac{\partial S}{\partial a_r} = 0.$$

Moreover, each v_i is a function of a_k; therefore,

$$(162\text{-}2) \qquad \frac{\partial S}{\partial a_k} \equiv \frac{\partial}{\partial a_k}(v_1^2 + v_2^2 + \cdots + v_n^2)$$

$$= 2v_1 \frac{\partial v_1}{\partial a_k} + 2v_2 \frac{\partial v_2}{\partial a_k} + \cdots + 2v_n \frac{\partial v_n}{\partial a_k}$$

$$= 2 \sum_{i=1}^{n} v_i \frac{\partial v_i}{\partial a_k}, \qquad (k = 1, 2, \cdots, r).$$

Equations (162-1) are called the *normal* equations.

If it happens that the r equations (162-1) are linear in the r unknowns $a_1, a_2, \cdots, a_r$, then these equations can be solved immediately.   This will certainly be the case if $f(x)$ is a polynomial.   For let

$$f(x) = \sum_{j=1}^{r} a_j x^{j-1} \quad \text{so that} \quad v_i = \sum_{j=1}^{r} a_j x_i^{j-1} - y_i.$$

Then, $\partial v_i / \partial a_k = x_i^{k-1}$, and the normal equations assume the form, with the aid of (162-2),

$$(162\text{-}3) \qquad \sum_{i=1}^{n} \left(\sum_{j=1}^{r} a_j x_i^{j-1} - y_i \right) x_i^{k-1} = 0, \quad (k = 1, 2, \cdots, r).$$

It should be noted that the equation which is obtained by setting $k = 1$ is $\sum_{i=1}^{n} v_i = 0$. Reordering the terms in (162-3), so as to collect the coefficients of the a_j, gives

$$(162\text{-}4) \qquad \sum_{j=1}^{r} \left(\sum_{i=1}^{n} x_i^{j+k-2} \right) a_j = \sum_{i=1}^{n} x_i^{k-1} y_i, \quad (k = 1, 2, \cdots, r).$$

The r linear equations (162-4) can then be solved for the values of the r unknowns $a_1, a_2, \cdots, a_r$.

This procedure may be clarified somewhat by writing out some of these expressions for a simple specific case. Consider the data given in the following table. Since the second differences

x	1	2	3	4
y	1.7	1.8	2.3	3.2

of the y_i are constant, the equation will have the form

$$f(x) = a_1 + a_2 x + a_3 x^2.$$

Then, $v_i = a_1 + a_2 x_i + a_3 x_i^2 - y_i$, and

$$\frac{\partial v_i}{\partial a_1} = 1, \qquad \frac{\partial v_i}{\partial a_2} = x_i, \qquad \frac{\partial v_i}{\partial a_3} = x_i^2.$$

The normal equations

$$\sum_{i=1}^{4} v_i \frac{\partial v_i}{\partial a_k} = 0, \qquad (k = 1, 2, 3),$$

are

$$\sum_{i=1}^{4} (a_1 + a_2 x_i + a_3 x_i^2 - y_i) \cdot 1 = 0,$$

$$\sum_{i=1}^{4} (a_1 + a_2 x_i + a_3 x_i^2 - y_i) \cdot x_i = 0,$$

$$\sum_{i=1}^{4} (a_1 + a_2 x_i + a_3 x_i^2 - y_i) \cdot x_i^2 = 0.$$

If the coefficients of the a_j are collected and the normal equations put in the form (162-4), one obtains the three equations

$$4a_1 + \left(\sum_{i=1}^{4} x_i\right) a_2 + \left(\sum_{i=1}^{4} x_i^2\right) a_3 = \sum_{i=1}^{4} y_i,$$

$$\left(\sum_{i=1}^{4} x_i\right) a_1 + \left(\sum_{i=1}^{4} x_i^2\right) a_2 + \left(\sum_{i=1}^{4} x_i^3\right) a_3 = \sum_{i=1}^{4} x_i y_i,$$

$$\left(\sum_{i=1}^{4} x_i^2\right) a_1 + \left(\sum_{i=1}^{4} x_i^3\right) a_2 + \left(\sum_{i=1}^{4} x_i^4\right) a_3 = \sum_{i=1}^{4} x_i^2 y_i.$$

Now,

$$\sum_{i=1}^{4} x_i = 1 + 2 + 3 + 4 = 10, \quad \sum_{i=1}^{4} x_i^2 = 1 + 4 + 9 + 16 = 30,$$

$$\sum_{i=1}^{4} x_i y_i = 1.7 + 3.6 + 6.9 + 12.8 = 25, \text{ etc.}$$

The equations become

$$4a_1 + 10a_2 + 30a_3 = 9,$$
$$10a_1 + 30a_2 + 100a_3 = 25,$$
$$30a_1 + 100a_2 + 354a_3 = 80.8;$$

and the solutions are $a_1 = 2$, $a_2 = -0.5$, $a_3 = 0.2$.

Even when Eqs. (162-1) are not linear in the unknowns, it may be possible to solve them easily. However, in most cases it is convenient to replace the exact residuals by approximate residuals which are linear in the unknowns. This is accomplished by expanding $y = f(x)$, treated as a function of $a_1, a_2, \cdots, a_r$, in Taylor's series in terms of $a_i - \bar{a}_i \equiv \Delta a_i$, where the $\bar{a}_i$ are approximate values of the a_i. The values of $\bar{a}_i$ may be obtained by graphical means or by solving any r of the equations $y_i = f(x_i)$. The expansion gives

$$(162\text{-}5) \quad y = f(x, a_1, \cdots, a_r) \equiv f(x, \bar{a}_1 + \Delta a_1, \cdots, \bar{a}_r + \Delta a_r)$$

$$= f(x, \bar{a}_1, \cdots, \bar{a}_r) + \sum_{k=1}^{r} \frac{\partial f}{\partial \bar{a}_k} \Delta a_k$$

$$+ \frac{1}{2!} \sum_{j,k=1}^{r} \frac{\partial^2 f}{\partial \bar{a}_j \, \partial \bar{a}_k} \Delta a_j \Delta a_k + \cdots,$$

where

$$\frac{\partial f}{\partial \bar{a}_k} \equiv \left.\frac{\partial f}{\partial a_k}\right|_{a_k = \bar{a}_k}, \quad \frac{\partial^2 f}{\partial \bar{a}_j \, \partial \bar{a}_k} \equiv \left.\frac{\partial^2 f}{\partial a_j \, \partial a_k}\right|_{\substack{a_j = \bar{a}_j \\ a_k = \bar{a}_k}}, \text{ etc.}$$

Assuming that the $\bar{a}_i$ are chosen so that the Δa_i are small, the terms of degree higher than the first can be neglected and (162-5) becomes

$$y = f(x, \bar{a}_1, \cdots, \bar{a}_r) + \sum_{k=1}^{r} \frac{\partial f}{\partial \bar{a}_k} \Delta a_k.$$

The n observation equations are then replaced by the n approximate equations

$$(162\text{-}6) \qquad \bar{y}_i = f(x_i, \bar{a}_1, \cdots, \bar{a}_r) + \sum_{k=1}^{r} \frac{\partial f}{\partial \bar{a}_k} \Delta a_k.$$

If (162-6) is used, the residuals v_i will be linear in the Δa_k, and hence the resulting conditions, which become

$$(162\text{-}7) \qquad \frac{\partial S}{\partial (\Delta a_k)} = 0, \quad (k = 1, 2, \cdots, r),$$

also will be linear in the Δa_k. Equations (162-7) are called the normal equations in this case.

In order to illustrate the application of the method of least squares, two examples will be given. In the first the polynomial form of $f(x)$ permits the use of (162-4), whereas the second requires the expansion in Taylor's series.

Example 1. Compute the values of the constants appearing in the equation of Example 1, Sec. 160.

The equation is $y = a_0 + a_1 x + a_2 x^2 + a_3 x^3$, and from the given data it appears that the normal equations are

$$8a_0 + \left(\sum_{i=1}^{8} x_i \right) a_1 + \left(\sum_{i=1}^{8} x_i{}^2 \right) a_2 + \left(\sum_{i=1}^{8} x_i{}^3 \right) a_3 = \sum_{i=1}^{8} y_i,$$

$$\left(\sum_{i=1}^{8} x_i \right) a_0 + \left(\sum_{i=1}^{8} x_i{}^2 \right) a_1 + \left(\sum_{i=1}^{8} x_i{}^3 \right) a_2 + \left(\sum_{i=1}^{8} x_i{}^4 \right) a_3 = \sum_{i=1}^{8} x_i y_i,$$

$$\left(\sum_{i=1}^{8} x_i{}^2 \right) a_0 + \left(\sum_{i=1}^{8} x_i{}^3 \right) a_1 + \left(\sum_{i=1}^{8} x_i{}^4 \right) a_2 + \left(\sum_{i=1}^{8} x_i{}^5 \right) a_3 = \sum_{i=1}^{8} x_i{}^2 y_i,$$

$$\left(\sum_{i=1}^{8} x_i{}^3 \right) a_0 + \left(\sum_{i=1}^{8} x_i{}^4 \right) a_1 + \left(\sum_{i=1}^{8} x_i{}^5 \right) a_2 + \left(\sum_{i=1}^{8} x_i{}^6 \right) a_3 = \sum_{i=1}^{8} x_i{}^3 y_i.$$

From the form of the coefficients of the a_k, it is seen that it is convenient to make a table of the powers of the x_i and to form the sums

$\Sigma x_i{}^j$ and $\Sigma x_i{}^j y_i$ before attempting to write down the equations in explicit form.

x_i	$x_i{}^2$	$x_i{}^3$	$x_i{}^4$	$x_i{}^5$	$x_i{}^6$
1	1	1	1	1	1
2	4	8	16	32	64
3	9	27	81	243	729
4	16	64	256	1,024	4,096
5	25	125	625	3,125	15,625
6	36	216	1,296	7,776	46,656
7	49	343	2,401	16,807	117,649
8	64	512	4,096	32,768	262,144
$\Sigma x_i{}^j$ 36	204	1,296	8,772	61,776	446,964

x_i	y_i	$x_i y_i$	$x_i{}^2 y_i$	$x_i{}^3 y_i$
1	2.105	2.105	2.105	2.105
2	2.808	5.616	11.232	22.464
3	3.614	10.842	32.526	97.578
4	4.604	18.416	73.664	294.656
5	5.857	29.285	146.425	732.125
6	7.451	44.706	268.236	1,609.416
7	9.467	66.269	463.883	3,247.181
8	11.985	95.880	767.040	6,136.320
$\Sigma x_i{}^j y_i$	47.891	273.119	1,765.111	12,141.845

When the values given in the tables are inserted, the normal equations become

$$8a_0 + 36a_1 + 204a_2 + 1{,}296a_3 = 47.891,$$
$$36a_0 + 204a_1 + 1{,}296a_2 + 8{,}772a_3 = 273.119,$$
$$204a_0 + 1{,}296a_1 + 8{,}772a_2 + 61{,}776a_3 = 1{,}765.111,$$
$$1{,}296a_0 + 8{,}772a_1 + 61{,}776a_2 + 446{,}964a_3 = 12{,}141.845.$$

The solutions are

$$a_0 = 1.426, \qquad a_1 = 0.693, \qquad a_2 = -0.028, \qquad a_3 = 0.013.$$

Therefore, the equation, as determined by the method of least squares, is

$$y = 1.426 + 0.693x - 0.028x^2 + 0.013x^3.$$

It will be observed that these values of the constants are very nearly the same as those obtained by the method of averages.

Example 2. Compute the constants that appear in the equation that represents the following data:

t	1	2	3	4
θ	51.66	44.46	38.28	32.94

Since the observed values are such that the t_i form an arithmetic progression and the θ_i approximately form a geometric progression, the equation expressing the relation is of the form

$$\theta = ka^t.$$

If the points are plotted on semilogarithmic paper, it is found that $k = 60$ and $a = 10^{-0.065} = 0.86$, approx. This suggests using $k_0 = 60$ and $a_0 = 0.9$ as the first approximations. The first two terms of the expansion in Taylor's series in terms of $\Delta k = k - 60$ and $\Delta a = a - 0.9$ are

$$\theta = 60(0.9)^t + \left(\frac{\partial \theta}{\partial k}\right)_{\substack{k=60 \\ a=0.9}} \Delta k + \left(\frac{\partial \theta}{\partial a}\right)_{\substack{k=60 \\ a=0.9}} \Delta a$$

$$= 60(0.9)^t + (0.9)^t \Delta k + 60t(0.9)^{t-1} \Delta a.$$

If the values (t_i, θ_i) are substituted in this equation, four equations result, namely,

$$\theta_i = 60(0.9)^{t_i} + (0.9)^{t_i} \Delta k + 60t_i(0.9)^{t_i-1} \Delta a, \qquad (i = 1, 2, 3, 4).$$

The problem of obtaining from these four equations the values of Δk and Δa, which furnish the most probable values of θ_i, is precisely the same as in the case in which the original equation is linear in its constants. The residual equations are

$$v_i = (0.9)^{t_i} \Delta k + 60t_i(0.9)^{t_i-1} \Delta a + 60(0.9)^{t_i} - \theta_i, \qquad (i = 1, 2, 3, 4).$$

Therefore,

$$S \equiv \sum_{i=1}^{4} v_i{}^2 = \sum_{i=1}^{4} [(0.9)^{t_i} \Delta k + 60t_i(0.9)^{t_i-1} \Delta a + 60(0.9)^{t_i} - \theta_i]^2,$$

and the normal equations

$$\frac{\partial S}{\partial (\Delta k)} = 0 \qquad \text{and} \qquad \frac{\partial S}{\partial (\Delta a)} = 0$$

become

$$2 \sum_{i=1}^{4} [0.9^{t_i} \Delta k + 60t_i(0.9)^{t_i-1} \Delta a + 60(0.9)^{t_i} - \theta_i]0.9^{t_i} = 0$$

and

$$2 \sum_{i=1}^{4} [0.9^{t_i} \, \Delta k + 60 t_i (0.9)^{t_i-1} \, \Delta a + 60(0.9)^{t_i} - \theta_i] 60 t_i (0.9)^{t_i-1} = 0.$$

When these equations are written in the form

$$p \, \Delta k + q \, \Delta a = r,$$

with all common factors divided out, they are

$$\sum_{i=1}^{4} (0.9)^{2t_i} \, \Delta k + 60 \sum_{i=1}^{4} t_i (0.9)^{2t_i-1} \, \Delta a = \sum_{i=1}^{4} \theta_i (0.9)^{t_i} - 60 \sum_{i=1}^{4} (0.9)^{2t_i}$$

and

$$\sum_{i=1}^{4} t_i (0.9)^{2t_i-1} \, \Delta k + 60 \sum_{i=1}^{4} t_i^2 (0.9)^{2t_i-2} \, \Delta a = \sum_{i=1}^{4} \theta_i t_i (0.9)^{t_i-1}$$
$$- 60 \sum_{i=1}^{4} t_i (0.9)^{2t_i-1}.$$

As in Example 1, the coefficients are computed most conveniently by the use of a table.

t_i	1	2	3	4	Totals
$(0.9)^{t_i}$	0.9	0.81	0.729	0.6561	
$(0.9)^{2t_i}$	0.81	0.6561	0.531441	0.43046721	2.42800821
$t_i(0.9)^{2t_i-1}$	0.9	1.458	1.77147	1.9131876	6.0426576
$t_i^2(0.9)^{2t_i-2}$	1	3.24	5.9049	8.503056	18.647956
$(\theta_i)(0.9)^{t_i}$	46.494	36.0126	27.90612	21.611934	132.024654
$(\theta_i t_i)(0.9)^{t_i-1}$	51.66	80.028	93.0204	96.05304	320.76144

Substituting the values of the sums from the table gives

$$2.42800821 \, \Delta k + 362.559456 \, \Delta a = 132.024654 - 145.6804926$$

and

$$6.0426576 \, \Delta k + 1118.87736 \, \Delta a = 320.76144 - 362.559456.$$

Reducing all the numbers to four decimal places gives the following equations to solve for Δk and Δa:

$$2.4280 \, \Delta k + 362.5595 \, \Delta a = -13.6558,$$
$$6.0427 \, \Delta k + 1118.8774 \, \Delta a = -41.7980.$$

The solutions are

$$\Delta k = -0.238 \quad \text{and} \quad \Delta a = -0.036.$$

Hence, the required equation is

$$\theta = 59.762(0.864)^t.$$

PROBLEMS

1. Find the constants in the equation for the data given in Prob. 1, Sec. 161.   Use the method of least squares.

2. Use the method of least squares to determine the values of the constants in the equation that represents the following data:

x	0.2	0.4	0.6	0.8	1
y	1.25	1.60	2.00	2.50	3.20

3. Apply the method of least squares to the data given in Prob. 1, Sec. 158.

4. Apply the method of least squares to determine the values of a and b in Prob. 4, Sec. 161.

163. Method of Moments.   Since the method of moments is one of the most popular methods in use by the statisticians and economists, a brief discussion of it will be presented.   For certain types of equations, especially those which are linear in their constants, it provides a simple method of determining the constants.   If the equation has the form

$$y = \sum_{k=0}^{r-1} a_k x^k,$$

this method gives results identical with those obtained by the method of least squares.   In this case the method has a theoretical background that justifies its use.   When the method is applied to other types of equations, there is, in general, no such justification.   However, in modified forms it is convenient for computation and often gives very good results.

Let the set of observed values be (x_i, y_i), $(i = 1, 2, \cdots, n)$, and the equation that represents these data be $y = f(x)$.   When the values $x = x_i$ are substituted in $f(x)$, there result the corresponding computed values of y, which will be designated by

$\bar{y}_i$. The moments of the observed values y_i and of the computed values $\bar{y}_i$ are defined, respectively, by

$$\gamma_k = \sum_{i=1}^{n} x_i^k y_i \qquad \text{and} \qquad \mu_k = \sum_{i=1}^{n} x_i^k \bar{y}_i.$$

If $f(x)$ contains r undetermined constants, the method of moments is based on the assumption that

$$(163\text{-}1) \qquad\qquad \gamma_k = \mu_k, \qquad (k = 0, 1, 2, \cdots, r - 1).$$

Since $\bar{y}_i$ is a function of the r undetermined constants, Eqs. (163-1) give r simultaneous equations in these constants.

The method of moments in this form is most useful when $f(x)$ is linear in its r constants, so that the r equations (163-1) can be solved immediately. Various modifications and devices are used to simplify the computation in case $f(x)$ is not linear in its constants. These will not be discussed here.*

In the special case in which $f(x)$ is a polynomial, that is,

$$f(x) = \sum_{j=0}^{r-1} a_j x^j,$$

the values of $\bar{y}_i$ are given by

$$\bar{y}_i = \sum_{j=0}^{r-1} a_j x_i^j$$

and therefore

$$\mu_k = \sum_{i=1}^{n} x_i^k \sum_{j=0}^{r-1} a_j x_i^j = \sum_{j=0}^{r-1} \sum_{i=1}^{n} x_i^{j+k} a_j, \ (k = 0, 1, 2, \cdots, r - 1).$$

Then Eqs. (163-1) assume the form

$$\sum_{j=0}^{r-1} \sum_{i=1}^{n} x_i^{j+k} a_j = \sum_{i=1}^{n} x_i^k y_i, \qquad (k = 0, 1, 2, \cdots, r - 1),$$

which are identical with the normal equations (162-4) obtained by the method of least squares. Hence, the two methods lead to identical results for this form of $f(x)$.

164. Harmonic Analysis. The problem of obtaining the expansion of a periodic function in an infinite trigonometric

* For a discussion, see Frechet and Romann, Représentation des lois empiriques; Rietz, Handbook of Mathematical Statistics.

series was considered in Chap. II. In this section will be given a short discussion of the problem of fitting a finite trigonometric sum to a set of observed values (x_i, y_i) in which the values of y are periodic.

Let the set of observed values

$$(x_0, y_0), (x_1, y_1), \cdot \cdot \cdot , (x_{2n-1}, y_{2n-1}), (x_{2n}, y_{2n}), \cdot \cdot \cdot$$

be such that the values of y start repeating with y_{2n} (that is, $y_{2n} = y_0$, $y_{2n+1} = y_1$, etc.). It will be assumed that the x_i are equally spaced, that $x_0 = 0$, and that $x_{2n} = 2\pi$. [If $x_0 \neq 0$ and the period is c, instead of 2π, the variable can be changed by setting

$$\theta_i = \frac{2\pi}{c} (x_i - x_0).$$

The discussion would then be carried through for θ_i and y_i in place of the x_i and y_i used below.] Under these assumptions

$$x_i = i \cdot \frac{2\pi}{2n} = \frac{i\pi}{n}.$$

The equation

$$(164\text{-}1) \qquad y = A_0 + \sum_{k=1}^{n} A_k \cos kx + \sum_{k=1}^{n-1} B_k \sin kx$$

contains the $2n$ unknown constants

$$A_0, A_1, A_2, \cdot \cdot \cdot , A_n, B_1, B_2, \cdot \cdot \cdot , B_{n-1},$$

which can be determined so that (164-1) will pass through the $2n$ given points (x_i, y_i) by solving the $2n$ simultaneous equations

$$y_i = A_0 + \sum_{k=1}^{n} A_k \cos kx_i + \sum_{k=1}^{n-1} B_k \sin kx_i,$$

$$(i = 0, 1, 2, \cdot \cdot \cdot , 2n - 1).$$

Since $x_i = i\pi/n$, these equations become

$$(164\text{-}2) \quad y_i = A_0 + \sum_{k=1}^{n} A_k \cos \frac{ik\pi}{n} + \sum_{k=1}^{n-1} B_k \sin \frac{ik\pi}{n},$$

$$(i = 0, 1, 2, \cdot \cdot \cdot , 2n - 1).$$

The solution of Eqs. (164-2) is much simplified by means of a scheme somewhat similar to that used in determining the Fourier coefficients. Multiplying both sides of each equation by its coefficient of A_0 (that is, by unity) and adding the results give

$$\sum_{i=0}^{2n-1} y_i = 2nA_0 + \sum_{k=1}^{n}\left(\sum_{i=0}^{2n-1} \cos \frac{ik\pi}{n}\right) A_k + \sum_{k=1}^{n-1}\left(\sum_{i=0}^{2n-1} \sin \frac{ik\pi}{n}\right) B_k.$$

It can be established that

$$\sum_{i=0}^{2n-1} \cos \frac{ik\pi}{n} = 0, \qquad (k = 1, 2, \cdots, n),$$

and

$$\sum_{i=0}^{2n-1} \sin \frac{ik\pi}{n} = 0, \qquad (k = 1, 2, \cdots, n-1).$$

Therefore,

(164-3) $$2nA_0 = \sum_{i=0}^{2n-1} y_i.$$

Multiplying both sides of each equation by its coefficient of A_j, $(j = 1, 2, \cdots, n - 1)$, and adding the results give

$$\sum_{i=0}^{2n-1} y_i \cos \frac{ij\pi}{n} = \sum_{k=1}^{n}\left(\sum_{i=0}^{2n-1} \cos \frac{ik\pi}{n} \cos \frac{ij\pi}{n}\right) A_k$$
$$+ \sum_{k=1}^{n-1}\left(\sum_{i=0}^{2n-1} \sin \frac{ik\pi}{n} \cos \frac{ij\pi}{n}\right) B_k$$

for $j = 1, 2, \cdots, n - 1$. But

$$\sum_{i=0}^{2n-1} \cos \frac{ik\pi}{n} \cos \frac{ij\pi}{n} = 0, \qquad \text{if } k \neq j,$$
$$= n, \qquad \text{if } k = j;$$

and

$$\sum_{i=0}^{2n-1} \sin \frac{ik\pi}{n} \cos \frac{ij\pi}{n} = 0$$

for all values of k. Therefore,

(164-4) $$nA_j = \sum_{i=0}^{2n-1} y_i \cos \frac{ij\pi}{n}, \qquad (j = 1, 2, \cdots, n - 1).$$

In order to determine the coefficient of A_n the procedure is precisely the same, but

$$\sum_{i=0}^{2n-1} \cos \frac{ik\pi}{n} \cos i\pi = 0, \qquad \text{if } k \neq n,$$

$$= 2n, \qquad \text{if } k = n.$$

Hence,

$$(164\text{-}5) \qquad 2nA_n = \sum_{i=0}^{2n-1} y_i \cos i\pi.$$

Similarly, by multiplying both sides of each equation of (164-2) by its coefficient of B_k and adding, it can be established that

$$(164\text{-}6) \qquad nB_j = \sum_{i=0}^{2n-1} y_i \sin \frac{ij\pi}{n}, \qquad (j = 1, 2, \cdots, n-1).$$

Equations (164-3), (164-4), (164-5), and (164-6) give the solutions for the constants in (164-1). A compact schematic arrangement is often used to simplify the labor of evaluating these constants. It will be illustrated in the so-called "6-ordinate" case, that is, when $2n = 6$. The method is based on the equations that determine the constants, together with relations such as

$$\sin \frac{\pi}{n} = \sin \frac{(n-1)\pi}{n} = -\sin \frac{(n+1)\pi}{n} = -\sin \frac{(2n-1)\pi}{n},$$

$$\cos \frac{\pi}{n} = -\cos \frac{(n-1)\pi}{n} = -\cos \frac{(n+1)\pi}{n} = \cos \frac{(2n-1)\pi}{n}, \text{ etc.}$$

Six-ordinate Scheme. Here, $2n = 6$, the given points are (x_i, y_i), where $x_i = i\pi/3$, $(i = 0, 1, 2, 3, 4, 5)$, and Eq. (164-1) becomes

$$y = A_0 + A_1 \cos x + A_2 \cos 2x + A_3 \cos 3x + B_1 \sin x + B_2 \sin 2x.$$

Make the following table of definitions:

	y_0 y_1 y_2	v_0 v_1	w_0 w_1
	y_3 y_4 y_5	v_2	w_2
Sum.....	v_0 v_1 v_2	p_0 p_1	r_0 r_1
Difference	w_0 w_1 w_2	q_1	s_1

It can be checked easily that Eqs. (164-3), (164-4), (164-5), and (164-6), with $n = 3$, become

$$6A_0 = p_0 + p_1, \qquad 3A_1 = r_0 + \tfrac{1}{2}s_1, \qquad 3A_2 = p_0 - \tfrac{1}{2}p_1,$$

$$6A_3 = r_0 - s_1, \qquad 3B_1 = \frac{\sqrt{3}}{2}\, r_1, \qquad 3B_2 = \frac{\sqrt{3}}{2}\, q_1.$$

In particular, suppose that the given points are

x	0	$\dfrac{\pi}{3}$	$\dfrac{2\pi}{3}$	π	$\dfrac{4\pi}{3}$	$\dfrac{5\pi}{3}$	2π
y	1.0	1.4	1.9	1.7	1.5	1.2	1.0

Upon using these values of y in the table of definitions above,

```
           1.0                1.4               1.9
           1.7                1.5               1.2
   v₀ =    2.7        v₁ =    2.9       v₂ =    3.1
   w₀ = −0.7          w₁ = −0.1         w₂ =    0.7
           2.7                2.9              −0.7              −0.1
                              3.1                                0.7
   ────────────       ────────────      ────────────      ────────────
   p₀ = 2.7           p₁ = 6.0          r₀ = −0.7         r₁ =   0.6
                      q₁ = −0.2                           s₁ = −0.8
```

Therefore, the equations determining the values of the constants are

$$6A_0 = 2.7 + 6.0 = 8.7 \qquad \text{and} \qquad A_0 = 1.45,$$
$$3A_1 = -0.7 - 0.4 = -1.1 \qquad \text{and} \qquad A_1 = -0.37,$$
$$3A_2 = 2.7 - 3.0 = -0.3 \qquad \text{and} \qquad A_2 = -0.10,$$
$$6A_3 = -0.7 + 0.8 = 0.1 \qquad \text{and} \qquad A_3 = 0.02,$$
$$3B_1 = \frac{\sqrt{3}}{2}(0.6) = 0.3\sqrt{3} \qquad \text{and} \qquad B_1 = 0.17,$$
$$3B_2 = \frac{\sqrt{3}}{2}(-0.2) = -0.1\sqrt{3} \qquad \text{and} \qquad B_2 = -0.06.$$

Hence, the curve of type (164-1) that fits the given data is

$$y = 1.45 - 0.37\cos x - 0.10\cos 2x + 0.02\cos 3x + 0.17\sin x - 0.06\sin 2x.$$

A convenient check upon the computations is furnished by the relations

$$A_0 + A_1 + A_2 + A_3 = y_0 \qquad \text{and} \qquad B_1 + B_2 = \frac{\sqrt{3}}{3}(y_1 - y_5).$$

Substituting the values found above in the left-hand members gives

$$1.45 - 0.37 - 0.10 + 0.02 = 1.0 \qquad \text{and} \qquad 0.17 - 0.06 = 0.11,$$

which check with the values of the right-hand members.

Similar tables can be constructed for 8-ordinates, 12-ordinates, etc.*

PROBLEMS

1. Use the 6-ordinate scheme to fit a curve of the type (164-1) to the data in the following table:

x	0	$\dfrac{\pi}{3}$	$\dfrac{2\pi}{3}$	π	$\dfrac{4\pi}{3}$	$\dfrac{5\pi}{3}$	2π
y	0.8	0.6	0.4	0.7	0.9	1.1	0.8

2. Make a suitable change of variable, and apply the 6-ordinate scheme to the data given in the table

x	0	$\dfrac{\pi}{6}$	$\dfrac{\pi}{3}$	$\dfrac{\pi}{2}$	$\dfrac{2\pi}{3}$	$\dfrac{5\pi}{6}$	π
y	0.6	0.9	1.3	1.0	0.8	0.5	0.6

165. Interpolation Formulas. When an equation has been obtained to represent the relation existing between x and y, as indicated by a given set of observed values (x_i, y_i), this equation can be used to determine approximately the value of y corresponding to an arbitrary value of x. It would be expected that the equation would furnish a good approximation to the value of y corresponding to an x which lies within the range of the observed values x_i. The equation may provide a good approximation for y even if x is chosen outside this range, but this must not be assumed.

Frequently, it is desired to obtain an approximation to the y corresponding to a certain value of x without determining the relation that connects the variables. Interpolation formulas have been developed for this purpose and for use in numerical integration (mechanical quadrature).† The formulas to be

---

* See CARSE and SHEARER, A Course in Fourier Analysis and Periodogram Analysis.

† See Secs. 167 and 168.

discussed here all assume that the desired value for y can be obtained from the equation

$$y = a_0 + a_1x + a_2x^2 + \cdots + a_mx^m,$$

in which the a_i have been determined so that this equation is satisfied by $m + 1$ pairs of the observed values (x_i, y_i). These $m + 1$ pairs may include the entire set of observed values, or they may be a subset chosen so that $|x - x_i|$ is as small as possible.

The first interpolation formula of this discussion assumes that the set of $m + 1$ observed values x_0, x_1, x_2, $\cdots$, x_m is an arithmetic progression, that is, that

(165-1) $x_k = x_{k-1} + d = x_0 + kd,$ $(k = 1, 2, \cdots, m).$

Since there are $m + 1$ pairs of observed values, there is only one mth difference $\Delta^m y$, and all differences of order higher than m are zero. Hence, by (159-3),

$$y_k = y_0 + k\,\Delta y_0 + \frac{k(k-1)}{2!}\,\Delta^2 y_0 + \cdots$$
$$+ \frac{k(k-1)\cdots(k-m+1)}{m!}\,\Delta^m y_0.$$

But, from (165-1), it follows that

$$k = \frac{x_k - x_0}{d},$$

so that the expression for y_k becomes

(165-2) $$y_k = y_0 + \frac{x_k - x_0}{d}\,\Delta y_0 + \frac{(x_k - x_0)(x_k - x_0 - d)}{2!\,d^2}\,\Delta^2 y_0 +$$
$$\cdots + \frac{(x_k - x_0)(x_k - x_0 - d)\cdots(x_k - x_0 - md + d)}{m!\,d^m}\,\Delta^m y_0.$$

Relation (165-2) is satisfied by every one of the $m + 1$ pairs of observed values. Now, assume that the value of the y which corresponds to an arbitrary x also can be obtained from (165-2). Then,

(165-3) $$y = y_0 + \frac{(x - x_0)}{d}\,\Delta y_0 + \frac{(x - x_0)(x - x_0 - d)}{2!\,d^2}\,\Delta^2 y_0 +$$
$$\cdots + \frac{(x - x_0)(x - x_0 - d)\cdots(x - x_0 - md + d)}{m!\,d^m}\,\Delta^m y_0.$$

Equation (165-3) represents the mth-degree parabola which passes through the $m + 1$ points whose coordinates are (x_i, y_i). It assumes a more compact form and is more convenient for computation purposes when $\dfrac{x - x_0}{d}$ is replaced by X. Then,

$$(165\text{-}4) \quad y = y_0 + X \, \Delta y_0 + \frac{X(X - 1)}{2!} \, \Delta^2 y_0 + \cdots$$

$$+ \frac{X(X - 1) \, \cdots \, (X - m + 1)}{m!} \, \Delta^m y_0.$$

Example. Using the data given in Example 1, Sec. 160, determine an approximate value for the y corresponding to $x = 2.2$.

First, let y be determined by using only the two neighboring observed values (hence, $m = 1$). Then, $x_0 = 2$, $y_0 = 2.808$, $\Delta y_0 = 0.806$, and $X = \dfrac{2.2 - 2}{1} = 0.2$. Hence,

$$y = 2.808 + 0.2(0.806) = 2.969,$$

which has been reduced to three decimal places because the observed data are not given more accurately. Obviously, this is simply a straight-line interpolation by proportional parts.

If the three nearest values are chosen, $m = 2$, $x_0 = 1$, $y_0 = 2.105$, $\Delta y_0 = 0.703$, $\Delta^2 y_0 = 0.103$, and $X = 2.2 - 1 = 1.2$. Then,

$$y = 2.105 + 1.2(0.703) + \frac{(1.2)(0.2)}{2!} (0.103) = 2.961,$$

correct to three decimal places.

If the four nearest values are chosen, $m = 3$, $x_0 = 1$, $y_0 = 2.105$, $\Delta y_0 = 0.703$, $\Delta^2 y_0 = 0.103$, $\Delta^3 y_0 = 0.081$, and $X = 1.2$. Therefore,

$$y = 2.105 + 1.2(0.703) + \frac{(1.2)(0.2)}{2} (0.103)$$

$$+ \frac{(1.2)(0.2)(-0.8)}{6} (0.081) = 2.958,$$

correct to three decimal places.

The value obtained by substituting $x = 2.2$ in the equation

$$y = 1.426 + 0.693x - 0.028x^2 + 0.013x^3,$$

obtained by the method of least squares (see Example 1, Sec. 162) is 2.954. It might be expected that a better approximation to this value could be obtained by choosing $m = 4$, but investigation shows that the additional term is too small to affect the third decimal place.

166. Lagrange's Interpolation Formula. The interpolation formula developed in Sec. 165 applies only when the chosen set of x_i is an arithmetic progression.   If this is not the case, some other type of formula must be applied.

As in Sec. 165, select the $m + 1$ pairs of observed values for which $|x - x_i|$ is as small as possible, and denote them by (x_i, y_i), $(i = 0, 1, 2, \cdots, m)$.   Let the mth-degree polynomials $P_k(x)$, $(k = 0, 1, 2, \cdots, m)$, be defined by

$$(166\text{-}1) \quad P_k(x) = \frac{(x - x_0)(x - x_1) \cdots (x - x_m)}{x - x_k} \equiv \prod_{\substack{i=0 \\ i \neq k}}^{m} (x - x_i).$$

Then, the coefficients A_k of the equation

$$y = \sum_{k=0}^{m} A_k P_k(x)$$

can be determined so that this equation is satisfied by each of the $m + 1$ pairs of observed values (x_i, y_i).   For if $x = x_k$, then

$$A_k = \frac{y_k}{P_k(x_k)},$$

since $P_k(x_i) = 0$, if $i \neq k$.   Therefore,

$$(166\text{-}2) \qquad y = \sum_{k=0}^{m} \frac{y_k P_k(x)}{P_k(x_k)}$$

is the equation of the mth-degree parabola which passes through the $m + 1$ points whose coordinates are (x_i, y_i).   If x is chosen as any value in the range of the x_i, (166-2) determines an approximate value for the corresponding y.

Equation (166-2) is known as Lagrange's interpolation formula. Obviously, it can be applied when the x_i are in arithmetic progression, but (165-4) is preferable in that it requires less tedious calculation.   Since only one mth-degree parabola can be passed through $m + 1$ distinct points, it follows that (165-3), or its equivalent (165-4), and (166-2) are merely different forms of the same equation and will furnish the same value for y.

Example.   Using the data given in Prob. 1, Sec. 160, apply Lagrange's formula to find the value of p corresponding to $v = 21$.

If the two neighboring pairs of observed values are chosen, so that $m = 1$,

$$p = 0.675 \frac{21 - 22.5}{15 - 22.5} + 1.519 \frac{21 - 15}{22.5 - 15} = 1.350,$$

correct to three decimal places.

If the three nearest values are chosen, so that $m = 2$,

$$p = 0.3 \frac{(21 - 15)(21 - 22.5)}{(10 - 15)(10 - 22.5)} + 0.675 \frac{(21 - 10)(21 - 22.5)}{(15 - 10)(15 - 22.5)}$$
$$+ 1.519 \frac{(21 - 10)(21 - 15)}{(22.5 - 10)(22.5 - 15)} = 1.323,$$

correct to three decimal places.

The value of p obtained from the equation $p = 0.003v^2$, which represents the given data, is also 1.323.

PROBLEMS

1. Using the data given in Prob. 2, Sec. 160, find an approximate value for θ when $t = 2.3$. Use $m = 1$, 2, and 3.

2. Find an approximate value for the y corresponding to $x = 2$, using the data given in Example 3, Sec. 160. Use $m = 1$ and $m = 2$.

3. If the observed values are given by the data of Prob. 3, Sec. 160, find an approximate value of H when $C = 21.6$. Use $m = 1$, 2, and 3.

4. Using the data of Prob. 1, Sec. 160, find an approximate value for p when $v = 30$. Use $m = 1$ and $m = 2$.

167. Numerical Integration.* The definite integral $\int_a^b f(x)\, dx$ is interpreted geometrically as the area under the curve $y = f(x)$ between the ordinates $x = a$ and $x = b$. If the function $f(x)$ is such that its indefinite integral $F(x)$ can be obtained, then from the fundamental theorem of the integral calculus it follows that

$$\int_a^b f(x)\, dx = F(b) - F(a).$$

However, if the function $f(x)$ does not possess an indefinite integral expressible in terms of known functions or if the value of $f(x)$ is known only for certain isolated values of x, some kind of approximation formula must be used in order to secure a value for $\int_a^b f(x)\, dx$.

A formula of numerical integration, or mechanical quadrature, is one that gives an approximate expression for the value of $\int_a^b f(x)\, dx$. The discussion given here is restricted to the case in which $m + 1$ pairs of values (x_i, y_i), or $[x_i, f(x_i)]$, are given [either by observation or by computation from $y = f(x)$ if the form of $f(x)$ is known] and where this set of given values is represented by (165-3) or (166-2).

The formulas of numerical integration that are most frequently used are based on the assumption that the x_i form an arith-

* For discussion of the accuracy of the formulas given here, see Steffensen, Interpolation; and Kowalewski, Interpolation und genäherte Quadratur.

metic progression, that is, that $x_k = x_0 + kd$.   In that case, all
the $m + 1$ points (x_i, y_i), $(i = 0, 1, 2, \cdots, m)$, lie on the
parabola whose equation is given by (165-3).   The area bounded
by the x-axis and this parabola between $x = x_0$ and $x = x_m$
is an approximation to the value of $\int_{x_0}^{x_m} f(x) \, dx$.

Upon using (165-4) and recalling that

$$X = \frac{x - x_0}{d},$$

it follows that

$$(167\text{-}1) \quad \int_0^m y \, dX = \int_0^m \left[y_0 + X \, \Delta y_0 + \frac{X(X - 1)}{2!} \Delta^2 y_0 \right.$$
$$\left. + \cdots + \frac{X(X - 1) \cdots (X - m + 1)}{m!} \Delta^m y_0 \right] dX.$$

If $m = 1$, (167-1) becomes

$$\int_0^1 y \, dX = \int_0^1 (y_0 + X \, \Delta y_0) \, dX$$
$$= y_0 + \frac{\Delta y_0}{2} = y_0 + \frac{y_1 - y_0}{2} = \frac{1}{2} (y_0 + y_1).$$

But

$$x_m = x_0 + md \quad \text{and} \quad X = \frac{x - x_0}{d},$$

so that

$$dX = \frac{dx}{d}$$

and the formula becomes

$$(167\text{-}2) \quad \int_{x_0}^{x_1} y \, dx = \frac{d}{2} (y_0 + y_1).$$

If $n + 1$ pairs of values are given, (167-2) can be applied
successively to the first two pairs, the second and third pairs,
the third and fourth pairs, etc.   There results

$$(167\text{-}3) \quad \int_{x_0}^{x_n} y \, dx = \int_{x_0}^{x_1} y \, dx + \int_{x_1}^{x_2} y \, dx + \cdots + \int_{x_{n-1}}^{x_n} y \, dx$$
$$= \frac{d}{2} (y_0 + y_1) + \frac{d}{2} (y_1 + y_2) + \cdots$$
$$+ \frac{d}{2} (y_{n-1} + y_n)$$
$$= \frac{d}{2} (y_0 + 2y_1 + 2y_2 + \cdots + 2y_{n-1} + y_n).$$

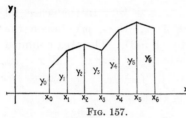

FIG. 157.

Formula (167-3) is known as the trapezoidal rule, for it gives the value of the sum of the areas of the n trapezoids whose bases are the ordinates $y_0, y_1, y_2, \cdots,$ y_n. Figure 157 shows the six trapezoids in the case of $n = 6$.

If $m = 2$, (167-1) becomes

$$\int_0^2 y\, dX = \int_0^2 \left[y_0 + X\, \Delta y_0 + \frac{(X^2 - X)}{2}\, \Delta^2 y_0 \right] dX$$

$$= 2y_0 + 2\,\Delta y_0 + \frac{1}{2}\left(\frac{8}{3} - 2\right) \Delta^2 y_0$$

$$= 2y_0 + 2(y_1 - y_0) + \frac{1}{3}(y_2 - 2y_1 + y_0)$$

$$= \frac{1}{3}\, y_0 + \frac{4}{3}\, y_1 + \frac{1}{3}\, y_2,$$

or

(167-4) $$\int_{x_0}^{x_2} y\, dx = \frac{d}{3}(y_0 + 4y_1 + y_2).$$

Suppose that there are $n + 1$ pairs of given values, where n is even. If these $n + 1$ pairs are divided into the groups of three pairs with abscissas $x_{2i},\ x_{2i+1},\ x_{2i+2},\ \left(i = 0, 1, \cdots, \frac{n-1}{2}\right)$, then (167-4) can be applied to each group. Hence,

(167-5) $$\int_{x_0}^{x_n} y\, dx = \int_{x_0}^{x_2} y\, dx + \int_{x_2}^{x_4} y\, dx + \cdots + \int_{x_{n-2}}^{x_n} y\, dx$$

$$= \frac{d}{3}(y_0 + 4y_1 + y_2) + \frac{d}{3}(y_2 + 4y_3 + y_4)$$

$$+ \cdots + \frac{d}{3}(y_{n-2} + 4y_{n-1} + y_n)$$

$$= \frac{d}{3}[y_0 + y_n + 4(y_1 + y_3 + \cdots + y_{n-1})$$

$$+ 2(y_2 + y_4 + \cdots + y_{n-2})].$$

Formula (167-5) is known as Simpson's rule with $m = 2$. Interpreted geometrically, it gives the value of the sum of the areas under the second-degree parabolas that have been passed through the points (x_{2i}, y_{2i}), (x_{2i+1}, y_{2i+1}), and (x_{2i+2}, y_{2i+2}), $[i = 0, 1, 2, \cdots, (n-1)/2]$.

If $m = 3$, (167-1) states that

$$\int_0^3 y \, dX = \int_0^3 \left(y_0 + X \, \Delta y_0 + \frac{X^2 - X}{2} \Delta^2 y_0 \right.$$
$$\left. + \frac{X^3 - 3X^2 + 2X}{6} \Delta^3 y_0 \right) dX$$
$$= 3y_0 + \frac{9}{2} \Delta y_0 + \left(\frac{9}{2} - \frac{9}{4} \right) \Delta^2 y_0 + \left(\frac{27}{8} - \frac{9}{2} + \frac{3}{2} \right) \Delta^3 y_0$$
$$= 3y_0 + \frac{9}{2} (y_1 - y_0) + \frac{9}{4} (y_2 - 2y_1 + y_0)$$
$$+ \frac{3}{8} (y_3 - 3y_2 + 3y_1 - y_0)$$
$$= \frac{3}{8} (y_0 + 3y_1 + 3y_2 + y_3),$$

or

$$(167\text{-}6) \qquad \int_{x_0}^{x_3} y \, dx = \frac{3d}{8} (y_0 + 3y_1 + 3y_2 + y_3).$$

If $n + 1$ pairs of values are given and if n is a multiple of 3, then (167-6) can be applied successively to groups of four pairs of values to give

$$(167\text{-}7) \qquad \int_{x_0}^{x_n} y \, dx = \frac{3d}{8} [y_0 + y_n + 3(y_1 + y_2 + y_4 + y_5 + \cdots$$
$$+ y_{n-2} + y_{n-1}) + 2(y_3 + y_6 + \cdots + y_{n-3})].$$

Formula (167-7) is called Simpson's rule with $m = 3$. It is not encountered so frequently as (167-3) or (167-5). Other formulas for numerical integration can be derived by setting $m = 4, 5, \cdots$ in (167-1), but the three given here are sufficient for ordinary purposes. In most cases, better results are obtained by securing a large number of observed or computed values, so that d will be small, and using (167-3) or (167-5).

Example. Using the data given in Example 1, Sec. 160, find an approximate value for $\int_1^7 y \, dx$.

Using the trapezoidal rule (167-3) gives

$$\int_1^7 y \, dx = \tfrac{1}{2}(2.105 + 5.616 + 7.228 + 9.208 + 11.714$$
$$+ 14.902 + 9.467) = 30.120.$$

Using (167-5) gives

$$\int_1^7 y \, dx = \tfrac{1}{3}[2.105 + 9.467 + 4(2.808 + 4.604 + 7.451)$$
$$+ 2(3.614 + 5.857)] = 29.989.$$

Using (167-7) gives

$$\int_1^7 y \, dx = \tfrac{3}{8}[2.105 + 9.467 + 3(2.808 + 3.614$$
$$+ 5.857 + 7.451) + 2(4.604)] = 29.989.$$

168. A More General Formula. If numerical integration is to be used in a problem in which the form of $f(x)$ is known, the set of values (x_i, y_i) can usually be chosen so that the x_i form an arithmetic progression and one of the formulas of Sec. 167 can be applied. Even if it is expedient to choose values closer together for some parts of the range than for other parts, the formulas of Sec. 167 can be applied successively, with appropriate values of d, to those sets of values for which the x_i form an arithmetic progression. However, if the set of given values was obtained by observation, it is frequently convenient to use a formula that does not require that the x_i form an arithmetic progression.

Suppose that a set of pairs of observed values (x_i, y_i), ($i = 0$, 1, 2, $\cdots$, m), is given. The points (x_i, y_i) all lie on the parabola whose equation is given by (166-2). The area under this parabola between $x = x_0$ and $x = x_m$ is an approximation to the value of $\int_{x_0}^{x_m} y \, dx$. The area under the parabola (166-2) is

$$(168\text{-}1) \qquad \int_{x_0}^{x_m} y \, dx = \sum_{k=0}^{m} \frac{y_k}{P_k(x_k)} \int_{x_0}^{x_m} P_k(x) \, dx,$$

in which the expressions for the $P_k(x)$ are given by (166-1).

If $m = 1$, (168-1) and (166-1) give

$$(168\text{-}2) \qquad \int_{x_0}^{x_1} y \, dx = \frac{y_0}{x_0 - x_1} \int_{x_0}^{x_1} (x - x_1) \, dx$$
$$+ \frac{y_1}{x_1 - x_0} \int_{x_0}^{x_1} (x - x_0) \, dx$$
$$= \frac{x_1 - x_0}{2} (y_0 + y_1).$$

Formula (168-2) is identical with (167-2), as would be expected, but the formula corresponding to (167-3) is

$$(168\text{-}3) \quad \int_{x_0}^{x_n} y\, dx = \tfrac{1}{2}[(x_1 - x_0)(y_0 + y_1) + (x_2 - x_1)(y_1 + y_2)$$
$$+ \cdots + (x_n - x_{n-1})(y_{n-1} + y_n)].$$

If $m = 2$, (168-1) becomes

$$(168\text{-}4) \quad \int_{x_0}^{x_2} y\, dx = \frac{y_0}{P_0(x_0)} \int_{x_0}^{x_2} (x - x_1)(x - x_2)\, dx$$

$$+ \frac{y_1}{P_1(x_1)} \int_{x_0}^{x_2} (x - x_0)(x - x_2)\, dx$$

$$+ \frac{y_2}{P_2(x_2)} \int_{x_0}^{x_2} (x - x_0)(x - x_1)\, dx$$

$$= \frac{y_0}{P_0(x_0)} \left[\frac{x_2^3 - x_0^3}{3} - \frac{(x_1 + x_2)(x_2^2 - x_0^2)}{2} \right.$$

$$\left. + x_1 x_2 (x_2 - x_0) \right]$$

$$+ \frac{y_1}{P_1(x_1)} \left[\frac{x_2^3 - x_0^3}{3} - \frac{(x_0 + x_2)(x_2^2 - x_0^2)}{2} \right.$$

$$\left. + x_0 x_2 (x_2 - x_0) \right]$$

$$+ \frac{y_2}{P_2(x_2)} \left[\frac{x_2^3 - x_0^3}{3} - \frac{(x_0 + x_1)(x_2^2 - x_0^2)}{2} \right.$$

$$\left. + x_0 x_1 (x_2 - x_0) \right]$$

$$= \frac{(x_2 - x_0)^2}{6} \left[\frac{y_0}{P_0(x_0)} (3x_1 - 2x_0 - x_2) \right.$$

$$\left. + \frac{y_1}{P_1(x_1)} (x_0 - x_2) + \frac{y_2}{P_2(x_2)} (2x_2 + x_0 - 3x_1) \right].$$

Formula (168-4) reduces to (167-4) when $x_1 - x_0 = x_2 - x_1 = d$. The formula that corresponds to (167-5) is too long and complicated to be of practical importance, and hence it is omitted here. It is simpler to apply (168-4) successively to groups of three values and then add the results.

Example. Using the data given in Example 3, Sec. 160, find an approximate value of $\int_{0.16}^{6.25} y\, dx$.

Using (168-3) determines

$$\int_{0.16}^{6.25} y\, dx = \tfrac{1}{2}[0.24(4.210) + 0.6(4.631) + 1.5(5.082)$$

$$+ 3.75(5.590)] = 16.187.$$

Applying (168-4) successively to the first three values and to the last three values gives

$$\int_{0.16}^{6.25} y\, dx = \frac{(0.84)^2}{6}\left[\frac{2(1.2-0.32-1)}{(-0.24)(-0.84)} + \frac{2.210(-0.84)}{(0.24)(-0.6)}\right.$$
$$\left. + \frac{2.421(2+0.16-1.2)}{(0.84)(0.6)}\right]$$
$$+ \frac{(5.25)^2}{6}\left[\frac{2.421(7.5-2-6.25)}{(-1.5)(-5.25)} + \frac{2.66(-5.25)}{(1.5)(-3.75)}\right.$$
$$\left. + \frac{2.929(12.5+1-7.5)}{(5.25)(3.75)}\right] = 17.194.$$

PROBLEMS

1. Determine an approximate value for $\int_1^7 y\, dx$, using the data given in Example 2, Sec. 160, and applying (167-3). Find the approximate value if (167-5) is used.

2. Apply (168-3) to determine an approximate value for $\int_{10}^{50.625} p\, dv$, using the data given in Prob. 1, Sec. 160.

3. Work the preceding problem by applying (168-4).

4. Apply (167-3) and (167-5) to the data given in Prob. 3, Sec. 160, in order to determine $\int_{19}^{25} H\, dC$.

5. Find the approximate values of $\int_0^6 \sqrt{4+x^3}\, dx$ obtained by using $x = 0, 1, 2, 3, 4, 5, 6$ and applying (167-3) and (167-5).

ANSWERS

CHAPTER I

1. (a) convergent; (b) divergent; (c) divergent; (d) convergent;
   (e) convergent; (f) divergent; (g) convergent; (h) divergent.
2. (a) convergent; (b) divergent.
4. (a) divergent; (b) convergent; (c) divergent; (d) divergent;
   (e) convergent; (f) convergent; (g) divergent; (h) convergent;
   (i) convergent; (j) divergent.

Page 22

3. (a) $-1 < x \le 1$; (b) all finite values; (c) $-1 < x < 1$;
   (d) $x > 1$ and $x \le -1$.
4. (a) $-\frac{4}{3} \le x < 4$; (b) 0; (c) $-1 < x < 1$.

Pages 39–40

1. (a) $1 + x + \dfrac{x^2}{2!} + \dfrac{x^3}{3!} + \cdots$;

   (b) $x - \dfrac{x^3}{3!} + \dfrac{x^5}{5!} - \dfrac{x^7}{7!} + \cdots$;

   (c) $1 - \dfrac{x^2}{2!} + \dfrac{x^4}{4!} - \dfrac{x^6}{6!} + \cdots$;

   (d) $x - \dfrac{x^3}{3} + \dfrac{x^5}{5} - \dfrac{x^7}{7} + \cdots$;

   (e) $x + \dfrac{1}{2}\dfrac{x^3}{3} + \dfrac{1 \cdot 3}{2 \cdot 4}\dfrac{x^5}{5} + \cdots$;

   (f) $1 + \dfrac{x^2}{2!} + \dfrac{5x^4}{4!} + \dfrac{61x^6}{6!} + \cdots$;

   (g) $x + \dfrac{x^3}{3} + \dfrac{2}{15}x^5 + \dfrac{17}{315}x^7 + \cdots$;

   (h) $1 + x + \dfrac{x^2}{2!} - \dfrac{3x^4}{4!} - \dfrac{8x^5}{5!} - \dfrac{3x^6}{6!} + \cdots$.

2. (a) $(x - 1) - \frac{1}{2}(x - 1)^2 + \frac{1}{3}(x - 1)^3 - \cdots$;

   (b) $1 + 2\left(x - \dfrac{\pi}{4}\right) + 2\left(x - \dfrac{\pi}{4}\right)^2 + \dfrac{8}{3}\left(x - \dfrac{\pi}{4}\right)^3 + \cdots$;

   (c) $e^2\left[1 + (x - 2) + \dfrac{(x - 2)^2}{2!} + \dfrac{(x - 2)^3}{3!} + \cdots\right]$;

   (d) $\dfrac{1}{2}\left[1 + \sqrt{3}\left(x - \dfrac{\pi}{6}\right) - \dfrac{1}{2!}\left(x - \dfrac{\pi}{6}\right)^2 - \dfrac{\sqrt{3}}{3!}\left(x - \dfrac{\pi}{6}\right)^3 + \cdots\right]$;

   (e) $7 + 29(x - 1) + 76(x - 1)^2 + 110(x - 1)^3 + 90(x - 1)^4$
   $+ 39(x - 1)^5 + 7(x - 1)^6$

4. All finite values of x. 6. $x^2 < 1$.

Pages 45–46

1. 0.984808; $2 \cdot 10^{-11}$.   **3.** 0.5446.

2. 9.   **5.** 2.03617.

8. (a) 0.3103; (b) 0.0201; (c) 0.9461;

(d) $x - \dfrac{x^3}{3} + \dfrac{x^5}{5 \cdot 2!} - \dfrac{x^7}{7 \cdot 3!} + \dfrac{x^9}{9 \cdot 4!} - \cdots$;

(e) $x - \dfrac{x^5}{5 \cdot 2!} + \dfrac{x^9}{9 \cdot 4!} - \dfrac{x^{13}}{13 \cdot 6!} + \cdots$; (f) 0.937; (g) -0.1026;

(h) $2\sqrt{x}\left(1 - \dfrac{x^2}{5 \cdot 2!} + \dfrac{x^4}{9 \cdot 4!} - \dfrac{x^6}{13 \cdot 6!} + \cdots\right)$;

(i) $x + \dfrac{x^2}{2!} + \dfrac{x^3}{3!} + \dfrac{3x^4}{4!} + \dfrac{9x^5}{5!} + \dfrac{37x^6}{6!} + \cdots$.

11. $\alpha \leq 0.24$ radian or $14°$.

Pages 53–55

5. $\pi/2$.   **15.** 1.05.

6. 214.5 ft.; 25.1 ft.   **16.** 1.69; 0.881.

14. $2\sqrt{2}\, E(\sqrt{2}/2, \pi/2) = 3.825$.

CHAPTER II
Pages 75–76

2. $\dfrac{\pi}{2}\sin x - \dfrac{16}{\pi}\displaystyle\sum_{n=1}^{\infty} \dfrac{n}{(4n^2 - 1)^2}\sin 2nx$;

$$1 - \dfrac{1}{2}\cos x - 2\displaystyle\sum_{n=2}^{\infty}\dfrac{(-1)^n}{n^2 - 1}\cos nx.$$

Pages 77–78

2. (a) $\dfrac{4}{\pi}\displaystyle\sum_{n=1}^{\infty}\dfrac{1}{2n-1}\sin\dfrac{(2n-1)\pi x}{2}$, 1;

(b) $\dfrac{2}{\pi}\displaystyle\sum_{n=1}^{\infty}\dfrac{(-1)^{n+1}}{n}\sin n\pi x$, $\dfrac{1}{2} - \dfrac{4}{\pi^2}\displaystyle\sum_{n=1}^{\infty}\dfrac{1}{(2n-1)^2}\cos(2n-1)\pi x$;

(c) $\dfrac{18}{\pi^3}\left[\left(\dfrac{\pi^2}{1} - \dfrac{4}{1^3}\right)\sin\dfrac{\pi x}{3} - \dfrac{\pi^2}{2}\sin\dfrac{2\pi x}{3} + \left(\dfrac{\pi^2}{3} - \dfrac{4}{3^3}\right)\sin\dfrac{3\pi x}{3}\right.$

$\left. - \dfrac{\pi^2}{4}\sin\dfrac{4\pi x}{3} + \left(\dfrac{\pi^2}{5} - \dfrac{4}{5^3}\right)\sin\dfrac{5\pi x}{3} - \cdots\right]$,

$$3 + \dfrac{36}{\pi^2}\displaystyle\sum_{n=1}^{\infty}\dfrac{(-1)^n}{n^2}\cos\dfrac{n\pi x}{3}.$$

CHAPTER III
Page 85

1. (a) $2, 4, -0.75$; (b) $1.22, -0.73$; (c) $1.08, -0.55, -0.77$; (d) -0.57.

2. 4.49.

Page 91

(a) 1.618, -1, -0.618.　(b) 13.968, $-6.984 \pm 0.291i$.

(c) 3, -1, -1.　　　　(d) -1, 1, 2.

(e) $2 + \sqrt[3]{4} + \sqrt[3]{2}$, $2 + \sqrt[3]{4}\omega + \sqrt[3]{2}\omega^2$, $2 + \sqrt[3]{4}\omega^2 + \sqrt[3]{2}\omega$.

(f) -6, $i\sqrt{3}$, $-i\sqrt{3}$.　(g) $-\dfrac{1}{2}$, $\dfrac{-1 \pm i\sqrt{3}}{2}$.

Pages 94–95

1. (a) 2, -2, -2; (b) 2, -1, $-\frac{1}{2}$; (c) $\pm\frac{1}{2}$, ω, ω^2; (d) 2, $-\frac{1}{2}$, $\pm i$.

2. (a) $(-1, 0)$, $(0, 1)$, $(2, 3)$; (b) $(-3, -2)$, $(-1, 0)$, $(0, 1)$;

(c) $(-4, -3)$, $(-2, -1)$, $(-1, 0)$; (d) $(-3, -2)$, $(-1, 0)$, $(0, 1)$,

$(2, 3)$.

Page 97

1. 2.924.

2. 1.618, -1, -0.618.

3. 2.061.

4. 1.398.

5. -0.879, 1.347, 2.532.

6. -0.418.

7. 1.226.

Pages 101–102

1. 1.226; $\frac{4}{3}$.

2. 2.310 radians.

3. 0.3574, 2.1533.

4. 0.739.

5. 4.494.

6. -0.567.

7. -0.725, 1.221.

Pages 105–106

1. 41; -35; 1.

2. (a) $(3\frac{7}{23}, 2\frac{9}{23})$; (b) $(1, 0, -1)$; (c) $(5, 4, -3)$; (d) $(1, -\frac{1}{2}, \frac{1}{2})$.

Page 114

1. 20; -126; -212.

2. (a) $(2, -1, 1)$; (b) $(1, \frac{3}{2}, -\frac{1}{2})$; (c) $(3, -1, 2)$; (d) $(1, -1, -2, 3)$

Pages 121–122

1. (a) $(1, -1)$; (b) inconsistent; (c) inconsistent; (d) $(1, 3k - 2, k)$.

2. (a) $(-k/7, 5k/7, k)$; (b) $(0, 0)$; (c) $(0, 0, 0)$;

(d) $(k/4, 7k/8, k)$; (e) $(k, 2k, 0)$; (f) $(0, 0, 0)$.

CHAPTER IV

Page 126

1. (a) $\dfrac{-y}{x^2}$, $\dfrac{1}{x}$; (b) $3x^2y - \dfrac{y}{x^2 + y^2}$, $x^3 + \dfrac{x}{x^2 + y^2}$;

(c) $y\cos xy + 1$, $x\cos xy$; (d) $e^x\log y$, e^x/y;

(e) $2xy + \dfrac{1}{\sqrt{1 - x^2}}$, x^2.

2. (a) $2xy - z^2$, $x^2 + z$, $y - 2xz$;　(b) $yz + \dfrac{1}{x}$, $xz + \dfrac{1}{y}$, xy;

(c) $\dfrac{z}{\sqrt{y^2 - x^2}}$, $\dfrac{-zx}{y\sqrt{y^2 - x^2}}$, $\sin^{-1}\dfrac{x}{y}$;

(d) $\dfrac{x}{\sqrt{x^2 + y^2 + z^2}}$, $\dfrac{y}{\sqrt{x^2 + y^2 + z^2}}$, $\dfrac{z}{\sqrt{x^2 + y^2 + z^2}}$;

(e) $\dfrac{-x}{(x^2 + y^2 + z^2)^{3/2}}$, $\dfrac{-y}{(x^2 + y^2 + z^2)^{3/2}}$, $\dfrac{-z}{(x^2 + y^2 + z^2)^{3/2}}$.

Pages 129–130

1. $\pi/6$ cu. ft.

2. 11.7 ft.

3. 0.139 ft.

4. 2250.

5. 10.85.

6. \$3.46.

7. 0.112; 0.054.

8. 53.78; 0.93.

9. 0.003π; 0.3 per cent.

10. 1.6π; π.

Pages 135–136

1. $ka^2(\theta \cos 2\theta + \frac{1}{2} \sin 2\theta)$.

2. $2r \cos 2\theta$; $-2r^2 \sin 2\theta$.

3. $2r - t$; $t - 2s$; $s - r$.

4. $\dfrac{e^{xy}}{u^2 + v^2}(uy + vx)$; $\dfrac{e^{xy}}{u^2 + v^2}(vy - ux)$.

7. (a) $e^{t^2}\left(2t \sin \dfrac{t-1}{t} + \dfrac{1}{t^2}\cos\dfrac{t-1}{t}\right)$;

(b) $2r(1 - 3\tan^2\theta)$, $-6r^2 \tan\theta \sec^2\theta$.

8. (a) $2x$, $2(x + \tan x \sec^2 x)$;

(b) $\cos\theta\,\dfrac{\partial V}{\partial x} + \sin\theta\,\dfrac{\partial V}{\partial y}$, $r\left(\cos\theta\,\dfrac{\partial V}{\partial y} - \sin\theta\,\dfrac{\partial V}{\partial x}\right)$, $\dfrac{\partial V}{\partial z}$.

9. $\dfrac{1}{x^2 + y^2}\left(x\sqrt{x^2 + y^2}\,\dfrac{\partial f}{\partial u} - y\,\dfrac{\partial f}{\partial v}\right)$; $\dfrac{1}{x^2 + y^2}\left(y\sqrt{x^2 + y^2}\,\dfrac{\partial f}{\partial u} + x\,\dfrac{\partial f}{\partial v}\right)$;

$(x^2 + y^2)^{-1/2}\sqrt{(x^2 + y^2)\left(\dfrac{\partial f}{\partial u}\right)^2 + \left(\dfrac{\partial f}{\partial v}\right)^2}$.

Pages 141–143

1. $\dfrac{-9x^2 - 4u}{12v^2(u + v)}$; $\dfrac{1 - 4vy^2}{4u^2(u + v)}$, $\dfrac{-4uy^2 - 1}{4v^2(u + v)}$.

2. $\dfrac{y - x^2}{y^2 - x}$.

4. $\dfrac{ye^v - xy - uve^v - v}{e^{v+y} - xe^v - ue^v - 1}$; $\dfrac{-ve^{v+y} - x}{e^{v+y} - xe^v - ue^v - 1}$.

6. (a) $-2, 3, 1, -1$; (b) $\dfrac{-u}{u^2 + v^2}$, $\dfrac{v}{u^2 + v^2}$, $\dfrac{v}{u^2 + v^2}$, $\dfrac{u}{u^2 + v^2}$.

8. $-\dfrac{u + 2v^2}{1 + 4uv}$; $\dfrac{2u^2 - v}{1 + 4uv}$.

11. $2r$; 0.

13. (a) $-\dfrac{\sec y + 3x^2y^2}{x \sec y \tan y + 2x^3y}$; (b) $\dfrac{3x^2y}{\cos z - 3z^2}$, $\dfrac{x^3}{\cos z - 3z^2}$.

14. $2(z - y): 2(x - z): 2(y - x)$.

Pages 145–146

3. $\frac{1}{2}[3\sqrt{3} + 1 + e(\sqrt{3} + 1)]$ or 6.811.

4. $2\sqrt{x^2 + y^2}$.

Page 149

1. $\sqrt{3}/3.$

2. (a) $2x + 3y + 2z = 6, \dfrac{x-1}{4} = \dfrac{y-1}{6} = \dfrac{z-\frac{1}{2}}{4};$

   (b) $6x + 2y - 3z = 6, \dfrac{x-4}{2} = \dfrac{y-3}{\frac{2}{3}} = \dfrac{z-8}{-1};$

   (c) $\dfrac{x_0 x}{a^2} + \dfrac{y_0 y}{b^2} + \dfrac{z_0 z}{c^2} = 1, \dfrac{a^2}{x_0}(x-x_0) = \dfrac{b^2}{y_0}(y-y_0) = \dfrac{c^2}{z_0}(z-z_0).$

Pages 152–153

6. $dx/ds = 1/\sqrt{14}, \; dy/ds = 2/\sqrt{14}, \; dz/ds = 3/\sqrt{14}.$ **9.** $27°.$

Pages 154–155

3. $10; 20.$

4. $f_{xx}\cos^2\theta + f_{xy}\sin 2\theta + f_{yy}\sin^2\theta;$
$f_{xx}r^2\sin^2\theta - f_{xy}r^2\sin 2\theta + f_{yy}r^2\cos^2\theta - f_x r\cos\theta - f_y r\sin\theta.$

Pages 157–158

1. $\dfrac{\pi^2}{4} + \left(\dfrac{\pi^2}{4} - \dfrac{\pi}{2}\right)(x-1) + (\pi-1)\left(y - \dfrac{\pi}{2}\right)$

$\quad + \dfrac{1}{2!}\left[2(\pi-1)(x-1)\left(y-\dfrac{\pi}{2}\right) + 2\left(y-\dfrac{\pi}{2}\right)^2 \right]$

$\quad + \dfrac{1}{3!}\left[\dfrac{\pi^3}{8}(x-1)^3 + \dfrac{3\pi^2}{4}(x-1)^2\left(y-\dfrac{\pi}{2}\right) \right.$

$\quad\quad\quad \left. + 3\left(2+\dfrac{\pi}{2}\right)(x-1)\left(y-\dfrac{\pi}{2}\right)^2 + \left(y-\dfrac{\pi}{2}\right)^3 \right] + \cdots.$

2. $e\left\{ 1 + (x-1) + (y-1) + \dfrac{1}{2!}[(x-1)^2 + 4(x-1)(y-1) \right.$

$\quad\quad\quad\quad\quad\quad\quad \left. + (y-1)^2] + \cdots \right\}.$

3. $1 + x + \dfrac{1}{2!}(x^2 - y^2) + \dfrac{1}{3!}(x^3 - 3xy^2) + \dfrac{1}{4!}(x^4 - 6x^2y^2 + y^4)$

$\quad\quad\quad\quad\quad\quad\quad\quad\quad\quad\quad\quad + \cdots.$

Page 160

1. (a) $(3, -26)$ minimum;

   (b) $(3, 108)$ maximum, $(5, 0)$ minimum;

   (c) No maxima or minima.

2. $x = 1/e.$

4. (a) $\cos x = -\frac{1}{2}$ and $\sin x = 0$, inflection;

   (b) $\cos x = \frac{1}{2}$ and $\sin x = 0$, inflection;

   (c) $\sin x = 0$, inflection.

6. (a) $x = 1/e$; (b) $x = {}^{16}\!/_{25}$, maximum, $x = {}^{64}\!/_{225}$, inflection.

Pages 162–163

1. $a/3, a/3, a/3.$ **2.** $8abc/3\sqrt{3}.$ **3.** $a/3, b/3, c/3.$
4. $\sqrt{3}P/(2\sqrt{3}+3), (\sqrt{3}+1)P/2(2\sqrt{3}+3), P/(2\sqrt{3}+3).$
5. $l = h = \dfrac{1}{5\pi}\sqrt[3]{60\pi^2 V}, d = \sqrt{5}l.$

Pages 170–171

1. $\dfrac{\pi \sin\dfrac{\pi\alpha}{2}}{2\alpha} + \dfrac{\cos\dfrac{\pi\alpha}{2} - 1}{\alpha^2}.$ **4.** $-\tan\alpha.$

2. $\alpha\pi.$ **5.** $2x^2.$

3. $\alpha\left(\dfrac{\pi}{2} - \log 2\right).$ **6.** $\alpha\pi(\alpha^2 - 1)^{-3/2}.$

CHAPTER V
Pages 190–191

1. $(a/5, a/5).$ **8.** $\pi a^2/2.$

2. $\pi a^4/16.$ **11.** $4a^2\left(\dfrac{\pi}{2} - 1\right).$

3. (a) $u\,du\,dv$; (b) $u^2v\,du\,dv\,dw.$ **12.** $\dfrac{4}{3}a^3\left(\dfrac{\pi}{2} - \dfrac{2}{3}\right).$

4. $(3\pi a/16, 0, 0).$ **13.** $8a^2$

5. $32a^3/9.$ **14.** $\bar{x} = a\cos^2\dfrac{\alpha}{2}.$

6. $(a/4, b/4, c/4).$ **15.** $\pi a^4 h/2.$

7. $\sigma\pi a^4 b/2.$ **16.** $I_z = \dfrac{4}{15}abc(a^2 + b^2).$

Page 195

1. 0.   **4.** $12\pi a^5/5.$

CHAPTER VI
Page 199

1. (a) $\dfrac{2}{3}$; (b) $\dfrac{19}{30}$; (c) $\dfrac{2}{3}$; (d) $\dfrac{13}{20}.$
2. (a) $-\dfrac{69}{10}$; (b) $-\dfrac{29}{4}.$
3. (a) $\dfrac{2}{3}$; (b) $\dfrac{2}{3}$; (c) $\dfrac{2}{3}$; (d) $\dfrac{2}{3}.$
4. (a) 0; (b) $\dfrac{1}{3}$; (c) $-\dfrac{4}{15}.$

Page 202

1. $\pi ab.$ **2.** $\dfrac{1}{2}.$ **3.** $3\pi a^2/8.$

Page 206

1. $-\dfrac{1}{28}.$ **2.** 0.   **3.** $-\dfrac{1}{12}.$ **4.** $\dfrac{3}{4}.$

Page 212

1. $1\dfrac{3}{5}.$ **3.** $\dfrac{1}{2}.$
5. (a) $\pi/2$; (b) $-\sqrt{3}/4$; (c) $1\dfrac{7}{9}.$

CHAPTER VII
Pages 230–231

1. $(y')^2 + 5xy' - y + 5x^2 = 0.$
2. $y'' + y = 0.$
3. $xy''' - y'' - xy' + y = 0.$
4. $xy' + (1 - x)y + 2e^{-x} = 0.$
5. $(y'')^2 = [1 + (y')^2]^3.$

6. $y'' - 2y' + 2y = 0.$
7. $x(y')^2 - yy' + 1 = 0.$
9. $x^3y''' - 3x^2y'' + 6xy' - 6y = 0.$
10. $2xy' - y = 0.$

Pages 254–256

1. 0.417 ft.
2. $\theta = \theta_0 + (\theta_1 - \theta_0)e^{-kt}$

9. $v = v_0(1 - e^{-gt/v_0}).$
11. 0.000667 cal.

Page 258

1. $\sin^{-1} y + \sin^{-1} x = c.$
2. $(y - 1)/(y + 1) = ce^{x^2}.$
3. $2 \cos y - \sin x \cos x + x = c.$
4. $\sec x + \tan y = c.$
5. $\tan^{-1} y - 2\sqrt{1 + x} = c.$
6. $xe^x - e^x - \sqrt{1 - y^2} = c.$
13. $x \sin^{-1} x + \sqrt{1 - x^2} + \dfrac{y^2}{2} - e^y(y - 1) = c.$

7. $1 + y = c(1 + x).$
8. $\log\left[(y - 1)/y\right] + e^{-x} = c.$
9. $2 \tan^{-1} e^y + \log \tanh x/2 = c.$
10. $\dfrac{1}{x} - \dfrac{1}{y} - \log y = c.$
11. $y(2 - \log y) = \tfrac{1}{2} \tan^2 x + c.$
12. $x(1 + 4y^2)^{3/4} = c.$

14. $y = c\sqrt{1 - x^2}.$
15. $y - x - \log xy = c.$
16. $\tan^{-1} y - \tan^{-1} x = c.$
17. $-\dfrac{1}{y + 1} + \dfrac{1}{x - 1} = c.$

18. $-\dfrac{1}{y} + \dfrac{1}{x} + \log xy = c.$
19. $y = c(1 + x)(1 - y).$
20. $1 + y^2 = c(1 + x^2).$
23. $(B - x)/(A - x) = Ce^{(B-A)kt}.$

Pages 261–262

1. $\left[\dfrac{y}{x}\left(3 + \dfrac{y^2}{x^2}\right)\right]^{1/3} = \dfrac{c}{x}.$
2. $\sin^{-1}(y/x) - \log x = c.$
3. $\sin(y/x) + \log x = c.$
4. $x^2 - 2xy - y^2 = c.$
5. $\log y + x^3/(3y^3) = c.$
11. $h = \dfrac{a_2b_3 - a_3b_2}{a_1b_2 - a_2b_1},\ k = \dfrac{a_3b_1 - a_1b_3}{a_1b_2 - a_2b_1}.$
12. $y + ce^{y/x} = 0.$
14. $x + y + 2 \log(2x + y - 3) = c.$
16. $xy^2 = c(x + 2y).$
17. $x^3 + y^3 = cxy.$
18. $x[4(y/x)^2 + 1]^{3/8} = c.$

6. $x = ce^{x/y}.$
7. $y = ce^{-2\sqrt{x/y}}.$
8. $x = ce^{2\sqrt{y/x}}.$
9. $\log x + e^{-y/x} = c.$
10. $x = ce^{(1/x)\sqrt{x^2-y^2}}.$
13. $x^2 + y^2 + cy = 0.$
19. $x + ce^{y^2/(2x^2)} = 0.$
20. $y^2 + 2xy - x^2 = c.$

Pages 264–265

1. $\sin xy + x^2 = c.$
2. $x^2 y + xy^2 + x = c.$
3. $e^x + x + y = c.$
4. $x^3 y - y^3 x = c.$
5. Not exact.
6. $\sin(y/x) = c.$
7. $x^2 \log y = c.$
8. $(1 - x^2)(1 - y^2) = c.$
9. $e^x \log y + x^2 = c.$
10. Not exact.
11. Not exact.
13. $x \sin 2y = c.$

Pages 268–269

1. $\sin^{-1} y \pm x = c.$
2. $y = \pm \frac{1}{2}(x \sqrt{1 - x^2} + \sin^{-1} x) + c.$
3. $x + y - \tan^{-1} y = c.$
4. $y - ce^{3x} = 0,\ y - ce^{-x} = 0.$

Pages 278–279

1. $y = cx.$
2. $x^2 - y^2 = c.$
3. $x^2 + ny^2 = c.$
9. $y = ce^{x/k}.$

Pages 280–283

5. $s = (44/k)(1 - e^{-kt}).$
9. $y = -\dfrac{g}{2v_0^2 \cos^2 \alpha} x^2 + x \tan \alpha.$
12. $p = p_0 e^{-kh}.$

Pages 285–286

1. $1 + \sqrt{x^2 + 1} = cxe^{-y\sqrt{x^2+1}}.$
2. $y = \dfrac{x^3 + c}{3(x^2 + 1)}.$
3. $y = e^{-x^2}(x + c).$
4. $y = 1 + ce^{-x^2/2}.$
5. $y = \cos^2 x + 2(\sin x - 1) + ce^{-\sin x}.$
6. $y = 2 \sin x - x \cos x + \dfrac{2}{x} \cos x + \dfrac{c}{x}.$
7. $y = 1 + ce^{\tan^{-1} x}.$
8. $I = (E/R)(1 - e^{-Rt/L}).$
9. $y = \sin x + ce^x.$
10. $y = c \tan x + e^x.$
11. $x = 1 + ce^{-y^2/2}.$
12. $x = ce^{-2y} + \dfrac{y}{2} - \dfrac{1}{4}.$
13. $y = \tan x - 1 + ce^{-\tan x}.$
14. $y = (x + 1)(e^x + c).$
15. $y = e^{3x} + ce^{2x}.$

Page 287

1. $y^4 = (48x^{-2} - 96x^{-4} - 4) \cos x + (16x^{-1} - 96x^{-3}) \sin x + cx^{-4}.$
2. $y^{-2} = x + \frac{1}{2} + ce^{2x}.$
3. $y^{-5} = \frac{5}{2}x^3 + cx^5.$
4. $x = y \log cx.$
5. $y^{-1} = 1 + \log x + cx.$
6. $y^{-2} = 1 + x^2 + ce^{x^2}.$
7. $x^{-2} = y + \frac{1}{2} + ce^{2y}.$
8. $y^{-1} = -1 + c\sqrt{1 - x^2}.$

Page 291

2. $e^{-ax} \displaystyle\int e^{(a+m)x}\, dx.$
3. $e^{-ax} \displaystyle\int e^{ax} \cos mx\, dx.$

Pages 294–295

1. (a) $y = c_1 e^{-9x} + c_2 e^{6x}$; (b) $y = c_1 e^{3x} + c_2 e^{2x}$;
(c) $y = (c_1 + c_2 x)e^{-x}$; (d) $y = (c_1 + c_2 x)e^x + c_3$;
(e) $y = (c_1 + c_2 x + c_3 x^2)e^{-x} + c_4$; (f) $y = c_1 \cos kx + c_2 \sin kx$
$$+ c_3 \cosh kx + c_4 \sinh kx.$$

Pages 298–299

1. $y = c_1 e^{-3x} + \dfrac{(x^3 - x^2)}{3} + \dfrac{2x}{9} - \dfrac{2}{27}.$

2. $y = c_1 e^{-3x} + c_2 e^{-2x} + \dfrac{e^x}{12}.$ **3.** $y = (c_1 + c_2 x)e^x + x + 2.$

4. $y = c_1 e^{-kx} + c_2 e^{kx} + (w/2P)(x^2 - lx + 2k^{-2})$, where $k = \sqrt{P/EI}.$

5. $y = c_1 e^x + c_2 e^{-x} + c_3 e^{2x} - x.$ **6.** $y = c_1 e^{-x} + c_2 e^{x/2} + 2 \sin x.$

7. $y = (c_1 + c_2 x)e^x + c_3 e^{-2x} + \sin x.$

Pages 305–307

1. $y = 2 \cos \sqrt{10}t,\ \sqrt{10}/(2\pi);\ y = 2 \cos \sqrt{10}t + \sqrt{10} \sin \sqrt{10}t.$

3. $y = 10 \cos \sqrt{245}t.$

4. $y = 10e^{-5t}\left(\cos \sqrt{220}t + \dfrac{5}{\sqrt{220}} \sin \sqrt{220}t\right);\ R = 400 \sqrt{245}$ dynes.

5. $V = 100 \sqrt{2}e^{-500t} \cos\left(500t - \dfrac{\pi}{4}\right);\ V = 100e^{-500\sqrt{2}t}(1 + 500 \sqrt{2}t).$

6. $V = 20 \sqrt{5}e^{-50000t}(5 \sinh 10000 \sqrt{5}t + \sqrt{5} \cosh 10000 \sqrt{5}t).$

10. $10 \dfrac{d^2y}{dt^2} + 10gy = 0$; maximum $y = \sqrt{3}$, total drop $2 + \sqrt{3}.$

Pages 314–315

1. $x = \tfrac{2}{3}c_1 e^t - c_2 e^{-4t} + \tfrac{2}{5}te^t - \tfrac{2}{15}e^t - \tfrac{1}{4}t - \tfrac{7}{16},$
$y = c_1 e^t + c_2 e^{-4t} + \tfrac{3}{5}te^t - \tfrac{3}{4}t -- \tfrac{9}{16}.$

3. Cycloid of radius $mE/(eH^2).$

Pages 317–318

1. No.   **2.** Yes.   **3.** No.

Pages 321–322

3. $y = -(x^2 \log x)/9.$ **4.** $y = c_1 e^x + c_2 x + x^2 + 1.$

Pages 324–325

2. $y = c_1 x^{-2} + c_2 x^{-1} + \tfrac{1}{2} \log x - \tfrac{3}{4}.$

3. $y = c_1 x^2 + c_2 x^3.$ **4.** $y = c_1 x^m + c_2 x^{-m-1}.$

5. $y = c_1 x^2 + c_2 x^{(5+\sqrt{21})/2} + c_3 x^{(5-\sqrt{21})/2} - \tfrac{1}{2}.$

6. $y = c_1 x^{(1+\sqrt{3}i)/2} + c_2 x^{(1-\sqrt{3}i)/2} + \dfrac{x^2}{3}.$

7. $y = c_1 x^2 + c_2 x - x[(\log x)^2/2 + \log x].$

Page 329

1. $y = c_1 \left(x - \dfrac{x^3}{3!} + \dfrac{x^5}{5!} - \cdots \right) + c_2 \left(1 - \dfrac{x^2}{2!} + \dfrac{x^4}{4!} - \cdots \right).$

2. $y = c \left(1 + x + \dfrac{x^2}{2!} + \dfrac{x^3}{3!} + \cdots \right).$

3. $y = c_1 \left(1 - x + \dfrac{x^2}{2!} - \dfrac{x^3}{3!} + \cdots \right) + c_2(1 + x + x^2 + x^3 + \cdots).$

CHAPTER VIII
Pages 356–357

1. (a) $2 \dfrac{\partial z}{\partial x} + \dfrac{\partial z}{\partial y} = 10$; (b) $y \dfrac{\partial z}{\partial x} - x \dfrac{\partial z}{\partial y} = 0$;

   (c) $\dfrac{\partial z}{\partial x} + \dfrac{\partial z}{\partial y} = z$; (d) $\dfrac{\partial^2 z}{\partial x \partial y} = \dfrac{1}{z} \dfrac{\partial z}{\partial x} \dfrac{\partial z}{\partial y}.$

Page 361

1. (a) $z = F_1(y + ax) + F_2(y - ax)$;
   (b) $z = F_1(y - 2x) + F_2(y + x)$;
   (e) $z = F_1(y - x) + xF_2(y - x)$.
2. (a) xy; (c) $x^2y/2 - x^3/3$.

Page 372

1. 0.44883; 0.14922; 0.00004.

Pages 375–377

2. 35.5; 41.9.

Pages 385–386

1. $u = 50 + \dfrac{200}{\pi} \displaystyle\sum_{n=1}^{\infty} \dfrac{1}{(2n-1)a^{2n-1}} r^{2n-1} \sin (2n-1)\theta.$

3. $u = \dfrac{400}{\pi} \displaystyle\sum_{n=1}^{\infty} \dfrac{1}{(2n-1)a^{2n-1}} r^{2n-1} \sin (2n-1)\theta.$

4. $u = \displaystyle\sum_{n=1}^{\infty} A_n e^{-\alpha^2 k_n^2 t} J_0(k_n r)$, where $1 = \displaystyle\sum_{n=1}^{\infty} A_n J_0(k_n r).$

Pages 390–391

2. $V = \dfrac{3x}{50} + \dfrac{4}{\pi} \displaystyle\sum_{n=1}^{\infty} \dfrac{1}{n} \sin \dfrac{n\pi x}{100} e^{-n^2\pi^2 t/0.0024}.$

7. $I = 0.6 + 1.1 \displaystyle\sum_{n=1}^{\infty} (-1)^n \cos \dfrac{n\pi x}{1000} e^{-n^2\pi^2 t/0.6}.$

CHAPTER IX
Pages 398–399

1. 0.5640.   2. $(10 \sqrt{3}/3)(\mathbf{i} + \mathbf{j} + \mathbf{k})$.

Pages 403–404

5. $3i + 12j + 4k.$ **6.** $19\sqrt{3}/3;\ (\sqrt{3}/3)(8i + j - 9k).$

Page 409

1. $\dfrac{du}{ds} = \dfrac{\partial u}{\partial x}\dfrac{dx}{ds} + \dfrac{\partial u}{\partial y}\dfrac{dy}{ds} + \dfrac{\partial u}{\partial z}\dfrac{dz}{ds}.$

2. (a) $iyz + jxz + kxy;$ (b) $i2x + j2y + k2z;$
(c) $(x^2 + y^2 + z^2)^{-\frac{1}{2}}(ix + jy + kz);$
(d) $2(x^2 + y^2 + z^2)^{-1}(ix + jy + kz).$

5. $26\sqrt{2}/5.$ **6.** $9.$

Pages 414–415

1. (a) $3;$ (b) $2/r;$ (c) $0.$

3. $i\dfrac{\partial}{\partial x}\left(\dfrac{\partial A_x}{\partial x} + \dfrac{\partial A_y}{\partial y} + \dfrac{\partial A_z}{\partial z}\right) + j\dfrac{\partial}{\partial y}\left(\dfrac{\partial A_x}{\partial x} + \dfrac{\partial A_y}{\partial y} + \dfrac{\partial A_z}{\partial z}\right)$
$$+ k\dfrac{\partial}{\partial z}\left(\dfrac{\partial A_x}{\partial x} + \dfrac{\partial A_y}{\partial y} + \dfrac{\partial A_z}{\partial z}\right).$$

Pages 420–421

1. (a) $0;$ (b) $0;$ (c) $0.$

Pages 432–433

4. $\Psi = cy.$ **5.** $\Phi = x^2 - y^2.$

Page 439

1. $\varrho_1\dfrac{\partial\Phi}{\partial\rho} + \dfrac{\theta_1}{\rho}\dfrac{\partial\Phi}{\partial\theta} + z_1\dfrac{\partial\Phi}{\partial z};\ \varrho_1\dfrac{\partial\Phi}{\partial\rho} + \dfrac{\theta_1}{\rho}\dfrac{\partial\Phi}{\partial\theta} + \dfrac{\varphi_1}{\rho\sin\theta}\dfrac{\partial\Phi}{\partial\varphi}.$

3. $\varrho_1\left[\dfrac{1}{\rho}\dfrac{\partial A_z}{\partial\theta} - \dfrac{\partial A_\theta}{\partial z}\right] + \theta_1\left[\dfrac{\partial A_\rho}{\partial z} - \dfrac{\partial A_z}{\partial\rho}\right] + z_1\dfrac{1}{\rho}\left[\dfrac{\partial(\rho A_\theta)}{\partial\rho} - \dfrac{\partial A_\rho}{\partial\theta}\right];$

$\varrho_1\dfrac{1}{\rho\sin\theta}\left[\dfrac{\partial(\sin\theta A_\varphi)}{\partial\theta} - \dfrac{\partial A_\theta}{\partial\varphi}\right] + \theta_1\left[\dfrac{1}{\rho\sin\theta}\dfrac{\partial A_\rho}{\partial\varphi} - \dfrac{1}{\rho}\dfrac{\partial(\rho A_\varphi)}{\partial\rho}\right]$
$$+ \varphi_1\dfrac{1}{\rho}\left[\dfrac{\partial(\rho A_\theta)}{\partial\rho} - \dfrac{\partial A_\rho}{\partial\theta}\right]$$

10. $3p\cos\theta/r^4;\ 0.$

CHAPTER X
Pages 443–444

1. (a) $2,\ 60°;$ (b) $2\sqrt{2},\ 45°;$ (c) $1,\ 90°.$

9. (a) $\dfrac{x}{x^2 + (y - 1)^2} + i\dfrac{-y + 1}{x^2 + (y - 1)^2};$

(b) $\dfrac{x^2 + y^2 - 1}{x^2 + (y + 1)^2} + i\dfrac{-2x}{x^2 + (y + 1)^2};$

(d) $\dfrac{x^2 - y^2}{(x^2 - y^2)^2 + (2xy + 1)^2} + i\dfrac{-2xy - 1}{(x^2 - y^2)^2 + (2xy + 1)^2}.$

Pages 447–448

4. $\dfrac{\sin 2x}{\cos 2x + \cosh 2y} + i\,\dfrac{\sinh 2y}{\cos 2x + \cosh 2y}.$

5. $\sin x \cosh y + i \cos x \sinh y.$

7. (a) $e^{-\pi/4}[\cos\,(\log \sqrt{2}) + i \sin\,(\log \sqrt{2})];$

    (b) $\sqrt{2}e^{-\pi/4}\left[\cos\left(-\dfrac{\pi}{4} - \log \sqrt{2}\right) + i \sin\left(-\dfrac{\pi}{4} - \log \sqrt{2}\right)\right].$

Pages 452–453

3. (a) z^2; (b) $1/z$; (c) z; (d) $\log z$; (e) $\cos z.$ **7.** $x^3 - 3xy^2.$

Page 461

3. 2   **4.** $\pi i.$ **5.** 0.   **6.** $2\pi i.$ **7.** 0.

Page 469

2. (a) $u = \cos x \cosh y,\ v = -\sin x \sinh y;$

    (b) $u = e^x \cos y,\ v = e^x \sin y;$

    (c) $u = x^3 - 3xy^2,\ v = 3x^2y - y^3;$

    (d) $u = \log\,(x^2 + y^2)^{1/2},\ v = \tan^{-1}\,(y/x);$

    (e) $u = x/(x^2 + y^2),\ v = -y/(x^2 + y^2).$

CHAPTER XI
Page 495

1. $\tfrac{1}{6}$; $\tfrac{1}{18}.$ **2.** $\tfrac{3}{20}$; $\tfrac{1}{2}$; $\tfrac{7}{20}$; $\tfrac{9}{38}$; $1323/46189.$

Page 497

1. $33/16660.$ **4.** $\tfrac{49}{50}.$

2. $\tfrac{31}{32}$; $\tfrac{1}{32}.$ **5.** $\tfrac{3}{32}$; $\tfrac{5}{32}$; $\tfrac{9}{32}.$

3. $\tfrac{1}{74088}.$

Pages 499–500

1. $\tfrac{41}{60}.$ **5.** $n > \log 2/(\log 6 - \log 5).$

2. $\tfrac{1}{6}$; $\tfrac{5}{36}.$ **6.** $\tfrac{3}{10}$; $\tfrac{9}{20}.$

3. $46413/78125.$ **7.** $\tfrac{162}{315}.$

4. $\tfrac{2}{9}.$ **8.** $91854/100000.$

Page 501

1. 0.775; 0.0000265; $\$47.50.$ **2.** \$11.   **3.** 6.

Page 504

1. (a) $\tfrac{125}{3888}$; (b) $\tfrac{23}{648}.$

2. $(0.65)^{10} + 10(0.65)^9(0.35) + 45(0.65)^8(0.35)^2 + 120(0.65)^7(0.35)^3.$

3. $5(\tfrac{1}{6})^6 + 4(\tfrac{1}{6})^5(\tfrac{5}{6}) + 45(\tfrac{1}{6})^4(\tfrac{5}{6})^2 + 40(\tfrac{1}{6})^3(\tfrac{5}{6})^3 + 15(\tfrac{1}{6})^2(\tfrac{5}{6})^4.$

4. $\tfrac{741}{2728}.$

Page 508

    50; $_{100}C_{50}(\tfrac{1}{2})^{100}$; $_{1000}C_{500}(\tfrac{1}{2})^{1000}.$

Page 512

1. $1/\sqrt{125\pi}$. **2.** $200;\ \sqrt{3/(1000\pi)}$. **3.** $1/\sqrt{50\pi};\ 1/\sqrt{500\pi}$.

Page 516

1. $(200)^{10}e^{-200}/10!$ **2.** $(20)^{100}e^{-20}/100!$
3. $0.136;\ 0.272;\ 0.272;\ 0.181;\ 0.091;\ 0.036$.

Pages 523–524

4. $0.00896;\ 0.00850$. **5.** $0.976;\ 0.983$. **6.** First set.

CHAPTER XII
Page 527

1. $y = x/2 + \tfrac{1}{2}$. **2.** $y = 2.5x^{0.5}$. **3.** $y = 0.3(10^{0.2x})$.

Pages 533–534

1. $p = av^n$. **2.** $\theta = ka^t$.
3. $H = a_2C^2 + a_1C + a_0$.

Pages 535–536

1. $y = 4.99 - 3.13x + 1.26x^2$. **2.** $H = \tfrac{1}{4}C^2 - \tfrac{1}{2}C + \tfrac{1}{4}$.
3. $y = 2.547 + 1.064x - 0.593x^2 + 0.100x^3$.
4. $y = 1.3 + 0.2e^x$. **5.** $y = 0.3e^x - 1.1\sin x + 1.5x^2$.

Page 544

1. $y = 4.99 - 3.13x + 1.26x^2$. **2.** $y = 10^{0.5x}$.

Page 550

1. $y = 0.75 + 0.10\cos x - 0.05\cos 3x - 0.29\sin x$.
2. $y = 0.85 - 0.25\cos 2x - 0.05\cos 4x + 0.05\cos 6x + 0.26\sin 2x$
$- 0.03\sin 4x$.

Page 554

1. $42.61;\ 42.50;\ 42.51$. **3.** $106.15;\ 106.09;\ 106.09$.
2. $2.581;\ 2.627$. **4.** $2.784;\ 2.700$.

Page 560

1. $25.252;\ 25.068$. **4.** $666.25;\ 666.00$.
2. 132.137. **5.** $39.30;\ 38.98$.
3. 128.6.

INDEX

C